Weather Studies

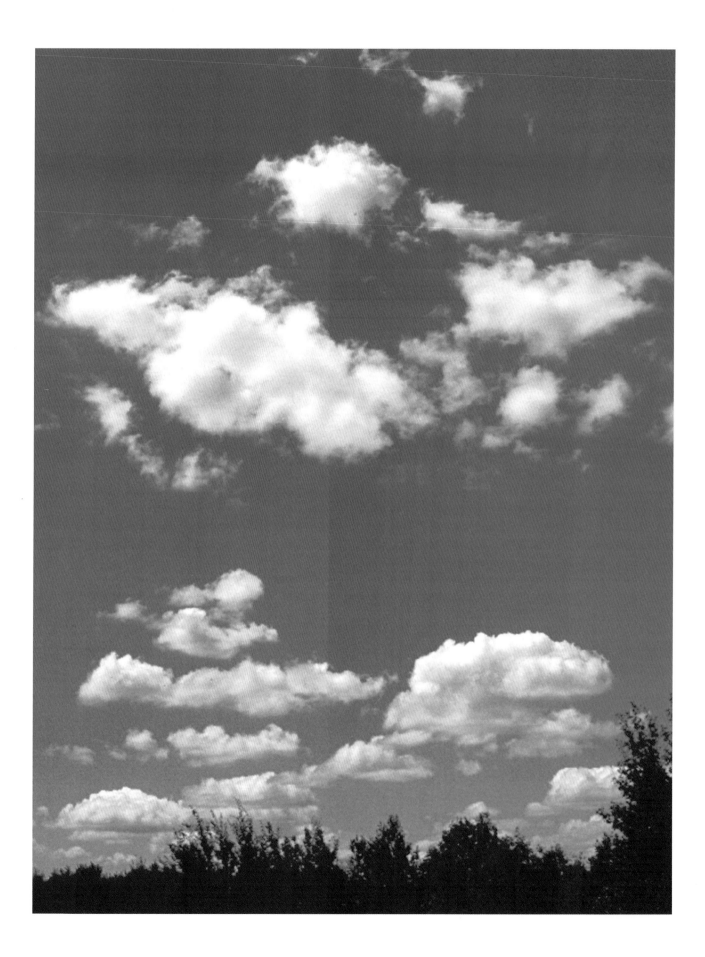

Weather Studies
Introduction to Atmospheric Science

3rd Edition

Joseph M. Moran

Education Program

American Meteorological Society

The American Meteorological Society
Education Program

The American Meteorological Society (AMS), founded in 1919, is a **scientific and professional** society. Interdisciplinary in its scope, the Society actively promotes the development and dissemination of information on the atmospheric and related oceanic and hydrologic sciences. AMS has more than 10,000 professional members from more than 100 countries and over 135 corporate and institutional members representing 40 countries.

The Education Program is the initiative of the American Meteorological Society fostering the teaching of the atmospheric and related oceanic and hydrologic sciences at the precollege level and in community college, college and university programs. It is a unique partnership between scientists and educators at all levels with the ultimate goals of (1) attracting young people to further studies in science, mathematics and technology, and (2) promoting public scientific literacy. This is done via the development and dissemination of scientifically authentic, up-to-date, and instructionally sound learning and resource materials for teachers and students.

Online Weather Studies, a component of the AMS education initiative, is an introductory undergraduate meteorology course offered partially via the Internet in partnership with college and university faculty. **Online Weather Studies** provides students with a comprehensive study of the principles of meteorology while simultaneously providing classroom and laboratory applications focused on current weather situations. It provides real experiences demonstrating the value of computers and electronic access to time-sensitive data and information.

Developmental work for **Online Weather Studies** was supported by the Division of Undergraduate Education of the National Science Foundation under Grant No. DUE - 9752416.

This project was supported, in part, by the
National Science Foundation
Opinions expressed are those of the authors and not necessarily those of the Foundation

Weather Studies: Introduction to Atmospheric Science/ Joseph M. Moran. — 3rd edition
ISBN-10: 1-878220-74-8
ISBN-13: 978-1-878220-74-5
Copyright © 2006 by the American Meteorological Society

Published by the American Meteorological Society
45 Beacon Street, Boston, MA 02108

The previous editions of this book were published under the title *Online Weather Studies*.

Cover photograph © 2003 Roger Edwards, www.skypix.ws

Dedicated to the memory of

Roderick A. Scofield

*longtime friend, mentor and contributor
to the AMS Education Program*

BRIEF CONTENTS

CONTENTS

CHAPTER 3   SOLAR AND TERRESTRIAL RADIATION
49

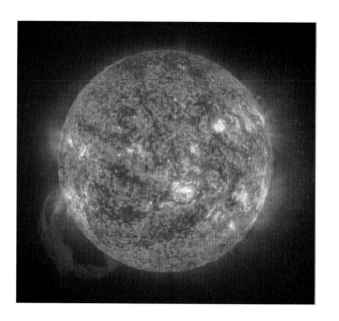

CHAPTER 4   HEAT, TEMPERATURE, AND ATMOSPHERIC CIRCULATION
83

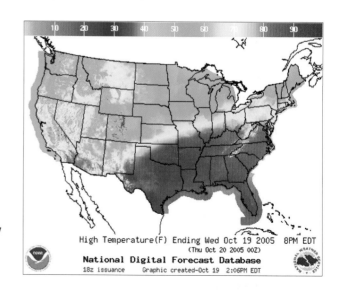

High Temperature(F) Ending Wed Oct 19 2005 8PM EDT
(Thu Oct 20 2005 00Z)
National Digital Forecast Database
18z issuance   Graphic created-Oct 19 2:06PM EDT

CHAPTER 5　　AIR PRESSURE　　111

CHAPTER 6　　HUMIDITY, SATURATION, AND STABILITY　　131

CHAPTER 7   CLOUDS, PRECIPITATION, AND WEATHER RADAR   163

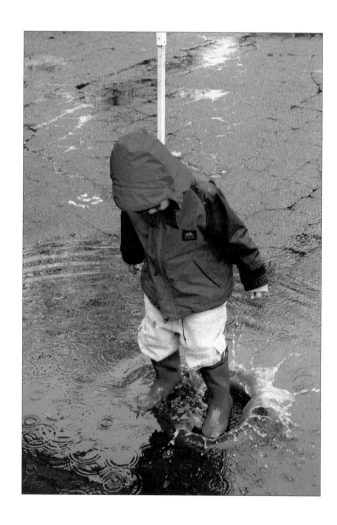

CHAPTER 8   WIND AND WEATHER

CHAPTER 9   ATMOSPHERE'S PLANETARY CIRCULATION

CHAPTER 10   WEATHER SYSTEMS OF MIDDLE LATITUDES   265

CHAPTER 11   THUNDERSTORMS AND TORNADOES

CHAPTER 12   TROPICAL WEATHER SYSTEMS

CHAPTER 13   WEATHER ANALYSIS AND FORECASTING   363

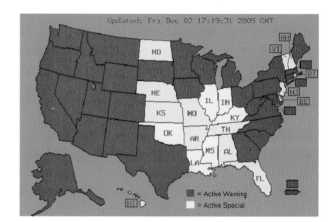

CHAPTER 14   LIGHT AND SOUND IN THE ATMOSPHERE   391

CHAPTER 15   CLIMATE AND CLIMATE CHANGE   409

PREFACE

Welcome to *Weather Studies*! You are about to embark on an exciting study of the science of the atmosphere. The purpose of this book is to provide you with background information on the properties of the atmosphere, the scientific principles that govern weather and climate, interactions between the atmosphere and the other components of the Earth system, and the implications of those interactions for humankind. *Weather Studies* was developed by the Education Program of the American Meteorological Society (AMS) with support from the National Science Foundation (NSF) and the National Oceanic and Atmospheric Administration (NOAA).

Weather Studies may serve as a stand alone textbook in a traditional undergraduate college course on the atmosphere, meteorology, or weather and climate. *Weather Studies* also serves as the reference book for *Online Weather Studies*, a turnkey distance learning course developed, licensed and nationally implemented by AMS. A companion *Investigations Manual* plus website provide students with twice-weekly investigations on weather partially delivered via the Internet. In this way the course can be offered partially or totally online.

Weather Studies introduces the reader to scientific inquiry and the scientific method. Atmospheric science is particularly suited to these aims because it is an applied science that readily lends itself to familiar everyday illustrations. The inquiry-based approach is designed to promote the development of critical thinking skills. The emphasis on scientific methodology provides a perspective on the accomplishments of atmospheric scientists and the challenges still facing them. Early on the reader realizes that weather is not an arbitrary act of nature, weather forecasting has its limits, and the climate future is uncertain. Integrated throughout the book are topics of special contemporary interest including, for example, threats to the stratospheric ozone shield, global climate change, and severe weather.

This book consists of 15 chapters. Each of the first 12 chapters corresponds to one week of the *Online Weather Studies* distance learning course. Chapters are organized so that concepts build logically one upon the other so that Earth's atmosphere emerges as an interactive system subject to physical laws. Investigations are tied directly to each chapter. Topics covered include sources of weather information (Chapter 1), composition and structure of the atmosphere (Chapter 2), the planet's radiation budget and controls of temperature (Chapters 3 and 4), air pressure (Chapter 5), humidity, clouds and precipitation (Chapter 6 and 7), forces governing atmospheric circulation (Chapter 8), planetary-scale circulation (Chapter 9), weather of middle latitudes (Chapter 10), thunderstorms and tornadoes (Chapter 11), and tropical storms and hurricanes (Chapter 12). The final three chapters cover weather analysis and forecasting (Chapter 13), atmospheric optics and acoustics (Chapter 14), and climate and climate change (Chapter 15). All chapters have accompanying investigations in the optional *Investigations Manual*.

Each chapter opens with a *Case-in-Point*, an authentic, relevant, and real-life event or issue that highlights or applies one or more of the main concepts covered in the chapter. In essence, the Case-in-Point previews the chapter and is intended to engage reader interest early on. Chapter 12 (Tropical Weather Systems), for example, opens with a discussion of Hurricane Katrina and its impact on the Gulf Coast. The Case-in-Point is followed by a sample *Driving Question*, a broad-based query that links chapter concepts and provides a central focus for that week's study. Chapter content is science-rich and informs additional driving questions. Each chapter closes with a list of *Basic Understandings* and questions for *Review* and *Critical Thinking*. One or more *Essays* at the end of each chapter address in some depth specific topics that complement or supplement a concept covered in the narrative. Examples include *The Atmosphere of Mars*, *Hazards of Solar Ultraviolet Radiation*, *Human Responses to Changes in Air Pressure*, and *Santa Ana Winds and California Fire Weather*. All terms bold-faced in the narrative are defined in the *Glossary* at the back of the book. Appendixes cover unit conversions, milestones in the history of atmospheric science, and climate classification.

In this third edition, we have updated the science and case studies, included more Essays, and added new photographs and line drawings. New, expanded or significantly revised topics include Evolution of the Atmosphere (Chapter 2), The Gas Law (Chapter 5), Acid Deposition (Chapter 7), Monsoon Circulation (Chapter 9), El Niño and La Niña (Chapter 9), Ocean/Atmosphere

Oscillations (Chapter 9), Trends in Severe Weather (Chapter 11), Hurricane Threat to the Southeastern United States (Chapter 12), Weather Prediction (Chapter 13), Atmospheric Acoustics (Chapter 14), and Potential Impacts of Climate Change (Chapter 15).

The distance-learning course package, *Online Weather Studies*, is pedagogically guided by a teaching approach (*project-based science*) that seeks to engage learners in exploring their world by investigating meaningful questions. *Weather Studies* offers one driving question per chapter but each chapter plus investigations inspire and explore many other driving questions. Each investigation has printed and electronic components that make use of weather and climate data available via the course website. Investigations engage participants in observation, prediction, data analysis, inference, and critical thinking (processes of science). The course presents opportunities for collaboration among participants as together they negotiate understanding. Application of information-age technology helps participants to develop their ability to retrieve and analyze real-world data and share interpretations. Throughout the course, participants assemble learning materials (artifacts) for assessment purposes.

Development work leading to *Online Weather Studies* was originally supported by the National Science Foundation under Grant No. DUE-9752416. Subsequent development of *Online Weather Studies* was funded by the National Science Foundation through its Opportunities for Enhancing Diversity in the Geosciences (OEDG) Program, Grant No. GEO-0119740, and its Course, Curriculum and Laboratory Improvement–National Dissemination (CCLI-ND) Program, Grant No. DUE-0126032.

Weather Studies is the product of collaboration among many individuals having considerable teaching experience in the atmospheric sciences. This book is primarily the work of Joseph M. Moran, Associate Director of the American Meteorological Society's Education Program and Professor Emeritus of Earth Science at the University of Wisconsin-Green Bay. Development of this third edition benefited greatly from suggestions and critical reviews provided by Ira W. Geer, Bernard A. Blair, Elizabeth W. Mills, and W. Ross Foniri of the AMS Education Program, Robert S. Weinbeck of SUNY College at Brockport and the AMS Education Program, Edward J. Hopkins of the University of Wisconsin-Madison, James A. Brey of the University of Wisconsin-Fox Valley, Steven J. Meyer of the University of Wisconsin-Green Bay, Margaret F. Boorstein of the C.W. Post Campus of Long Island University, and William A. Porter of Elizabeth City State University (NC). For numerous helpful comments and suggestions, special thanks are extended to all past instructors of *Online Weather Studies*.

Norman J. Frisch of Brockport, NY did an excellent job of turning line drawings into final art. Unless otherwise indicated, Joseph M. Moran supplied photographs. Bernard A. Blair of the AMS Education Program met the numerous technical challenges in turning the original manuscript into this book with his usual skill, attention to detail, dedication, enthusiasm, and perseverance. Thanks also to Ashley L. Boivin of the University of Wisconsin-Green Bay for her thorough library research.

A special note concerns the use of units in *Weather Studies*. Generally the International System of Units (abbreviated SI, for Systéme Internationale d'Unitès) is employed with equivalent English or other units following in parentheses. Exceptions are units used by convention or convenience in meteorology or the user community (e.g., knots, calories, millibars). Also, the equivalence between units is given in context; that is, where general estimates are used, approximate values are shown in all units. Conversion factors are given in Appendix I.

Ira W. Geer
AMS Education Program

CHAPTER 1

MONITORING THE WEATHER

Case in Point

Cloud-to-ground lightning during a night-time thunderstorm in Norman, Oklahoma. [Courtesy NOAA Photo Library, OAR/ERL/ National Severe Storms Laboratory]

On the morning of 12 January 1888, an unusually ferocious blizzard swept southeastward across eastern Montana and bore down on the Dakota Territory and Nebraska. Gale-force winds ushered in a frigid arctic air mass with wind-chill temperatures plummeting to near −40 °C (−40 °F) in some places. Wind-driven snow reduced visibility to near zero. The storm struck the small towns and isolated farms abruptly, without warning and with tragic results.

In the Dakota Territory and Nebraska, the day began mild, almost spring-like, a welcome respite from several weeks of bitter cold on the prairie. Farmers took advantage of the pleasant weather to attend to chores that took them into their fields well away from the safety of their homes. When the blizzard struck, many became disoriented and were unable to find their way to shelter. In Nebraska, the storm hit just as schools were letting out for the day. Because the day started mild, many students were inadequately dressed for the rapidly deteriorating conditions as they trudged home through the snow and cold winds. All told, an estimated 250 to 500 people perished from the storm—many of them school children. For this reason, the storm is referred to as the *Children's Blizzard.*

About two months later, on 12-14 March 1888, a powerful coastal storm accompanied by heavy snow and strong winds blasted the Eastern Seaboard from Washington, DC northward into southern New England. The so-called *Blizzard of '88* brought to a standstill virtually all activity (Figure 1.1). Particularly hard hit was New York City where the three-day snowfall total was 53 cm (21 in.) and 65 km (40 mi) per hr winds whipped snow into drifts 4.5 to 6.0 m (15 to 20 ft) deep. Much greater snowfalls (generally 100 to 125 cm or 40 to 50 in.) and deeper snowdrifts (to 12 m or 40 ft) were reported over southeastern New York, western Connecticut and western Massachusetts. An estimated 300 people (200 in New York City) lost their lives to exposure, accidents, or overexertion; almost 200 ships were sunk or damaged with nearly 100 lives lost; hundreds of trains stalled in deep snow drifts, marooning passengers for days; and telephone and telegraph lines were severed.

The *Children's Blizzard* and the *Blizzard of '88* were total surprises for the people impacted by these storms. At the time, the U.S. Army Signal Corps had operated the nation's weather service for more than 17 years, and observers at some 154 weather stations nationwide

FIGURE 1.1
Scenes of the aftermath of the blizzard of 12-14 March 1888 in New York City (top) and Farmington, CT (bottom). [NOAA Photo Library, Historic NWS Collection]

telegraphed weather observations three times daily to headquarters in Washington, DC. *Indications* (later called weather forecasts) were issued based on surface weather observations alone. In St. Paul, MN an experimental office was charged with forecasting cold waves and blizzards for the Northern Plains. The technology of the day and the limited understanding of the workings of the atmosphere put meteorologists at a distinct disadvantage in forecasting storms, especially storms that tracked offshore, parallel to the Atlantic coast (so-called *nor'easters*). There were no means of monitoring the upper atmosphere, no satellites, no radar, no wireless communications with ships at sea, and no computer models.

Communicating weather warnings to the public was another serious short coming. This was before radio, television, and the Internet so that the public received most (if any) of their weather information from newspapers that may have been a day old. The officer in charge at the St. Paul office knew that the blizzard was heading toward the Dakota Territory and Nebraska and sent warnings via telegraph. However, the telegraph lines ran along the railroad tracks, too far away from most of the region's residents for them to receive any advance warning.

More than a century later, in December 2000, a powerful coastal storm threatened to paralyze the major metropolitan areas from Washington, DC northeastward to Boston with heavy snow and strong, gusty winds. This time, weather forecasters were much better prepared and there would be no surprises. Satellites continually monitored the storm's developing cloud shield and tracked its movements; radar located heavy snow bands sweeping onshore; a flood of weather observational data from the surface and upper atmosphere fed into sophisticated computer models running on supercomputers. Well in advance of the storm's arrival, the National Weather Service issued winter storm watches and warnings that were rapidly communicated via the electronic media to the public and public service agencies. Some school districts announced closings more than 12 hours before the first snowflake was expected, and people stocked up on food, videos, and other supplies in case they were marooned at home.

But in spite of the great technological advances in weather observation, forecasting, and communications since 1888, the much anticipated snowstorm of 2000 spared the major metropolitan areas. Washington, DC, for example, reported only a few snowflakes. What happened? Post-event analysis by meteorologists revealed that the storm failed to intensify where expected over the ocean because sea-surface temperatures were too low. One of the computer models they relied on for forecasting the development of the storm uses satellite-derived sea-surface temperatures. But persistent cloudiness off the East Coast in the weeks before the storm prevented updating of sea-surface temperature data. Using the earlier-obtained temperatures that were too high, the model overestimated the amount of ocean-water evaporation, key to the intensification of the storm. Although the forecast failed to verify, meteorologists learned from the experience. Today, new technology that provides sea-surface temperatures under all sky conditions adds information that is incorporated in computerized storm-prediction models, thereby benefiting future forecasts. The December 2000 storm reminds us, however, that while weather analysis and forecasting have greatly benefited from advances in science and technology, we still have more to learn about the workings of Earth's atmosphere.

Driving Question:

What are some basic characteristics of the atmosphere and weather?

We are about to embark on a systematic study of our continually changing atmospheric environment. We will observe weather as it happens while becoming familiar with some of the basic scientific principles and understandings that govern the atmospheric environment. As our study progresses, we will combine our observational experiences with what we have learned in exploring a wide variety of atmospheric phenomena ranging from cold waves to hurricanes. Long before the end of the course, we will understand that the behavior of the atmosphere is not arbitrary; its workings are explainable in scientific terms, drawn from many scientific disciplines, such as physics and chemistry. At the same time, questions are likely to persist regarding past, present, and future weather and climate.

If you are counting on studying storms, tornadoes, fronts, hailstorms, and the like right away, you will not be disappointed. Significant weather events will be observed and discussed as they happen via information delivered by the Internet, and they will be explored in greater detail after relevant scientific foundations have been established. You can begin some activities now—today in fact—that will involve you in weather events, and enrich and enliven your study of the atmosphere. Our objective in this first chapter is to introduce and describe some of the tools and basic understandings that will guide your investigation.

Weather and Climate

Everyone has considerable experience with (and understanding of) the subject matter of this book. After all, each of us has been living with weather all our lives. Regardless of where we live or what we do, we are well aware of the far-reaching influence of weather. To a large extent, weather dictates how we dress, how we drive, and even our choice of recreational activities. Before setting off in the morning, most of us check the latest weather forecast on radio or TV or glance out the window to look at the sky or read the thermometer. Every day, we acquire information on weather through our senses, the media, and perhaps our own weather instruments. From that information, we acquire a basic understanding of how the atmosphere functions. We are now hearing that our

climate is changing and that these changes could affect society in significant ways.

Weather is defined as the state of the atmosphere at some place and time, described in terms of such quantitative variables as temperature, humidity, cloudiness, precipitation, and wind speed and direction. Thousands of weather stations around the world monitor these weather variables at Earth's surface at least on an hourly basis. A place and time must be specified when describing weather because the atmosphere is dynamic and its state changes from one place to another and with time. At the same hour, the weather may be cold and snowy in New York City, warm and humid in Miami, and hot and dry in Phoenix. *If you don't like the weather, wait a minute* is an old saying that is not far from the truth in many areas of the nation. From personal experience, we know that tomorrow's weather may differ markedly from today's weather. **Meteorology** is the study of the atmosphere and the processes that cause weather.

While day to day weather can be variable, we are aware that the weather of a particular location tends to follow reasonably consistent seasonal variations, with temperatures higher in summer and lower in winter. In addition, we associate the tropics with warmer weather and smaller seasonal contrasts than polar latitudes. Because arithmetic averages of weather elements (e.g., temperature, precipitation) taken over a span of years are often the easiest way of describing typical weather conditions, **climate** is popularly defined as weather conditions at some locality averaged over a specified time period. By international convention, average values of climatic elements are computed over a 30-year period beginning with the first year of a decade. At the close of a decade, the averaging period is moved forward ten years. For the first decade of the twenty-first century, 1971-2000 is the official averaging period. Thirty-year average monthly and annual temperatures and precipitation totals are commonly used to describe the climate of some locality. Other useful climatic parameters include average seasonal snowfall, length of growing season, percent of possible sunshine, and number of days with dense fog. Climate is the ultimate environmental control in that it governs, for example, what crops can be cultivated, the fresh water supply, and the average heating and cooling requirements for homes.

In addition to average values of weather elements, the description of a locale's climate encompasses extremes in weather (e.g., highest and lowest temperature, greatest 24-hr snowfall, most intense rainfall). Tabulation of extreme values usually covers the entire period of record (or at least the period when observations were made at the same location). Records of weather extremes provide information on the variability of climate at a particular place and give a more complete and useful description of climate. Farmers, for example, are interested in knowing not only the average summer rainfall, but also the frequency of extremely wet or dry summers. **Climatology** is the study of climate, its controls, and spatial and temporal variability.

Sources of Weather Information

Until now, for most of us, keeping track of the weather has been a casual part of daily life. From now on, or at least for the duration of this course, weather observation will be a more formal and regular activity. As a key part of this course, you are encouraged to access current weather data via the Internet frequently each week. In addition, we suggest that you tune to a televised weathercast at least once a day. Weathercasts are routine segments of the local morning, noon, and evening news reports. If you have cable television, you may choose to watch *The Weather Channel*, a 24-hour-a-day telecast devoted exclusively to weather reports and forecasts, both nationally and locally.

If television is not available, weather information may be obtained by reading local or national newspapers or by listening to radio broadcasts. Most newspapers include a weather column or page featuring maps and statistical summaries. Radio stations provide the latest local weather conditions and forecasts, but often do not include a summary of weather conditions across the nation unless some newsworthy event has occurred such as a hurricane or tornado outbreak.

A valuable source of local weather information is the **NOAA Weather Radio (NWR)**. As a public service, the *National Oceanic and Atmospheric Administration (NOAA)*, the parent organization of the *National Weather Service (NWS)*, operates low-power, VHF high band FM radio transmitters that broadcast continuous weather information (e.g., regional conditions, local forecasts, marine warnings, and local climatological statistics) directly from NWS forecast offices 24 hrs a day. A series of messages is repeated every 4 to 6 minutes and some messages are updated hourly. When weather-related hazards threaten, NWS forecasters interrupt routine reports

and issue watches, warnings, and advisories appropriate to the hazard.

The NWR is an all-hazards radio network. Working with other federal agencies and the Federal Communications Commission's Emergency Alert System, the NWR provides the public with warnings and post-event information for all types of hazards: weather, natural (e.g., earthquakes, tsunamis, volcanic eruptions), technological (e.g., oil spills, chemical leaks), and other non-weather emergencies (e.g., terrorist attacks, Amber alerts).

A special *weather radio* is required to receive NWR transmissions because the seven broadcast frequencies (from 162.40 to 162.55 MHz) are outside the range of standard AM/FM radios (Figure 1.2). Some weather radios are designed to sound a tone alarm or switch on automatically when a weather watch or warning or other emergency information is issued. The latest generation weather radio is equipped with the *Specific Area Message Encoding (SAME)* feature that sounds an alarm only if a weather watch or warning is issued specifically for a county or limited local area programmed (selected) by the user. Depending on terrain, the maximum range of NOAA weather radio broadcasts is about 65 km (40 mi). As of this writing, about 900 transmitters are operating in the 50 states, the District of Columbia, Puerto Rico, the U.S. Virgin Islands, and the U.S. Pacific Territories. Expansion of this service is expected to eventually bring 95% of the U.S. population within range of NOAA weather radio broadcasts. In many communities, NOAA weather radio broadcasts are also available on cable TV and broadcast television's secondary audio programming channels. *Environment Canada* has

FIGURE 1.2
At the push of a button, this weather radio monitors weather reports, forecasts, watches and warnings issued by the National Weather Service.

167 transmitters in its Weatheradio network, operating on the same seven frequencies as the NWR network and broadcasting in the nation's two official languages.

Another rich source of weather information is the Internet. The World Wide Web provides real-time access to weather maps, satellite images, national weather radar summaries, and weather forecasts, plus updates on environmental issues, such as trends in global climate, stratospheric ozone, and air quality. All NWS forecast offices maintain homepages that provide a variety of current meteorological, climatological, and hydrological information. This course's website also brings you a host of real-time weather data via the Internet.

Weather Systems and Weather Maps

Weather information received via Internet, television, or newspapers may include: (1) national and regional weather maps; (2) satellite or radar images (or video loops) depicting large-scale cloud, precipitation and atmospheric circulation patterns; (3) data on current and past (24-hr) weather conditions; and (4) weather forecasts for the short-term (24 to 48 hrs) and long-term (up to 7 days or longer). So that your weather watching is more meaningful and useful, the remainder of this chapter is devoted to a description of what to watch for, beginning with features plotted on the national weather map.

Temperature, dewpoint, wind, and air pressure are among the many atmospheric variables that are routinely monitored by instruments at surface weather stations (Figure 1.3). These data are transmitted to a central facility where they are assembled and plotted on surface weather maps. In order to represent the state of the atmosphere at a particular time, weather observations are taken simultaneously around the world. (For information on time keeping see the first Essay at the end of this chapter.) Special symbols are used on national weather maps to identify and locate the principal weather-makers, that is, pressure systems and fronts (Figure 1.4). (For an historical sketch on the origins of weather maps, refer to this chapter's second Essay.)

Pressure systems are of two types, *highs* (or anticyclones) and *lows* (or cyclones). The high and low designations refer to air pressure. We can think of **air pressure** as the weight per unit area of a column of air that stretches upward from the Earth's surface (or any altitude within the atmosphere) to the top of the atmosphere. At any specified time, air pressure at the Earth's surface varies from one place to another across the continent.

FIGURE 1.3
The National Weather Service's Automated Surface Observing System (ASOS) consists of electronically operated meteorological sensors, computers, and communications ports that record and transmit atmospheric conditions (e.g., temperature, humidity, wind) automatically 24 hrs per day.

On a weather map, *H* or *High* symbolizes the center of regions where the air pressure is relatively high compared to surrounding areas. Conversely, *L* or *Low* signifies the center of regions where the air pressure is relatively low compared to surrounding areas.

As you examine weather maps, note the following about pressure systems:

1. Usually highs are accompanied by fair weather and hence are described as *fair-weather systems*. Highs that originate in northwestern Canada bring cold, dry weather in winter and cool, dry weather in summer to much of the coterminous United States. Highs that develop further south over land may bring hot, dry weather in summer and mild, dry weather in winter.

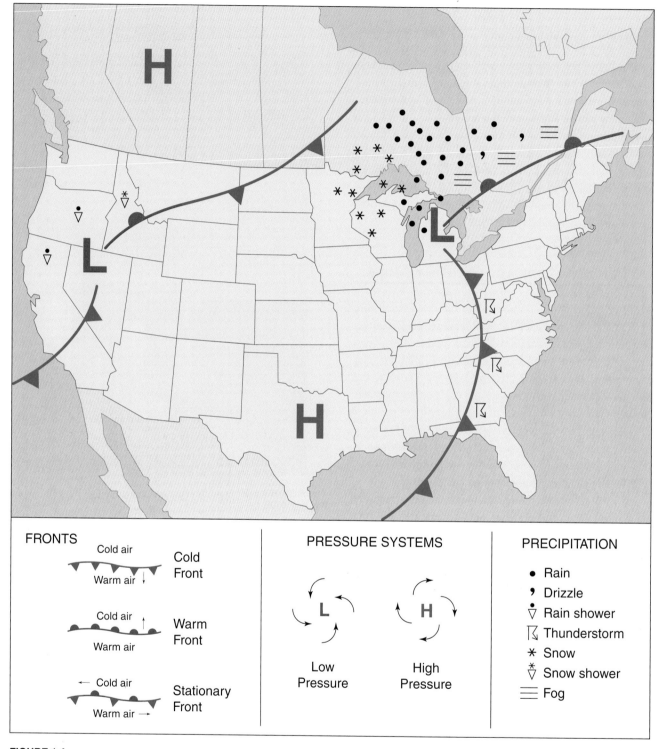

FIGURE 1.4
On a weather map, special symbols represent the state of the atmosphere over a broad geographical area at a specific time.

2. Viewed from above in the Northern Hemisphere, surface winds in a high-pressure system blow in a clockwise and outward spiral as shown in Figure 1.5A. Calm conditions or light winds are typical over a broad area at the center of a high.

3. Most lows produce cloudy, rainy or snowy weather and are often described as *stormy-weather systems*. An exception may be lows that

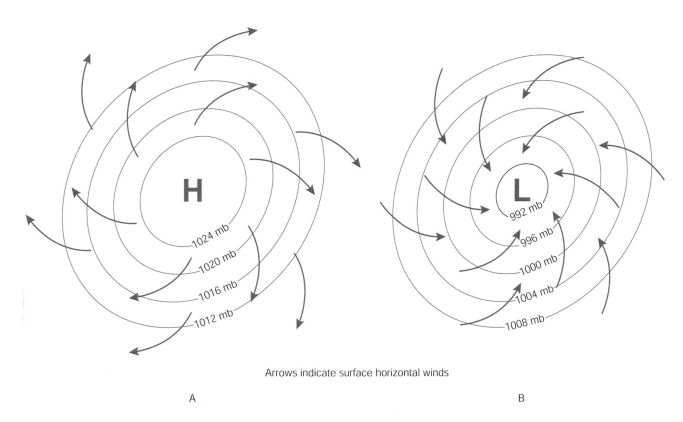

Arrows indicate surface horizontal winds

A   B

FIGURE 1.5
Viewed from above in the Northern Hemisphere, winds near the Earth's surface blow (A) clockwise and outward from a high-pressure system, and (B) counterclockwise and inward into a low-pressure system. Blue lines are isobars, passing through places having the same air pressure in millibars (mb). Isobars are drawn at intervals of 4 millibars.

develop over arid or semiarid terrain, such as the Desert Southwest, especially in summer. In such areas, intense solar heating of the ground raises the air temperature and lowers the surface air pressure, producing a low that remains stationary over the hot ground and is not accompanied by stormy weather.

4. Viewed from above in the Northern Hemisphere, surface winds in a low-pressure system blow in a counterclockwise and inward spiral as shown in Figure 1.5B.

5. Both highs and lows move with the prevailing wind several kilometers above the surface, generally eastward across North America, and as they do, the weather changes at places in their paths. Highs follow lows and lows follow highs resulting in alternating changes from inclement weather to fair weather (that can be monitored as changes in air pressure). As a general rule, highs track toward the east and southeast whereas lows track toward the east and northeast. An important exception is tropical cyclones (e.g.,

hurricanes, tropical storms) that often move from east to west over the tropical North Atlantic Ocean before turning north and then eastward in middle latitudes.

6. Lows that track across the northern United States or southern Canada are more distant from sources of moisture and usually produce less rain- or snowfall than lows that track further south (such as lows that travel out of eastern Colorado and move along the Gulf Coast or up the Eastern Seaboard).

7. Weather on the left side (west and north) of a midlatitude storm's track (path) tends to be relatively cold, whereas weather on the right (east and south) of a storm's track tends to be relatively warm. For this reason, winter snows are most likely to the west and north of the path of a low-pressure system.

Air masses and fronts are also important weather-makers. An **air mass** is a huge volume of air covering hundreds of thousands of square kilometers that is horizontally relatively uniform in temperature and humidity, typically associated with a large high pressure system. The specific characteristics of an air mass depend on the types of surface over which the air mass forms (its *source region*) and travels. Cold air masses form at higher latitudes over surfaces that are often snow or ice covered, whereas warm air masses form in the lower latitudes where the Earth's surface is relatively warm. Humid air masses form over moist maritime surfaces (e.g., Pacific Ocean, Gulf of Mexico), whereas dry air masses develop over dry continental surfaces (e.g., Desert Southwest, northwestern Canada). The four basic types of air masses are cold and dry, cold and humid, warm and dry, and warm and humid.

A **front** is a narrow transition zone between air masses that differ in temperature, humidity, or both. Fronts form where contrasting air masses meet, and the associated air movements often give rise to cloudiness and precipitation. The most common fronts are stationary, cold, and warm; weather map symbols for all three are shown in Figure 1.4. As the name implies, a *stationary front* is just that, stationary (or nearly so). On both sides of a stationary front, winds blow roughly parallel to the front but in opposite directions. A shift in wind direction may cause a portion of a stationary front to advance northward (becoming a warm front) or southward (becoming a cold front). At the same pressure, warm air is less dense than cold air so that a warm air mass advances by gliding up and over a retreating cold air mass. The cold air forms a wedge under the warm air and the leading edge of warm air at

the Earth's surface is plotted on a weather map as a *warm front* (Figure 1.6A). On the other hand, cold air advances by sliding under and pushing up the less dense warm air and the leading edge of cold air at the Earth's surface is plotted on a weather map as a *cold front* (Figure 1.6B). Consequently, the boundary between warm and cold air associated with a warm front slopes more gently with altitude than does the boundary between warm and cold air associated with a cold front.

FIGURE 1.6

The two most common types of fronts are (A) a warm front that marks the boundary between advancing relatively warm (less dense) air and retreating cold (more dense) air, and (B) a cold front that marks the boundary between advancing cold air and retreating warm air. In both diagrams the fronts are shown in vertical cross-section with the vertical scale greatly exaggerated.

As you examine surface weather maps, note the following about air masses and fronts:

1. In response to regular seasonal changes in the duration and intensity of sunlight, polar air masses are much colder in winter and milder in summer. By contrast, in the tropics, sunlight is nearly uniform in duration and intensity throughout the year so that tropical air masses are warm and exhibit less seasonal variation in temperature.

2. An air mass modifies (becomes warmer, colder, more humid, drier) as it moves away from its source region with the degree of modification dependent on the properties of the surface over which the air mass travels. For example, a cold air mass warms more if it travels over ground that is bare rather than snow-covered.

3. Fronts are three-dimensional and the map symbol for a front is plotted where the frontal surface intersects Earth's surface.

4. Most cloudiness and precipitation associated with a warm front occur over a broad band, often hundreds of kilometers wide, in advance of where the front intersects Earth's surface. Widespread precipitation ahead of a warm front generally is light to moderate in intensity and may persist at a particular location from 12 to 24 hrs or longer.

5. Most cloudiness and precipitation associated with a cold front occur as a narrow band along or just ahead of where the front intersects Earth's surface. Although precipitation often is showery and may last from a few minutes to a few hours, its intensity can be very heavy.

6. Wind direction (and at times wind speed) differs on opposite sides of a front.

7. Some fronts are not accompanied by cloudiness or precipitation. A shift in wind direction, together with changes in air pressure, temperature and/or humidity typically accompany the passage of the front.

8. In summer, air temperatures can be nearly the same ahead of and behind a cold front. In that case, the air masses on opposite sides of the front differ primarily in humidity; that is, the air mass ahead of the advancing front is more humid (and therefore less dense) and the air mass behind the front is drier (denser). With passage of the front, refreshingly drier air replaces uncomfortably humid air.

9. Cold and warm fronts are plotted on a weather map as heavy lines that are usually anchored at the center of a low-pressure system. The counterclockwise and inward circulation about a low brings contrasting air masses together to form fronts. By contrast, the outward flow of relatively homogeneous air from a high precludes development of fronts.

10. A low-pressure system may develop along a stationary front and travel rapidly like a large ripple from west to east along the front.

11. Thunderstorms and associated severe weather (e.g., tornadoes, hail) most often develop south and southeast of the center of a low-pressure system, that is, in the warm, humid air mass located between the cold front and the warm front.

As you monitor national and regional weather maps, also watch for the following:

1. Cool sea breezes or lake breezes may push inland perhaps 10 to 50 km (6 to 30 mi) and lower summer afternoon temperatures in coastal areas.

2. Beginning in late fall and continuing through much of the winter, lake-effect snows fall in narrow bands on the downwind (eastern and southern) shores of the Great Lakes and Utah's Great Salt Lake. Such snowfalls are highly localized and can be very heavy.

3. Severe thunderstorms and tornadoes are most common in spring and early summer across the central United States, especially from east Texas northward to Nebraska and from Iowa eastward to central Indiana.

4. Thunderstorms are most frequent in Florida, on the western High Plains and eastern slopes of the Rockies, but are relatively rare along the Pacific coast and on the Hawaiian Islands.

5. Tropical storms and hurricanes occasionally impact the Atlantic and Gulf coasts, primarily from August through October. However, these tropical weather systems are rare on the West Coast.

Describing the State of the Atmosphere

Internet, television, and newspaper weather reports usually include statistical summaries of present and past weather conditions. These data are compiled to form a climatology for a locale. It is useful to briefly comment on the meaning of the most common weather parameters:

- *Maximum temperature.* The highest air temperature recorded over a 24-hr period, usually between midnight of one day and midnight of the next day. Typically, but not always, the day's maximum temperature occurs in the early to mid-afternoon. In the United States, surface air temperatures are reported in degrees Fahrenheit (°F) and in most other countries in degrees Celsius (°C).

- *Minimum temperature.* The lowest air temperature recorded over a 24-hr period, usually between midnight of one day and midnight of the next day. Typically, but not always, the minimum temperature occurs around sunrise.

- *Dewpoint* (or *frost point*). The temperature to which air must be cooled at constant pressure to become saturated with water vapor and for dew (or frost) to begin forming on relatively cold surfaces.

- *Relative humidity.* A measure of the actual concentration of the water vapor component of air compared to the concentration the air would have if saturated with water vapor. Relative humidity is always expressed as a percentage. Because the saturation concentration varies with air temperature so too does the relative humidity. On most days, the relative humidity is highest during the coldest time of day (around sunrise) and lowest during the warmest time of day (early to mid-afternoon).

- *Precipitation amount.* Depth of rainfall or melted snowfall over a 24-hr period, usually from midnight of one day to midnight of the next, measured to one-hundredth of an inch in the United States and in millimeters elsewhere. On average, 10 inches of freshly fallen snow melt down to 1 inch of water.

- *Air pressure.* The weight of a column of air over a unit area of the Earth's surface. With a mercury barometer, the traditional instrument for measuring air pressure, the pressure exerted by the atmosphere supports a column of mercury to a certain height and the mercury column fluctuates up and down as the air pressure rises and falls. This is the reason air pressure is commonly reported in units of length, that is, inches or millimeters of mercury. In the United States,

meteorologists express air pressure in millibars (mb), a unit of pressure. The average air pressure at sea-level is 1013.25 mb, corresponding to the pressure exerted by a 29.92 in. (760 mm) column of mercury. Falling air pressure over a span of several hours often signals an approaching low-pressure system and a turn to stormy weather. Rising air pressure, on the other hand, indicates an approaching high-pressure system, with clearing skies or continued fair weather.

- *Wind direction* and *wind speed*. According to meteorological tradition, wind direction is the compass direction *from which* the wind blows (Figure 1.7). For example, a southeast wind blows from the southeast toward the northwest and a west wind blows from the west toward the east. As a general rule, at middle latitudes a wind shift from east to northeast to north to northwest is accompanied by falling air temperatures. On the other hand, a wind shift from east to southeast to south usually brings warmer weather. Over a broad area about the center of a high-pressure system calm air or light winds prevail. Wind speed tends to increase markedly as a cold front

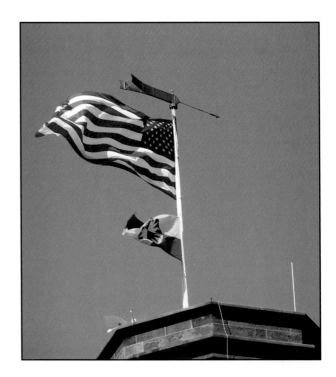

FIGURE 1.7
Wind vane atop the Smithsonian Building in Washington, DC. The arrow of the wind vane points in the direction from which the wind is blowing, as confirmed by the flags that are stretched out in the downwind direction. [Photo by R.S. Weinbeck]

passes a location and winds are particularly strong and gusty in the vicinity of thunderstorms.

- *Sky cover.* Based on the fraction of the sky that is cloud covered, the sky is described as clear (no clouds), a few clouds (1/8 to 2/8 cloud cover), scattered clouds (3/8 to 4/8), broken clouds (5/8 to 7/8), and overcast (completely cloud-covered). All other factors being equal, nights are coldest when the sky is clear and the air is relatively dry. An overcast sky elevates the day's minimum temperature and lowers the day's maximum temperature.
- *Weather watch.* Issued by the National Weather Service when hazardous weather (e.g., tornadoes, heavy snowfall) is considered possible based on current or anticipated atmospheric conditions.
- *Weather warning.* Issued by the National Weather Service when hazardous weather is imminent or actually taking place.

Weather Satellite Imagery

Satellite images and video loops (composed of successive images) are routine components of many televised and Internet-delivered weather reports. Some newspaper weather pages also feature satellite images. Sensors on weather satellites orbiting Earth provide a unique and valuable perspective on the state of the atmosphere over broad areas and enable meteorologists to remotely measure temperature and humidity as well as to locate and track weather systems.

The weather satellite images most familiar to us are those obtained by sensors onboard a **Geostationary Operational Environmental Satellite (GOES)** orbiting Earth about 36,000 km (22,300 mi) above the planet's surface. A GOES satellite orbits the planet at a rate that matches Earth's rotation and in the same eastward direction so that it is always positioned over the same spot on the Earth's surface and its sensors have the same field of view (Figure 1.8). The *subsatellite point*, the location on Earth's surface directly below the satellite, is essentially on the equator. Two geostationary satellites, one over South America (near 75 degrees W longitude) and the other over the eastern Pacific (approximately 135 degrees W longitude), provide a complete view of much of North America and adjacent portions of the Pacific and Atlantic Oceans to latitudes of about 60 degrees. Considerable distortion sets in near the edge of this field of view so that polar-orbiting satellites complement geostationary satellites in monitoring the planet.

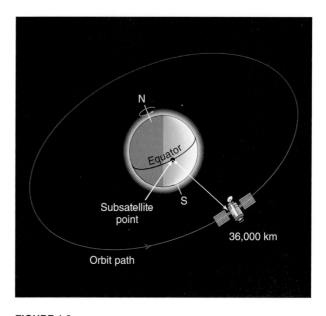

FIGURE 1.8
A geostationary weather satellite (GOES) orbits Earth so that it is always positioned over the same spot on Earth's surface.

A **Polar-orbiting Operational Environmental Satellite (POES)** travels in a relatively low (800 to 1000 km) nearly north-south orbit passing close to the poles (Figure 1.9). The satellite's orbit defines a plane in space while the planet continually rotates on its axis

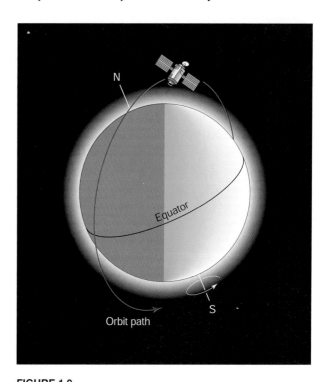

FIGURE 1.9
A polar-orbiting weather satellite (POES) orbits Earth in a nearly north-south direction passing near the poles.

through the plane of the satellite's orbit. With each orbit, points on Earth's surface (except near the poles) move eastward so that onboard sensors sweep out successive overlapping north-south strips. Sun-synchronous polar-orbiting weather satellites pass over essentially the same area twice every 24 hrs.

A weather satellite's onboard sensors receive two types of signals from Earth: reflected sunlight and emitted infrared radiation (IR). Sunlight reflected by Earth's surface and atmosphere produces images that are essentially black and white photographs of the planet. Sun-lit, highly reflective surfaces such as cloud tops and snow-covered ground appear bright white whereas less reflective surfaces such as evergreen forests and the ocean appear much darker. Cloud patterns on a **visible satellite image** are of particular interest to meteorologists (Figure 1.10). From analysis of cloud patterns displayed on the image, they can identify not only a specific type of weather system (such as a hurricane), but also the stage of its life cycle and its direction of movement when a sequence of images is animated.

A second type of sensor onboard a weather satellite detects infrared radiation (IR). IR is an invisible form of radiation emitted by all objects continually, both day and night. Hence, an **infrared satellite image** of the planet can provide useful information at any time whereas visible weather satellite images are available only during daylight hours. (Because of around-the-clock availability, infrared satellite images are usually shown on television.) IR signals are routinely calibrated to give the temperature of objects in the sensor's field of view. This is possible because the intensity of IR emitted by an object depends on its surface temperature; that is, relatively warm objects emit more intense IR than do relatively cold objects. IR-derived temperatures are calibrated on a gray scale such that the brightest white indicates the lowest temperature and dark gray indicates the highest temperature. Alternately, a color scale is used so that, for example, reds and oranges represent high temperatures and blues and violets signal low temperatures.

The temperature dependency of IR emission makes it possible, for example, to distinguish low clouds from high clouds on an IR satellite image. In the part of the atmosphere where most clouds occur (the lowest 10 km or 6 mi or so), air temperature usually drops with increasing altitude. The tops of high clouds are colder than the tops of low clouds and emit less intense IR

Visible Image   1415Z 22 APR 2005

NCEP/NWS/NOAA

FIGURE 1.10
A sample visible satellite image from sensors onboard a geostationary satellite.

Infrared Image   1415Z 22 APR 2005

NCEP/NWS/NOAA

FIGURE 1.11
A sample infrared satellite image from sensors onboard a geostationary satellite, taken at the same time as Figure 1.10.

radiation. In the sample IR satellite image in Figure 1.11, high clouds appear bright white whereas low clouds are darker. IR sensors are tuned to detect those wavelength bands where some of the radiation emitted from Earth's surface in cloud-free areas passes directly out to space.

Water vapor satellite imagery is a valuable tool in weather analysis and forecasting, enabling meteorologists to track the movement of moisture plumes over distances of thousands of kilometers. Water vapor is an invisible gas and its presence is not detectable on visible or conventional infrared satellite images. But water vapor efficiently absorbs and emits certain wavelength bands of IR so that sensors onboard weather satellites that are sensitive to these wavelength bands can detect water vapor. Water vapor imagery displays the water vapor concentration between altitudes of about 5000 and 12,000 m (16,000 and 40,000 ft) on a gray scale (Figure 1.12). At one extreme, dark gray indicates almost no water vapor whereas at the other extreme, milky white signals a relatively high concentration of water vapor. Upper-level clouds appear milky to bright white on water vapor images, masking water vapor concentrations in the image.

Weather Radar

Weather radar complements satellite surveillance of the atmosphere by locating and tracking the movement of areas of precipitation and monitoring the circulation within small-scale weather systems such as thunderstorms. Weather radar continually emits pulses of microwave energy that are reflected by atmospheric targets such as raindrops, snowflakes, or hailstones. The reflected signal is displayed as blotches (*radar echoes*) on a television-type screen with a superimposed map of the region surrounding the radar. The heavier the precipitation, the more intense is the echo. Echo intensity is calibrated on a color scale so that light green indicates light rain whereas dark red signals heavy rain or hail. Some radar images appearing on weather broadcasts or the Internet are color coded according to precipitation type, so the public can distinguish between snow, rain, and freezing rain. From analysis of radar echoes, meteorologists can determine the intensity of thunderstorms, track the movement of areas of precipitation, and predict when precipitation is likely to begin or end at a particular place. Composite maps of radar echoes from a number of weather radars around the

Water Vapor Image   1415Z 22 APR 2005

NCEP/NWS/NOAA

FIGURE 1.12
A sample water vapor satellite image from sensors onboard a geostationary satellite, taken at the same time as Figure 1.10.

nation are useful in following the progress of large-scale weather systems (Figure 1.13). By overlaying radar echoes on satellite images, areas of precipitation and clouds can be displayed simultaneously, thereby helping to determine the most active portion of a weather system (Figure 1.14). These composites are often animated.

Weather radar also monitors the movement of raindrops, snowflakes, and hailstones within a storm system. Using the same operating principle as the device that measures the speed of a pitched baseball (*Doppler effect*), weather radar detects the motion of precipitation particles within the storm system,

FIGURE 1.13
A sample composite national radar image (approximately the same time as Figure 1.10.)

FIGURE 1.14
A sample infrared satellite image of eastern United States, overlaid with radar echoes.

which then can provide an indication of the system's circulation. Early identification of the circulation within a thunderstorm cloud that is a precursor of a developing tornado is a potentially life-saving application of Doppler weather radar. With advance warning of a tornado before a funnel cloud touches the ground, people have time to seek shelter or move out of its path.

Sky Watching

At this beginning stage in our study of the atmosphere and weather, it is also a good idea to develop the habit of observing the sky, watching for changes in clouds and cloud cover. As the ancients before us found, sky watching makes us more aware of the dynamic nature of the atmosphere and may reveal clues to future weather. Here are some things to watch for:

1. Clouds are aggregates of tiny water droplets, ice crystals, or some combination of both. Ice-crystal clouds occur at high altitudes where air temperatures are relatively low; they have a fibrous or wispy appearance (Figure 1.15). Water-droplet clouds occur at lower altitudes where temperatures are higher; their edges tend to be more sharply defined (Figure 1.16).

2. A cloud that is very near or actually in contact with Earth's surface is fog. By convention, *fog* is

FIGURE 1.15
These high thin cirrus clouds appear fibrous because they are composed of mostly tiny ice crystals.

a suspension of tiny water droplets or ice crystals in air that reduces horizontal visibility to less than 1000 m (0.621 mi).

3. Some clouds form horizontal layers (*stratiform clouds*) whereas others appear puffy (*cumuliform clouds*). Stratiform clouds develop where air ascends gently over a broad region whereas cumuliform clouds are produced by more vigorous ascent of air over a much smaller area. Often stratiform clouds develop ahead of a warm front while cumuliform clouds, especially those having great vertical development, form along or just ahead of a cold front.

FIGURE 1.16
These relatively low clouds are composed of tiny water droplets and have more sharply defined edges than ice-crystal clouds.

FIGURE 1.17
Fair-weather cumulus clouds are most common during the warmest time of the day.

FIGURE 1.19
Clouds at different altitudes may move horizontally in different directions indicating a change in wind direction with altitude.

4. Arrival of high, thin clouds in the western sky at a middle latitude location is often the first sign of an approaching warm front. In time, clouds gradually lower and thicken so that eventually they block out the sun during the day or the moon at night.

5. The day may begin clear but after several hours of bright sunshine, small white clouds appear, resembling puffs of cotton floating in the sky (Figure 1.17). These fair-weather *cumulus clouds* usually vaporize rapidly near sunset.

6. During certain atmospheric conditions, cumulus clouds build vertically and merge laterally, eventually forming a thunderstorm cloud, called a *cumulonimbus cloud* (Figure 1.18). All thunderstorms produce lightning and thunder. Severe thunderstorms can produce torrential rains, large hail, strong and gusty winds, and even tornadoes.

7. Clouds at different altitudes sometimes move horizontally in different directions and perhaps at different speeds (Figure 1.19). Because most clouds move with the wind, this observation indicates that the horizontal wind shifts direction (and speed) with increasing altitude.

Conclusions

We can learn much about the atmosphere and weather by keeping track of local, regional, and national weather patterns via the Internet, television, radio, and newspapers. Weather maps, satellite images, and radar displays are particularly valuable in obtaining the "big picture" when following the development and movement of weather systems across a broad region. In addition, we are well advised to develop the habit of watching the sky for changing conditions locally and to monitor weather instruments if they are available. In this way, we are able to get involved with the subject matter of this course from the beginning and what we learn becomes more meaningful and practical. Our study of the atmosphere, weather, and climate continues in the next chapter with an examination of the evolution and fundamental properties of the atmosphere.

FIGURE 1.18
Cumulonimbus (thunderstorm) clouds always produce lightning and sometimes heavy rain, hail, or strong and gusty surface winds.

Basic Understandings

- From the experiences of everyday life, all of us have developed basic understandings of the workings of the atmosphere, weather, and climate.

- Weather is the state of the atmosphere at some place and time, described quantitatively in terms of such variables as temperature, humidity, and cloudiness. Climate is weather conditions at some locality averaged over a specified time period plus extremes in weather.

- Sources of weather information include televised news programs, *The Weather Channel*, newspaper weather pages or columns, standard AM/FM radio, the NOAA weather radio, and the Internet.

- A weather map is a graphical portrayal of weather across a broad region at a given time. On a weather map, H or High symbolizes a locale where air pressure is relatively high compared to the surrounding area. Viewed from above in the Northern Hemisphere, surface winds blow clockwise and outward about the center of a high. In general, a high is a fair-weather system.

- On a weather map, L or Low symbolizes a locale where air pressure is relatively low compared to the surrounding area. Viewed from above in the Northern Hemisphere, surface winds blow counterclockwise and inward about the center of a low. In general, a low is a stormy weather system.

- An air mass is a huge volume of air covering hundreds of thousands of square kilometers that is relatively uniform horizontally in temperature and humidity. The temperature and humidity of an air mass depend on the properties of its source region and the nature of the surface over which the air mass travels.

- A front is a narrow transition zone between air masses that contrast in temperature and/or humidity. Fronts form where air masses meet and associated air movements often give rise to cloudiness and precipitation that have characteristics dependent on the type of front. The most common types of fronts are stationary, warm, and cold.

- Sensors onboard weather satellites orbiting the planet provide a unique and valuable perspective on the state of the atmosphere and enable meteorologists to remotely measure temperature and humidity and track weather systems. These sensors measure two types of radiation: sunlight that is reflected or scattered by Earth and infrared radiation that is emitted by Earth. Weather satellites are in either geostationary or polar orbits and generate data that are processed into visible and infrared images.

- Weather radar continually emits pulses of microwave radiation that are reflected by raindrops, snowflakes, or hailstones. The reflected signal appears as blotches, known as radar echoes, on a television-type screen. From analysis of radar echoes, meteorologists determine the intensity and track the movement of areas of precipitation. Using the Doppler effect, weather radar can also monitor the circulation of air within a storm system and provide advance warning of severe weather.

- Observing the development, type, and movement of clouds may provide clues as to future weather.

Review

1. What sources of current weather information are available to the public?
2. Distinguish between the weather that usually accompanies a high (anticyclone) and a low (cyclone).
3. What determines the temperature and humidity characteristics of an air mass?
4. Distinguish between a warm front and a cold front in terms of their typical movements.
5. Compare the cloudiness and precipitation pattern usually associated with a warm front with that associated with a cold front.
6. Compare and contrast infrared satellite images versus visible satellite images.
7. How is it possible for satellite sensors to observe continuously the same area of Earth?
8. Describe the capabilities of weather radar in monitoring weather systems.
9. Why do high thin clouds (such as cirrus) appear fibrous?
10. Compare fog to other types of clouds.

Critical Thinking

1. How and why have technological advances of the 20th century improved weather observation and forecasting?
2. Should a severe storm threaten your area, what are the advantages of having access to a NOAA weather radio?
3. Explain why simultaneous weather observations are essential for plotting weather maps.
4. Should New Englanders expect heavier precipitation from a slow-moving winter storm that tracks northward along the Atlantic coastline or a fast-moving winter storm that tracks southeastward out of southern Canada? Justify your response.
5. Why are clouds and precipitation often associated with fronts?
6. Residents of Chicago look to the west for an indication of what tomorrow's weather might be. Explain why.
7. Speculate on why the day's lowest air temperature usually occurs around sunrise. Under what circumstances might the day's minimum air temperature occur in mid-afternoon?
8. What are the advantages of infrared satellite images over visible satellite images for monitoring storm systems that travel across the nation?
9. How can a composite weather radar image be used to locate a cold front?
10. Explain how it is possible for clouds at different altitudes to be moving in different directions?

ESSAY: Time Keeping

Weather observations are made simultaneously at weather stations around the world. Simultaneous observations are necessary if the state of the atmosphere over a large area is to be portrayed accurately on a weather map at a specific time. (This portrayal is also the basis for weather forecasting.) The weather maps used in this course are given in *Z time*. The meaning of Z time and the conventional basis for time keeping are subjects of this Essay.

For millennia, humans have kept track of their activities by the daily motions of the sun. Local noon was a convenient reference, marking the time of day when the sun was at its highest point in the observer's sky. However, locations only a few tens of kilometers to the east or west would have different *sun times*. Beginning in the mid-1800s, with advances in transportation and communication made possible by railroads and telegraphy, travel east or west could be confusing and even potentially dangerous because of local time differences. To eliminate the confusion, the railroads argued for the standardized time keeping scheme we use today. Civil time zones were instituted in the United States and Canada on 18 November 1883 to standardize time keeping in North America. The concept of international time zones was officially adopted on 22 October 1884 at the International Meridian Conference, held in Washington, DC.

Time zones were established based on longitude, which is measured as so many degrees east and west of the *prime meridian*, that is, zero degrees longitude. Because some of the best early astronomical determinations of time had been made at The Old Royal Observatory in Greenwich, England, the 1884 Conference designated the meridian of longitude passing through the observatory as the prime meridian. For more than 50 years, Greenwich Mean Time (GMT) was used for essentially all meteorological observations. GMT is based upon the daily rotation of Earth with respect to a "mean sun." Often the single letter *Z* (phonetically pronounced "zulu") designated the time within the Greenwich time zone (centered on the prime meridian). Today, the preferred time system is the more precise Coordinated Universal Time or Universel Temps Coordinné (UTC), based on an atomic clock and reckoned according to the stars. For practical purposes, GMT and UTC are equivalent.

Earth makes one complete rotation (360 degrees) on its axis with respect to the sun once every 24 hrs. Hence, Earth rotates through 15 degrees of longitude every hour (360 degrees divided by 24 hrs equals 15 degrees per hr). Ideally, Earth should be divided into 24 civil time zones each having a width of 15 degrees of longitude. The central meridian of each time zone is defined as a longitude that is evenly divisible by 15. For example, the central meridian of the Central Time Zone in North America is 90 degrees W longitude. Ninety degrees divided by 15 equals 6 so that Central Standard Time (CST) is six hours different from the time at Greenwich. Earth rotates eastward so that Greenwich time is ahead of CST by 6 hrs. When it is noon at Greenwich, it is 7 a.m. Eastern Standard Time (EST), 6 a.m. CST, 5 a.m. Mountain Standard Time (MST), and 4 a.m. Pacific Standard Time (PST).

Boundaries between some time zones have been adjusted to accommodate political boundaries of various nations. In a few cases, nations adhere to a local civil time that may differ by one half hour from the central meridian of that time zone. To head off potential confusion, time is expressed according to a 24-hr clock so that, for example, 7:45 a.m. is 0745 and 2:20 p.m. is 1420. While most of the United States observes Daylight Saving Time from April through October, UTC is fixed and does not shift to a summer schedule. Hence, you will have to adjust the time by one hour where and when Daylight Saving Time is observed. For example, during summer, residents of the U.S. Central Time Zone lag Greenwich time by 5 instead of 6 hrs. Hence, 0700 Central Daylight Time (CDT) = 0600 Central Standard Time (CST) = 1200 Z. The Energy Policy Act of 2005 mandates a change in dates for Daylight Saving Time in the U.S. Beginning in 2007 Daylight Saving Time will begin on the second Sunday of March and end the first Sunday of November.

By international agreement, surface weather observations are taken at least four times per 24 hrs, that is, at 0000 Z, 0600 Z, 1200 Z, and 1800 Z, with upper-air measurements via balloon-borne instruments (radiosondes) made at 0000 Z and 1200 Z. In the United States, surface observations are taken hourly (at the top of the hour), composite radar charts are also issued hourly at 35 minutes past the hour, and fronts are analyzed on weather maps every 3 hrs beginning at 0000 Z.

ESSAY: Weather Maps, Historical Perspective

Weather maps shown on television, the Internet, or in newspapers are graphical models that display weather observations. The purpose of a weather map is to represent the state of the atmosphere over a broad geographical area at a specific time thereby permitting the identification of weather systems such as fronts, cyclones and anticyclones. Analyzing a sequence of weather maps enables meteorologists to determine the movement of weather systems, a key component of weather forecasting.

In meteorology, *weather analysis* refers to the sequence of steps involved in the interpretation of a graphical (e.g., weather map) display of the distribution of one or more weather elements (e.g., temperature, air pressure). Typically, an important part of the analysis consists of drawing isopleths. An *isopleth* is a contour line that joins places having the same value of some weather element. Examples include *isotherms*, connecting locales with the same temperature, and *isobars*, joining places with the same air pressure. Isopleths plotted on a weather map form patterns that are interpreted by meteorologists.

During the 18th century, European and North American scientists made weather observations because of their interest in weather for its own sake and weather's influence on agriculture and human health. By the early 19th century, some weather observers had assembled reasonably continuous weather records, but typically they were not part of an organized reporting network. Their observations were primarily for the purpose of describing the climate. Lacking any means for rapid communication of weather observations, these data were not useful for weather analysis and forecasting.

The first weather maps appeared in the early 19th century but took years to assemble because of sparse data, non-standard observation practices, and poor communications systems. Heinrich Wilhelm Brandes (1777-1834), a professor at the University of Breslau (in modern Poland), was one of the first to recognize the value of the spatial display of weather data in depicting the state of the atmosphere. Credit goes to Brandes for drawing the first weather map in 1819 showing an intense storm centered over the English Channel on 6 March 1783. However, the 36-year time delay meant that his analysis could hardly be useful for weather forecasting. In 1819, Brandes also plotted 365 daily weather maps for the year 1785.

The source of data for Brandes' weather maps was the network of 39 volunteer weather observers in 18 nations (mostly European) operated by the Meteorological Society of the Palatinate in Mannheim. This first attempt at organized international weather observation lasted from 1781 to 1792. The Society published the data (i.e., wind, temperature, pressure, humidity, precipitation) but no maps in a series of a dozen volumes from 1783 to 1795. Brandes plotted departures (anomalies) from normal air pressure and drew isopleths joining locations having the same departure value. He also plotted winds on the same map and observed how air rotated around a storm and converged inward toward the storm center. By viewing a progressive series of weather maps based on simultaneous observations, Brandes concluded that reduced air pressure was associated with a storm system.

In the United States, the first weather maps appeared in the fourth and fifth decades of the 19th century. In 1837, James P. Espy (1785-1860) published the first U.S. weather map based on observations from widely spaced locales. Espy's map had no isobars and only arrows to represent wind directions associated with a storm system centered near Silver Lake, NY on 20 June 1836. Elias Loomis (1811-1889), professor of mathematics at Western Reserve College in Cleveland, OH, employed a similar approach as Brandes in his 1843 study of a storm that occurred on 16 February 1842. Loomis analyzed a series of maps on which were plotted simultaneous observations from 131 locations to determine the circulation and track of the storm. In so doing, Loomis produced the first *synoptic weather map* with pressure, temperature, wind, sky condition, and precipitation on the same map.

Until the mid-1800s, the utility of weather maps for forecasting purposes was stymied by a lack of a rapid means of communicating observational data. That changed with the invention of the electric telegraph in 1844. Now weather observations could be transmitted rapidly over long distances making possible up-to-date weather maps and the first practical system of weather analysis and forecasting. The first telegraph-linked weather observation networks in the U.S. were operated by Cleveland Abbe (1838-1916) at Cincinnati's Mitchell Astronomical Observatory, Joseph Henry (1797-1878) at the Smithsonian Institution, and the U.S. Army Signal Corps (predecessor to the U.S. Weather

Bureau and National Weather Service) (Figure 1). Through the years with technological advances in instrumentation and communications, weather maps became more accurate in their portrayal of the state of the atmosphere and more useful for weather analysis and forecasting (Chapter 2).

FIGURE 1

A U.S. Army Signal Corps weather map dated 1 September 1872 based on observations telegraphed to Washington, DC. The Signal Corps weather network was the predecessor to the U.S. Weather Bureau and National Weather Service. (NOAA Photo Library)

CHAPTER 2

ATMOSPHERE: ORIGIN, COMPOSITION, AND STRUCTURE

The National Weather Service Forecast Office at La Crosse, WI.

Case in Point

For many years, scientists suspected that significant amounts of red iron- and clay-rich soils on islands throughout the Caribbean and in Bermuda owed their composition partially to dust transported by northeast trade winds from the arid lands of North Africa. They also proposed that wind-borne North African dust supplies nutrients to the Amazon rain forest. Remote sensing by satellite now confirms transport of dust from North Africa to the western North Atlantic, Caribbean Sea, and Gulf of Mexico (Figure 2.1). In recent years, scientists have found evidence that a pool of warm dusty air originating over the Saharan Desert may suppress tropical cyclone activity (e.g., hurricanes) in the North Atlantic, adversely affect air quality over the southeastern United States, and when the dust settles into the ocean, may contribute to toxic red tides in the Gulf of Mexico and threaten coral reefs in the Caribbean.

As weather systems sweep across North Africa (i.e., the Saharan Desert and Sub-Saharan Africa), their strong turbulent winds lift dust particles from the dry topsoil and can carry them to altitudes of 5000 m (16,500 ft) or higher. The prevailing northeast trade winds then transport plumes of the smallest dust particles across the Atlantic and over the Caribbean, Central America, and the southeastern United States. (Florida receives more than half of all North African dust delivered to the United States.) This transoceanic journey takes about 1 to 2 weeks and dust plumes are observed primarily from June to October, peaking in July. Persistent drought in sub-Saharan Africa (from the mid-1960s through the early 1990s) may explain a recent increase in the volume of dust transported to the western North Atlantic.

A

B

FIGURE 2.1

(A) A massive dust storm over northwest Africa and the Sahara Desert. This satellite image was acquired on 11 February 2001 by SeaWiFS. [Courtesy of the SeaWiFS Project, NASA/Goddard Space Flight Center and ORBIMAGE.] (B) This satellite image taken by NASA's Total Ozone Mapping Spectrometer (TOMS) instrument shows dust and smoke blowing off land sources in North Africa and moving westward across the Atlantic as a dust plume on 2 July 1999. [Courtesy of NASA.]

In 2004, scientists reported on a new satellite-based technique that enables them to analyze and track the westward movement of the so-called *Saharan air layer (SAL)*. They found that the SAL is uniformly warm and dusty, extends to an altitude approaching 5500 m (18,000 ft), and covers an area somewhat larger than the 48 contiguous United States. Over the Atlantic Ocean, the SAL is underlain by a shallow (900-1800 m or 3000-5900 ft) layer of cool, humid air (the *marine layer*). Remarkably, the SAL retains its warm dusty characteristics as it travels many thousands of kilometers across the Atlantic. Absorption of solar radiation by the suspended dust particles is one reason why the SAL remains warm. For reasons given in Chapter 12, conditions in the SAL tend to inhibit the formation of tropical cyclones. When the SAL engulfs a hurricane (or a precursor to a hurricane), the system weakens.

North African dust contributes to a reddish haze and colorful sunsets over much of the southeastern United States. The dust particles also can harbor in their microscopic cracks and crevasses, bacteria and fungi, potential disease-causing organisms that may pose a health risk for people suffering from respiratory illnesses or having weakened immune systems. Even without these pathogens, the dust is known to trigger allergic and respiratory reactions. Furthermore, the North African dust arrives over the southeastern United States at the

time of year when photochemical air pollutants are at their highest levels, further exacerbating regional air quality problems.

In the summer of 2001, scientists reported that the iron in North African dust particles fertilizes the Gulf of Mexico waters, increasing the probability of toxic algae blooms, commonly known as *red tides*. Red tides have been implicated in the die-off of great numbers of fish, shellfish, marine mammals, and birds as well as respiratory problems and skin irritations in humans. Enhanced levels of iron enable specialized bacteria to convert nitrogen in the water to a form that can be used by other marine life, triggering an explosive growth in populations of toxic algae. North African dust may also harm coral reefs in the Caribbean through nutrient enrichment that spurs the growth of populations of algae and phytoplankton that colonize the same environment as coral and interfere with its growth.

The story of North African dust transport illustrates how our investigation of the atmosphere is key to a better understanding not only of weather and climate but also of environmental issues that involve the atmosphere and atmospheric processes. Hence, our study focuses on the atmosphere's interactions with the other components of the Earth system, including land, ocean, and living organisms. The significance of these interactions will become evident as we develop basic understandings in atmospheric science.

Driving Question:

What is the composition and structure of the atmosphere?

Almost everyone seems to be interested in the weather, probably because it affects virtually every aspect of daily life—our clothing, the price of orange juice and coffee in the grocery store, and sometimes even the outcome of a football game. Tranquil, pleasant weather allows us to enjoy a variety of outdoor activities (Figure 2.2). A turn to stormy weather can bring mixed blessings: heavy rains wash out picnics but also benefit crops wilting under the searing summer sun. Occasionally, the weather is severe, and the impact may range from mere inconvenience to a disaster that is costly in human lives and property. Thick fog causes flight delays and cancellations, a night of subfreezing temperatures takes its toll on Florida citrus, and heavy snowfall snarls commuter traffic (Figure 2.3). But these impacts pale in comparison to the death, injury, and property damage that a tornado or hurricane can cause.

Regardless of where we live, each of us is well aware from personal experience that weather is variable. This variability prompted Mark Twain, not one to shy from exaggeration, to quip of spring weather in New England: "In the spring I have counted one hundred and thirty-six different kinds of weather inside of four-and-

FIGURE 2.3
Heavy snowfall can disrupt motor vehicle traffic and cause considerable inconvenience.

twenty hours."[1] Of course, weather is not equally variable everywhere. For example, the temperature contrast between winter and summer is much more pronounced in the Dakotas, where summers are very warm and winters are bitterly cold, than in south Florida, where the weather is usually warm year round.

This chapter covers the evolution of the atmosphere, the composition of air, how meteorologists monitor surface and upper-air properties of the atmosphere, the average temperature profile of the atmosphere, the thermal subdivisions of the atmosphere, and the special electromagnetic characteristics of the upper atmosphere.

Evolution of the Atmosphere

The atmosphere is the site of weather and climate, the main subjects of this book. Earth's **atmosphere** is a relatively thin envelope of gases and tiny, suspended particles that encircles the globe. The atmosphere is one component of a planetary system that also consists of the hydrosphere (ocean, glaciers, lakes, ground water), the geosphere, and the biosphere. All components of the Earth system interact with one another in ways that maintain a habitable environment.

Compared to the planet's diameter (12,740 km or 7918 mi), the atmosphere is like the thin skin of an apple. About half the atmosphere's mass is concentrated within about 5500 m (18,000 ft) of Earth's surface and

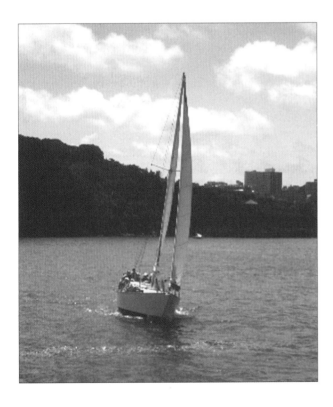

FIGURE 2.2
The variability of weather makes possible a wide variety of outdoor recreational activities.

---

1 "Address of Mr. Samuel L. Clemens: The Weather in New England," New England Society in the City of New York, Annual Report, 1876, p. 59.

99% of its mass is below an altitude of 32 km (20 mi).[2] Yet, this thin atmospheric skin is essential for life and the orderly functioning of physical and biological processes on Earth.   The atmosphere shields organisms from exposure to hazardous levels of solar ultraviolet radiation; it has the gases necessary for life-sustaining processes of photosynthesis and cellular respiration; and it supplies the water required by all forms of life.

The ancient Greeks thought that air was one of the four elements (earth, air, water, and fire). However, by the beginning of the 19th century, chemists such as Joseph Black, Daniel Rutherford and Joseph Priestley had isolated various constituent gases from the air, demonstrating that air is a mixture of gases that are either elements or compounds. Chemists have identified a chemical *element*, such as hydrogen or oxygen, to consist of atoms that cannot be broken down farther by ordinary means whereas a *compound* contains molecules consisting of chemically bonded atoms of various elements in fixed proportions, such as water (H_2O) or carbon dioxide (CO_2). Mixtures, like Earth's atmosphere, contain a collection of elements or compounds that can be separated by ordinary physical means.

Earth's atmosphere is the product of a lengthy evolutionary process that began at the planet's birth more than 4.5 billion years ago. Astronomers scanning the solar system and geologists analyzing evidence obtained from meteorites, rocks, and fossils have given us a reasonable, albeit incomplete, account of the origins of the atmosphere. At least one thing is known with a high degree of confidence: The evolution of the atmosphere was closely linked to the formation of the ocean and the coming of life on the planet.

PRIMEVAL PHASE

According to astronomers, Earth, the sun, and the entire solar system evolved from an immense rotating cloud of dust, ice and gases, called a **nebula**, more than 4.5 billion years ago. Temperature, density, and pressure were highest at the center of the nebula, decreasing gradually toward its outer limits. Extreme conditions at the nebula's center vaporized ice and light elements and drove them toward the outer reaches of the nebula. Consequently, dry rocky masses formed the inner planets (including Earth). Farther out, meteorites and the less-dense giant planets Saturn and Jupiter formed. While meteorites are about 10% ice by mass and the giant planets contain some ice, most of the water in the nebula condensed in comets at distances

beyond Saturn and Jupiter. A **comet** is a relatively small body composed of meteoric dust and ices that follows a parabolic or highly elliptical orbit around the sun.

Although it began as a dry rocky mass, today Earth is appropriately described as the watery planet with about 71% of its surface covered by ocean water and 10% of its land area overlain by glacial ice. The ocean is the ultimate source of water that is a key component of the atmosphere, responsible for clouds and precipitation. Water vapor also slows the escape of Earth's heat to space. Where did the water originally come from? Scientists do not have a complete explanation but popular hypotheses attribute water on Earth to the bombardment of the planet by comets and/or **planetesimals**, large meteorites a few kilometers across.

Comets are about half ice. During the latter stages of Earth's formation, comets impacted the planet's surface delivering a veneer of water.   Jupiter's strengthening gravitational attraction may have drawn a multitude of ice-rich comets from the outer to the inner reaches of the solar system on a collision course with Earth. The hypothesis that comets delivered most of Earth's water remained popular until the past decade when scientists discovered that water on Earth and ice in comets are not chemically equivalent. Spectral analyses of three comets that approached Earth in recent years revealed that comet ice contains about twice as much deuterium as the water on Earth. *Deuterium* is an isotope of hydrogen whose nucleus consists of one proton plus one neutron and is very rare on Earth; a normal hydrogen atom has a single proton. Based on this finding, some scientists estimate that comets accounted for no more than half the water on Earth and perhaps much less. The water in planetesimals, on the other hand, contains less deuterium than comet ice; they may have impacted Earth during the latter stages of the planet's formation. However, the ratio of some other chemical components of planetesimals is not the same as the ratio of those same components on Earth. Yet another possibility is that Earth's water is indigenous; that is, the center of the nebula may have been cooler than previously assumed and some of the materials present in the inner solar system that formed Earth were water-rich.

At the very beginning, Earth's atmosphere was probably mostly hydrogen (H) and helium (He) plus some hydrogen compounds including methane (CH_4) and ammonia (NH_3). Because these atoms and molecules are relatively light with high molecular speeds, this earliest atmosphere eventually escaped to space as Earth's gravity was too weak and the temperature too high. In time, volcanic activity began spewing huge quantities of lava,

---

2 For unit conversions, see Appendix I.

ash, and gases. By about 4.4 billion years ago, the planet's gravitational field was sufficiently strong to retain a thin gaseous envelope of volcanic origin, Earth's primeval atmosphere.

The principal source of Earth's early atmosphere was **outgassing**, the release of gases from rock through volcanic eruptions and the impact of meteorites on the planet's rocky surface. Perhaps as much as 85% of all outgassing took place within a million or so years of the planet's formation, but outgassing continues to this day (Figure 2.4) although at a slower pace. Outgassing produced a *primeval atmosphere* that was mostly carbon dioxide (CO_2), with some nitrogen (N_2) and water vapor (H_2O), along with trace amounts of methane, ammonia, sulfur dioxide (SO_2), and hydrochloric acid (HCl). Radioactive decay of an isotope of potassium (potassium-40) in the planet's bedrock added argon (Ar), an inert (chemically non-reactive) gas, to the evolving atmosphere. Dissociation of water vapor into its constituent atoms, hydrogen and oxygen, by high-energy solar ultraviolet radiation contributed a small amount of free oxygen to the primeval atmosphere. (The lighter hydrogen—with its relatively high molecular speeds—escaped to space.) Also, some oxygen combined with other elements in various chemical compounds such as carbon dioxide.

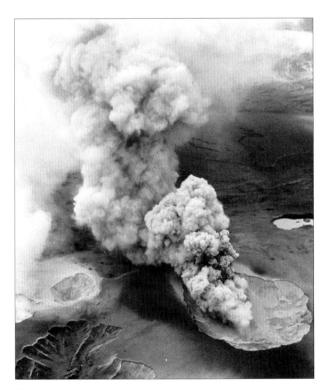

Figure 2.4
Steam and gas venting at Spirit Lake, Mt. St. Helens. [Courtesy of United States Geological Survey].

Scientists suggest that between 4.5 and 2.5 billion years ago, the sun was about 30% fainter than it is today. This did not mean a cooler planet, however, because of the abundance of carbon dioxide. Earth's CO_2-rich atmosphere was perhaps 10 to 20 times denser than the present atmosphere. Carbon dioxide slows the escape of Earth's heat to space, contributing to average surface temperatures that may have been as high as 85 °C to 110 °C (185 °F to 230 °F).

By perhaps 4 billion years ago, the planet started to cool and the atmosphere underwent major changes. Cooling caused atmospheric water vapor to condense into clouds that produced rain. Precipitation plus runoff from landmasses gave rise to the ocean that eventually may have covered as much as 95% of the planet's surface. The global water cycle (which helped further cool the Earth's surface through evaporation) and its largest reservoir (the ocean) were in place. Rains also helped bring about a substantial decline in the concentration of atmospheric CO_2. Carbon dioxide dissolves in rainwater producing weak carbonic acid that reacts chemically with bedrock. The net effect of this large-scale geochemical process was increasing amounts of carbon chemically locked in rocks and minerals while less and less CO_2 remained in the atmosphere. The physical and chemical breakdown of rock (*weathering*) plus erosion on land delivered some carbon-containing sediment to the ocean. Also, rains washed dissolved carbon dioxide directly into the sea and some atmospheric CO_2 dissolved in ocean water as sea surface temperatures fell. In this way, the ocean eventually emerged as the major reservoir in the global carbon cycle.

Although carbon dioxide has been a minor component of the atmosphere for at least 3.5 billion years, its concentration fluctuated from time to time in the geologic past with important implications for climate. All other factors being equal, more CO_2 in the atmosphere means higher temperatures at the Earth's surface. For example, geologic evidence points to a burst of volcanic activity on the Pacific Ocean floor about 100 to 120 million years ago. Some CO_2 released during that activity eventually found its way to the atmosphere and elevated the global mean temperature by as much as 10 Celsius degrees (18 Fahrenheit degrees). During the Pleistocene Ice Age (1.7 million to 10,500 years ago), atmospheric carbon dioxide levels fluctuated, decreasing during episodes of glacial expansion and increasing during episodes of glacial recession (although it is not clear whether variations in atmospheric CO_2 were the cause or effect of these global-scale climate changes).

Living organisms also played an important role in Earth's evolving atmosphere, primarily through **photosynthesis**, the process whereby green plants use sunlight, water, and carbon dioxide to manufacture their food. A byproduct of photosynthesis is oxygen (O_2). (Although vegetation is also a sink for carbon dioxide, photosynthesis probably was not as important as the geochemical processes just described in removing carbon dioxide from the atmosphere.) Photosynthesis dates to at least 2.5 billion years ago with the first appearance of primitive forms of life (blue-green algae) in the ocean. During the subsequent 500 million years, most oxygen generated via photosynthesis combined with ocean sediments while very little entered the atmosphere. By about 2.3 billion years ago, however, oxidation of ocean sediments tapered off. Oxygen generated by marine plants via photosynthesis initially dissolved in ocean water. Eventually, oxygen saturated surface ocean waters and began cycling into the atmosphere, ultimately building to near modern levels. With the concurrent decline in CO_2, within 500 million years, oxygen became the second most abundant atmospheric gas after nitrogen.

With oxygen emerging as a major component of Earth's atmosphere, the ozone shield formed. In the portion of the upper atmosphere known as the *stratosphere*, incoming solar ultraviolet (UV) radiation powers reactions that convert oxygen to ozone (O_3) and ozone to oxygen (Chapter 3). Absorption of UV radiation in these reactions prevents potentially lethal intensities of UV radiation from reaching Earth's surface. By about 438 million years ago, formation of the stratospheric ozone shield made it possible for organisms to live and evolve on land. UV radiation does not penetrate ocean water to any great depth so that marine life was able to exist in the ocean depths prior to the formation of the ozone shield. But with the ozone shield, marine life was able to thrive in surface waters.

Nitrogen (N_2), a product of outgassing, became the most abundant atmospheric gas because it is relatively inert chemically and its molecular speeds are too slow for this gas to readily escape Earth's gravitational pull. Furthermore, compared to other atmospheric gases, such as oxygen and carbon dioxide, nitrogen is less soluble in water. All these factors greatly limit the rate at which nitrogen cycles out of the atmosphere. While nitrogen continues to be generated as a minor component of volcanic eruptions, today the principal source of free nitrogen entering the atmosphere is the denitrification process involved in bacterial decay of the remains of plants and animals. But this input is countered by an amount removed from the atmosphere by *biological fixation* (i.e.,

direct nitrogen uptake by leguminous plants such as clover and soybeans) and *atmospheric fixation* (i.e., the process whereby the high temperatures associated with lightning causes nitrogen to combine with oxygen to form nitrates that are subsequently washed by rains to Earth's surface).

MODERN PHASE

Ultimately, these gradual evolutionary processes produced the modern atmosphere. The lower atmosphere continually circulates so that the principal atmospheric gases are well mixed and occur almost everywhere in about the same relative proportions up to an altitude of about 80 km (50 mi). That portion of the atmosphere is called the **homosphere**. Above 80 km, gases are stratified such that concentrations of the heavier gases decrease more rapidly with altitude than do concentrations of the lighter gases. The region of the atmosphere above 80 km is known as the **heterosphere**.

Nitrogen and oxygen are the chief gaseous components of the homosphere. Not counting water vapor (which has a highly variable concentration), nitrogen (N_2) occupies 78.08% by volume of the homosphere, and oxygen (O_2) is 20.95% by volume. Henry Cavendish (1731-1810) discovered this basic gaseous composition of air in 1781. The next most abundant gases are argon (0.93%) and carbon dioxide (0.0376%). As shown in Table 2.1, the atmosphere also has small quantities of helium (He), methane (CH_4),

TABLE 2.1
Gases Composing Dry Air in the Lower Atmosphere (below 80 km)

Gas	% by Volume	Parts per Million
Nitrogen (N_2)	78.08	780,840.0
Oxygen (O_2)	20.95	209,460.0
Argon (Ar)	0.93	9,340.0
Carbon dioxide (CO_2)	0.03756	375.6
Neon (Ne)	0.0018	18.0
Helium (He)	0.00052	5.2
Methane (CH_4)	0.00014	1.4
Krypton (Kr)	0.00010	1.0
Nitrous oxide (N_2O)	0.00005	0.5
Hydrogen (H)	0.00005	0.5
Xenon (Xe)	0.000009	0.09
Ozone (O_3)	0.000007	0.07

hydrogen (H), ozone (O_3), and many other gases. Unlike the atmosphere's principal gases, the percent volume of some of these trace gases varies with time and location within the homosphere.

In the heterosphere, above about 150 km (95 mi), oxygen is the chief atmospheric gas but occurs primarily in the atomic (O) rather than diatomic (O_2) form. Solar ultraviolet radiation dissociates O_2 into its constituent atoms. Two oxygen atoms can recombine to form a molecule only by colliding with another atom or molecule, but the number of molecules per unit volume (the *number density*) at these high altitudes is so low that such collisions are infrequent. At lower altitudes the intensity of incoming solar ultraviolet radiation is less, thereby reducing the rate of dissociation of O_2. Also, with more molecules per unit volume at lower altitudes, molecular collisions are more frequent. Below about 100 km (60 mi), oxygen atoms recombine at a faster rate than oxygen molecules dissociate, so that oxygen occurs mostly as O_2.

Earth's nitrogen/oxygen-dominated atmosphere contrasts strikingly with the CO_2-rich atmospheres of our neighboring planets Venus and Mars. The atmosphere of Venus is almost 100 times denser than Earth's atmosphere and features an average surface temperature of about 460 °C (860 °F). The Martian atmosphere, on the other hand, is much thinner than Earth's atmosphere and has an average surface temperature ranging from about −60 °C (−76 °F) at the equator to as low as −123 °C (−189 °F) at the poles. These differences exist even though all three planets likely began with chemically similar atmospheres. The atmospheres of Earth, Mars, and Venus evidently followed different evolutionary paths; for more on the Martian atmosphere, see this chapter's first Essay.

In addition to gases, Earth's atmosphere contains minute liquid and solid particles, collectively called **aerosols**. A flashlight beam in a darkened room reveals an abundance of suspended dust particles. Most aerosols individually are too small to be visible but in aggregates, such as the water droplets and ice crystals that compose clouds, they may be visible. Most aerosols occur in the lower atmosphere near their sources on Earth's surface and are derived from wind erosion of soil, ocean spray, forest fires, volcanic eruptions, and industrial and agricultural activities. Also, some aerosols, such as meteoric dust, enter the atmosphere from above.

We may be tempted to dismiss as unimportant those substances that make up only a small fraction of the atmosphere, but the significance of an atmospheric gas or aerosol is not necessarily related to its relative abundance. Water vapor, carbon dioxide, and ozone (O_3) occur in minute concentrations, yet they are essential for life. By volume, no more than about 4% of the lowest kilometer of the atmosphere is water vapor even in the warm, humid air over tropical seas and rainforests. Without water vapor, however, there would be no clouds, and no rain or snow to replenish soil moisture, rivers, lakes, and seas. Although comprising only 0.0376% of the homosphere, carbon dioxide is essential for photosynthesis. Furthermore, water vapor and carbon dioxide absorb and emit infrared radiation, elevating the temperature of the lower atmosphere to a range that makes life possible on Earth. Although the volume percentage of ozone is minute, the formation and dissociation of this essential gas shields organisms, including ourselves, from exposure to potentially lethal intensities of ultraviolet radiation from the sun.

The aerosol concentration of the atmosphere is also relatively small, yet these suspended particles participate in important processes. As demonstrated in Chapter 7, some aerosols function as nuclei for the development of clouds. Furthermore, certain aerosols such as sulfurous particles can influence air temperature by interacting with incoming solar radiation (Chapter 15).

AIR POLLUTION

Human activity also plays a role in the composition of air primarily by contributing air pollutants. An **air pollutant** is a gas or aerosol that occurs at a concentration that threatens the wellbeing of living organisms (especially humans) or disrupts the orderly functioning of the environment. Many of these substances occur naturally in the atmosphere. Sulfur dioxide (SO_2) and carbon monoxide (CO), for example, are normal minor gaseous components of the atmosphere that become pollutants when their concentrations approach or exceed the tolerance limits of organisms. At sufficiently high concentrations, sulfur dioxide irritates the throat and lungs and impairs the respiratory system's defenses against foreign particles and bacteria. Carbon monoxide is a colorless, odorless, and tasteless asphyxiating agent (reducing the blood's oxygen-carrying ability). Certain air pollutants, however, do not occur naturally in the atmosphere, and some of these are hazardous to human health even at very low concentrations. An example is benzene, which is known to cause cancer.

A substance that is harmful immediately upon emission into the atmosphere is designated a *primary air pollutant*. Carbon monoxide in automobile exhaust is an example. In addition, within the atmosphere, chemical reactions involving primary air pollutants, both gases and aerosols, produce *secondary air pollutants*. An example is *photochemical smog*, a mixture of aerosols, ozone, nitrogen oxides, and hydrocarbons, generated by the action of sunlight on motor vehicle exhaust, some industrial emissions, and volatile organic compounds emitted by certain vegetation.

Air pollutants are products of both natural events and human activities. Natural sources of air pollutants include forest fires, dispersal of pollen, wind erosion of soil, decay of dead plants and animals, and volcanic eruptions. The single most important human-related source of air pollutants is the internal combustion engine that propels most motor vehicles. Many industrial sources also contribute to air quality problems. Unless emissions are controlled, pulp and paper mills, zinc and lead smelters, oil refineries, and chemical plants can be major sources of air pollutants. Additional pollutants come from fuel combustion for space heating and generation of electricity (Figure 2.5), refuse burning, and various agricultural activities such as crop dusting.

The U.S. Environmental Protection Agency (EPA) has set ambient air quality standards for six criteria air pollutants: carbon monoxide, lead, nitrogen oxides, ozone, particulate matter, and sulfur dioxide. *Ambient air* is the outside air that we breathe. Standards for the six criteria air pollutants are based on scientific studies that demonstrate that adverse effects are likely only after concentrations exceed a specific threshold value (hence, the *criteria* designation). Standards are of two types, primary and secondary. *Primary air quality standards* are defined as the maximum exposure levels that can be tolerated by humans without ill effects. *Secondary air quality standards* are defined as the maximum levels that are allowable to minimize the impact on crops, visibility, personal comfort, and climate. Emission standards for stationary sources (e.g., coal-fired electric power plants) and mobile sources (e.g., motor vehicles) are set to ensure, theoretically at least, that once pollutants enter the atmosphere, ambient air quality standards are not exceeded.

A geographical region where the ambient air meets or does better than primary air quality standards is designated an *attainment area*. Compliance is established by direct sampling of air over specified time periods. A region where the ambient air does not meet the primary standard for one or more criteria air pollutants is designated a *nonattainment area* for those pollutants. In that case, remedial action (i.e., reduction of emissions) is required.

Investigating the Atmosphere

Our understanding of the atmosphere, weather, and climate is the culmination of centuries of painstaking inquiry by scientists representing many disciplines. Physicists, chemists, astronomers, and others have applied basic scientific principles in unlocking the mysteries of the atmosphere. The roots of modern meteorology, in fact, go back to around 350-340 B.C. and Aristotle's *Meteorologica*, the first treatise on atmospheric science.[3] Although much progress has been made over the years, many questions remain regarding the workings of the atmosphere, weather, and climate. Today's atmospheric scientists (meteorologists and climatologists) continue the efforts of their predecessors, and although armed with more sophisticated tools such as satellites, radar, and supercomputers, they still rely on the scientific method of inquiry.

THE SCIENTIFIC METHOD

The **scientific method** is a systematic form of inquiry involving observation, interpretation, speculation, and reasoning. The Antarctic ozone hole illustrates how scientists apply the scientific method. In 1985, the British Antarctic Survey team reported a drastic decline in the amount of stratospheric ozone over Antarctica during the Southern Hemisphere spring (mainly in September and October). The region of depleted ozone covered an area almost as large as North America and was later dubbed the *Antarctic Ozone Hole*. In checking records,

FIGURE 2.5
Unless emissions are controlled, a coal-fired electric power plant can be a source of air pollutants including sulfur dioxide and particulates.

---

3 For a timeline of historical events in meteorology, see Appendix II.

scientists found evidence from ground-based instruments of massive ozone depletion during each of the eight prior Antarctic springs.

At first, scientists dismissed the Antarctic ozone hole as a product of instrument error—not unexpected considering the brutal environmental conditions in Antarctica. Other scientists argued that the Antarctic ozone hole was real and the product of natural seasonal changes in the polar atmospheric circulation. A third hypothesis attributed the Antarctic ozone hole to pollution. In an effort to solve the mystery, an intensive field study was launched during the Antarctic spring of 1987 involving monitoring of the Antarctic stratosphere by satellites, specially outfitted aircraft, and instrumented balloon probes. That field investigation not only confirmed the existence of the Antarctic ozone hole, but also detected exceptionally high levels of chlorine monoxide (ClO), a gas known from laboratory studies to be a product of chemical reactions that destroy ozone. For many scientists, discovery of ClO in the Antarctic stratosphere was the "smoking gun" linking ozone depletion to a group of chemicals known as chlorofluorocarbons (CFCs). We have more to say about CFCs and the threat to stratospheric ozone in Chapter 3.

From our Antarctic ozone example, it is evident that the scientific method involves a sequence of steps in which scientists (1) identify specific questions related to the problem at hand; (2) propose an answer to one of these questions in the form of an educated guess; (3) state the educated guess in such a way that it can be tested, that is, formulate a **hypothesis**; (4) predict the outcome of the test if the hypothesis were correct; (5) test the hypothesis by checking to see if the prediction is correct; and (6) reject or revise the hypothesis if the prediction is wrong. A hypothesis that has stood the test of time and is generally accepted by the scientific community is a **scientific theory**.

In our Antarctic ozone illustration we divided the scientific method into a sequence of steps but in actual practice, scientists do not always follow this scheme cookbook style, and discrete steps often combine into a seamless avenue of inquiry. Furthermore, the scientific method is not a formula for creativity because it does not provide the key idea, hunch, or educated guess that spontaneously springs to mind and forms the basis of a hypothesis. Rather, it is a technique for assessing the validity of a creative idea regardless of how it originates.

As in the Antarctic ozone hole example, a hypothesis is a tool that suggests new field studies, experiments or observations, or opens new avenues of inquiry. Hence, even a rejected hypothesis may be fruitful. Above all, scientists must keep in mind that a hypothesis is merely a working assumption that may be accepted, modified, or rejected. They must be objective in evaluating a hypothesis and not allow personal biases or expectations to cloud that evaluation. In fact, scientists search for observations or information that could disprove their hypothesis. If they find such evidence, they revise their hypothesis to account for disparate observations or information. Inquiry, creative thinking, and imagination are stifled when a hypothesis is considered immutable.

A new hypothesis (or an old, resurrected one) is sometimes hotly debated within the scientific community. History attests to the natural human reluctance to accept new ideas that threaten to displace long-held notions. Also, disagreements among scientists on a particularly controversial issue sometimes receive considerable media attention, which may confuse the general public. For some time now, atmospheric scientists have been engaged in a sometimes contentious public debate as to if, when, and to what extent burning coal and oil for power might impact global climate. In some cases, public reaction may be summed up as follows: "Well, if the so-called experts can't agree among themselves, who should I believe? Is there really a problem after all?" Debate and disagreement among scientists are essential steps in the process of reaching understanding; they generate useful suggestions, stimulate new thinking, and uncover errors. In fact, debate and skepticism buffer the scientific community from too hastily accepting new ideas. If a hypothesis survives the scrutiny and skepticism of scientists and the public, it is probably correct.

ATMOSPHERIC MODELS

In applying the scientific method, scientists often find that models aid inquiry and this is certainly the case in the atmospheric sciences. Because we use models throughout this book, we consider at the outset the general objectives and limitations of scientific models, especially as they apply to meteorology and climatology.

A **scientific model** is an approximate representation or simulation of a real system. A **system** is an entity having components that function and interact with one another in an orderly and predictable manner that can be described by fundamental physical principles (or natural laws). The **Earth-atmosphere system**, for example, encompasses the Earth's surface (i.e., continents, ocean, ice sheets) plus atmosphere. A model includes only what are considered to be the essential variables or characteristics of a system. For example, to learn how to improve the fuel efficiency of automobiles, engineers might examine a scale-model automobile in a wind tunnel. An automobile can be designed to minimize its air resistance, thereby increasing its fuel efficiency (miles per gallon). The shape of the model automobile is the critical variable and is the focus of study. Other variables, such as the color of the model automobile or whether it is equipped with a miniature CD-player, are irrelevant to the experiment and are ignored. In constructing a model, trial and error often determine which variables are or are not essential.

Because models are not cluttered with extraneous and distracting details, they may provide important insights as to how things interact, or they may facilitate critical thinking about complex phenomena. Models also are used to predict how a real system might respond to internal or external forcing (i.e., environmental change). Depending on their particular function, scientific models are classified as conceptual, graphical, physical, or numerical.

A *conceptual model* is an abstract idea that represents some fundamental law or relationship. The geostrophic wind (described in Chapter 8) is a conceptual model that relates the interaction of certain forces operating in the atmosphere to straight, horizontal winds blowing at altitudes of 1000 m (3300 ft) or higher. A *graphical model* compiles and displays data in a format that readily conveys meaning. For example, a weather map (Figure 1.4) integrates weather observations taken simultaneously at hundreds of locations into a coherent representation of the state of the atmosphere at a specific time.

A *physical model* is a miniaturized version of some system. Almost half a century ago, scientists studied the patterns exhibited by a fluid in a flat rotating pan in experiments designed to simulate the planetary scale atmospheric circulation. More recently, Purdue University scientists simulated a tornadic circulation in a specially designed Tornado Vortex Chamber, measuring 5 m wide, 5 m deep, and 8 m high (Figure 2.6). Precision instruments monitored air motions within small tornado-like vortices (swirls) that developed. Using this model, scientists improved their understanding of the internal characteristics of real tornadoes.

Today, atmospheric scientists usually depend on *numerical models* rather than physical models for investigating the atmosphere, weather, and climate. A numerical model consists of one or more mathematical equations that describe the relationship among variables of a system. Numerical models of the Earth-atmosphere system are usually programmed on a computer that can accommodate enormous quantities of data and perform numerous and often repetitive calculations

A

B

FIGURE 2.6

(A) External view of Purdue University's Tornado Vortex Chamber, used to simulate the circulation within tornadoes (B). [Courtesy of John T. Snow, University of Oklahoma, and C.R. Church, Miami University of Ohio]

with lightning speed. Variables in the numerical model (e.g., temperature, winds, cloud cover) are manipulated, individually or in groups, to assess their influence on the behavior of the system.

Numerical models have been used to forecast weather since the 1950s. More recently, other types of numerical models have been used to predict the potential impact on the global climate of rising levels of atmospheric carbon dioxide and other infrared-absorbing gases. As discussed in more detail in Chapters 3 and 15, the atmospheric carbon dioxide concentration has been rising for more than a century, primarily as a byproduct of fossil fuel (coal, oil, and natural gas) burning. Higher air temperatures may be the consequence because, as noted earlier, carbon dioxide slows the escape of Earth's heat to space. Atmospheric scientists employ numerical global climate models in experiments to compute the magnitude of warming that might accompany a continued increase in atmospheric carbon dioxide concentration. Essentially they follow three steps: (1) Design a global climate model that incorporates the various controls of climate to accurately depict the long-term average pattern of air temperature worldwide. (2) Holding all other climate-control variables constant, elevate the carbon dioxide concentration (typically, it is doubled), and the global climate model computes a new worldwide average air temperature pattern. (3) Subtract the present temperature pattern from the temperature pattern predicted for the CO_2-enriched atmosphere to obtain the net temperature change.

All models simulate reality and as such are subject to error. A weather map portrays the state of the atmosphere at a particular time based on weather observations at discrete locations (weather stations), which may be hundreds of kilometers apart. (Weather satellite imagery provides a much more continuous field of view but the spatial resolution of satellite sensors is still limited.) This state of the atmosphere is used as a starting point for numerical models that are used to forecast the weather. Missing or erroneous observational data may mean that numerical models are not properly initialized reducing the likelihood of an accurate forecast. Another potential difficulty with numerical models concerns the accuracy of their component equations. Equations only approximate the way a system really works in nature, and may not adequately account for all relevant variables. This is one reason why the skill of long-range weather forecasting, based on numerical models of the Earth-atmosphere system, declines in accuracy as the forecast period lengthens (Chapter 13).

Monitoring the Atmosphere

Much of what we know about Earth's atmosphere, weather, and climate is derived from direct (*in situ*) and remote sensing of the Earth-atmosphere system. Since invention of the first weather instruments in the 17th century, monitoring of the atmosphere has undergone considerable refinement. Denser monitoring networks, more sophisticated instruments and communications systems, and better trained observers have produced an increasingly detailed, reliable, and representative record of weather and climate. Monitoring has progressed on two fronts: surface and upper-air observations.

SURFACE OBSERVATIONS

Early weather observers used primitive instruments or made qualitative assessments of the weather, jotting down observations in journals or diaries. The first systematic weather observations in North America were made in 1644-45 at Old Swedes Fort (now Wilmington, DE). The observer was John Campanius Holm (1601-83), chaplain of the Swedish military expedition. Holm did not have any weather instruments, however. In his diary, he recorded qualitative descriptions of temperature, humidity, wind, and weather. After Holm's return to Sweden in 1648, some 50 years passed before his grandson published his weather observations, which were later translated into English.

Long-term instrument-based temperature records began in Philadelphia in 1731; Charleston, SC in 1738; and Cambridge, MA in 1753. The New Haven, CT temperature record began in 1781 and continues uninterrupted today. Thomas Jefferson (third President of the United States) and the Reverend James Madison (president of the College of William and Mary) are credited with taking the nation's first simultaneous weather observations. Over a six-week period in 1778, they recorded temperature, air pressure, and wind at their respective homes in Monticello and Williamsburg, VA.

On 2 May 1814, James Tilton, M.D., U.S. Surgeon General, issued an order that in retrospect was the first step in the eventual establishment of a national network of weather-observing stations. Tilton directed the Army Medical Corps to begin a diary of weather conditions at army posts, with responsibility for observations falling to the post's chief medical officer. Tilton's objective was to assess the relationship between weather and the health of the troops, for it was a popular notion at the time that weather and its seasonal changes were important factors in the onset of disease. (Even well into the 20th century, more troops lost their lives to disease than combat.) He also wanted to learn more about the climate of the then sparsely populated interior of the continent.

The ongoing War of 1812 prevented immediate compliance with Tilton's order. In 1818, Joseph Lovell, M.D., succeeded Tilton as Surgeon General and issued formal instructions for taking weather observations. Reports soon began trickling into the Army Medical Department and by 1838, 16 army posts had compiled at least 10 complete (although not always successive) years of weather records. By the close of the American Civil War, weather records had been tabulated for varying periods at 143 army posts. In 1826, Lovell began compiling, summarizing and publishing the data and for this reason Lovell, rather than Tilton, is sometimes credited with founding the federal government's system of weather observation.

In the mid-1800s, Joseph Henry (1797-1878), first secretary of the Smithsonian Institution in Washington, DC, established a national network of volunteer observers who mailed in monthly weather reports. The number of citizen observers (consisting of farmers, educators, and public servants) peaked at nearly 600 just prior to the U.S. Civil War. Henry understood the value of rapid communication of weather data and was quick to realize the potential of the newly invented telegraph in achieving this goal. In 1849, Henry persuaded the heads of several telegraph companies to direct their telegraphers in major cities to take weather observations at the opening of each business day and transmit them free of charge. Henry supplied thermometers and barometers (for measuring air pressure). Using simultaneous weather observations, in 1850 Henry prepared the first national weather map and later regularly displayed the daily weather map for public viewing in the Great Hall of the Smithsonian building. By 1860, some 42 telegraph stations, mostly east of the Mississippi River, were participating in the Smithsonian network.

In the 1860s, growing public alarm over the great loss of life and property from shipwrecks caused by surprise storms sweeping across the Great Lakes spurred the federal government to take a greater role in weather observation and forecasting. In 1868 and 1869 alone, storms on the Great Lakes sunk or damaged 3078 vessels with the loss of 530 lives. In response, the naturalist Increase A. Lapham (1811-1875) of Milwaukee, WI urged his congressman, Halbert E. Paine (1826-1905), to persuade Congress to establish a telegraph-based storm-warning system for the Great Lakes. Lapham's proposal was inspired by the success of Henry's Smithsonian network and another telegraph-based network operated by

Cleveland Abbe (1838-1916) at the Mitchell Astronomical Observatory in Cincinnati, OH. President Ulysses S. Grant signed the resolution into law on 9 February 1870 and the network, initially composed of 24 stations, began operating on 1 November 1870 under the auspices of the U.S. Army Signal Corps.

Although the storm-warning network was originally authorized for the Great Lakes, in 1872 Congress appropriated funds to expand the network to the entire nation. The new weather-observing network soon encompassed stations previously operated by the Surgeon General, the Smithsonian Institution, the U.S. Army Corps of Engineers, and Cleveland Abbe. The number of Signal Corps stations regularly reporting daily weather observations by telegraph reached 110 by 1880.

On 1 July 1891, the nation's weather network was transferred from military to civilian hands in a new Weather Bureau within the U.S. Department of Agriculture, with a special mandate to provide weather and climate guidance for farmers. Later, aviation's growing need for weather information spurred the shift of the Weather Bureau to the Commerce Department on 1 July 1940. Many cities saw their Weather Bureau offices relocated from downtown to an airport usually in a rural area well outside the city. In 1965, the Weather Bureau was reorganized as the National Weather Service (NWS) within the Environmental Science Services Administration (ESSA), which became the National Oceanic and Atmospheric Administration (NOAA) in 1971.

During the early and mid-1990s, facilities of the National Weather Service underwent extensive modernization with the goal of upgrading the quality and reliability of weather observations and forecasts. As part of this $4.5 billion project, new or restructured NWS Forecast Offices were established at 122 locations across the nation (Figure 2.7). Some 862 automated weather stations, many of them at airports, replaced the old system of manual hourly observations. This **Automated Surface Observing System (ASOS)** consists of electronic sensors, computers, and fully automated communications ports (Figure 1.3). Twenty-four hours a day, ASOS feeds data to NWS Weather Forecast Offices and airport control towers.

Besides the numerous weather stations that provide observational data for weather forecasting and aviation, another 11,700 cooperative weather stations are scattered across the nation (Figure 2.8). These stations (rooted in the old Army Medical Corps and Smithsonian networks) are cooperative in that volunteers supply their time and labor to monitor instruments and the National Weather Service provides instruments and data

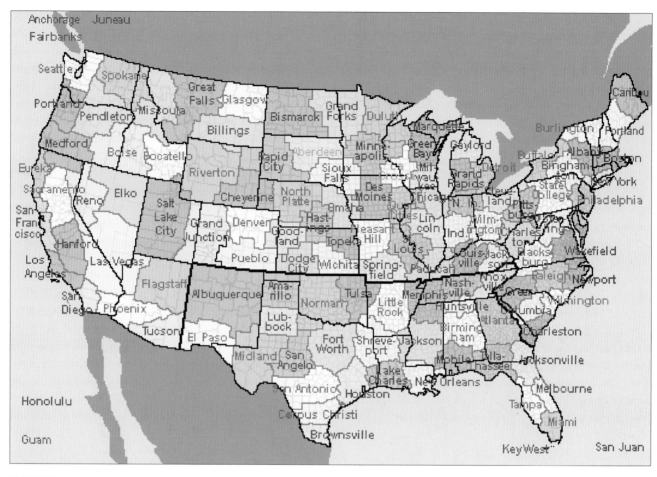

FIGURE 2.7
Locations of National Weather Service Forecast Offices and their geographic areas of responsibility.

FIGURE 2.8
This NWS cooperative observer station at Mount Mary College, Milwaukee, WI is equipped with a standard rain gauge and thermometers housed in a wooden instrument shelter.

management. The principal function of member stations of the **NWS Cooperative Observer Network** is to record daily precipitation and maximum/minimum temperatures for hydrologic, agricultural, and climatic purposes.

UPPER-AIR OBSERVATIONS

Weather stations were established on mountain-tops during the 19th century but the influence of the mountain itself meant that observations were not representative of conditions in the free atmosphere. Kites were an early means of investigating the upper atmosphere. In July 1749 in Glasgow, Scotland, Alexander Wilson attached several thermometers to six paper kites and flew them in tandem. Wilson designed the apparatus so that the thermometers would fall to the ground unbroken at predetermined intervals. In this way, he was the first to obtain a free-air temperature profile of the lower atmosphere (up to an altitude of perhaps 60 m or 200 ft).

Benjamin Franklin (1706-1790), an inventive genius, is credited with performing an experiment using a kite to demonstrate the electrical nature of lightning. On 10 June 1752, during a developing thunderstorm, Franklin touched a metal key that he had attached to the end of a kite string. Fortunately, lightning did not strike the kite because a single bolt could have killed him. Franklin detected static electricity that had built up along the kite string, an observation that inspired him the next year to extol the effectiveness of lightning rods in his *Poor Richard's Almanac*.

On 27 August 1804, the French scientists J. L. Gay-Lussac (1778-1850) and Jean Biot ushered in the age of manned balloon exploration of the atmosphere. They took air samples, measured temperature and humidity, and on one ascent reached an altitude of 7000 m (23,000 ft). On 5 September 1862, the British scientist James Glaisher (1822-1911) and his fellow aeronaut Henry Coxwell took weather instruments aloft in a balloon ascent over Wolverhampton, England. In less than an hour, they ascended to about 7600 m (25,000). They nearly perished from severe cold and oxygen deprivation in reaching an altitude of 9000 m (29,500 ft) setting a new manned balloon altitude record.

Through the early part of the 20th century, weather instruments borne by kites, aircraft, and balloons provided data chiefly on the lowest 5000 m (16,000 ft)

of the atmosphere. On 4 August 1894 at Harvard's Blue Hill Observatory near Boston, MA, kites were used for the first time to carry aloft a self-recording thermometer (*thermograph*). This instrument provided a vertical profile of air temperature to an altitude of 427 m (1400 ft) above the ground. The next year, scientists conducted kite experiments for meteorological purposes at Mount Weather Observatory, VA, about 80 km (50 mi) west of Washington, DC. Box kites of various sizes and shapes were secured by piano wire to rotating steel drums. Kites were equipped with a recording instrument, called a *meteorograph*, which profiled air pressure, temperature, humidity, and wind speed. Wind direction was determined from the ground using a theodolite, an instrument that measures azimuth and elevation angles. On 3 October 1907, a box kite equipped with a meteorgraph set a new world record in climbing to an altitude of 7044 m (23,111 ft). On 5 May 1910, a train of 10 instrumented kites reached an altitude of 7265 m (23,835 ft).

The success of kite experiments convinced the U.S. Weather Bureau in 1907 to begin operating a network of weather kite stations at several locations, mostly in the central part of the nation (Figure 2.9). Box kites equipped with meteorgraphs profiled the atmosphere up to a maximum

FIGURE 2.9
In the early 20th century, scientists probed the atmosphere up to altitudes of about 3000 m (10,000 ft) using recording weather instruments attached to box kites. [NOAA Photo Library]

altitude of about 3000 m (10,000 ft). The longest and last operating station, at Ellendale, ND was closed in 1933. Among reasons cited for discontinuing the kite network was the relatively low maximum altitude reached by kites and the interruption in observations during periods of light winds or calm air. For several years afterward, the U.S. Weather Bureau relied mostly on regular 5 a.m. (EST) aircraft observations originating at as many as 30 locations to probe the atmosphere to altitudes up to 4900 m (16,000 ft), but this practice proved too hazardous and costly.

A leap forward in monitoring higher altitudes came in the late 1920s with invention of the first radiosonde. A **radiosonde** is a small instrument package equipped with a radio transmitter that is carried aloft by a helium- (or hydrogen-) filled balloon. This device transmits altitude readings, called a **sounding**, of temperature, air pressure, and dewpoint (a measure of humidity) to a ground station. Radiosonde data are received immediately; no recovery of a recording instrument is required. The first official U.S. Weather Bureau radiosonde was launched at East Boston, MA in 1937. By World War II, meteorologists were tracking radiosonde movements from ground stations using radio direction-finding antennas, thereby monitoring variations in wind direction and speed with altitude. A radiosonde used in this way is called a **rawinsonde**.

Today, radiosondes are launched simultaneously at 12-hr intervals (at 0000Z and 1200Z) from hundreds of ground stations around the world (Figure 2.10). The

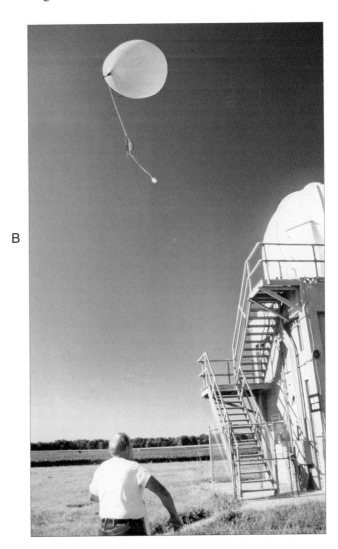

FIGURE 2.10

A radiosonde (A) is a small instrument package equipped with a radio transmitter. Borne by a hydrogen or helium-filled balloon (B), a radiosonde measures vertical profiles of air temperature, pressure, and dewpoint (C) up to an altitude of about 30,000 m (100,000 ft). Tracking horizontal movements of the radiosonde gives a profile of wind speed and direction (symbols on right).

balloon bursts at an altitude of about 30,000 m (100,000 ft), and the instrument package descends to the surface under a parachute. In the United States, about 20% of radiosondes are recovered, refurbished, and reused. Each radiosonde contains a prepaid mailbag and instructions to its finder for returning the instrument to the National Weather Service.

A **dropwindsonde** is similar to a rawinsonde except that instead of being launched by a balloon from a surface station, it is dropped from an aircraft. The instrument package descends on a parachute at about 18 km (11 mi) per hr and along the way radios data back to the aircraft every few seconds. The dropwindsonde was developed at the National Center for Atmospheric Research (NCAR) in Boulder, CO to obtain soundings over the ocean where conventional rawinsonde stations are few and far between. Dropwindsondes provide vertical profiles of air temperature, pressure, dewpoint, and wind. They are often deployed by "hurricane hunter" aircraft that fly out to investigate offshore tropical storms and hurricanes that are approaching the Gulf or East Coast.

REMOTE SENSING

Remote sensing refers to the measurement of environmental conditions by processing signals that are either emitted by an object or reflected back to a signal source. Remote sensing instruments are never in direct contact with whatever is being measured. In meteorology and climatology, radar and satellites are used in remote sensing of the atmosphere.

Radar (acronym for *ra*dio *d*etection *a*nd *r*anging) is a valuable tool for determining the location, movement, and intensity of areas of precipitation. Weather radar emits microwave signals and receives reflected signals from targets as it continually scans the lower atmosphere. The first reported use of radar for meteorological purposes was on 20 February 1941, when a radar unit on the south coast of England tracked a thunderstorm a distance of 11 km (7 mi). More widespread application of radar for weather analysis began shortly after World War II.

Early weather radars were short-range surplus military units. Not until the mid-1950s, following major tornado and hurricane disasters, did the U.S. Congress authorize funds for purchase and installation of new long-range radar units designed specifically for meteorological purposes. In 1959, these units, called *WSR-57* radars, went into service for hurricane detection along the Atlantic and Gulf Coasts and for tornado and severe thunderstorm surveillance over the central United States. By 1964, *WSR-57* radars were operating at 32 sites

and by the late 1960s were a routine feature of televised weathercasts in many parts of the nation. Weather radar was upgraded in 1974 with installation of *WSR-74* radars. During the early and mid-1990s, as a key component of the modernization of the National Weather Service, the obsolete *WSR-57* and *WSR-74* radars were replaced by the more technologically sophisticated *WSR-88D* radars (Figure 2.11). (*WSR* stands for Weather Surveillance Radar; the number refers to the year of development; and, *D* is for Doppler.) As of this writing a network of 113 *WSR-88D* weather radar units monitors atmospheric conditions over much of the nation. Weather radar is discussed in greater detail in Chapter 7.

FIGURE 2.11
This radome for a *WSR-88D* radar unit houses a rotating dish antenna that sends out pulses of microwave energy and receives microwave energy reflected by precipitation particles.

Robert H. Goddard (1882-1945) is credited with conducting the first rocket probe of the atmosphere in 1929. The payload of Goddard's primitive rocket included a thermometer and a barometer. World War II spurred advances in rocketry so that by the late 1940s, instrumented rockets were investigating the composition of the middle and upper atmosphere. *Rocketsondes* have been used routinely during the past five decades to monitor winds, density, and ozone concentration above levels attained by radiosondes. A small rocket is launched carrying an instrument package similar to a radiosonde that parachutes back to Earth's surface.

In March 1947, a vertically fired V2 rocket was equipped with a camera that took the first successful photographs of Earth's cloud cover from altitudes of 110-165 km (70-100 mi). This and subsequent rocket probes of the upper atmosphere convinced scientists of the value of cloud pattern photography in monitoring weather systems and inspired the first serious proposals for orbiting a weather satellite. In the mid- to late 1950s, the United States' fledgling space program was directed at developing a launch vehicle (rocket) capable of putting a satellite in orbit. With the former Soviet Union's successful orbiting of Sputnik I on 4 October 1957, the age of remote sensing by satellite had begun. On 1 April 1960 the United States orbited the world's first weather satellite, *TIROS-1 (Television and Infrared Observation Satellite)*. Since then, a series of weather satellites equipped with increasingly sophisticated sensors have been orbited.

Weather satellites are invaluable tools in weather observation and storm surveillance. These *eyes in the sky* offer distinct advantages over the network of surface weather stations by providing a broad and nearly continuous field of view. Surface weather stations are discrete and often widely spaced data sources, and weather observations are sparse or absent over vast areas of Earth's surface, especially the ocean. Five geostationary satellites provide nearly complete coverage of the globe poleward to about 60 degrees latitude. Onboard weather satellites are sensors capable of monitoring cloud patterns, temperature, water vapor concentration, upper-air winds, rainfall, and the life cycles of severe storms. By the early 1990s, vertical profiling of the atmosphere's temperature and humidity by satellite became routine practice.

Today, a variety of technologies provides detailed information on the state of the atmosphere. The remainder of this chapter considers two important properties of the atmosphere: its average vertical temperature profile and electromagnetic characteristics of the upper atmosphere.

Temperature Profile of the Atmosphere

Earlier in this chapter, we described the vertical structure of the atmosphere in terms of composition (*homosphere* versus *heterosphere*). However, for convenience of study, the atmosphere typically is subdivided into concentric layers based upon the vertical profile of the average air temperature, as shown in Figure 2.12. Almost all weather occurs within the lowest layer, the **troposphere**, which extends from Earth's surface to an average altitude ranging from about 6 km (3.7 mi) at the poles to about 20 km (12 mi) at the equator. Normally, but not always, the temperature within the troposphere falls with increasing altitude. Hence, the air temperature is usually lower on mountaintops than in surrounding lowlands (Figure 2.13). On average, within the troposphere, the air temperature drops 6.5 Celsius degrees for every 1000 m increase in altitude (3.5 Fahrenheit degrees per 1000 ft). The upper boundary of the troposphere, called the **tropopause**, is a transition zone between the troposphere and the next higher layer, the stratosphere.

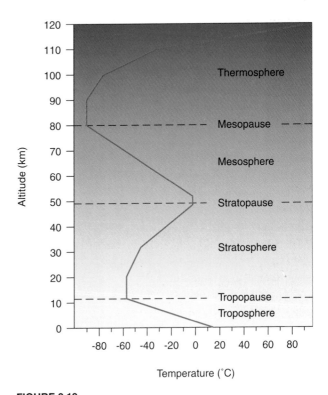

FIGURE 2.12
Variation in average air temperature with altitude within the atmosphere. Based on this vertical temperature profile, the atmosphere is subdivided vertically into the troposphere, stratosphere, mesosphere, and thermosphere.

FIGURE 2.13
Within the troposphere, average air temperature falls with increasing altitude so that it is generally colder on mountain peaks than in lowlands.

The **stratosphere** extends from the tropopause up to about 50 km (31 mi). On average, the temperature does not change with increasing altitude through the lower portion of the stratosphere. A constant temperature condition is described as *isothermal*. Above about 20 km (12 mi), the temperature rises with increasing altitude up to the top of the stratosphere, the **stratopause**. At the stratopause, the temperature is not much lower than it is at sea level. The stratosphere is ideal for jet aircraft travel because it is above the weather, offering excellent visibility and generally smooth flying conditions. But because little air is exchanged between the troposphere and the stratosphere, pollutants that reach the lower stratosphere may persist there for lengthy periods. Gases and aerosols thrown into the stratosphere during violent volcanic eruptions, for example, can reside there for many months to years and perhaps trigger short-term variations in climate (Chapter 15). Other pollutants (e.g., CFCs) threaten the protective ozone layer within the stratosphere (Chapter 3).

The stratopause is the transition zone between the stratosphere and the next higher layer, the **mesosphere** (or "middle" layer). Within this layer, the temperature once again falls with increasing altitude. The mesosphere extends up to the **mesopause**, which is about 80 km (50 mi) above Earth's surface and features the lowest average temperature in the atmosphere (about -95 °C or -139 °F). Above this layer is the **thermosphere**, where temperatures at first are isothermal and then rise rapidly with increasing altitude. Within the thermosphere, air temperature is particularly sensitive to incoming solar radiation and is more variable with time than in any other region of the atmosphere.

The Ionosphere and the Aurora

A third way of describing the vertical structure of the atmosphere is in terms of concentration of ions, especially in the upper atmosphere. The **ionosphere**, located primarily within the thermosphere, from a base of 70 to 80 km (43 to 50 mi) to an indefinite altitude, is a region of the atmosphere defined by a relatively high concentration of ions and electrons. An **ion** is an atomic-scale particle that carries an electrical charge. High-energy solar radiation entering the upper atmosphere strips electrons from oxygen and nitrogen atoms and molecules, converting them to positively charged ions. The highest concentration of ions is in the lower portion of the thermosphere. Changes in the concentration of the principal constituents of the ionosphere with altitude are plotted in Figure 2.14.

FIGURE 2.14
Average variation with altitude of the particle density of the principal constituents of the ionosphere at 45 degrees N on the equinox. [National Center for Atmospheric Research High Altitude Observatory and The COMET Program.]

FIGURE 2.15
Aurora borealis (northern lights) nearly directly overhead, photographed at Menasha, WI at 9:30 p.m. CST on 5 November 2001. The curving arcs of orange light are reflections from a light at a nearby parking lot. [Courtesy of John Beaver, University of Wisconsin, Fox Valley]

Although conditions in the upper atmosphere apparently do not influence day-to-day weather in the troposphere, the ionosphere reflects radio waves and is important for conventional long-distance radio transmission. Radio signals travel in straight lines and bounce back and forth between Earth's surface and the ionosphere. By repeated reflections, a radio signal may travel completely around the globe. For more on this phenomenon, see this chapter's second Essay.

The ionosphere is also the site of the spectacular **aurora** (Latin for "dawn")—*aurora borealis* (northern lights) in the Northern Hemisphere and *aurora australis* (southern lights) in the Southern Hemisphere. Auroras often appear in the night sky as a variety of visual displays including overlapping curtains of greenish-white light, occasionally fringed with pink (Figure 2.15). The bottom of the curtains is at an altitude of about 100 km (62 mi) and the top is at 400 km (250 mi) or higher.

An aurora is triggered by the **solar wind**, a stream of super-hot electrically charged subatomic particles (protons and electrons) that continually emanates from the sun and travels through space at speeds of 400 to 500 km (250 to 300 mi) per second. Like a rock in a mountain stream, Earth's magnetic field deflects the solar wind and, in so doing, is deformed into a teardrop-shaped cavity surrounding the planet known as Earth's **magnetosphere** (Figure 2.16). The solar wind compresses the front end of the magnetosphere and elongates the back end. A complex interaction between the solar wind and the magnetosphere generates beams of electrons that collide with atoms and molecules within the ionosphere. Collisions rip apart molecules, excite atoms, and increase ion and electron densities. As atoms shift down from their excited (energized) state and ions combine with free electrons, they emit radiation, part of which is visible as the aurora. Excited nitrogen molecules emit pinkish or magenta light, whereas excited oxygen atoms emit greenish light.

The aurora is usually visible only at higher latitudes. Earth's magnetic field channels some solar

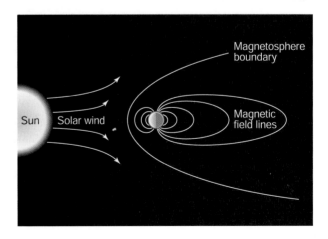

FIGURE 2.16
Earth's magnetic field deflects the solar wind and is thereby deformed into the teardrop-shaped magnetosphere that surrounds the planet.

wind particles into two doughnut-shaped belts that are centered on the planet's north and south geomagnetic poles. These belts of more or less continuous auroral activity, known as *auroral ovals*, are located between 20 and 30 degrees of latitude from the geomagnetic poles and bulge equatorward on the dark (night) side of the planet. The Northern Hemisphere auroral oval is centered on the northwest tip of Greenland at latitude 78.5 degrees N and longitude 69 degrees W.

Auroral activity varies directly with solar activity. When the sun is quiet, the auroral oval shrinks, but when the sun is active, the auroral oval expands toward the equator, and the aurora may be visible across southern Canada and the northern United States or, rarely, further south. Solar activity follows a roughly 11-year cycle, with the most recent solar maximum in 2000 (Chapter 15). In 1989, during a particularly active solar phase, the aurora was visible as far south as Mexico's Yucatán Peninsula. Gigantic explosions, called *solar flares*, characterize an active sun. A solar flare is a brief event (lasting perhaps an hour) that produces a shock wave that propagates rapidly (500 to 1000 km per sec) through the solar wind. Collision of the shock wave with the magnetosphere causes the auroral oval to expand equatorward. During some active solar episodes, the phenomenon that produces auroras also disrupts the operation of electric power grids, telecommunications systems, and satellites.

Conclusions

In this chapter we covered the origin, evolution, composition, and structure of the atmosphere. We emphasized the importance of minor gases in the functioning of the atmosphere, and surveyed some of the various technologies used to monitor the atmosphere. We also saw how the vertical profile of average air temperature is a convenient basis for subdividing the atmosphere into four layers. Because the primary focus of this course is weather and climate, we will be concerned primarily with atmospheric processes operating within the troposphere.

Our next major objective is to examine the driving force behind weather. To do so, we require an understanding of energy input and energy conversions within the Earth-atmosphere system. In the next chapter we learn how the sun supplies the energy that drives the atmosphere's circulation. As we will see, circulation of the atmosphere ultimately is responsible for variations in weather from one place to another and with time.

Basic Understandings

- Earth's atmosphere encircles the planet as a thin envelope of gases and suspended solid and liquid particles (aerosols).

- The modern atmosphere is the product of a lengthy evolutionary process that began about 4.5 billion years ago. Outgassing (the release of gases from rock through volcanic eruptions and meteorite impacts) played a key role in the evolution of the atmosphere by contributing water vapor, carbon dioxide, and nitrogen. Photosynthesis is the principal source of free oxygen in the atmosphere.

- Within the homosphere, the lowest 80 km (50 mi) of the atmosphere, the principal atmospheric gases, nitrogen (N_2) and oxygen (O_2), occur everywhere in the same relative proportion (about 4 to 1). Suspended in the atmosphere are minute solid and liquid particles, collectively called aerosols.

- The significance of an atmospheric gas or aerosol is not necessarily related to its relative concentration. Water vapor, carbon dioxide, and ozone are minor in concentration but extremely important in the life-sustaining roles they play on Earth.

- An air pollutant is a gas or aerosol occurring in concentrations that adversely affect the wellbeing of organisms (especially humans) or disrupt the orderly functioning of the environment. Human activities and natural processes are sources of air pollutants.

- The scientific method is a systematic form of inquiry that requires the formulation and testing of hypotheses. A hypothesis is a working assumption that may be accepted, modified, or rejected. Debate and disagreement among scientists on controversial issues are usual and important elements of the scientific method.

- A scientific model is a simulation of a real system and may be conceptual, graphical, physical, or numerical. Examples of models commonly used in meteorology and climatology include weather maps and global climate models.

- The Army Medical Corps operated the nation's first weather observation network in the 1800s. Invention of the telegraph made possible rapid communication of simultaneous weather observations and the first near real-time weather maps.

- In the 1860s, growing public concern over the great loss of life and property from surprise storms sweeping the Great Lakes spurred the federal government to create a telegraph-linked national weather observation network in 1870 under the auspices of the U.S. Army Signal Corps, forerunner of today's National Weather Service.

- Through the years, tools for investigating the upper atmosphere advanced from instrumented kites and manned balloons to rockets, radiosondes, radar, and satellites.

- A radiosonde consists of an instrument package and radio transmitter carried aloft by balloon to altitudes up to 30,000 m (100,000 ft); it provides vertical profiles (called soundings) of air temperature, pressure, and dewpoint (a measure of humidity).

- Remote sensing refers to the measurement of environmental conditions by processing signals that are either emitted by an object or reflected back to a signal source. In meteorology and climatology, radar and satellites are examples of remote sensing methods.

- The atmosphere is subdivided into four concentric layers (troposphere, stratosphere, mesosphere, and thermosphere) based on the average vertical temperature profile. Almost all weather takes place in the troposphere, the lowest subdivision of the atmosphere.

- The ionosphere is a region of electrically charged particles situated primarily within the thermosphere and consists of a relatively high concentration of charged particles (ions and electrons).

- An aurora (northern or southern lights) is a spectacular visual display in the night sky at higher latitudes, sometimes appearing as curtains of colors. It develops in the ionosphere when the solar wind interacts with Earth's magnetic field and varies with solar activity.

Review

1. Define Earth's atmosphere and describe some of the ways whereby it interacts with the other components of the Earth system.
2. Describe the role of outgassing in the evolution of Earth's atmosphere.
3. What is the ratio of nitrogen (N_2) to oxygen (O_2) in the troposphere? Does this ratio change within the stratosphere?
4. Present several examples of how *minor* constituents of the atmosphere are essential for life on Earth.
5. How does human activity influence the composition of the atmosphere?
6. What role is played by scientific models in understanding atmospheric processes?
7. In what way was invention of the radiosonde a major step forward in monitoring the upper atmosphere?
8. Does the normal temperature profile of the troposphere imply that the troposphere is heated from above or from below? Justify your response.
9. How does the troposphere differ from the stratosphere?
10. Why is the aurora visible only at high latitudes?

Critical Thinking

1. Photosynthesis occurs chiefly during the growing season. Speculate on how variations in the rate of photosynthesis through the course of a year might influence the concentration of carbon dioxide in the atmosphere.
2. Radiosonde balloons typically burst at altitudes above about 30,000 m (100,000 ft). Why would a rising balloon eventually burst?
3. Speculate on how changes in the average temperature of the troposphere might affect the altitude of the tropopause.
4. Mountaintops are closer to the sun than are lowlands, and yet mountaintops are colder than lowlands. Why?
5. List the advantages of a numerical model over a physical model.
6. By convention, monthly mean temperatures and precipitation are computed for a recent 30-year period. Speculate on whether a 30-year summary of weather is representative of climate and its variability.
7. Explain why the ratio of nitrogen (N_2) to oxygen (O_2) is constant at about 4 to 1 throughout the homosphere.
8. Identify some natural processes and some human activities that can change the concentration of carbon dioxide (CO_2) in the atmosphere. What might be the consequence of a change in CO_2 concentration for climate?
9. How do scientific models aid scientific inquiry and critical thinking?
10. What type of events led to establishment of a national weather service? What do you think is the principal purpose of NOAA's National Weather Service?

ESSAY: The Atmosphere of Mars

In 1976, sensors onboard the National Aeronautics and Space Administration's (NASA's) Viking spacecraft confirmed much earlier speculation that the Martian atmosphere differs considerably from Earth's atmosphere. The Martian atmosphere is 95% carbon dioxide, 2% to 3% nitrogen, 1% to 2% argon, and 0.1% to 0.4% oxygen. Also, the Martian atmosphere is much thinner; its average surface pressure is only 0.6% of Earth's mean sea-level air pressure. In the beginning, more than 4 billion years ago, however, the atmospheres of both planets probably were quite similar in composition, but for several reasons, followed different evolutionary paths.

Outgassing produced the primeval atmospheres of both Earth and Mars. Gases were released from ancient planetary rock through volcanic eruptions and the impact of meteorites on the rocky surfaces of both planets. The gases were probably the same because the source rocks on both planets were chemically equivalent. Through outgassing, the primeval atmosphere of the two planets was mostly carbon dioxide, with some nitrogen and water vapor and trace amounts of other gases. As noted elsewhere in this chapter, geochemical processes plus photosynthesis gradually altered Earth's primeval atmosphere so that eventually nitrogen and oxygen became the principal gases and carbon dioxide was reduced to minor status. From the beginning, however, carbon dioxide has remained the chief gaseous constituent of the Martian atmosphere, although through the eons its density declined significantly with major implications for the planet's climate.

Contrasts in the volcanic histories of Earth and Mars may help to explain why the atmospheres of the two planets evolved differently. On Mars, the bulk of volcanic activity apparently took place during the planet's first 2 billion years, whereas on Earth, volcanism has been more or less continuous throughout the planet's history. The decline in volcanism on Mars cut the supply of nitrogen, and much of the original nitrogen escaped Mars' relatively weak gravitational field. Gravity, the force that holds an atmosphere to a planet, is about 38% weaker on Mars than on Earth because Mars is less massive than Earth (11% of Earth's mass).

In the beginning, the CO_2-rich Martian atmosphere produced a surface pressure perhaps three times that of Earth's modern atmosphere. However, diminishing volcanic activity on Mars meant less CO_2 released to the planet's atmosphere. At the same time, other geological processes removed carbon dioxide from the Martian atmosphere. Enormous amounts of CO_2 escaped to space, some adhered to the dust that blankets the planet's surface, and some may have been locked up in carbonate rocks. Carbon dioxide slows the loss of the planet's heat to space so that as CO_2 thinned, more heat escaped and surface temperatures on Mars fell.

Today, the mean temperature on the Martian surface ranges from about −60 °C (−76 °F) at the equator to as low as −123 °C (−189 °F) at the poles. The planet's surface temperature is much too low for liquid water to exist on the planet but sensors on Mars-orbiting spacecraft have detected water ice buried under several meters of dust. The ice layer is estimated to be roughly equivalent to twice the volume of water in Lake Superior, the largest of the North American Great Lakes. Perennial polar ice caps are mostly water ice with a covering of dry ice (solid carbon dioxide). Severe cold on Mars means no life, no photosynthesis, and hence, only a trace of free oxygen and no ozone in the Martian atmosphere.

Planetary scientists believe that during at least the first billion years of its existence, Mars was sufficiently warm that liquid water flowed on the planet's surface. In recent decades, sensors onboard Mars-orbiting satellites and rovers (robots) placed on the planet have analyzed its surface for signs of liquid water in the past. Mariner satellite missions of the 1960s and Viking orbiter missions of the 1970s photographed vast flood channels and networks of valleys on the Martian surface. Scientists proposed that these features were eroded by running water. About two decades later, NASA's Pathfinder mission to Mars confirmed this hypothesis. On 4 July 1997, the Pathfinder spacecraft landed on an ancient floodplain that had been scoured by catastrophic flooding billions of years ago. Also, Pathfinder's tiny rover, *Sojourner*, photographed pebbles and rocks on the Martian surface having physical properties indicative of transport by running water. In 2005, images taken by sensors onboard the European Space Agency's Mars Express spacecraft revealed a frozen body of water in a flat area near the equator that at one time was about the size of the North Sea. A layer of ash or dust about 1 to 20 m thick mantles the surface thereby preventing the ice from sublimating.

In January 2004, twin Mars Exploration Rovers (MERs), *Opportunity* and *Spirit*, landed at sites on opposite sides of Mars. Both uncovered conclusive evidence that liquid water once flowed on Mars. *Spirit* located a rock showing signs of chemical alteration by water. *Opportunity* detected minerals (i.e., salts, evaporates), and rock features (e.g., mud cracks, ripple marks) indicating that water not only altered rock but that rock formed from sediment that settled out of a shallow saline sea.

Today Mars is a frigid and foreboding place swept by strong winds and massive dust storms that sometimes encircle the entire planet (Figure 1). Although Mars' primeval atmosphere was probably similar in composition to that of Earth, a reduction in volcanic outgassing and a weaker gravitational field on Mars caused its atmosphere to follow a distinctly different evolutionary path. On Mars, carbon dioxide has remained the principal atmospheric gas although its concentration declined significantly causing surface temperatures to plunge. Evidence that water now frozen under a dusty mantle once flowed as liquid on the Martian surface confirms this planetary-scale climate change.

FIGURE 1
The surface of Mars viewed from space is marked by numerous craters produced by meteorite impacts. Running water apparently cut canyons up to 8 km (5 mi) deep and flowed into a large basin in the upper right of the image. Volcanoes (dark spots) are visible on the left side of the image. [Courtesy of NASA and the U.S. Geological Survey]

ESSAY: Radio Transmission and the Ionosphere

Reception of distant radio signals (waves) at night is not at all unusual. Late-night radio listeners in Illinois can, for example, routinely pick up WBZ, a Boston radio station (1030 on the AM dial) even though the station's transmitter is more than 1500 km (930 mi) away and its signals receive no help from orbiting satellites.

Arrival of distant radio waves at night and their subsequent disappearance during sunlit hours is due to interactions of those waves with the ionosphere. A radio wave is a form of *electromagnetic radiation* that travels in essentially straight paths in all directions away from its source transmitter (Chapter 3). Earth is essentially a sphere so its surface gradually curves under and away from direct radio waves. A *quiet zone*, where direct radio waves are not received, begins about 160 km (100 mi) from a transmitter tower of average height. At night, beyond the distant edge of the quiet zone, reception resumes because radio waves are reflected back to Earth's surface from the upper ionosphere.

Recall from elsewhere in this chapter that the ionosphere is a region of ions and free electrons. Highly energetic solar radiation splits molecular nitrogen (N_2) and molecular oxygen (O_2) into atoms, positively charged ions, and free electrons. The production rate of ions and electrons depends on two factors, both of which vary with altitude: (1) the *number density* of atoms and molecules available for ionization, which decreases rapidly with altitude, and (2) the intensity of solar radiation, which increases with altitude. Combined, these two factors maximize the concentration of ions and free electrons in the ionosphere.

By convention, the ionosphere is subdivided vertically into several layers. From lowest to highest, layers are designated D (upper mesosphere below 100 km), E (100 to 120 km), F_1 (150 to 190 km), and F_2 (above 200 km). The original basis for this subdivision was the belief that each layer is a distinct zone of maximum electron density. Measurements by rockets and satellites, however, show that the ionosphere is not made up of discrete layers; rather, electron density increases nearly continuously with altitude to a maximum at an average altitude close to 300 km (186 mi). The D, E, F_1, and F_2 labels in this discussion refer to regions within the ionosphere.

Radio waves that enter the ionosphere interact with free electrons in the D, E, and F regions and are either absorbed or reflected back toward Earth's surface. At night, in the absence of ionizing radiation, the D region virtually disappears as ions and electrons recombine into neutral particles. The recombination rate depends on air density; that is, the higher the density, the greater the likelihood of collision of particles and capture of electrons by positive ions. In the E, F_1, and F_2 regions, air is so rarefied that collisions are infrequent, and although the E region weakens, these regions persist through the night. Radio waves that reach the F region are reflected back toward Earth's surface. (Exceptions are radio waves that enter the F region at nearly a right angle; these waves pass on into space.) At night, because of F-region reflection, radio waves propagate many hundreds of kilometers from their point of origin.

With the return of the sun's ionizing radiation during the day, the D region redevelops. Most radio waves that reach the D region are absorbed instead of propagating into the E and F regions. The F region reflects waves that penetrate the D region back to the D region where they are absorbed. Consequently, during sunlit hours, radio-wave propagation is not aided by F-region reflection. In summary, radio waves travel greater distances at night because the upper ionosphere reflects them back to Earth's surface.

Ionizing radiation from the sun generates the ionosphere so that any solar activity that disturbs the flow of this radiation may affect ion density and consequently, radio communication on Earth. *Sudden ionospheric disturbances* (*SIDs*), typically lasting 15 to 30 minutes, are caused by bursts of ultraviolet radiation emitted from the sun. Ionization temporarily increases, D-region absorption strengthens, and radio transmissions fade. The same solar activity responsible for the aurora also increases ionization and causes radio fadeout.

CHAPTER 3

SOLAR AND TERRESTRIAL RADIATION

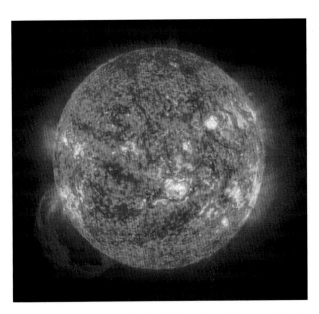

A large solar prominence (a cloud of erupting solar gas retained above the sun's surface by the sun's magnetic field). [Courtesy of the Space Environment Center, NOAA]

Case in Point

Ancient peoples were well aware of the sun's annual cycle and the progression of the seasons. Knowing when the seasons began and ended was critical to the timing of planting and harvesting of crops. In monsoon climates, the timing of the rainy and dry seasons is closely tied to the solar cycle. While these people did not possess a calendar in the modern sense, their knowledge of the path of the sun through the sky and other regular astronomical events inspired them to construct astronomical calculators in the form of elaborate megaliths.

Probably the best known of the ancient astronomical calculators is Stonehenge located in Southern England, the earliest portion of which dates to about 2950 B.C. As early as the 18th century, scientists noticed that the horseshoe arrangement of great stones opened in the direction of sunrise on the summer solstice. Stones also point in the direction of the mid-winter sunset. In more recent years, scientists discovered that the arrangement of stones and other features at Stonehenge could be used to predict solar and lunar eclipses. People living at Cahokia (just east of modern St. Louis, MO) erected similar solar calendars consisting of wooden posts arranged in circles. These so-called Woodhenge calendars date from the period 900 to 1100 A.D.

Predating Stonehenge by some two thousand years, the oldest astronomical calculator discovered so far consists of megaliths and a stone circle, located near Nab-ta in the present-day Nubian Desert of southern Egypt. A global positioning satellite confirms the stones' alignment with the position of the rising sun on the summer solstice (as it would have been 6000 years ago). For people living there at the time this was a very significant date because monsoon rains typically begin shortly after the summer solstice.

Driving Question:

How does energy flow into and out of the Earth-atmosphere system maintain a habitable planet?

The sun drives the atmosphere; that is, the sun is the source of energy that drives the circulation of the atmosphere and powers winds and storms. **Energy** is defined as the capacity for doing work and occurs in many different forms such as radiation and heat. The circulation of the atmosphere ultimately is responsible for weather and its temporal and spatial variability.

The sun ceaselessly emits energy to space in the form of electromagnetic radiation. A very small portion of that energy is intercepted by the Earth-atmosphere system and converted to other forms of energy including, for example, heat and the kinetic energy of the winds. Energy cannot be created nor destroyed although it can be converted from one form to another. This is the **law of energy conservation** (also known as the *first law of thermodynamics*).

In this chapter, we examine the basic properties of electromagnetic radiation, laws governing electromagnetic radiation, how solar radiation interacts with the components of the Earth-atmosphere system, and the conversion of solar radiation to heat. The Earth-atmosphere system responds to solar heating by emitting infrared radiation. Some of this infrared radiation is absorbed by certain atmospheric gases. In turn, those gases radiate infrared downward, elevating the temperature of Earth's surface and lower atmosphere to levels that make life possible (the so-called *greenhouse effect*). We begin with the nature of electromagnetic radiation and some of the properties of its various forms.

Electromagnetic Spectrum

Planet Earth is bathed continuously in **electromagnetic radiation**, so named because this form of energy has both electrical and magnetic properties. Essentially all objects absorb and emit electromagnetic radiation. Forms of electromagnetic radiation include radio waves, microwaves, infrared radiation, visible light, ultraviolet radiation, X-rays, and gamma radiation. Together, they make up the **electromagnetic spectrum**, illustrated in Figure 3.1.

Electromagnetic radiation travels as waves, described in terms of wavelength or frequency. **Wavelength** is the distance between successive wave crests (or equivalently, wave troughs), as shown in Figure 3.2. **Wave frequency** is defined as the number of crests (or troughs) that pass a given point in a specific period of time, usually 1 second. Passage of one complete wave is called a *cycle*, and a frequency of 1 cycle per second equals 1.0 hertz (Hz). Wave frequency is inversely proportional to wavelength; that is, the higher the frequency, the shorter is the wavelength. Radio waves have frequencies in the millions of hertz with wavelengths up to hundreds of kilometers. At the other end of the electromagnetic spectrum, by contrast, gamma rays have frequencies as high as 10^{24} (a trillion trillion) Hz and wavelengths as short as 10^{-14} (a hundred trillionth) m. Furthermore, higher frequency radiation with shorter wavelengths has higher energy than lower frequency (or longer wavelength) radiation.

Electromagnetic waves travel through space and may pass through gases, liquids, and solids. In a vacuum, all electromagnetic waves travel at maximum possible speed, that is, 300,000 km (186,000 mi) per sec, commonly called the *speed of light*. All forms of electromagnetic radiation slow down when passing through materials, their speed varying with wavelength and type of material. As electromagnetic radiation passes from one medium into another, it may be reflected or refracted (that is, bent) at the interface. This happens, for example, when

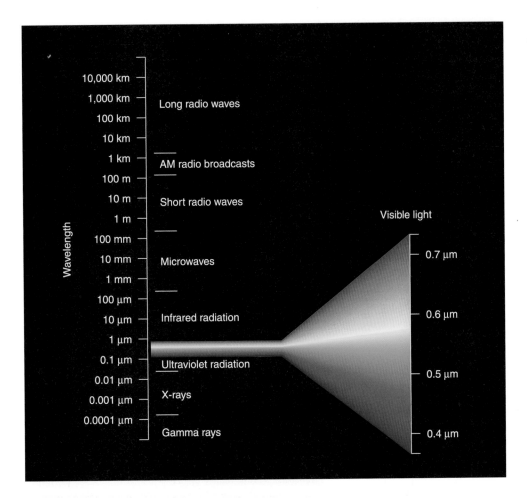

FIGURE 3.1

The electromagnetic spectrum consists of many forms of radiation distinguished by wavelength.

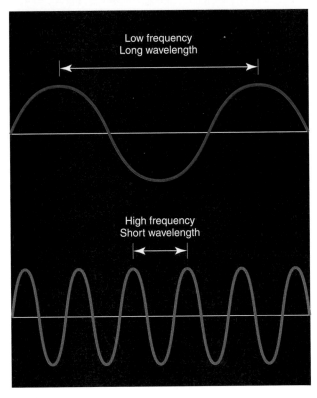

solar radiation strikes the ocean surface at an oblique angle—some radiation is reflected into the atmosphere and some bends (is refracted) as it penetrates the water. Electromagnetic radiation may also be absorbed, that is, converted to heat.

Although the electromagnetic spectrum is continuous, different names are assigned to different segments because we detect, measure, generate, and use those segments in different ways. Furthermore, the various types of electromagnetic radiation do not begin or end at precise points along the spectrum. For example, red light shades into invisible infrared radiation (infrared, meaning *below red*). At the other end of the visible portion of the electromagnetic spectrum, violet light shades into invisible ultraviolet radiation (ultraviolet, meaning *beyond violet*).

FIGURE 3.2

Wavelength is the distance between two successive crests or, equivalently, between two successive troughs. Wavelength is inversely related to wave frequency.

Beyond visible light on the electromagnetic spectrum and in order of increasing energy level, increasing frequency, and decreasing wavelength are ultraviolet radiation (UV), X-rays, and gamma radiation. All three types of radiation occur naturally and all can be produced artificially. All have medical uses: ultraviolet radiation is a potent germicide; X-rays are used as a powerful diagnostic tool; and both X-rays and gamma radiation are used to treat cancer patients. These three highly energetic types of radiation are dangerous as well as useful. Ultraviolet radiation can cause irreparable damage to the light-sensitive cells of the eye. Staring at the sun (for instance, during a partial solar eclipse) can permanently blind a person unless a filter is used to block out ultraviolet radiation. Also, overexposure to UV, X-rays, or gamma radiation can cause sterilization, cancer, mutations, or damage to a fetus. Fortunately, Earth's atmosphere blocks most incoming ultraviolet radiation and virtually all X-rays and gamma radiation through absorption by the rarefied gases in the ionosphere and stratosphere. Without this protective atmospheric shield, life as we know it would perish.

At lower frequencies and longer wavelengths, UV radiation shades into **visible radiation**, that is, radiation that is perceptible by the human eye. White light is *polychromatic*, composed of multiple colors associated with individual wavelength bands. The wavelength of visible light ranges from about 0.40 micrometer at the violet end to approximately 0.70 micrometer at the red end. (One *micrometer* is a millionth of a meter, about one-tenth the thickness of a human hair.) Visible light is essential for many activities of plants and animals. In plants, light provides the energy needed for photosynthesis; it also regulates the opening of buds and flowers in spring and the dropping of leaves in autumn. For animals, light governs the timing of reproduction, hibernation, and migration and makes vision possible.

Between red light and microwave radiation on the electromagnetic spectrum is **infrared radiation (IR)**. IR is not visible, but we can feel the heat it generates when it is intense, as it is, for example, when emitted by a hot stove. Actually, every known object, including you and this book, emit small amounts of infrared radiation. And, as we will see later in this chapter, absorption and emission of IR by certain atmospheric gases is responsible for significant warming of the lower atmosphere (the *greenhouse effect*).

At longer wavelengths is the microwave portion of the electromagnetic spectrum, which spans wavelengths of about 0.1 to 1000 millimeters. Some microwave frequencies are used for radio communication, in microwave ovens, and in weather radar. At the low energy, low frequency, long wavelength end of the electromagnetic spectrum are radio waves. Wavelengths range from a fraction of a centimeter up to hundreds of kilometers, and frequencies can extend to a billion Hz. FM (frequency modulation) radio waves, for example, span 88 million to 108 million Hz; hence, the familiar 88 and 108 at opposite ends of the FM radio dial.

Radiation Laws

Several physical laws describe the properties of electromagnetic radiation emitted by a perfect radiator, a so-called blackbody. By definition, a **blackbody** at a constant temperature absorbs all radiation that is incident on it and emits all the radiant energy it absorbs. A blackbody is both a perfect absorber and perfect emitter of radiation. The wavelengths of emitted radiation are related to the temperature of the blackbody. Surfaces of real objects may approximate blackbodies for certain wavelengths of radiation but not for others. Freshly fallen snow, for example, is very nearly a blackbody for infrared radiation but not for visible light. (Note that *blackbody* does not refer to color.) Although neither the sun nor Earth is a blackbody, their absorption and emission of radiation is sufficiently close to that of a blackbody that we can apply blackbody radiation laws to them with some very useful results. Here we apply two blackbody radiation laws: Wien's displacement law and the Stefan-Boltzmann law.

All known objects emit and absorb all forms of electromagnetic radiation. However, the wavelength of most intense radiation (λ_{max}) emitted by a blackbody is inversely proportional to the absolute temperature (T) of the object. That is,

$$\lambda_{max} = C/T$$

where C, a constant of proportionality, has the value of 2897 if λ_{max} is expressed in micrometers, and T is in kelvins. *Absolute temperature* is the number of kelvins above absolute zero (-273.15 °C or -459.67 °F). This is a statement of **Wien's displacement law**. As shown in Figure 3.3, a significant portion of the radiation emitted (or absorbed) by an object is found around this peak maximum wavelength.

According to Wien's displacement law, hot objects (such as the sun) emit radiation that peaks at relatively short wavelengths, whereas cold objects (such as the Earth-atmosphere system) emit peak radiation at longer wavelengths. The top heating elements of an electric range

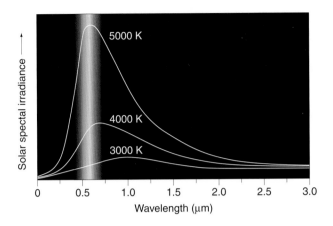

FIGURE 3.3
With increasing absolute temperature (K), the wavelength of maximum radiation emitted or absorbed by an object decreases. This is known as Wien's displacement law.

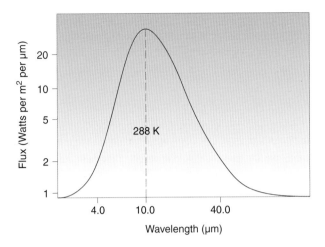

FIGURE 3.5
Flux of radiation as a function of wavelength emitted by a blackbody radiating at about the same average temperature as Earth's surface, that is, 15 °C (288 K).

provide an illustration of Wien's displacement law. After switching on a heating element, its metal coils warm and we readily feel the heat. We are actually feeling invisible infrared radiation. As the coil temperature continues to rise, the coils emit more intense infrared radiation with peak emission at progressively shorter wavelengths. That is, as the coil temperature rises, the coil's peak radiation is displaced from the infrared toward the near-infrared portion of the electromagnetic spectrum. The highest setting on the stove will cause the heating element to glow dull red in a dark room.

Radiation emitted by the sun is similar to that emitted by a blackbody at temperature of about 6000 °C (11,000 °F). Figure 3.4 shows the flux (rate of energy transfer per unit time per unit area) of solar radiation

received at the top of the atmosphere as a function of wavelength. The sun emits a band of radiation (at wavelengths mostly between 0.25 and 2.5 micrometers) that is most intense at a wavelength of about 0.5 micrometer (in the green of visible light). The flux of radiation emitted by Earth's surface is similar to that emitted by a blackbody at a temperature of about 15 °C (59 °F) peaking in the infrared (Figure 3.5). Earth's surface emits a broad band of infrared radiation (at wavelengths mostly between 4 and 24 micrometers) with peak intensity at a wavelength of about 10 micrometers.

The area under the blackbody curves in Figures 3.4 (for the sun) and 3.5 (for Earth's surface) represent the total radiation energy emitted per unit time per unit surface area at all wavelengths. The vertical scales in the two figures are much different because the sun emits immensely more total radiational energy than does Earth's surface. According to the **Stefan-Boltzmann law**, the total energy flux emitted by a blackbody across all wavelengths (E) is proportional to the fourth power of the absolute temperature (T^4) of the object; that is,

$$E \sim T^4.$$

This relationship implies that a small change in the temperature of a blackbody results in a much greater change in the total amount of radiational energy emitted by the blackbody. The sun radiates at a much higher temperature than does Earth's surface, so that the Stefan-Boltzmann law predicts that the sun's energy output per square meter is about 190,000 times that of the Earth-atmosphere system.

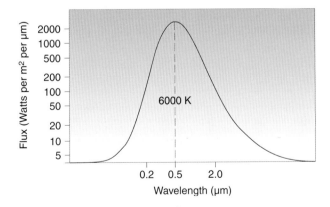

FIGURE 3.4
The flux of solar radiation incident at the top of the atmosphere as a function of wavelength. Radiation emitted by the sun is similar to that emitted by a blackbody at a temperature of about 6000 °C (about 6000 K).

As solar radiation travels away from the sun and spreads outward into space in all directions, its intensity (energy per unit time per unit area) diminishes rapidly, as the inverse square of the distance traveled. The radiation emanating in all directions from a nearly point source like the sun spreads out as ever increasing spheres, with the intensity being reduced as a function of the surface area of the sphere. According to this **inverse square law**, doubling the distance traversed by radiation reduces its intensity to $(1/2)^2$ or 1/4 of its initial value. Earth orbits the sun at a distance such that it receives an intensity of solar radiation which results in a temperature range that supports life as we know it (Figure 3.6). Venus is closer to the sun, receives nearly twice as much solar radiation as Earth and is too hot for life, with surface temperatures averaging about 460 °C (860 °F). Mars is farther away from the sun, receives slightly less than one-half the solar radiation as Earth and is too cold for life, with surface temperatures averaging about −65 °C (−85 °F).

Based upon several decades of satellite measurements as well as a relatively constant planetary temperature, we can assume that the total energy (in the form of solar radiation) absorbed by planet Earth is equal to the total energy (in the form of infrared radiation) emitted by the Earth-atmosphere system to space. This balance between energy input and energy output for the

Earth-atmosphere system is known as **global radiative equilibrium** and is an example of the *law of energy conservation*. We examine this important concept in more detail in the next chapter.

Input of Solar Radiation

The sun, the closest star to Earth, is a huge gaseous body composed almost entirely of hydrogen (about 80% by mass) and helium with internal temperatures that may exceed 20 million °C. The ultimate source of solar energy is a continuous nuclear fusion reaction in the sun's interior. Simply put, in this reaction, four hydrogen nuclei (protons) fuse to form one helium nucleus (alpha particle). However, the mass of the four hydrogen nuclei is about 0.7% greater than the mass of one helium nucleus. This mass lost in the fusion of hydrogen to helium is converted to energy as described by Albert Einstein's mass-energy equivalence principle:

$$E = mc^2$$

where mass, m, is related to energy, E, and c is the speed of light (300,000 km per sec). Note that c^2 is a huge number so that even a very small mass is converted to an enormous quantity of energy. Some of the energy produced by nuclear fusion in the sun is used to bind the helium nucleus together. The rest of the energy is radiated and convected to the sun's surface, and then radiated in all directions to space.

At radiating temperatures near 6000 °C (11,000 °F), the visible surface of the sun, known as the **photosphere**, is much cooler than the sun's interior. A network of huge, irregularly shaped convective cells, called *granules*, gives the photosphere its honeycomb appearance. A typical granule is about 1000 km (600 mi) across, although some so-called *supergranules* may be 30,000 to 50,000 km (18,500 to 31,000 mi) in diameter. Most granules have a life expectancy of only a few minutes and consist of a broad central area of rising hot gas surrounded by a thin layer of cooler gas sinking back toward the center of the sun. This zone of convective activity encompasses the outer 200,000 km (125,000 mi) of the sun.

Relatively dark, cool areas, called **sunspots**, dot the surface of the photosphere. Sunspot temperatures may be 400 to 1800 Celsius degrees (720 to 3240 Fahrenheit degrees) lower than the photosphere's average temperature. Bright areas, known as *faculae*,

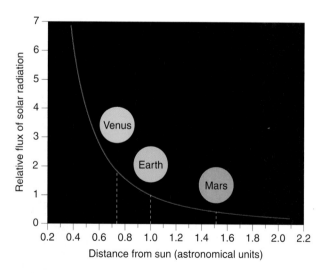

FIGURE 3.6
As radiation flows from the sun into space, its intensity decreases as the inverse square of the distance traveled. Venus, closer to the sun than Earth, receives about twice as much solar radiation as Earth. Mars, on the other hand, is farther from the sun than Earth and receives roughly half as much solar radiation as Earth. [Courtesy of E.J. Hopkins]

usually occur near sunspots. Changes in the number of sunspots and faculae accompany changes in solar energy output and may influence Earth's climate (Chapter 15).

Outward from the photosphere is the **chromosphere**, consisting of ions of hydrogen and helium at 4000 °C to 40,000 °C (7200 °F to 72,000 °F). Beyond this zone is the outermost portion of the sun's atmosphere, the **solar corona**, a region of extremely hot (1 to 4 million °C) and highly rarefied ionized gases (predominantly hydrogen and helium) that extends millions of kilometers into space. The solar wind originates in the corona and is intensified by solar flares that erupt from the photosphere into the corona (Chapter 2). In its orbit about the sun, planet Earth intercepts only about one two-billionth of the enormous quantity of energy continually radiated by the sun to space.

SOLAR ALTITUDE

Our experience at middle latitudes tells us that the intensity of solar radiation striking Earth's surface varies significantly with the season. At local noon, the summer sun is higher in the sky than the winter sun, and solar rays striking Earth's surface are more concentrated in summer than in winter. Even over the course of a single day, regular changes occur in incoming solar radiation striking the Earth's surface; that is, the solar beam is more concentrated at noon than at sunrise or sunset. Evidently, the angle of the sun above the horizon, called the **solar altitude**, influences the intensity of solar radiation received at the Earth's surface. When and where the sun is directly overhead, the solar altitude has its maximum value of 90 degrees and solar rays are most concentrated (Figure 3.7). When the sun is positioned lower in the sky (that is, as the solar altitude is lower), solar radiation spreads over a larger area of Earth's horizontal surface and thus is less intense.

Earth is so distant from the sun (a mean distance of about 150 million km or 93 million mi) that solar radiation reaches the planet as essentially parallel beams of uniform intensity. But the nearly spherical Earth presents a curved surface to incoming solar radiation so that the noon solar altitude always varies with latitude (Figure 3.8). The intensity of solar radiation actually striking Earth's surface is greatest at the latitude where the noon sun is in the zenith (solar altitude of 90 degrees) and decreases with distance north and south of that latitude.

Solar altitude also influences the interaction between solar radiation and the atmosphere. Decreasing solar altitude lengthens the path of the sun's rays through

FIGURE 3.7
The intensity of solar radiation striking Earth's surface per unit area varies with the solar altitude. (Top) Incident solar radiation is most intense when the sun is directly overhead (solar altitude of 90 degrees). (Bottom) With decreasing solar altitude, solar radiation received at Earth's surface spreads over an increasing area (*y* is greater than *x*) so that radiation is less concentrated (less radiational energy per unit area).

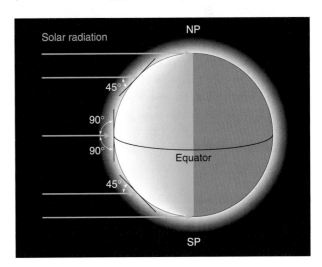

FIGURE 3.8
On any day of the year, the noon solar altitude always varies with latitude because Earth presents a curved surface to the incoming solar beam. In this example for an equinox, the solar altitude is 90 degrees at the equator and decreases with latitude (toward the poles). Hence, solar radiation striking horizontal surfaces per unit area is most intense at the equator and least intense at the poles.

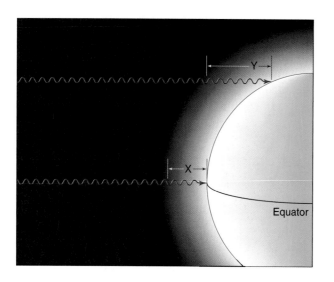

FIGURE 3.9
Solar radiation's path through the atmosphere lengthens with decreasing solar altitude, that is, as the sun moves lower in the sky. *X* is the path length at high solar altitude and *Y* is the path length at low solar altitude. Path *Y* may be 30 times longer than *X*.

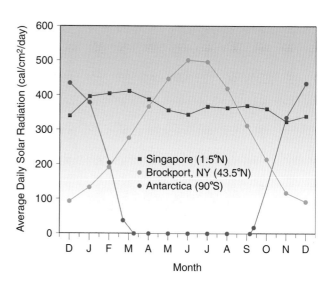

FIGURE 3.10
Average daily solar radiation (in calories per cm² per day) by month at Singapore, Brockport, NY, and Antarctica. During part of the year, the polar (Antarctic) and mid-latitude (Brockport) locations receive more solar radiation daily than the near-equator location (Singapore).

the atmosphere (Figure 3.9). As the path lengthens, the greater interaction of solar radiation with clouds, gases and aerosols reduces its intensity. Even if skies are cloud-free, the longer the path of solar radiation through the atmosphere, the less intense is the radiation striking Earth's surface. The nature of the interactions between solar radiation and the atmosphere (scattering, reflection, and absorption) is described later in this chapter.

While solar altitude influences the intensity of solar radiation striking Earth's surface per unit area, the length of daylight affects the total amount of radiational energy that is received each day. For example, in summer the altitude of the noon sun is lower at high latitudes than at middle latitudes. Nonetheless, the greater length of daylight at high latitudes may translate into more total radiation striking Earth's surface during a 24-hr day (Figure 3.10). Variations in both solar altitude and length of daylight accompany the annual march of the seasons. Before examining these relationships, first consider the fundamental motions of Earth in space: rotation of the planet on its spin axis and the planet's orbit about the sun.

EARTH'S MOTIONS IN SPACE AND THE SEASONS

Rotation of Earth on its axis accounts for day and night. Once every 24 hrs, the nearly spherical Earth completes one rotation with respect to the sun and at any instant, half the planet is illuminated by visible solar radiation (daylight) and the other half is in darkness (night).

Over the course of one year, which is actually 365.2422 days, Earth makes one complete revolution about the sun in a slightly elliptical orbit (Figure 3.11). Earth's orbital eccentricity, that is, its departure from a circular orbit, is so slight that the Earth-to-sun distance varies by only about 3.3% through the year. Earth is closest to the sun (147 million km or 91 million mi) on about 3 January and farthest from the sun (152 million km or 94 million mi) on about 4 July. These are the current dates of **perihelion** and **aphelion**, respectively. In the Northern Hemisphere, Earth is closest to the sun in winter and farthest from the sun in summer. Because of the spreading of radiation described by the inverse square law, Earth receives about 6.7% more solar radiation at perihelion than at aphelion. The eccentricity of Earth's orbit about the sun cannot explain the seasons. What does account for seasons?

The answer is found in the tilt of Earth's spin axis. Because of this tilt, Earth's equatorial plane is inclined 23 degrees 27 minutes to the plane defined by the planet's annual orbit about the sun (Figure 3.12). Equivalently, Earth's spin axis is tilted 23 degrees 27 minutes from a perpendicular to Earth's orbital plane. During its annual revolution about the sun, Earth's spin axis always remains in the same orientation relative to the stars with the North Pole aimed toward *Polaris*, the North Star, while its orientation to the sun changes in a periodic manner that we associate with our seasons. Accompanying these changes are regular variations

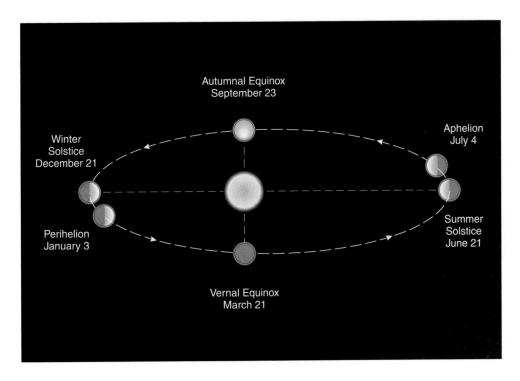

FIGURE 3.11
Earth's orbit is an ellipse with the sun located at one focus. Earth is closest to the sun at *perihelion* (about 3 January) and farthest from the sun at *aphelion* (about 4 July). Note that the eccentricity of Earth's orbit is greatly exaggerated in this drawing.

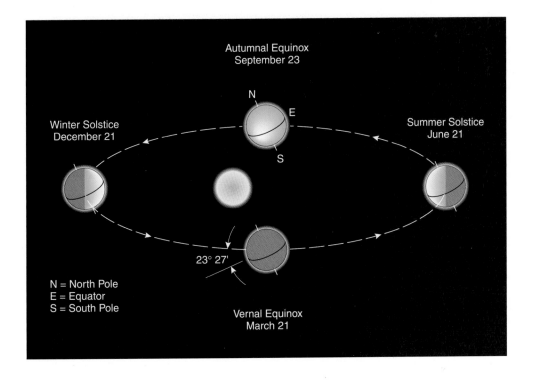

FIGURE 3.12
The seasons change because Earth's equatorial plane is inclined (at 23 degrees, 27 minutes) to its orbital plane. The seasons given are for the Northern Hemisphere. Note that the eccentricity of Earth's orbit is greatly exaggerated in this drawing.

in solar altitude and length of daylight, which in turn affect the intensity and total amount of solar radiation received at different latitudes on Earth's surface. If Earth's rotational axis were perpendicular to its orbital plane (no tilt), Earth's axis would always have the same orientation to the sun. Without an axial tilt, only the changes in the Earth-sun distance between aphelion and perihelion would produce a seasonal contrast and it would be slight.

How does Earth's orientation to the sun change over the course of a year? Viewed from Earth's surface, the latitude where the sun's rays are most intense (solar altitude of 90 degrees) shifts from 23 degrees 27 minutes south of the equator to 23 degrees 27 minutes north of the equator, and then back to 23 degrees 27 minutes S. On about 21 March and again on about 23 September, the sun's noon position is directly over the equator. At these times, day and night are approximately equal in length (12 hrs) everywhere, except at the poles (Figure 3.13). For this reason, these dates are the **equinoxes** (from the Latin for "equal nights").

Following the equinoxes, the sun continues its apparent journey toward its maximum poleward locations. On or about 21 June, the sun's noon rays are vertical at 23 degrees 27 minutes N, the latitude circle known as the **Tropic of Cancer**. As shown in Figure 3.14, daylight

FIGURE 3.13

At the autumnal and spring equinoxes, the noon solar altitude is greatest (90 degrees) at the equator. Day and night are about equal in length except at the poles, where the sun appears to travel along the local horizon for the entire day.

is continuous north of the **Arctic Circle** (66 degrees 33 minutes N) and absent south of the **Antarctic Circle** (66 degrees 33 minutes S). Elsewhere, days are longer than nights in the Northern Hemisphere, where it is the first day of astronomical summer, and days are shorter than nights

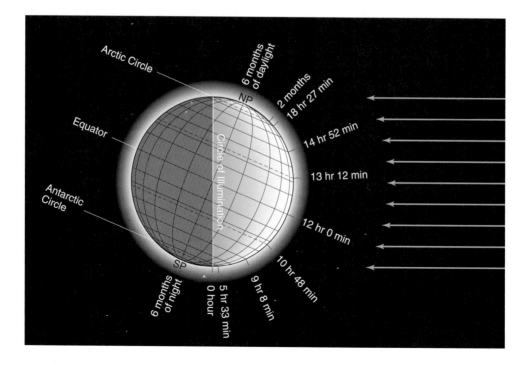

FIGURE 3.14

On the Northern Hemisphere summer solstice (about 21 June), the noon solar altitude is greatest (90 degrees) at 23 degrees 27 minutes N, and days are longer than nights everywhere north of the equator. Duration of daylight is given for every 20 degrees of latitude.

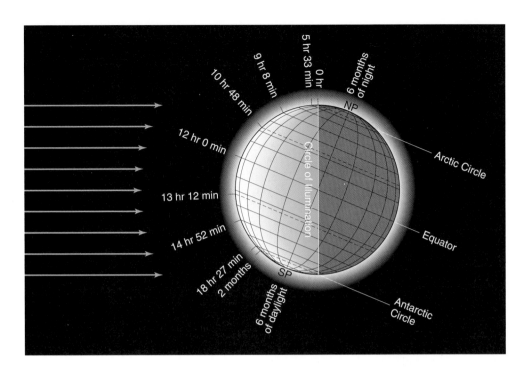

FIGURE 3.15
On the Northern Hemisphere winter solstice (about 21 December), the noon solar altitude is greatest (90 degrees) at 23 degrees 27 minutes S, and days are shorter than nights everywhere north of the equator. Duration of daylight is given for every 20 degrees of latitude.

in the Southern Hemisphere, where it is the first day of astronomical winter. Hence, this is a **solstice** date—the summer solstice in the Northern Hemisphere and winter solstice in the Southern Hemisphere. Solstice is from the Latin, *solstitium*, referring to the sun standing still.

On or about 21 December, the noon sun is directly over 23 degrees 27 minutes S, the latitude circle known as the **Tropic of Capricorn**, and the situation is reversed (Figure 3.15). Daylight is continuous south of the Antarctic Circle and absent north of the Arctic Circle. Elsewhere, nights are longer than days in the Northern Hemisphere, where it is the first day of winter, and days are longer than nights in the Southern Hemisphere, where it is the first day of summer. Thus this is the date of the winter solstice in the Northern Hemisphere and the summer solstice in the Southern Hemisphere.

As Earth's orientation to the sun changes through the course of a year, so does the daily path of the sun through the local sky. Figure 3.16 portrays the path of the sun through the sky from sunrise to sunset for solstices and equinoxes at the equator, a middle latitude Northern Hemisphere location, and the North Pole. The high point of each path is the sun's position at local solar noon. (Because of one's location within a civil time zone and the time of the year, along with daylight saving time, local solar noon may differ by as much as one hour from noon on a clock.) At the middle latitude location and North Pole, the altitude of the noon sun is greatest on the summer solstice but at the equator, the noon solar altitude

is greatest on the equinoxes (when the sun is directly overhead). Note that on the summer solstice at the North Pole, the sun circles the sky at a constant solar altitude (about 23.5 degrees) over the 24-hr day.

Solar radiation incident on horizontal Earth surfaces is at maximum intensity where the noon sun is directly overhead. North and south of that latitude, the intensity of noontime solar radiation diminishes because the solar altitude decreases. At the equinoxes, solar rays are most intense at the equator at noon and decrease with latitude toward the poles. At the Northern Hemisphere summer solstice, solar rays are most intense at local noon along the Tropic of Cancer and decrease to zero at the Antarctic Circle. On that day, the noon sun has the same altitude at 47 degrees N as at the equator. On the Northern Hemisphere winter solstice, solar rays are most intense along the Tropic of Capricorn and decrease to zero at the Arctic Circle.

As noted earlier, days and nights are approximately equal in length (12 hrs) everywhere on Earth (except at the poles) on only two days of the year, the spring and autumnal equinoxes. The length of daylight on the equinoxes is not precisely 12 hrs because of the optical effects of the atmosphere on the solar beam. Times of sunrise and sunset refer to the hour and minute when the outer edge of the sun (not its center) is on the horizon. The atmosphere refracts (bends) the incoming solar beam downward so that the sun appears to be higher than it actually is, lengthening the period

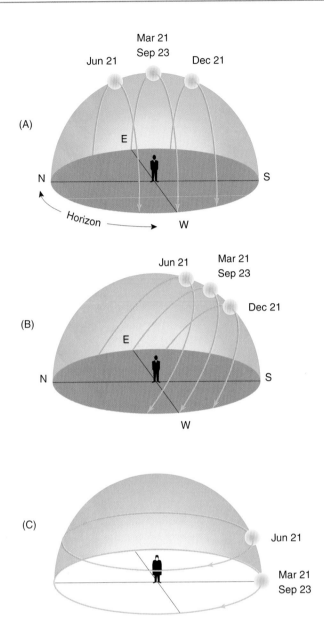

FIGURE 3.16
Path of the sun through the sky on the solstices and equinoxes at (A) the equator, (B) middle latitudes of the Northern Hemisphere, and (C) the North Pole.

of daylight. For example, at Washington, DC the day length is 12 hrs and 6 minutes on the autumnal equinox (on or about 23 September).

Between the March and September equinoxes, days are longer than nights in the Northern Hemisphere and days are shorter than nights in the Southern Hemisphere. Between the September and March equinoxes, days are shorter than nights in the Northern Hemisphere and days are longer than nights in the Southern Hemisphere. Furthermore, the seasonal (winter-to-summer) contrast in length of daylight increases with increasing latitude (Figure 3.17). At the equator, the period of daylight is essentially the same (slightly more than 12 hrs) year round. At 60 degrees N, the length of daylight varies from 5 hrs 53 minutes on 22 December to 18 hrs 52 minutes on 21 June.

THE SOLAR CONSTANT

For convenience of study, the solar energy input into the Earth-atmosphere system is often described as the solar constant. The **solar constant** is defined as the rate at which solar radiation falls on a surface located at the outer

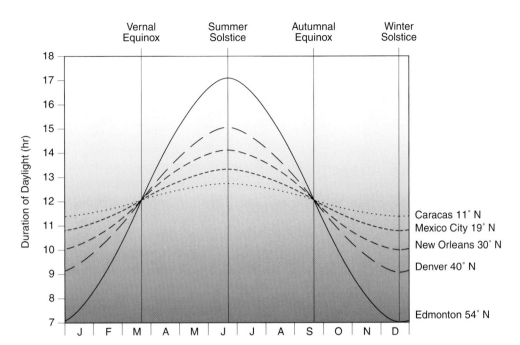

FIGURE 3.17
Variation in the length of daylight through the year increases with increasing latitude.

edge of the atmosphere and oriented perpendicular to the incoming solar beam when Earth is at its mean distance from the sun. The *constant* designation is misleading because solar energy output actually fluctuates by a very small fraction of a percent over a year and exhibits longer-term variations (Chapter 15). The solar constant averages about 1.97 calories per square centimeter per minute (cal/cm^2/min), or 1368 watts per square meter (W/m^2).

The rate of total solar energy input for the planet varies through the course of a year from a maximum when Earth is closest to the sun (perihelion) to a minimum when Earth is farthest from the sun (aphelion). At perihelion, Earth is about 3.3% closer to the sun than at aphelion. Applying the inverse square law, the planet intercepts about 6.7% more radiation at perihelion (2.04 cal/cm^2/min or 1417 W/m^2) than at aphelion (1.91 cal/cm^2/min or 1326 W/m^2).

The perihelion/aphelion contrast in solar energy input coupled with the seasonal variation in radiation has implications for global climate. The Southern Hemisphere receives more radiation during summer and less radiation during winter than does the Northern Hemisphere. Consequently, all other factors being equal, we might expect a greater winter-to-summer temperature contrast in the Southern Hemisphere. However, in the Southern Hemisphere the larger percentage of ocean surface area coupled with the relatively great thermal inertia of ocean water moderates seasonal temperature differences and largely offsets the greater seasonal contrast in incoming solar radiation (Chapter 4).

Solar Radiation and the Atmosphere

Solar radiation interacts with gases and aerosols as it travels through the atmosphere. These interactions consist of scattering, reflection, and absorption. Solar radiation that is not scattered or reflected back to space, or absorbed by gases and aerosols, reaches Earth's surface, where further interactions take place. Within the atmosphere, the percentage of solar radiation that is absorbed (*absorptivity*) plus the percentage scattered or reflected (*albedo*) plus the percentage transmitted to Earth's surface (*transmissivity*) must equal 100%. This relationship is another example of the *law of energy conservation*.

In the process of **scattering**, a particle disperses solar radiation in all directions—forward, backward, and also sideways. Within the atmosphere, both gas molecules and aerosols (including the tiny water droplets and ice crystals composing clouds) scatter solar radiation but with some important differences. Scattering by molecules is wavelength dependent and the preferential scattering of blue-violet light by nitrogen and oxygen molecules is the principal reason for the color of the daytime sky (Chapter 14). On the other hand, the tiny water droplets and ice crystals that compose clouds scatter visible solar radiation equally at all wavelengths so that clouds appear white.

Reflection, a special case of scattering, takes place at the interface between two different media, such as air and cloud, when some of the radiation striking that interface is redirected (backscattered). At such an

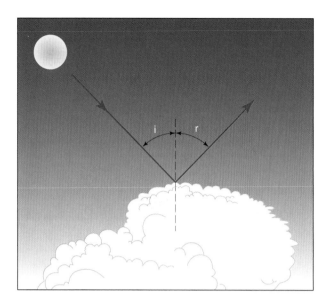

FIGURE 3.18
Reflection of a solar ray by the top of a cloud illustrates the law of reflection whereby the angle of incident radiation (*i*) equals the angle of reflected radiation (*r*).

interface (Figure 3.18), the angle of incident radiation (*i*) equals the angle of reflected radiation (*r*); this is known as the **law of reflection**. The fraction of incident radiation that is backscattered by airborne particles or reflected by a surface (or interface) is the **albedo** of that surface, that is,

albedo = [(reflected radiation)/(incident radiation)]

where albedo is expressed either as a percentage or a fraction. Surfaces having a high albedo reflect a relatively large fraction of incident solar radiation and appear light in color. Surfaces having a relatively low albedo reflect a relatively small fraction of incident solar radiation and appear dark in color. Because such surfaces absorb more sunlight, they typically are warmer than those that are lighter and have a higher albedo.

Within the atmosphere, the tops of clouds are the most important reflectors of solar radiation (Figure 3.19). Cloud top albedo depends primarily on cloud thickness and varies from under 40% for thin clouds (less than 50 m, or 165 ft, thick) to 80% or more for thick clouds (more than 5000 m, or 16,500 ft, thick). For this reason, during daytime, a high thin veil of cirrus clouds appears much brighter than the underside of a much thicker thunderstorm (cumulonimbus) cloud. The average albedo for all cloud types and thickness is about 55%, and at any point in time, clouds cover about 60% of the planet. All other factors

being constant, solar radiation reaching Earth's surface is more intense and daytime surface temperatures are higher when the sky is clear rather than cloudy.

Scattering and reflection within the atmosphere alter only the direction of incoming solar radiation. **Absorption**, however, is an energy conversion process whereby some of the radiation striking the surface of an object is converted to heat energy. Oxygen, ozone, water vapor, and various aerosols (including cloud particles) absorb a portion of the incoming solar radiation. Absorption by atmospheric gases varies by wavelength; that is, a specific gas may absorb strongly in some wavelengths, but weakly or not at all in other wavelengths. As a consequence of absorption, radiation in that wavelength band is removed.

Within the stratosphere, oxygen (O_2) and ozone (O_3) strongly absorb solar ultraviolet radiation at wavelengths shorter than 0.3 micrometer. Oxygen absorbs UV at very short wavelengths (less than 0.2 micrometer), and ozone absorbs longer UV (0.22 to 0.29 micrometer). The net effect of this absorption is twofold: (1) a significant reduction in the intensity of UV that reaches Earth's surface and (2) a marked warming of the upper stratosphere (Figure 2.12). The clear atmosphere is essentially transparent to solar radiation in the wavelength range between about 0.3 and 0.8 micrometer (mostly visible radiation). Water vapor absorbs solar infrared radiation in certain wavelength bands greater than 0.8 micrometer. Clouds are relatively poor absorbers of solar radiation, typically absorbing less than 10% of the solar radiation that strikes the cloud top, although exceptionally thick clouds such as thunderclouds absorb somewhat more.

FIGURE 3.19
Cloud tops strongly backscatter visible solar radiation and appear very bright as in this view from an airplane window.

Stratospheric Ozone Shield

Ozone (O_3) is a relatively unstable molecule made up of three atoms of oxygen, but has certain physical and chemical properties that make it differ from free oxygen (O_2). As shown in Figure 3.20, the greatest concentration of ozone occurs naturally in the atmosphere at altitudes near 40 km (25 mi). Depending on its location in the atmosphere, ozone has either a positive or negative impact on life. On the negative side, ozone in the lower troposphere is a serious air pollutant and one of the chief constituents of photochemical smog (Chapter 2). On the positive side, chemical reactions involved in the formation and dissociation of ozone in the stratosphere shields organisms at the Earth's surface from exposure to potentially lethal intensities of solar ultraviolet radiation. Without this so-called **stratospheric ozone shield**, life as we know it could not exist on Earth.

Within the stratosphere, two sets of competing chemical reactions, both powered by solar ultraviolet radiation, continually generate and destroy ozone (Figure 3.21). During ozone production, UV strikes an oxygen molecule (O_2) causing it to split into two free oxygen atoms (O). Free oxygen atoms then collide with molecules of oxygen to form ozone molecules (O_3). At the same time, ozone is destroyed. Ozone absorbs ultraviolet radiation, splitting the molecule into one free oxygen atom (O) and one molecule of oxygen (O_2). The free oxygen atom then collides with an ozone molecule to form two molecules of oxygen. The net effect of these opposing sets of chemical reactions is a minute reservoir of ozone that peaks at only about 10 parts per million (ppm) in the middle stratosphere.

Ultraviolet radiation (at different wavelengths) powers both sets of chemical reactions so that much, but not all, UV radiation is prevented from reaching Earth's surface. Prolonged exposure of the skin to the UV that does penetrate the ozone shield can cause serious health problems. A thinner ozone shield would likely mean more intense UV radiation received at Earth's surface and, for humans, a greater risk of skin cancer, cataracts of the eye, and immune deficiencies. As a general rule, every 1% decline in stratospheric ozone concentration translates into a 2% increase in the intensity of UV that passes through the ozone shield. Various studies suggest that a 2.5% thinning of the ozone shield could boost the rate of human skin cancer by 10%. The most dangerous portion of UV radiation that reaches Earth's surface, designated *UVB*, spans the wavelength band from 0.29 to 0.32 micrometer. The increase in UVB that actually reaches Earth's surface hinges on the cloudiness and dustiness of the atmosphere. For more on the human health hazards of overexposure to solar UV radiation, see this chapter's first Essay.

Chemicals that threaten to destroy stratospheric ozone are of natural and industrial origin (Figure 3.22). Since the 1970s, a group of chemicals known as *chlorofluorocarbons (CFCs)* have received considerable attention for their potential impact on the ozone shield. First synthesized in 1928, CFCs were widely used as chilling (heat-transfer) agents in refrigerators and air conditioners, for cleaning electronic circuit boards, and in the manufacture of foams used for insulation. Certain CFCs are inert (chemically non-reactive) in the troposphere, where they have accumulated for decades. Atmospheric circulation transports CFCs into the stratosphere where, at altitudes above about 25 km (15 mi), intense UV radiation breaks down CFCs, releasing chlorine (Cl), a gas that readily reacts with and destroys ozone. Products of this reaction are chlorine monoxide (ClO) and molecular oxygen (O_2). Chlorine (Cl) is a catalyst in chemical reactions that convert ozone to oxygen. In this way, each chlorine atom destroys perhaps tens of thousands of ozone molecules.

F.S. Rowland and M.J. Molina of the University of California at Irvine first warned of the threat of CFCs to the stratospheric ozone shield in 1974. Consequently, use of CFCs as propellants in common household aerosol sprays such as deodorants, hairsprays, and furniture polish was banned in the United States, Canada, Norway, and Sweden in 1979. For their pioneering research on the depletion of stratospheric ozone, Rowland, Molina (now at

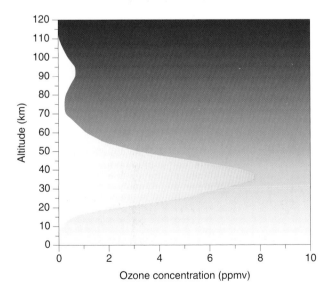

FIGURE 3.20
The concentration of ozone (O_3) peaks in the stratosphere.

FIGURE 3.21
Within the stratosphere, two sets of competing chemical reactions continually produce and destroy ozone (O₃). [Adapted from "Ozone: What is it and why do we care about it?" *NASA Facts*, NASA Goddard Space Flight Center, Greenbelt, MD, 1993.]

OZONE PRODUCTION

High energy ultraviolet radiation strikes an oxygen molecule...

...and causes it to split into two free oxygen atoms.

The free oxygen atoms collide with molecules of oxygen...

To form ozone molecules.

OZONE DESTRUCTION

Ozone absorbs a range of ultraviolet radiation...

...splitting the molecule into one free oxygen atom and one molecule of ordinary oxygen.

The free oxygen atom then can collide with an ozone molecule...

To form two molecules of oxygen.

the Massachusetts Institute of Technology), and P.J. Crutzen (of the Max Planck Institute for Chemistry, Germany) were awarded the 1995 Nobel Prize in chemistry.

Increasing world-wide acceptance of the threat of CFCs and other chemicals to the stratospheric ozone shield prompted the United Nations Environmental Program in 1987 to draw up the *Montreal Protocol on Substances that Deplete the Ozone Layer*. The original goal of the Montreal Protocol was to cut CFC production in half by 1992 (compared to 1986 levels). However, the seriousness of the problem led to subsequent amendments

expanding the list of regulated substances (e.g., to include bromine-containing halons) and requiring the worldwide phase out of the manufacture and use of CFCs beginning in January 1996.

As noted in Chapter 2, the first sign of thinning of the stratospheric ozone shield came from Antarctica. For about six weeks during the Southern Hemisphere spring (mainly in September and October), the ozone layer in the Antarctic stratosphere (mostly at altitudes from 11 to 23 km, or 7 to 14 mi) thins drastically and then recovers during November (Figure 3.23). The **Antarctic**

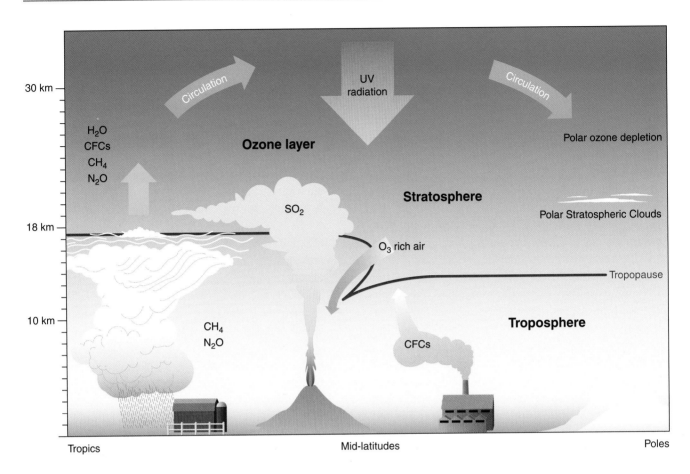

FIGURE 3.22
Chemicals that threaten to destroy stratospheric ozone have both natural and industrial sources. Chlorofluorocarbons (CFCs), methane (CH_4), nitrous oxide (N_2O), and water vapor enter the stratosphere via deep tropical convection currents. Within the stratosphere intense ultraviolet radiation breakdown these compounds forming substances such as chlorine monoxide (ClO) that readily reacts with and destroys ozone. [NASA Earth Observatory, adapted from Barbara Summey, SSAI]

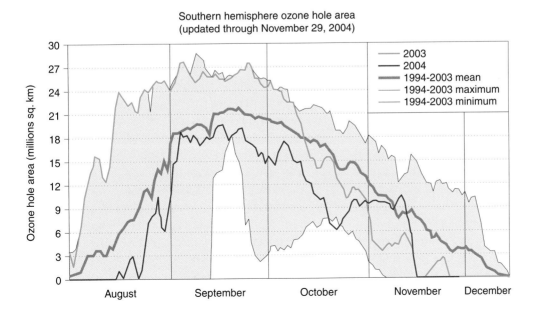

Southern hemisphere ozone hole area
(updated through November 29, 2004)

— 2003
— 2004
— 1994-2003 mean
— 1994-2003 maximum
— 1994-2003 minimum

FIGURE 3.23
The Antarctic ozone hole is a widespread area of stratospheric ozone depletion that develops over Antarctica during the Southern Hemisphere spring. The mean area encompassed by the Antarctic ozone hole during 1993-2003 increased from near zero at the beginning of August, peaked in September, and declined to zero in December. [NOAA and NASA Goddard Space Flight Center]

ozone hole is defined as the thinning of the ozone layer over the continent to levels significantly below pre-1979 levels. (Interestingly, prior to formation of the ozone hole, ozone levels in Antarctica were normally lowest in autumn.) Research conducted during the National Ozone Expeditions to the U.S. McMurdo Station in 1986-87 plus NASA aircraft flights into the Antarctic stratosphere in 1987 led to the discovery of relatively high concentrations of chlorine monoxide (ClO) in the Antarctic stratosphere. This discovery established a convincing link between the Antarctic ozone hole and CFCs.

The main source of information on stratospheric ozone levels is the *Total Ozone Mapping Spectrometer (TOMS)* flown aboard the satellites NIMBUS-7 (1978-93), Meteor-3 (1991-94), and NASA's Earth Probe (1996-present) and Aura (2004-present). Balloon-borne instruments and rocketsondes monitor the vertical structure of the ozone hole. Measurements indicate that the Antarctic ozone hole has steadily deepened (increasing depletion of ozone) since the late 1970s. The 2000 ozone hole was the largest on record, covering a maximum area of 29.2 million km^2 (11.5 million mi^2) on 10 September, larger than North America and exposing southern portions of Argentina and Chile to elevated levels of UV. On 24 September 2003, the ozone hole covered a near-record area of 28.7 million km^2 (11.1 million mi^2). In mid-September 2004, the ozone hole covered a maximum area of about 20 million km^2 (7.7 million mi^2).

What causes the Antarctic ozone hole and why does it fill in by November? During the long, dark Antarctic winter, extreme radiational cooling causes temperatures in the stratosphere to plunge below $-88\,°C$ ($-126\,°F$). At such frigid temperatures, **polar stratospheric clouds (PSCs)** form. These clouds (composed of tiny particles of water ice, nitric acid, and sulfuric acid) promote ozone depletion by providing surfaces on which chlorine and bromine compounds that are inert toward ozone are converted to active forms that destroy ozone. Once the sun reappears in spring, solar radiation supplies the energy that causes active forms of chlorine and bromine to begin destroying ozone.

Ozone depletion takes place while the Antarctic atmosphere is essentially cut off from the rest of the planetary-scale atmospheric circulation by the **circumpolar vortex**, a belt of strong winds that encircles the outer margin of the Antarctic continent. A month or so into spring, however, the circumpolar vortex begins to weaken, allowing warmer ozone-rich air from lower latitudes to invade the Antarctic stratosphere. Polar stratospheric clouds vaporize, and the stratospheric ozone concentration returns to normal levels; that is, the Antarctic ozone hole fills in. Year to year fluctuations in the depth and area of the Antarctic ozone hole are likely due to year to year variations in weather at high latitudes.

Scientists investigating stratospheric chemistry in the Arctic in early 1989 discovered ozone-destroying chlorine compounds and a slight thinning of ozone. Although some ozone depletion takes place in the Arctic during the Northern Hemisphere spring (March to May), an ozone hole comparable to the one over Antarctica is unlikely for two reasons. For one, in winter the Arctic stratosphere averages about 10 Celsius degrees (18 Fahrenheit degrees) warmer than the Antarctic stratosphere, making formation of polar stratospheric clouds unlikely. Secondly, the circumpolar vortex that surrounds the Arctic weakens earlier than its Antarctic counterpart. However, an exceptionally cold Arctic winter coupled with an unusually persistent circumpolar vortex could translate into significant ozone depletion in the Arctic, a region not very far from human population centers. In fact, this happened in the winters of 1996-97, 1999-2000, and 2002-03 with ozone losses over portions of Europe.

Discovery of the Antarctic ozone hole and its link to CFCs spurred questions regarding trends in stratospheric ozone elsewhere around the globe. In the spring of 1992, Richard Stolarski of NASA's Goddard Space Flight Center reported a downward trend in stratospheric ozone at middle latitude ground stations for all seasons since 1970. Shorter duration satellite measurements (about 12 years) revealed a negative ozone trend in both hemispheres except near the equator, where no significant change was detected. At middle latitudes, the greatest rate of depletion occurred in late winter and early spring and peaked at slightly more than 6% per decade. The first well-documented reports of a significant increase in ultraviolet radiation striking Earth's surface came from Toronto, Ontario. James Kerr and Thomas McElroy of Canada's Atmospheric Environment Service (AES) found that summer levels of UVB increased about 7% annually from 1989 to 1993. In the same period, winter levels of UVB climbed more than 5% per year.

CFCs and halons have long residence times in the atmosphere so that these substances will continue to threaten the stratospheric ozone shield for some time to come in spite of the phase out. Concentrations of ozone-depleting chlorine in the stratosphere are not expected to begin to decline until about 2010. And complete recovery of the Antarctic ozone layer is not likely until at least 2050.

Solar Radiation and Earth's Surface

Incoming solar radiation has both direct and diffuse components. Solar radiation that passes directly through the atmosphere to Earth's surface is the direct component that provides bright sunshine and casts shadows. Solar radiation that is scattered and/or reflected to Earth's surface is the diffuse component. Direct plus diffuse solar radiation that strikes Earth's surface is either reflected or absorbed depending on the surface albedo. The fraction that is not reflected is absorbed (that is, converted to heat) and the fraction that is not absorbed is reflected.

As noted earlier, light surfaces reflect more solar radiation than dark surfaces. Skiers and snow boarders who have been sunburned on the slopes on a sunny day are well aware of the high reflectivity of a snow cover. The albedo of fresh-fallen snow typically ranges between 75% and 95%; that is, 75% to 95% of the solar radiation striking a fresh snow cover is reflected, and the rest (5% to 25%) is absorbed (converted to heat). A fresh snow cover is highly reflective because the snow surface consists of a multitude of randomly oriented crystals each having many reflecting surfaces. As snow ages, the surface albedo declines as snow crystals convert to spherical ice particles having fewer reflecting surfaces. The albedo of old snow typically ranges between 40% and 60%. At the other extreme, the albedo of a dark surface, such as a black topped road or a spruce forest, may be as low as 5%. Differences in albedo explain why light-colored clothing is usually a more comfortable choice than dark-colored clothing on a sunny, hot day. Albedo values of some common surfaces are listed in Table 3.1.

In the visible satellite image in Figure 3.24, the ocean surface appears dark because of its low albedo and strong absorption of solar radiation. The albedo of the ocean (or lake) surface varies with the angle of the sun above the horizon (*solar altitude*). Under clear skies, the albedo of a flat, tranquil water surface decreases with increasing solar altitude (Figure 3.25). The albedo approaches a mirror-like 100% near sunrise and sunset (when the solar altitude is near 0 degrees) but declines sharply as the solar altitude approaches 20 degrees. With overcast skies, only diffuse solar radiation strikes the water surface and the albedo varies little with solar altitude and is uniformly less than 10%. On a global basis, the albedo of the ocean surface averages only about 8%; that is, the ocean absorbs on average 92% of incident solar radiation.

Whereas the clear atmosphere is relatively transparent to solar radiation, the ocean absorbs most solar radiation within relatively shallow depths. As shown

TABLE 3.1

Average Albedo (Reflectivity) of some Common Surface Types for Visible Solar Radiation

Surface	Albedo (% reflected)
Deciduous forest	15-18
Coniferous forest	9-15
Tropical rainforest	7-15
Tundra	15-35
Grasslands	18-25
Desert	25-30
Sand	30-35
Soil	5-30
Green crops	15-25
Sea ice	30-40
Fresh snow	75-95
Old snow	40-60
Glacial ice	20-40
Water body (high solar altitude)	3-10
Water body (low solar altitude)	10-100
Asphalt road	5-10
Urban area	14-18
Cumulonimbus cloud	90
Stratocumulus cloud	60
Cirrus cloud	40-50

FIGURE 3.24
In this visible satellite image of 20 June 2005 at 1815 UTC, water surfaces appear black because of their low albedo. Note the appearance of Lakes Michigan, Huron, Erie and Ontario, and the near-shore ocean from Massachusetts northward to Nova Scotia. Clusters of fair-weather cumulus clouds are visible from southern New York southwestward across the Ohio River Valley. The bright white blotch over Minnesota is widespread cirrus cloudiness from thunderstorm activity.

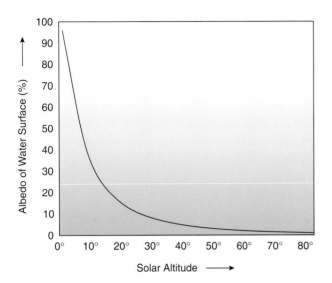

FIGURE 3.25
The albedo of a flat and undisturbed water surface under clear skies decreases with increasing solar altitude. A wave-covered water surface has a slightly higher albedo at high solar altitudes and a slightly lower albedo at low solar altitudes.

in Figure 3.26, solar radiation is selectively absorbed by wavelength as it passes through ocean waters. Water absorbs the longer wavelength light (i.e., reds and yellows) more efficiently than the shorter wavelength light (i.e., greens and blues) so that green and blue light penetrate to greater depths. Within clear, clean water, red light is completely absorbed within about 15 m (50 ft) of the surface, whereas green and blue-violet light may penetrate to depths approaching 250 m (800 ft). More green and

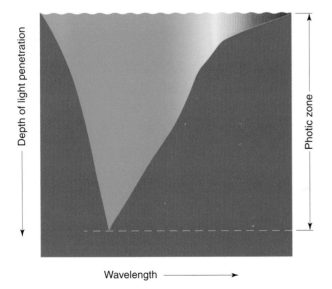

FIGURE 3.26
Visible solar radiation is selectively absorbed by wavelength as it penetrates the ocean's surface waters.

blue light is scattered to our eyes, explaining the blue/green color of the open ocean. Tiny particles suspended in water significantly boost absorption so that sunlight often is completely absorbed at shallower depths. In fact, some coastal waters are so turbid (murky) that little if any sunlight reaches much below 10 m (35 ft). Suspended particles preferentially scatter yellow and green light giving these waters their characteristic aqua color.

Significant changes in surface albedo occur seasonally and affect the fraction of incident solar radiation that is converted to heat. In autumn in forested areas, loss of leaves from deciduous trees raises the surface albedo. At middle and high latitudes, significant increases in surface albedo accompany the winter freeze-over of lakes, the formation of sea ice, and development of a persistent snow cover.

Global Solar Radiation Budget

Measurements by sensors onboard Earth-orbiting satellites indicate that the Earth-atmosphere system scatters or reflects back to space on average about 31% of the solar radiation intercepted by the planet. This is Earth's **planetary albedo**. By contrast, the moon's albedo is only about 7%, primarily because of the absence of clouds in the highly rarefied lunar atmosphere. Hence, Earth viewed from the moon (by American astronauts) is more than four times brighter than the moon viewed from Earth on a clear night.

The atmosphere (i.e., gases, aerosols, clouds) absorbs only about 20% of the total solar radiation intercepted by the Earth-atmosphere system. In other words, the atmosphere is relatively transparent to solar radiation. The remaining 49% of solar radiation (31% was scattered or reflected to space) is absorbed by Earth's surface, chiefly because of the low average albedo of ocean water covering about 71% of the surface of the globe. The global annual solar radiation budget is summarized in Table 3.2.

TABLE 3.2
Earth's Solar Radiation Budget

Reflected by the Earth-atmosphere system	31%
Absorbed by the atmosphere	20%
Absorbed by Earth's surface	49%
Total	100%

Earth's surface is the principal recipient of solar heating, and heat is transferred from Earth's surface to the atmosphere, which eventually radiates this energy to space. The Earth's surface is thus the main source of heat for the atmosphere; that is, the atmosphere is heated from below. This is evident in the vertical temperature profile of the troposphere. Normally, air is warmest close to the Earth's surface, and air temperature drops with increasing altitude within the troposphere, that is, away from the main source of heat (Figure 2.12). A secondary heat source is found at the top of the stratosphere, where absorption of ultraviolet radiation by oxygen and ozone molecules at altitudes below 50 km (31 mi) results in the relatively warm stratopause.

Infrared Response and the Greenhouse Effect

If solar radiation were continually absorbed by the Earth-atmosphere system without any compensating flow of heat out of the system to space, Earth's surface temperature would rise steadily. Eventually, life would be extinguished and the ocean would boil away. Actually, the global air temperature changes little from one year to the next. **Global radiative equilibrium** keeps the planet's temperature in check; that is, emission of heat to space in the form of infrared radiation balances solar radiational heating of the Earth-atmosphere system. Although solar radiation is supplied only to the illuminated portion of the planet, infrared radiation is emitted to space ceaselessly, day and night, by the entire Earth-atmosphere system. This explains why nights are usually colder than days and why air temperatures usually drop throughout the night.

While the clear atmosphere is relatively transparent to solar radiation, certain gases in the atmosphere impede the escape of infrared radiation to space thereby elevating the temperature of the lower atmosphere. This important climate control is the so-called *greenhouse effect*.

GREENHOUSE WARMING

The **greenhouse effect** refers to the heating of Earth's surface and lower atmosphere caused by strong absorption and emission of infrared radiation by certain atmospheric gases, known as **greenhouse gases**. Solar radiation and terrestrial infrared radiation peak in different portions of the electromagnetic spectrum, their properties differ, and they interact differently with the atmosphere. As noted earlier, the atmosphere absorbs only about 20% of the solar radiation intercepted by the planet. The atmosphere absorbs a greater percentage of the infrared radiation emitted by Earth's surface and the atmosphere, in turn, radiates some IR to space and some back to Earth's surface. Hence, Earth's surface is heated by absorption of both solar radiation and downwelling infrared radiation.

The similarity in radiational properties between infrared-absorbing atmospheric gases and the glass panes of a greenhouse is the origin of the term greenhouse effect. Window glass, like Earth's atmosphere, is relatively transparent to visible solar radiation but strongly absorbs infrared radiation. A greenhouse, where plants are grown, takes advantage of the radiational properties of glass and is constructed almost entirely of glass panes (Figure 3.27). Sunlight readily penetrates the glass and is absorbed (converted to heat) within the greenhouse. Objects in the greenhouse emit infrared radiation that is strongly absorbed by the glass panes. Glass, in turn, emits IR to the atmosphere and the greenhouse interior, thereby raising the temperature within the greenhouse. (Plastic sheeting commonly used in modern greenhouses in colder climates contains additives that enhance IR absorption thereby exhibiting the same radiational properties of glass.)

Although the greenhouse analogy is widely cited, absorption and emission of IR radiation by glass is only part of the reason why the interior of a greenhouse is relatively warm. A greenhouse is also a shelter from the wind and reduces heat loss to the external environment by conduction and convection (Chapter 4). As a rule, the thinner the greenhouse glass and the higher the external wind speed, the more important is the shelter

FIGURE 3.27
The glass of a greenhouse behaves similarly to certain gases (e.g., water vapor, carbon dioxide) in the atmosphere that are transparent to sunlight but strongly absorb and emit infrared radiation.

effect compared to the radiational effect. For this reason, some atmospheric scientists argue that the greenhouse analogy is inappropriate and the phenomenon should be renamed the *atmospheric effect*. However, use of the term greenhouse effect is so common among scientists, public policymakers, and the media that we continue use of the term in this book.

The greenhouse effect is responsible for considerable warming of Earth's surface and lower atmosphere. Viewed from space, the planet radiates at about −18 °C (0 °F), whereas the average temperature at the Earth's surface is about 15 °C (59 °F). The temperature difference is due to the greenhouse effect and amounts to

$$[15 \text{ °C} - (-18 \text{ °C})] = 33 \text{ Celsius degrees}$$
$$\text{or}$$
$$[59 \text{ °F} - 0 \text{ °F}] = 59 \text{ Fahrenheit degrees.}$$

Without the greenhouse effect, Earth would be too cold to support most forms of plant and animal life.

Water vapor is the principal greenhouse gas. Other greenhouse gases are carbon dioxide, ozone, methane (CH_4), and nitrous oxide (N_2O). As shown in Figure 3.28, the percentage of infrared radiation absorbed by each gas varies with wavelength. An **atmospheric window** is a range of wavelengths over which little or

no radiation is absorbed. A *visible atmospheric window* extends from about 0.3 to 0.9 micrometers and the major *infrared atmospheric window* is from about 8 to 13 micrometers. Significantly, this latter window includes the wavelength of the planet's peak infrared emission (about 10 micrometers). Through this window, most heat from the Earth's surface escapes to space as infrared radiation. This window is also used by those sensors onboard orbiting weather satellites that provide the traditional IR satellite imagery (Chapter 1).

Water vapor's contribution to the greenhouse effect is evident even at the local or regional scale. Consider an example. Locations in the American Desert Southwest and near the Gulf Coast are at about the same latitude and receive essentially the same amount of solar radiation on a clear summer day. In both places, summer afternoon high temperatures commonly top 32 °C (90 °F). At night, however, air temperatures often differ markedly. Air is relatively dry (low humidity) in the Southwest so that terrestrial infrared radiation readily escapes to space and air temperatures near Earth's surface may drop well under 15 °C (59 °F) by sunrise. People hiking or camping in the desert are aware of the dramatic fluctuations in temperature between day and night. Infrared radiation does not escape to space as readily through the Gulf Coast atmosphere where the air is more humid. Water vapor strongly absorbs outgoing IR and a significant portion of the IR it emits is directed downward to Earth's surface so that early morning low temperatures may dip no lower than the 20s Celsius (70s Fahrenheit). The smaller diurnal (day to night) temperature contrast along the Gulf Coast is due to more water vapor and a stronger greenhouse effect.

Clouds are composed of IR-absorbing water droplets and/or ice crystals and also contribute to the greenhouse effect. All other factors being equal, nights usually are warmer when the sky is overcast than when the sky is clear. Even high, thin cirrus clouds through which the moon is visible can reduce the temperature drop at Earth's surface by several Celsius degrees. Clouds thus affect climate in two opposing ways: By absorbing and radiating terrestrial IR, clouds warm Earth's surface and by reflecting solar radiation, clouds cool Earth's surface. On a global scale, which one of these two opposing effects is more important? Analysis of satellite measurements of incoming and outgoing radiation indicates that clouds have a net cooling effect on global climate. That is, all other factors being equal, a more extensive cloud cover would cool the planet whereas less extensive cloud cover would warm the planet.

FIGURE 3.28
Absorption of radiation by selected gaseous components of the atmosphere as a function of wavelength. *Absorptivity* is the fraction of radiation absorbed and ranges from 0 to 1 (0% to 100% absorption). Absorptivity is very low or near zero in *atmospheric windows*. Note the infrared windows near 8 and 10 micrometers.

GREENHOUSE GASES AND GLOBAL CLIMATE CHANGE

Many atmospheric scientists as well as public policymakers are concerned about the potential impact on global climate of the steadily rising concentrations of atmospheric carbon dioxide (CO_2) and other infrared absorbing gases. Higher levels of these gases enhance the natural greenhouse effect and could contribute to warming on a global scale.

Systematic monitoring of atmospheric carbon dioxide began in 1957 at NOAA's Mauna Loa Observatory in Hawaii under the direction of Charles D. Keeling (1928-2005) of Scripps Institution of Oceanography. The observatory is situated on the slope of a volcano 3400 m (11,200 ft) above sea level in the middle of the Pacific Ocean—sufficiently distant from major industrial sources of air pollution that carbon dioxide levels are considered representative of at least the Northern Hemisphere. Also since 1957, atmospheric CO_2 has been monitored at the South Pole station of the U.S. Antarctic Program and that record closely parallels the one at Mauna Loa. The Mauna Loa record shows a sustained increase in average annual atmospheric carbon dioxide concentration from about 315.98 ppmv (parts per million by volume) in 1959 to 377.6 ppmv in 2004 (Figure 3.29). Superimposed on this upward trend is an annual carbon dioxide cycle caused by seasonal changes in Northern Hemisphere vegetation. The carbon dioxide level falls during the growing season, reaching a minimum in September, and rises in winter, reaching a maximum in April, May, and June.

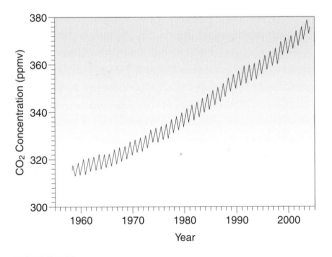

FIGURE 3.29
Concentration of atmospheric carbon dioxide (CO_2) as measured at the Mauna Loa Observatory, Hawaii. Annual cycles in photosynthesis and cellular respiration account for seasonal variations in CO_2. [Source: C.D. Keeling *et al.*, Scripps Institution of Oceanography, University of California, La Jolla, CA.]

The upward trend in atmospheric carbon dioxide was underway long before Keeling's monitoring and appears likely to continue well into the future. Human contributions to the buildup of atmospheric CO_2 began roughly three centuries ago with land clearing for agriculture and settlement. Land clearing contributes CO_2 to the atmosphere via burning, decay of wood residue, and reduced photosynthetic removal of carbon dioxide from the atmosphere. By the middle of the 19th century, growing dependency on coal burning associated with the beginnings of the Industrial Revolution spurred a more rapid rise in atmospheric CO_2 concentration. Carbon dioxide is a byproduct of the burning of coal and other fossil fuels. The concentration of atmospheric CO_2 has increased by an estimated 31% since 1750. The present atmospheric CO_2 concentration has not been exceeded over at least the past 420,000 years and the current rate of increase is unprecedented in the past 20,000 years. Fossil fuel combustion accounted for roughly 75% of the increase in atmospheric carbon dioxide over the past two decades while deforestation (and other land clearing) is likely responsible for the balance. If the growth in fossil fuel combustion continues, the atmospheric carbon dioxide concentration could top 550 ppmv (double the pre-industrial level) by the end of the 21st century.

Furthermore, rising levels of other infrared-absorbing gases (e.g., methane and nitrous oxide) could also enhance the natural greenhouse effect. Methane's concentration in the atmosphere has increased by 1060 ppb (parts per billion) (151%) since 1750. About half of all methane emissions are anthropogenic. Methane is a product of organic decay in the absence of oxygen and its concentration may be rising because of more rice cultivation, cattle, landfills, and/or termites, all sources of methane. The atmospheric concentration of nitrous oxide (N_2O) has increased by 46 ppb (17%) since 1750. The upward trend in nitrous oxide is likely linked to industrial air pollution, cattle feedlots, and agricultural soils. Although occurring in extremely low concentrations, methane and nitrous oxide are very efficient absorbers of infrared radiation (absorbing in the atmospheric windows mentioned earlier) and potentially could also contribute to global warming.

As noted in Chapter 2, atmospheric scientists use numerical global climate models to predict the magnitude of global warming that could accompany the upswing in atmospheric carbon dioxide. Based on runs of global climate models, in 2000 the *Intergovernment Panel on Climate Change (IPCC)*, a standing international committee sponsored by the United Nations, revised upward its earlier projections of the magnitude of global warming that could accompany an enhanced greenhouse effect. Various models project that the globally averaged surface temperature will rise by 1.4 to 5.8 Celsius degrees (2.5 to 10.4 Fahrenheit degrees) over the period 1990 to 2100. As discussed in more detail in Chapter 15, climate change is geographically non-uniform so that this projected magnitude of warming is not necessarily representative of what might happen everywhere. In any event, enhancement of the natural greenhouse effect could cause a climate change greater in magnitude than any prior climate change of the past 10,000 years.

POSSIBLE IMPACTS OF GLOBAL WARMING

What are the potential societal impacts of an enhanced greenhouse effect and global warming? According to estimates by the IPCC, North American climatic zones could shift northward by as much as 550 km (350 mi) and would likely affect all sectors of society. In some areas, heat and moisture stress would cut crop yields, and traditional farming practices would have to change. Across the North American grain belt, for example, higher temperatures and more frequent drought during the growing season might necessitate a switch from corn to wheat and require more irrigation.

Global warming may also cause sea level to rise in response to melting of land-based polar ice sheets and mountain glaciers, along with thermal expansion of seawater. (Melting of floating ice does not raise sea level.) Past large-scale climate changes apparently were amplified at higher latitudes, prompting speculation on the fate of the Greenland and West Antarctic ice sheets with global warming. Climate models predict that local warming over Greenland may be up to three times the global average. Tide gauging stations document a sea level rise of 10 to 20 cm (4 to 8 in.) over the past century and global climate models predict that this rise will accelerate. According to IPCC estimates, melting glaciers combined with thermal expansion of ocean water could raise global mean sea level by 9 to 88 cm (4 to 35 in.) over the period 1990 to 2100. This rise in sea level would accelerate coastal erosion and inundate islands and low-lying coastal plains, some of which are densely populated.

On the positive side, global warming would lengthen the growing season at high latitudes. Also, more atmospheric carbon dioxide is known to spur plant growth. Warmer winters would also lengthen the navigation season on lakes, rivers, and harbors where seasonal ice cover is a hindrance. For most Canadians and Americans living in the northern states, energy savings due to less space heating in winter would more than compensate for the greater energy requirements anticipated with more air conditioning in summer.

Is an enhanced greenhouse effect underway? Recent trends in climate are consistent with changes predicted by global climate models. In Spring 2000 the National Climatic Data Center (NCDC) reported that global warming accelerated during the final quarter of the 20th century and the ten warmest years in the instrument-based record have occurred since 1990. The year 2005 tied 1998 with the highest global mean annual surface temperature since reliable record keeping began in 1880; 2004 was the third warmest year on record. During 1997 and 1998, record high global mean surface temperatures were set over 16 consecutive months. In early 2001, the IPCC reported that the global mean annual surface temperature was about 0.6 Celsius degree (1.1 Fahrenheit degrees) higher at the end of the 20th century than at the close of the 19th century (Figure 3.30).

The IPCC also reports that according to satellite measurements, the extent of snow cover has decreased about 10% since the late 1960s. Ground-based observations show a reduction of about two weeks in the annual duration of lake- and river-ice cover at middle and high latitudes of the Northern Hemisphere during the 20th century. Many mountain glaciers are retreating in non-polar regions. Also, in Northern Hemisphere spring and summer, sea-ice extent has decreased by about 10% to 15% since the 1950s.

But before residents of low-lying coastal areas head for high ground to avoid rising ocean water, some words of caution are warranted. Even though some recent climate trends and environmental changes are consistent with changes expected to accompany greenhouse warming, little evidence exists of a direct cause-effect relationship. Climate controls other than (or in addition to) greenhouse gases may well be responsible for recent trends. Furthermore, the atmosphere is a complex and highly interactive system, so that in the future other processes may compensate for an enhanced greenhouse effect. For example, higher temperatures in polar latitudes may mean more snowfall and eventually more, not less, glacial ice.

The global climatic impact of the eruption of Mount Pinatubo in the Philippines underscores the dependency of climate on many variables. The June 1991 eruption, the most violent of the 20th century, injected huge quantities of sulfur dioxide (SO_2) into the stratosphere.

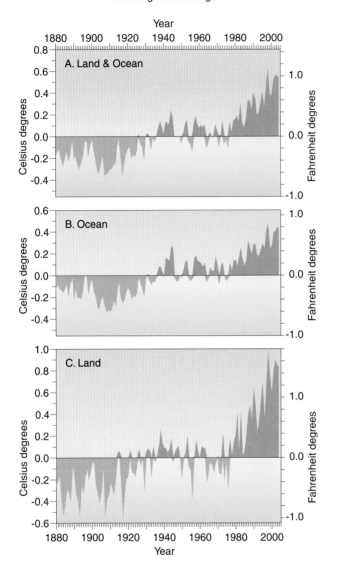

FIGURE 3.30
Anomalies in mean annual (A) global (land and ocean), (B) ocean, and (C) land temperatures. Anomalies are differences in degrees Celsius (left) and degrees Fahrenheit (right) from the long-term period average (1880-2004). [From NOAA, National Climatic Data Center, Asheville, NC]

SO_2 converted to tiny sulfuric acid droplets and sulfate particles that absorbed some solar radiation and scattered other solar radiation back to space. Less solar radiation reaching Earth's surface likely contributed to a temporary downturn in global mean temperature that persisted through 1992 and 1993. With the eventual cycling of sulfurous particles out of the stratosphere, warming resumed in 1994.

Some scientists question the integrity of the global mean temperature record that shows a gradual warming trend between the 1880s and 1990s. Questions center on the possible influence of (1) changes in the sophistication of instruments through the period of record, (2) warming caused by urbanization (Chapter 4), and (3) gaps in the spatial coverage of the networks of weather stations, especially over the ocean. Criticism is also directed at global climate models. For one, models vary in sophistication and in their ability to simulate the climatic influence of ocean currents, cloud cover, and atmospheric water vapor. Furthermore, the current generation of climate models does not do well in forecasting regional responses to hemispheric- or global-scale climate change.

In spite of scientific uncertainties, many experts argue that society has so much at stake that action should be taken immediately to head off possible enhanced greenhouse warming. They call for (1) sharp reductions in coal and oil consumption, (2) greater reliance on non-fossil fuel energy sources (see this chapter's Essay on solar power), (3) higher energy efficiencies (e.g., more vehicle miles per gallon), and (4) a halt to deforestation and massive reforestation. They hasten to point out that such actions are advisable even if greenhouse warming does not happen because they will help alleviate other serious environmental problems. For example, reducing reliance upon fossil fuels will also cut air pollution. Coal and oil burning produces not only CO_2, but also sulfur dioxide (SO_2) and particulate matter that are serious air pollutants. Chapter 15 has more on climate and climate change.

Monitoring Radiation

The **pyranometer** is the standard instrument for measuring the intensity of solar radiation striking a horizontal surface. The instrument consists of a sensor enclosed in a transparent hemisphere that transmits total (direct plus diffuse) solar short-wave (less than 3.0 micrometers) radiation (Figure 3.31). In one design, the sensor is a disk consisting of alternating black and white wedge-shaped segments forming a star-like pattern. Black wedges are highly absorptive whereas white wedges are highly reflective. Differences in absorptivity and albedo mean that the temperatures of the black and white portions of the sensor respond differently to the same intensity of solar radiation. The temperature contrast between the black and white segments is calibrated in terms of radiation flux (e.g., W/m²). A pyranometer may be linked electronically

FIGURE 3.31
Solar pyranometer, the standard instrument for monitoring solar radiation in the wavelength band from 0.3 to 3.0 micrometers.

to a pen recorder or computer that traces a continuous record of incident solar radiation. Special care must be taken in mounting and maintaining a pyranometer. The instrument should be situated where it will not be affected by shadows, any nearby highly reflective surface, or other sources of radiation which could interfere with measurement of solar radiation. The special enclosing bulb must also be kept clean and dry.

As discussed in Chapter 1, sensors onboard weather satellites measure two types of radiation emanating from the Earth-atmosphere system: scattered or reflected visible solar radiation and emitted infrared radiation. The first signal is processed into visible satellite images and the second is processed into infrared satellite images. An **infrared radiometer** is an instrument that measures the intensity of infrared radiation emitted by the surface of some object such as clouds or the ocean. The temperature dependency of IR emission means that infrared sensors can be calibrated to remotely sense the temperature of the Earth's surface or cloud tops.

As noted earlier in this chapter, for a *blackbody* (a perfect radiator) the wavelength of maximum radiation emission varies inversely with the radiation temperature (*Wien's displacement law*). Hence, a sensor that measures the intensity of radiation emitted by an object can determine the radiation temperature of that object. For a blackbody, the actual temperature equals the radiation temperature. For all other objects, the actual temperature is higher than the radiation temperature, the difference depending on the object's **emissivity**, a measure of how closely an object approximates a blackbody. The emissivity of a blackbody is 1.0 (or 100%) and less than 1.0 for all other objects. As a general rule, every 1% change in emissivity is associated with a change in the object's surface temperature of slightly less than 1.0 Celsius degree.

With adjustments made for differences in emissivity of objects within its field of view, an IR sensor (radiometer) onboard a weather satellite measures the temperature of land and sea surfaces and the tops of clouds. Based on measured differences in IR emission, sensors can distinguish low clouds, which are relatively warm, from high clouds, which are relatively cold. These measurements are calibrated on a gray scale (in which low clouds appear dark gray and high clouds appear bright white) or a color scale. One advantage of IR satellite images over visible satellite images is their availability both day and night.

Conclusions

Earth intercepts only a tiny fraction of the total radiational energy output of the sun. Movements of the planet in space (rotation on its spin axis and revolution about the sun) distribute this energy unequally within the Earth-atmosphere system. As solar radiation passes through the atmosphere, a portion is scattered and reflected back to space, a portion is absorbed (that is, converted to heat), while the rest is transmitted to Earth's surface either as direct or diffuse radiation. Overall, however, the atmosphere is relatively transparent to solar radiation and that which reaches Earth's surface is either reflected or absorbed. The Earth-atmosphere system responds to solar heating by emitting infrared radiation to space. Greenhouse gases and clouds absorb and emit IR to Earth's surface, thereby significantly elevating the average temperature of the lower troposphere (the greenhouse effect).

Net incoming solar radiation is balanced by the infrared radiation emitted to space by the Earth-atmosphere system. Absorption of solar radiation causes warming whereas emission of infrared radiation to space causes cooling. Within the Earth-atmosphere system, however, the rates of radiational heating and radiational cooling are not the same everywhere. In the next chapter, we examine the reasons for these energy imbalances and their implications for atmospheric circulation and weather. But first we distinguish between heat and temperature and describe heat transfer processes.

Basic Understandings

- All objects emit and absorb energy in the form of electromagnetic radiation. The many forms of electromagnetic radiation make up the electromagnetic spectrum and are distinguished on the basis of wavelength, frequency, and energy level.

- Earth and sun closely approximate perfect radiators (blackbodies) so that blackbody radiation laws may be applied to them with useful results.

- Wien's displacement law predicts that the wavelength of most intense radiation is inversely proportional to the absolute temperature of a radiating object. Hence, solar radiation peaks in the visible whereas the Earth-atmosphere (terrestrial) radiation peaks in the infrared (IR).

- According to the Stefan-Boltzmann law, the total energy radiated by an object at all wavelengths is directly proportional to the fourth power of the object's absolute temperature. Hence, the much hotter sun emits considerably more radiational energy per unit area per unit time than does the much cooler Earth-atmosphere system.

- The intensity of radiation emitted by the sun, assumed to be a point source, decreases as the square of the distance traversed by the radiation. Thus, the intensity of the solar radiation reaching Earth's orbit, equivalent to the solar constant, is sufficient to help maintain a habitable planet.

- The total energy (in the form of solar radiation) that is absorbed by the Earth-atmosphere system equals the total energy (in the form of infrared radiation) emitted by the Earth-atmosphere system to space. This balance of energy input and output is known as global radiative equilibrium and is the prevailing condition on planet Earth.

- Solar altitude, the angle of the sun above the horizon, influences the intensity of solar radiation that strikes Earth's surface. All other factors being equal, as the solar altitude increases, the intensity of solar radiation received at Earth's surface (energy per unit area) also increases.

- As a consequence of Earth's elliptical orbit about the sun, the planet's nearly spherical shape, and tilted spin axis, solar radiation is distributed unevenly over Earth's surface and changes through the course of a year.

- In the summer hemisphere, solar altitudes are higher and daylight is longer, resulting in the receipt of more solar radiation, and ultimately higher air temperatures. In the winter hemisphere, solar altitudes are lower, daylight is shorter, there is less solar radiation, and air temperatures are lower.

- Solar radiation that is not absorbed by the atmosphere (converted to heat) or scattered or reflected to space reaches Earth's surface.

- Absorption of ultraviolet radiation during the natural formation and destruction of ozone within the stratosphere shields organisms from exposure to potentially lethal levels of UV.

- Solar radiation that reaches Earth's surface is either reflected or absorbed depending on the surface albedo. Surfaces that appear light-colored have a relatively high albedo for visible radiation whereas surfaces that appear dark-colored have a relatively low albedo and typically have a higher surface temperature when exposed to sunlight.

- The atmosphere is heated primarily from below; that is, on average heat flows from Earth's surface to the overlying air. This is evident in the average temperature profile of the troposphere; that is, air temperature drops with increasing altitude.

- Water vapor, carbon dioxide, and several other atmospheric trace gases absorb outgoing IR and emit infrared radiation in all directions including downward, thereby significantly elevating the average temperature of the lower atmosphere. Clouds also contribute to this so-called greenhouse effect. Water vapor is the principal greenhouse gas.

- Rising levels of atmospheric CO_2 and several other IR-absorbing gases may enhance the natural greenhouse effect and cause global climate change. Combustion of fossil fuels and, to a lesser extent, deforestation are responsible for an upward trend in atmospheric carbon dioxide.

- The pyranometer is the standard instrument for monitoring the total flux of solar radiation whereas the infrared radiometer selectively monitors IR.

Review

1. What is a *blackbody*? Does *blackbody* refer to the color of a radiating object?
2. In the Northern Hemisphere, we are closer to the sun in winter than in summer. Why then are winters colder than summers?
3. What is the significance of the Tropic of Cancer and the Tropic of Capricorn? What is the significance of the Arctic Circle and the Antarctic Circle?
4. How and why does solar altitude affect the intensity of solar radiation received at the Earth's surface?
5. Distinguish between *reflection* and *scattering* of radiation.
6. Compare the average albedo of the ocean to the average albedo of clouds.
7. How does a snow cover influence the air temperature during the day and at night?
8. Describe how cloud-cover influences surface air temperatures during the day and at night.
9. What is the principal greenhouse gas?
10. What is the significance of the *greenhouse effect* for life on Earth?

Critical Thinking

1. For the entire globe, why must net incoming solar radiation balance the flux of infrared radiation emitted to space? What would be the consequences for global climate if this energy balance did not prevail?
2. If Earth had no atmosphere, the total solar radiation received per 24-hr day at the Earth's surface would reach a maximum in the Southern Hemisphere summer at the South Pole. Explain why the maximum is at the pole and not at the Tropic of Capricorn.
3. Why is the albedo of the moon considerably less than Earth's planetary albedo?
4. Speculate on what natural or human-related activities could raise or lower the Earth's planetary albedo. What are the implications of such changes for global climate?
5. What basic assumptions are made when blackbody radiation laws are applied to the sun and the Earth-atmosphere system?
6. About 18,000 years ago a massive glacial ice sheet covered much of what is now Canada and the northern tier states of the United States. Assuming that global cloud cover was essentially the same as it is now, how did the planetary albedo 18,000 years ago compare to what it is now? Justify your response.
7. In some locations, the noon solar altitude reaches 90 degrees on two days of the year. Where and when does this take place?
8. Speculate on what Earth would be like if the planet had no greenhouse effect.
9. Based on your personal experience, explain how you know that water vapor is a greenhouse gas.
10. Prepare a list of the possible impacts on your community of a warmer and drier climate. Be sure to consider all sectors of your community (e.g., agriculture, commerce, industry).

ESSAY: Hazards of Solar Ultraviolet Radiation

Most of us welcome sunny weather. Bright, sunny skies make possible a variety of outdoor activities and seem to energize and cheer most people. During warm weather, many people spend as much time as possible in the sun, some of them sunbathing for hours in pursuit of a tan (Figure 1). However, the evidence is now overwhelming that too much sun can cause premature aging of the skin and serious health problems, including skin cancer and cataracts of the eye. The culprit is overexposure to the ultraviolet portion of solar radiation.

Ultraviolet radiation is divided into segments: UVA (0.32-0.40 micrometers), UVB (0.29-0.32 micrometers), and UVC (0.20-0.29 micrometers). UVC rays, the most energetic of the three, readily kill exposed cells. Fortunately for life on Earth, the *stratospheric ozone shield* prevents UVC from reaching Earth's surface. Some UVB penetrates the ozone shield and strikes Earth's surface. Although less energetic than UVC, UVB rays are sufficiently intense to damage cells and cause sunburn, skin cancer, and other health problems. UVA, the weakest of the three forms of solar ultraviolet radiation, poses much less of a health risk than UVB but does accelerate the natural aging of the skin and exacerbates the damaging effects of UVB exposure.

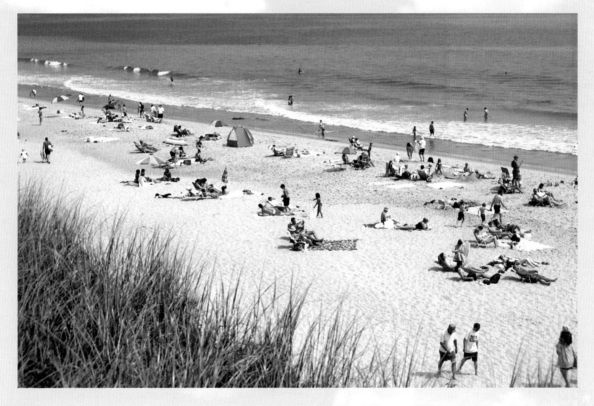

FIGURE 1
Sunbathers run the risk of excessive exposure to solar ultraviolet (UV) radiation that can cause serious health problems.

Some consequences of overexposure to solar ultraviolet radiation appear within hours (e.g., sunburn), but others typically take many years to show up (e.g., skin cancer and cataracts). Probably the most noticeable impact of long-term overexposure to the sun is premature aging of the skin, called *photoaging*. UV rays that penetrate the skin damage the structural proteins (i.e., collagen and elastin) that compose the elastic fibers responsible for skin's strength and resilience. As damage progresses, the skin develops a leathery texture, wrinkles, and irregular pigmentation. People who have had long-term exposure to the sun, perhaps because of an outdoor occupation or recreational interests, may exhibit symptoms of photoaging much earlier (prior to age 30) than people who minimize their exposure (after age 40).

Ultraviolet radiation contributes to certain types of cataracts, a major cause of vision impairment worldwide. A *cataract* is a cloudy (opaque) region that develops in the lens of the eye, the part of the eye that focuses light and produces sharp, clear images. If untreated, cataracts can cause partial or total blindness. Research suggests that 20% of all cataracts are related to UV exposure. In addition, excess exposure to UV rays suppresses the body's immune system.

Most troublesome is the role of UV radiation in the development of skin cancer, the most common form of cancer in the United States. The American Cancer Society estimates that each year more than 1 million people nationwide are diagnosed with skin cancer. About 1 in 5 Americans will contract this disease during their lifetime and perhaps 90% of these cases will stem from overexposure to the sun's UV rays. Researchers continue to accumulate evidence that links overexposure to UVB radiation to development of skin cancer, both melanoma and non-melanoma (i.e., basal cell carcinomas, squamous cell carcinomas). In each case, UVB damages the DNA in skin cells, resulting in uncontrolled cell growth and subsequent formation of tumors. Melanoma is the most virulent form of skin cancer and is responsible for 75% of skin cancer deaths. The number of cases of melanoma in the U.S. has more than doubled in the past decade with 50,000 new cases now reported each year. All types of skin cancers may be successfully treated if detected in their early stage.

How can you protect yourself from the health hazards of solar ultraviolet radiation? Begin by monitoring your level of exposure. In 1994, the National Weather Service (NWS) and the U.S. Environmental Protection Agency (EPA) introduced a special index that assists the general public in planning outdoor activities to avoid overexposure to UV radiation and thereby lowering their risk of adverse health effects. In 2004, the *Ultraviolet (UV) Index* was revised based on recommendations of the World Health Organization (WHO), the World Meteorological Organization (WMO), the United Nations Environment Programme, and the International Commission on Non-Ionizing Radiation Protection. The index is designed so that the higher the rating, the greater the expected exposure to UV and the quicker a person is likely to sunburn. As shown in Figure 2, values of the *UV Index* range from less than 2 (low risk) to 11 or higher (extreme risk).

UV INDEX

Exposure Category	UVI Range	Sun protection messages
Low	< 2	• Wear sunglasses on bright days. In winter, reflection off snow can nearly double UV strength. • If you burn easily, cover up and use sunscreen.
Moderate	3 to 5	• Take precautions, such as covering up and using sunscreen, if you will be outside. • Stay in shade near midday when the sun is strongest.
High	6 to 7	• Protection against sunburn is needed. • Reduce time in sun between 11 a.m. and 4 p.m. • Cover up, wear a hat and sunglasses, and use sunscreen.
Very high	8 to 10	• Take extra precautions. Unprotected skin will be damaged and can burn quickly. • Try to avoid the sun between 11 a.m. and 4 p.m. Otherwise, seek shade, cover up, wear a hat and sunglasses, and use sunscreen.
Extreme	11 +	• Take all precautions. Unprotected skin can burn in minutes. Beachgoers should know that white sand and other bright surfaces reflect UV and will increase UV exposure. • Avoid the sun between 11 a.m. and 4 p.m. • Seek shade, cover up, wear a hat and sunglasses, and use sunscreen.

FIGURE 2
The *Ultraviolet (UV) Index*, designed by the National Weather Service and the U.S. Environmental Protection Agency (EPA), to advise the public of the potential health hazards of exposure to solar ultraviolet radiation.

EPA and the NWS report the index based on the predicted intensity of UV (in the range of 0.29 to 0.40 micrometers) striking the ground at solar noon (when the sun is at its highest point in the sky). Satellite sensor measurements of current total ozone levels are used to forecast ozone levels for the following day. A model then predicts the UV intensity depending on the time of day (solar noon), day of the year, station elevation and latitude, and forecasted cloud cover. At present, the UV Index does not take into account the effects of air pollution, haze, or variations in surface properties (e.g., snow-covered versus bare ground). As of this writing, index values are issued for 58 major metropolitan areas across the nation. A sample UV Index forecast is shown in Figure 3.

The safe level of exposure to UVB depends upon skin phototype. People who never tan and always burn (most-sensitive phototype) can tolerate considerably less exposure to UV than people who always tan and rarely burn (least-sensitive phototype). The UV Index is intended only as a general guide. Because skin phototype varies considerably within human populations, some people will find that they require more protection from the sun than indicated by the UV Index.

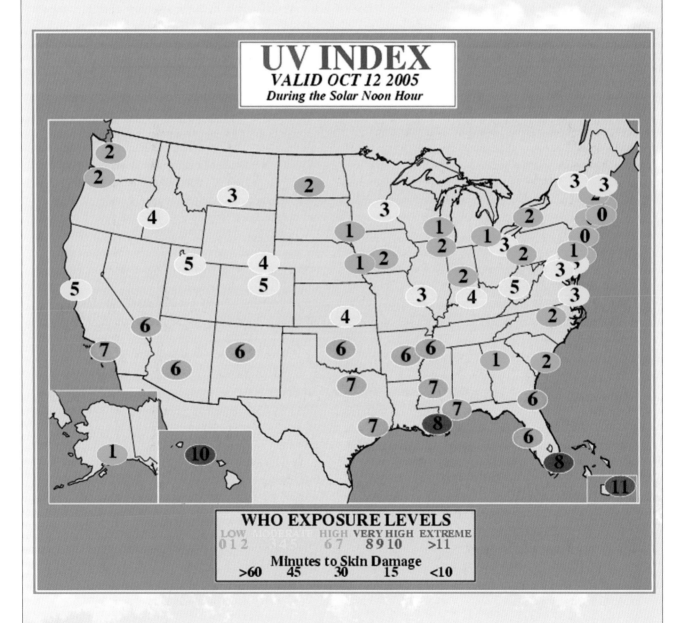

FIGURE 3
A sample UV Index forecast. [NOAA, National Climate Prediction Center]

If possible, people should avoid the sun when its rays are most intense, that is, between about 10 a.m. and 2 p.m. However, this general rule fails to account for the width of time zones (15 degrees of longitude typically), daylight saving time, and seasonal changes in solar altitude. Leith Holloway of the Geophysical Fluid Dynamics Laboratory in Princeton, NJ developed a simple and reliable guide for gauging UV exposure. Holloway found that on a clear midsummer day, as the solar altitude increases in the morning, the intensity of UV striking Earth's surface increases slowly until the sun is about 45 degrees above the horizon. At higher solar altitudes, the intensity of UV radiation striking Earth's surface increases rapidly as the solar beam passes through less and less atmosphere. In fact, total UV exposure at solar altitudes greater than 45 degrees is about 5 times greater than the total exposure during the remaining daylight hours. How then does a person determine if the solar angle is greater than or less then 45 degrees?

Shadows on a horizontal surface are shorter than the objects casting them when the solar angle is greater than 45 degrees (and vice versa). This is the basis for Holloway's *shadow rule*. If a person's shadow is shorter than he or she is tall, then the person should avoid the sun or apply a sunscreen to exposed skin; if a person's shadow is longer than she or he is tall, then the health risk is much less. Simply stated: "Short shadow? Seek shade!"

Solar altitudes are greatest in summer (May through August in the Northern Hemisphere) and in tropical latitudes so that UV intensity is also greatest at such times and locations. Unfortunately, summer is the season and the tropics are the place where people tend to spend more time outdoors and wear less protective clothing. Most skin cancers appear on exposed skin surfaces such as on the forearms, face, and neck. Hence, wearing protective clothing (e.g., wide-brimmed hat, long-sleeved shirt, long pants, tightly woven fabric) is a wise strategy. Sunglasses that are UV-rated worn along with a wide brimmed hat provide adequate eye protection.

Sunscreens have ingredients that selectively absorb UV wavelengths and should be applied to all exposed skin approximately 20 minutes before venturing outdoors. Be sure to read the label; medical experts strongly recommend a broad-spectrum sunscreen that provides protection against both UVB and UVA. Also be aware of the degree of protection offered, that is, the *sun protection factor* (*SPF*), a measure of the time that the skin can be safely exposed to the sun when wearing a particular sunscreen versus wearing no sunscreen. For example, if a person normally begins to turn pink after 10 minutes in the sun, applying a product with SPF 15 provides about 2.5 hrs of protection (10 minutes × 15 = 150 minutes). The higher the SPF, the longer the protection lasts. Health professionals recommend a minimum SPF of 15, but opting for a higher SPF is a good idea if a person is fair-skinned, spends a lot of time outdoors, or lives at a high elevation. (UV intensity increases by about 2% for every 300-m (1000-ft) increase in elevation.) Be sure to apply sunscreen liberally to all exposed skin to ensure optimal protection. Perspiration and water remove sunscreens (even so-called waterproof sunscreens) so they should be reapplied every two hours, even on cloudy days.

ESSAY: Solar Power

Solar power is a renewable energy source that will last as long as the sun, billions of years. Solar power is an environmentally attractive alternative to conventional energy sources, especially coal, oil, and nuclear fuels. Furthermore, the cost of solar power is becoming more competitive with the price of conventional fuels in a number of applications and environments.

If all the solar radiation that is transmitted through the day-lit atmosphere were distributed uniformly over Earth's surface, about 180 watts would illuminate every square meter. (By comparison, the *solar constant* is 1368 watts per m^2.) This amounts to about 4 kilowatt-hours per square meter per day, sufficient to meet nearly half the heating and cooling requirements of a typical American home. The total solar energy that falls yearly on America's land surface is about 600 times greater than the nation's total annual energy demand.

All technologies based on the collection of solar radiation are limited by the variability of the energy source. There is no solar radiation at night and its intensity varies with time of day, day of the year, latitude and cloud cover. Seasonal fluctuations in incident solar radiation are especially pronounced at middle and high latitudes. For example, in relatively sunny eastern Washington State, average annual solar radiation striking Earth's surface is 194 watts per m^2, but monthly mean values range from a low of 50 to a high of 343 watts per m^2, a sevenfold difference through the course of the year. The American Desert Southwest is the most promising area for solar power because of minimal cloud cover and less seasonal variability in solar radiation. Fluctuations in consumer demand for energy further complicate matters so that matching energy supply with demand requires use of energy storage systems. Solar collectors may produce more heat during the day than can be used at that time so that excess heat is usually stored in insulated water tanks or compartments filled with rocks. At middle and high latitudes, a conventional heating system is usually needed as a backup to solar collectors, particularly during extended spells of cloudy or very cold weather.

A traditional flat plate *solar collector* is basically a framed panel of glass that is designed to tap solar power. Sunlight passes through two layers of glass before being absorbed by a blackened (low albedo) metal plate. Heat is then conducted from the absorbing plate to either air or a liquid, which is conveyed by a fan or pump to wherever the heat is needed. Solar collectors typically capture 30% to 50% of the solar energy that strikes them and are most commonly used for space or water heating in small buildings such as homes, schools, and apartment houses. Flat plate solar collectors do not produce temperatures high enough to turn water into steam, so these devices are not suitable for most industrial purposes.

To partially compensate for the variability of incoming solar radiation due to changes in solar altitude, solar collectors are tilted toward the equator (to the south in the Northern Hemisphere). The advantage of tilted collectors over ones that are horizontal depends on the average cloud cover and latitude of the site. An optimal situation occurs in winter at a middle latitude locality favored by clear skies. There, tilted solar collectors can double the amount of solar radiation that is absorbed. Some solar collectors are designed to track the sun so that they are always oriented perpendicular to the solar beam (Figure 1). However, the cost of tracking devices usually exceeds the value of the energy obtained.

Scientists and engineers are developing ways to efficiently convert solar energy to electricity on a large scale. In one conversion method, a *power tower system*, an array of computer-controlled flat mirrors, called *heliostats*, track the sun and focus its radiation on a single heat collection point at the top of a tower. Concentrated sunlight in these systems can produce temperatures up to 480 °C (900 °F), high enough to convert water to high-pressure steam for driving turbines that generate electricity. Other designs utilize a large parabolic dish or trough as a collection device.

An alternative to solar-driven turbines for generating electricity is the *photovoltaic cell* (*PV cell*), also known as a *solar cell*. Solar cells convert solar radiation directly into electricity and routinely power many devices, including handheld calculators, parking lot lights, and space vehicles. Solar cells use sunlight to create a *voltage*, that is, a difference in electrical potential, in a *diode*. When sunlight strikes the diode, an electric current flows through the circuit to which it is connected. Only special materials develop the necessary voltage to produce a direct current when they are exposed to sunlight. These materials, called *semiconductors*, are composed of highly purified silicon to which tiny amounts of certain impurities have been added. Semiconductors are manufactured in the form of tiny wafers or sheets. Electricity travels through metal contact wires on the front and back of the wafer. Groups of wafers are wired together to form

FIGURE 1

A panel of interconnected photovoltaic cells, computer-controlled and designed to follow the sun and always present a horizontal surface to the incoming solar beam.

photovoltaic modules, and these are interconnected to form a photovoltaic panel. About 40 wafers must be linked to match the power output of a single automobile battery.

One serious drawback of today's solar cells is low efficiency. In this context, *efficiency* is defined as the percentage of solar radiation striking a photovoltaic cell that is converted to electrical energy. The efficiency of a handheld solar-powered calculator, for example, is only 3% or less. Some mass-produced photovoltaic panels have conversion efficiencies of 10% to 12%. In 1988, researchers at Sandia National Laboratories attained an all-time high efficiency rating of 31% by stacking two solar cells (a gallium arsenide cell on top and a silicon cell on the bottom). Among the many factors that contribute to low solar-cell efficiency are cell reflectivity, conversion of radiation to heat, and the sensitivity of cells to only a portion of the solar spectrum.

The main obstacle to greater use of solar cells for generating electricity is cost, although future prospects are encouraging. The cost of solar cell generated electricity has dropped substantially since 1980. Future cost reductions are unlikely to be achieved by boosting the efficiency of traditional solar cells because, as a general rule, production costs soar with increasing solar cell efficiency. A more promising alternative is further development of thin-film solar cells, which are less efficient but also much less expensive to manufacture than are traditional solar cells. A *thin-film solar cell* consists of a film of silicon or other light-sensitive substance deposited on a base material, whereas traditional solar cells consist of individual crystals.

Commercial-scale testing of the world's largest array of thin-film photovoltaic modules took place at Davis, CA in late 1992. By early the following year, the array was feeding electricity to a grid operated by the Pacific Gas and Electric Company. The photovoltaic system supplies up to 480 kilowatts, sufficient for the electrical needs of about 125 households.

About 50 megawatts of photovoltaic capacity are installed annually around the world. In the future, multi-megawatt solar-cell power plants are expected to routinely feed electricity into regional grids at costs that are competitive with conventional power plants. This outlook is based on current technological trends in developing more efficient thin-film solar cells (up to almost 18% efficient in 1996), plus declining manufacturing costs made possible by mass production and economy of scale. In addition, environmental concerns and the inevitable decline in supplies of fossil fuels should spur greater demand for solar power in the future.

CHAPTER 4

HEAT, TEMPERATURE, AND ATMOSPHERIC CIRCULATION

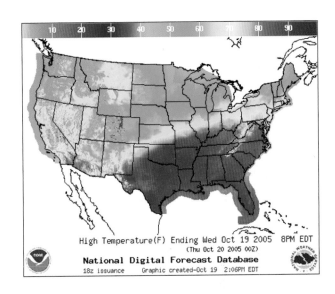

NOAA National Digital Forecast Database map showing temperatures forecast for the US. [Courtesy NOAA/NWS/NDFD]

Case in Point

Death Valley has the hottest and driest climate of any place in North America. Designated a National Monument in 1933 and a National Park in 1994, it is located in eastern central California near the Nevada border. The first permanent weather station in Death Valley was established in 1911 at Greenland Ranch, now known as Furnace Creek Ranch. Based on observations from 1911- 2001, the average daily high temperature ranges from 18 °C (65 °F) in December and January to 46 °C (115 °F) in July. The average daily low temperature for the same period ranges from 4 °C (39 °F) in December and January to 31 °C (88 °F) in July. Death Valley holds many North American high temperature records. On 10 July 1913, the temperature topped out at 56.7 °C (134 °F), second only to the 58 °C (136 °F) reading at Azizia, Libya on 13 September 1922, recognized as the highest temperature ever recorded on Earth. The temperature reached or exceeded 37.8 °C (100 °F) for a record 154 consecutive days in the summer of 2001. During the summer of 1996, the hottest summer on record at Death Valley, the temperature topped 48.9 °C (120 °F) on 40 successive days and 43.3 °C (110 °F) for 105 days in a row.

Air temperatures are recorded by standard thermometers mounted within instrument shelters. Shelters are located about 1.5 m (4.9 ft) above the surface and shield instruments from direct sunshine and precipitation. Temperatures at ground level are often considerably higher than shelter temperatures. For example, on 15 July 1972 the ground temperature at Furnace Creek reached a record high 93.9 °C (201 °F) while the shelter temperature was 53.3 °C (128 °F).

A combination of topographic setting, atmospheric circulation, and intense solar radiation is responsible for the extreme heat and desert conditions of Death Valley. The valley is a long, narrow basin—about 210 km (130 mi) long and 10 to 23 km (6 to 14 mi) wide—surrounded by high steep mountains. At its lowest point, the valley is 86 m (282 ft) below sea level. The prevailing west to east moist air flow inland from off the Pacific Ocean encounters four major mountain ranges before reaching Death Valley. For reasons discussed in detail in Chapter 6, clouds and precipitation develop where winds blow upslope and dry conditions prevail where winds blow down slope. By the time the winds reach Death Valley, they are exceptionally dry so that clear skies prevail. Average annual precipitation is only 4.9 cm (1.92 in.). The greatest total rainfall in a calendar year was 11.53 cm (4.54 in.) in 1913 and again in 1983 whereas the greatest rainfall in a 12-month stretch amounted to 15.47 cm (6.09 in.) in 1997-98. High temperatures and little moisture mean exceptionally stressful conditions for plants and animals living in Death Valley.

Intense solar radiation heats the dry desert surface consisting of rock, soil, and sparse vegetation. The lack of moisture means that most of the heat energy is used to raise the temperature of the ground surface rather than evaporate water. The hot surface heats the overlying air via conduction and convection (confined to the valley by the surrounding mountain rim). The air is so dry to begin with that the upward moving branch of convection currents usually does not produce clouds. The air in the downward moving branch of convection currents is compressed and heated (Chapter 5).

On the rare occasions when significant rain does fall in Death Valley, a spectacular bloom of colorful wild flowers spreads over the valley floor. However, if rainfall is locally heavy, flash flooding is likely. With little protective vegetative cover to anchor the soil, even a brief downpour can cause considerable erosion and property damage. For example, on 15 August 2004, rainfall estimated in the range of 2.5 to 5 cm (1 to 2 in.) washed out large sections of roadways and eroded trails in Death Valley. Two fatalities were reported.

Driving Question:

What are the causes and consequence of heat transfer within the Earth-atmosphere system?

Temperature is one of the most important and common variables used to describe the state of the atmosphere; it is a usual element in weather observations and forecasts. From everyday experience, we know that air temperature varies with time: from one season to another, between day and night, and even from one hour to the next. Air temperature also varies from one place to another: highlands and higher latitudes are usually colder than lowlands and lower latitudes.

We also know that temperature and heat are closely related concepts. Heating a pan of soup on the stove raises the temperature of the soup whereas dropping an ice cube into a warm beverage lowers the temperature of the beverage. Granted that the two concepts are related, what is the precise distinction between heat and temperature? This is one of the questions we consider in this chapter. We also compare temperature scales, describe how temperature is measured, explain how heat is transferred in response to a temperature gradient, and describe how the temperature of a substance responds to an addition or loss of heat.

This chapter then examines heat imbalances that develop within the Earth-atmosphere system and the various processes whereby heat is transferred from

Earth's surface to the troposphere and from the tropics to middle and high latitudes. All this enables us to better understand atmospheric circulation, energy conversions within the Earth-atmosphere system, and the controls of air temperature both globally and locally.

Distinguishing Temperature and Heat

All matter is composed of atoms or molecules that are in continual vibrational, rotational, and/or translational motion. The energy represented by this motion is called kinetic molecular energy or just *kinetic energy*, the energy of motion. In any substance, atoms or molecules actually exhibit a range of kinetic energy, as they are moving randomly at various speeds. **Temperature** is directly proportional to the *average* kinetic energy of the atoms or molecules composing a substance. At the same temperature, a drop of water has the same average kinetic molecular energy as a bathtub of water.

Internal energy encompasses all the energy in a substance, that is, the kinetic energy of atoms and molecules plus the potential energy arising from forces between atoms or molecules. If two objects have different temperatures (different average kinetic molecular energy) and are brought into contact, energy will be transferred between the two objects. **Heat** is the name given to this energy in transit. Heat transferred from one object reduces the internal energy of that object whereas heat absorbed by another object increases its internal energy.

Differences in temperature rather than differences in internal energy govern the direction of heat transfer. Heat energy is always transferred from a warmer object to a colder object. Heat is not necessarily transferred from an object having greater internal energy to an object with less internal energy. Consider, for example, a hot marble (at 40 ºC) that is dropped into 5 liters of cold water (at 5 ºC). The water has much more internal energy than the marble; nonetheless, heat is transferred from the warmer marble to the cooler water.

The following illustration makes clearer the distinction between temperature and heat. A cup of water at 60 ºC (140 ºF) is much hotter than a bathtub of water at 30 ºC (86 ºF); that is, the average kinetic energy of water molecules is greater at 60 ºC than at 30 ºC. Although lower in temperature, the greater volume of water in the bathtub means that it contains more total kinetic molecular energy than does the cup of water. If in both cases, the water is warmer than its environment, heat is transferred from water to its surroundings. However, much more heat

energy must be removed from the bathtub water than from the cup of water for both to cool to the same temperature, say a room temperature of 20 ºC (68 ºF).

From the above discussion, we might assume that any substance, including air, always changes temperature whenever it gains or loses heat. However, this is not necessarily the case. Water is a component of air and occurs in all three phases (ice crystals, droplets, and vapor), and, as we will see later in this chapter, heat must be added from or is released to the environment for water to change phase. Furthermore, air is a compressible mixture of gases; that is, an air sample can change volume. As discussed in Chapter 5, heat energy is required for the work of expansion or compression of air. Hence, as a sample of air gains or loses heat, that heat may be involved in some combination of temperature change, phase change of water, or volume change.

TEMPERATURE SCALES AND HEAT UNITS

When measuring temperature, a temperature scale is needed that is based upon recognizable and reproducible reference points. For most scientific purposes, temperature is measured on the Celsius scale. First popularized in 1742 by the Swedish astronomer Anders Celsius (1701-1744), the Celsius temperature scale has the numerical convenience of a 100-degree interval between the readily reproducible freezing point and boiling point of pure water at sea level. A German physicist, Gabriel Daniel Fahrenheit (1686-1736), introduced another scale in 1714 that was also based on the phase changes of water. Today, the United States is one of only a few nations still making public reports of surface weather conditions using this numerically more cumbersome Fahrenheit temperature scale. If a thermometer graduated in both scales is immersed in a beaker containing a mixture of ice and water, the temperature will be 0 degrees on the Celsius scale (0 ºC) and 32 degrees on the Fahrenheit scale (32 ºF). In boiling water at average sea level air pressure, the readings will be 100 ºC and 212 ºF.

The average kinetic molecular energy decreases with falling temperature. There is, theoretically at least, a temperature at which all molecular motion ceases, called **absolute zero**, corresponding to −273.15 ºC (−459.67 ºF). Actually, some atomic-level activity likely occurs at absolute zero, but an object at that temperature emits no electromagnetic radiation. On the Kelvin scale, temperature is the number of *kelvins* above absolute zero; hence, the Kelvin scale is a more direct measure of average kinetic molecular activity than either the Celsius or Fahrenheit temperature scales. The Kelvin scale is

FIGURE 4.1

A comparison of three temperature scales: Kelvin, Celsius, and Fahrenheit.

named for Lord Kelvin (William Thomson, 1824-1907) who developed it in the mid 19th century. Whereas units of temperature are expressed in degrees Celsius (°C) on the Celsius scale and degrees Fahrenheit (°F) on the Fahrenheit scale, temperature is expressed simply in kelvins (K) on the Kelvin scale. Nothing can be colder than absolute zero so the Kelvin scale has no negative values and a one-kelvin increment corresponds precisely to a one-degree increment on the Celsius scale. The three temperature scales are contrasted in Figure 4.1, and conversion formulas are presented in Table 4.1.

Most people would hardly notice a half-degree Celsius change in air temperature. But for operators of a Midwestern natural gas utility, a half-degree change in the average winter temperature can mean a significant change in consumer energy demand for space heating that translates into a major fluctuation in revenue stream for the utility. Energy utilities are not the only weather-sensitive businesses. An estimated 70% of all U.S. businesses are sensitive to temperature and other weather variables, representing at least $1 trillion of the nation's economic activity. Besides utilities, weather-sensitive businesses include transportation, agriculture, retail,

TABLE 4.1
Temperature Conversion Formulas

°F = 9/5 °C + 32°

°C = 5/9 (°F − 32°)

K = 5/9 (°F + 459.67)

K = °C + 273.15

tourism, recreation, and insurance. For example, a mild winter may mean fewer weather delays for aircraft and cross-country truckers, less risk of freezing temperatures in the Florida citrus groves, fewer northerners vacationing in southern Arizona, and reduced consumer demand for snow shovels, skis, and winter coats.

As described in detail in this chapter's first Essay, heating degree days are a measure of household energy consumption for space heating. Heating degree-days are computed for days when the average daily outdoor air temperature is less than 65 °F. For example, if the average temperature for the day is 35 °F, there are 65 − 35 = 30 heating degree-days for the day. The cumulative total of degree-days is tabulated throughout the heating season, from 1 July through the following 30 June.

Although temperature is a convenient way of describing the degree of hotness or coldness of an object, we can quantify heat energy directly. Until recently, meteorologists commonly measured heat energy in units called calories, where one **calorie (cal)** is defined as the quantity of heat needed to raise the temperature of 1 gram of water 1 Celsius degree (technically, from 14.5 °C to 15.5 °C). (The term *calorie* has two definitions, which can cause confusion. The calorie unit is also used to measure the energy content of food and is actually 1000 heat calories or 1.0 kilocalorie. Here we refer to the "small" calorie.) Today, the more usual unit for energy of any form, including heat, is the *joule (J)*. One calorie equals 4.1868 J. In the English system, heat is quantified as British thermal units. One **British thermal unit (Btu)** is defined as the amount of heat required to raise the temperature of 1 pound (lb) of water 1 Fahrenheit degree (technically, from 62 °F to 63 °F). One Btu is equivalent to 252 cal and to 1055 J.

MEASURING AIR TEMPERATURE

A **thermometer** is the usual instrument for measuring air temperature. Galileo Galilei (1564-1642) is credited with its invention in 1592. (Actually, Galileo invented a *thermoscope*, an instrument in which a fluid such as colored water responds to a gain or loss of heat but has no scale.) A common type of thermometer consists of a liquid-in-glass tube attached to a graduated scale (Figure 4.2). Typically, the liquid is either alcohol (which freezes at −117 °C or −179 °F) or mercury (which freezes at −39 °C or −38 °F). Both the glass and the liquid (alcohol or mercury) expand when heated but the liquid much more so than the glass. As air warms, heat is transferred to the thermometer, and the expanding liquid rises in the glass tube. The temperature can be read from the scale etched on the glass or

FIGURE 4.2
Liquid-in-glass thermometer. In this instrument, the liquid is alcohol.

printed on the surface of the plate on which the glass tube is mounted. As air cools, heat is transferred from the thermometer, and the liquid contracts, dropping in the tube. While this type of thermometer is relatively inexpensive and accurate, it must be read directly and not remotely.

A second type of thermometer uses a bimetallic sensing element to take advantage of the expansion and contraction that accompany the heating and cooling of metals. A bimetallic sensing element consists of strips of two different metals welded together back to back. The two metals have different rates of thermal expansion; that is, one metal expands more than the other in response to the same amount of heating. Because the two metals are bonded together, heating causes the bimetallic strip to bend; the greater the heating, the greater the bending. For example, the rate of thermal expansion of brass is about twice that of iron so that a bimetallic strip composed of those two metals will bend in the direction of the iron when heated. A series of gears or levers translates the response of the bimetallic strip to a pointer and a dial calibrated to read in °C or °F. Alternatively, this device may be rigged to a pen and a clock-driven drum to produce a continuous trace of temperature with time; this instrument is called a **thermograph**.

Another common type of thermometer employs an electrical conductor whose resistance changes with fluctuations in the temperature, permitting a calibration between electrical resistance and temperature. Figure 4.3 shows the change of temperature during passage of

a cold front as determined by an electronic thermometer. A radiosonde is equipped with this type of thermometer. Digital read-out thermometers widely available in a variety of consumer products are also of this type. Some electronic thermometers are designed to give remote temperature readings by mounting the sensor at the end of a long cable joined to the instrument. This system has replaced standard liquid-in-glass thermometers at National Weather Service facilities nationwide. Also, as described in Chapters 1 and 3, satellite sensors (radiometers) monitor surface temperatures remotely by measuring the intensity of emitted infrared radiation.

Regardless of the type of thermometer used, two important properties of the instrument are accuracy and response time. For most weather and climate purposes, a thermometer that is accurate to within 0.3 Celsius degree (0.5 Fahrenheit degree) will suffice. *Response time* refers to the instrument's capability of resolving changes in temperature. Electrical resistance thermometers have rapid response times, liquid-in-glass somewhat less, whereas bimetallic thermometers tend to be more sluggish.

For representative measurements of air temperature, ideally a thermometer should be adequately ventilated, in thermal equilibrium with its surroundings, and shielded from precipitation, direct sunlight, and the night sky. Enclosing temperature sensors (and other weather instruments) in a white, louvered wooden shelter had been standard practice for official temperature measurements. The sensor for the National Weather Service electronic thermometer is mounted inside a ventilated shield made of white plastic and the digital read-out box is located indoors (Figure 4.4). So that temperature readings are comparable, an instrument shelter should be located in an open grassy area well away from trees, buildings, or other obstacles, and at a standard height (1.5 m or about 5 ft) above the ground. As a general rule, the shelter should be no closer than four times the height of the nearest obstacle. If a shelter is not available, mounting a thermometer outside a window on the shady north side of a building is usually sufficient for general purposes.

In addition to using standard thermometers, air temperature can sometimes be determined in unconventional ways. One interesting and surprisingly accurate method is to count cricket chirps. Crickets are cold-blooded organisms so their activity (including frequency of chirping) depends on air temperature. For air temperatures above about 12 °C (54 °F), the number of cricket chirps heard in an 8-second period plus 4 approximates the air temperature in °C.

FIGURE 4.3
Record of air temperature over a 24-hr period showing the passage of a cold front.

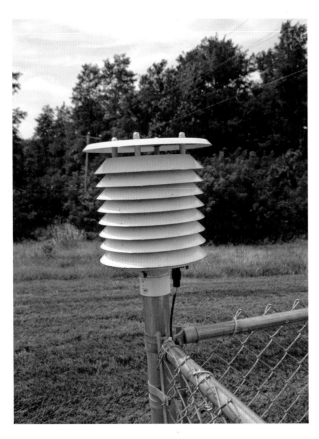

FIGURE 4.4
Enclosure for the National Weather Service electronic temperature sensor shields the instrument from direct sunshine and precipitation.

Heat Transfer

Air temperature varies from one place to another in large part because of imbalances in rates of radiational heating and radiational cooling within the Earth-atmosphere system. A change in temperature with distance is known as a **temperature gradient**. A familiar temperature gradient prevails between the hot equator and the cold poles (a horizontal temperature gradient). Another is the vertical temperature gradient between the relatively mild Earth's surface and the relatively cold tropopause (Figure 2.12).

Heat flows in response to a temperature gradient, according to the **second law of thermodynamics**. Simply put, this law states that all systems tend toward a state of disorder. You probably have personal experience with some implications of the second law. If you avoid cleaning up your home, for example, it rapidly becomes more and more disorganized. The presence of a gradient of any kind within a system signals order within that system. Hence, as a system tends toward disorder, gradients decrease.

The second law predicts that where a temperature gradient exists, heat is transferred in a direction so as to eliminate the gradient; that is, heat flows from locations of higher temperature toward locations of lower temperature. In addition, the greater the temperature difference (i.e., the steeper the temperature gradient), the more rapid is the rate of heat flow. Within the Earth-atmosphere system, heat is transferred via radiation, conduction, convection, and phase changes of water (i.e., latent heating).

RADIATION

Radiation is both a form of energy and a means of energy transfer (Chapter 3). Electromagnetic radiation consists of a spectrum of waves traveling at the speed of light. Unlike conduction and convection, radiation requires no intervening physical medium; that is, it can travel through a vacuum. Although not actually a vacuum, interplanetary space is so highly rarefied that conduction and convection play essentially no role in transporting heat from the sun to Earth (or any other planet). Rather, radiation is the principal means whereby the Earth-atmosphere system gains heat from the sun. Radiation is also the principal means whereby heat escapes from the planet to space to maintain a habitable environment.

As we saw in Chapter 3, absorption of radiation involves the conversion of electromagnetic energy to heat. In contrast, emission of electromagnetic energy is a loss of heat from the radiating object to the environment. All objects both absorb and emit electromagnetic radiation. If an object absorbs radiation at a greater rate than it emits radiation, the temperature of the object will rise. This type of imbalance in the flux of radiation is known as **radiational heating**. If an object emits radiation at a greater rate than it absorbs radiation, the temperature of the object will fall. This type of imbalance in the flux of radiation is called **radiational cooling**. At radiative equilibrium, when absorption and emission of radiation are equal, the object's temperature remains constant.

Radiative equilibrium does not necessarily mean that the temperature stays constant among all components of a system. The entire Earth-atmosphere system is in radiative equilibrium with its surroundings so that the planetary temperature remains relatively constant through the year. Nonetheless, heat may be redistributed among the various components of the Earth-atmosphere system (for example, among the ocean, land, and glaciers) so that air temperature at a specified location may undergo significant short- and long-term variations. Hence, global radiative equilibrium does not preclude changes in weather and climate.

CONDUCTION AND CONVECTION

Conduction occurs within a substance or between substances that are in direct physical contact. **Conduction (of heat)** refers to the transfer of kinetic energy of atoms or molecules via collisions between neighboring atoms or molecules. This is why a metal spoon heats and its temperature rises when placed in a steaming cup of coffee. As the more energetic molecules of the hot coffee collide with the less energetic atoms of the cooler spoon, some kinetic energy is transferred to the atoms of the spoon. These atoms then transmit some of their heat energy, via collisions, to neighboring atoms, so that heat is conducted up the handle of the spoon and eventually the handle becomes hot to the touch.

Some substances are better conductors of heat than others. **Heat conductivity** is defined as the ratio of the rate of heat transport across an area to a temperature gradient. Hence, in response to a specified temperature gradient, substances having higher heat conductivities have greater rates of heat transport. As a rule, solids are better conductors of heat than are liquids, and liquids are better heat conductors than gases. At one extreme, metals are excellent conductors of heat whereas at the other extreme, still air is a very poor conductor of heat. Heat conductivities of some common substances are listed in Table 4.2, ranked from most to least conductive.

Differences in heat conductivity can be the reason one object feels colder than another, even though both objects have the same temperature. For example, at the same relatively low temperature, a metallic object feels colder than a wooden object. The heat conductivity of metals is much greater than that of wood so that when you grasp the two objects, your hand more rapidly conducts heat to the metallic object than to the wooden object. Consequently, you have the sensation that the metal is colder than the wood.

The relatively low heat conductivity of air makes it a good heat insulator. Heat conductivity is lower for still air than for air in motion so to take maximum advantage of air as a heat insulator, air must be confined. For example, in a fiberglass blanket used as attic insulation, the motionless air trapped between individual fiberglass fibers is primarily responsible for inhibiting heat loss. In time, the fibers settle, air is excluded, and the blanket loses much of its insulating value. Similarly, the heat conductivity of a fresh snow cover is low because of the air trapped between individual snowflakes. A thick snow cover (20 to 30 cm or 8 to 12 in.) can thus inhibit or prevent freezing of the underlying soil, even though the temperature of the overlying air drops well below freezing. In time, however, like the fiberglass blanket, a snow cover loses some of its insulating property as the snow settles. As snow settles, air escapes, snow density increases, and heat conductivity increases as shown in Figure 4.5.

During the day, heat is conducted from sun-warmed ground to cooler overlying air, but because air

TABLE 4.2

Heat Conductivity of Some Familiar Substances[a]

Copper	0.92
Aluminum	0.50
Iron	0.16
Ice (at 0 °C)	0.0054
Limestone	0.0048
Concrete	0.0022
Water (at 10 °C)	0.0014
Dry sand	0.0013
Air (at 20 °C)	0.000061
Air (at 0 °C)	0.000058

[a]*Heat conductivity* is defined as the quantity of heat (in calories) that would flow through a unit area of a substance (cm^2) in one second in response to a temperature gradient of one Celsius degree per centimeter. Hence, heat conductivity has units of calories per cm^2 per sec per C° per cm.

FIGURE 4.5
A thick layer of fresh snow is a good heat insulator primarily because of air trapped between the individual snowflakes. (Air is a poor conductor of heat.) But in time, the snow settles, air escapes, snow density increases, and the snow cover's insulating property diminishes.

is a poor conductor of heat, conduction is significant only in a very thin layer of air in immediate contact with Earth's surface. Much more important than conduction in transporting heat vertically within the troposphere is convection. **Convection** is the transport of heat within a fluid via motions of the fluid itself. Although conduction takes place in solids, liquids, or gases, convection generally occurs only in liquids or gases. (An exception is the convection currents that likely occur in the Earth's interior under conditions of extremely high temperatures.)

Convection in the atmosphere is the consequence of differences in air density. At the same pressure, cold air is denser than warm air. As heat is conducted from the relatively warm ground to cooler overlying air, that air is heated, becoming less dense and thus more buoyant compared with the surrounding air. Cool, denser air from above sinks and forces the warmer, less dense air at the ground to rise. (This is similar to what happens when cold tap water flows into a tub of hot water; that is, the denser cold water sinks and forces the less dense hot water to rise.) Ascending warm air expands, cools and eventually sinks back to the ground. Meanwhile, air now in contact with the warm ground is heated and rises—displaced by the sinking cooler denser air. In this way, as illustrated in Figure 4.6, convection transports heat vertically from Earth's surface thousands of meters into the troposphere.

We can readily observe convection currents in a pan of water on a hot stove. By adding a drop or two of food coloring to the water, we actually see the circulating water redistributing heat that is conducted from the bottom of the pan into the water. In this example, as well as in the troposphere, conduction and convection work together in transferring heat.

PHASE CHANGES OF WATER

Another important heat transfer process operating within the Earth-atmosphere system involves phase changes of water. Water is one of the very few substances that can occur naturally in all three phases within the temperature and pressure ranges found at and near Earth's surface. Water occurs as a crystalline solid (ice or snow), liquid, and gas (water vapor), and is continually changing phase (Figure 4.7). Depending on the specific phase change, water either absorbs heat from its environment or releases heat to its environment. The quantity of heat that is involved in phase changes of water is known as **latent heat**, where the term "latent" refers to the heat that is "hidden" until released. Heat is required for phase changes because of differences in molecular activity represented by the three physical phases of water.

In the solid phase (ice), water molecules are relatively inactive and vibrate about a fixed location in an

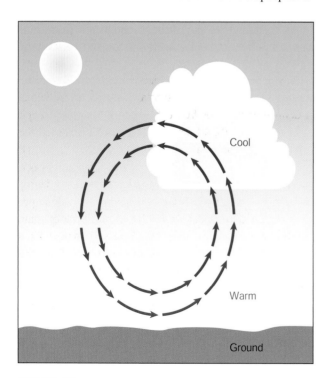

FIGURE 4.6
Convection currents transport heat from Earth's surface into the troposphere.

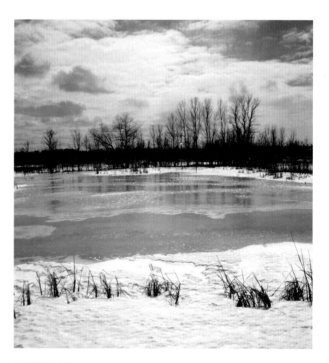

FIGURE 4.7
At and near Earth's surface, water occurs in all three phases: solid (ice and snow), liquid, and vapor. Clouds are composed of tiny water droplets and/or ice crystals.

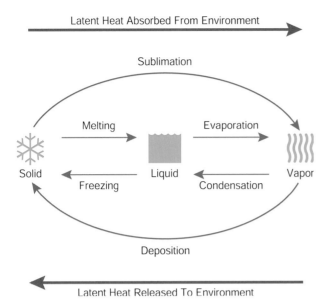

FIGURE 4.8
When water changes phase, heat energy is either absorbed from or released to the environment.

ice crystal lattice. Hence, at subfreezing temperatures, an ice cube or any other piece of ice maintains its shape. In the liquid phase, molecules move about with greater freedom, so that liquid water takes the shape of its container. In the vapor phase, water molecules exhibit maximum activity and diffuse readily throughout the entire volume of its container. A change in phase is thus linked to a change in level of molecular activity, which is brought about by either an addition or loss of heat (Figure 4.8). Heat is absorbed from the environment during those changes to higher energy states: *melting* (phase change from solid to liquid), *evaporation* (phase change from liquid to vapor), and *sublimation* (phase change directly from solid to vapor). Heat is released to the environment during those changes to lower energy states: *freezing* (phase change from liquid to solid), *condensation* (phase change from vapor to liquid), and *deposition* (phase change directly from vapor to solid). During any phase change, heat is exchanged between water and its environment. Although the temperature of the environment changes in response, the temperature of the water undergoing the phase change remains constant until the phase change is complete. That is, the available heat (latent heat) is involved exclusively in changing the phase of water and not its temperature.

Latent heating refers to the transport of heat from one location to another as a consequence of changes in the phase of water. For example, the latent heat that is supplied to change liquid water to vapor (evaporation) in one place is released to the environment when that

water vapor condenses at some other place. Prior to condensation, winds can transport water vapor thousands of kilometers and to altitudes of thousands of meters so that latent heating can involve long-range transport of heat. There is more on latent heating later in this chapter.

Heat transfer between the human body and its surroundings (via radiation, conduction and convection, and phase changes of water) is an important factor in human comfort and wellbeing. For example, the combination of strong winds and low air temperature may accelerate heat loss from the body to the extent that a person risks frostbite or hypothermia (a dangerous lowering of the body's core temperature). Hence, in winter in cold climates, weather forecasts usually include the *wind-chill equivalent temperature* (or simply *wind-chill*) along with the actual air temperature. The wind-chill is an air temperature index that takes into account the heat loss from exposed skin caused by the combined effect of wind and low air temperature. For more on wind-chill, refer to this chapter's second Essay.

Thermal Response and Specific Heat

Whether by radiation, conduction, convection, or latent heating, transfer of heat from one place to another within the Earth-atmosphere system is accompanied by changes in temperature. A heat gain causes a rise in temperature whereas a heat loss causes a drop in temperature.

The temperature change associated with an input (or output) of a specified quantity of heat varies from one substance to another. The amount of heat that will raise the temperature of 1 gram of a substance by 1 Celsius degree is defined as the **specific heat** of that substance. Joseph Black (1728-1799), a Scottish chemist, first proposed the concept of specific heat in 1760. The specific heat of all substances is measured relative to that of liquid water, which is defined as 1 calorie per gram per Celsius degree (at 15 °C). The specific heat of ice is about 0.5 calorie per gram per Celsius degree (near 0 °C). Specific heats of some familiar substances are listed in Table 4.3, ranked from high to low values. The variation in specific heat from one substance to another implies that different materials have different capacities for storing internal energy.

In response to the same input of heat energy, a substance with a low specific heat undergoes a greater temperature rise than a substance with a high specific heat. Water has the greatest specific heat of any naturally occurring substance. From Table 4.3, water's specific heat is about five times that of dry sand. One calorie of heat will raise the temperature of 1 gram of water 1 Celsius

FIGURE 4.3
<u>**Specific Heat of Some Familiar Substances**[a]</u>

Water	1.000
Wet mud	0.600
Ice (at 0 °C)	0.478
Wood	0.420
Aluminum	0.214
Brick	0.200
Granite	0.192
Sand	0.188
Dry air[b]	0.171
Copper	0.093
Silver	0.056
Gold	0.031

[a]Calories per gram per Celsius degree.
[b]At constant volume.

degree, whereas 1 calorie of heat will raise the temperature of 1 gram of dry sand by 5 Celsius degrees. This contrast in specific heat helps explain why at the beach in summer the sand feels considerably hotter to bare feet than the water (Figure 4.9). This also largely explains why wet sand feels cooler than dry sand.

Water's exceptional capacity to store heat has important implications for weather and climate, especially at middle and high latitudes. A large body of water (such as the ocean or Great Lakes) can significantly influence the climate of downwind localities. The most persistent influence is on air temperature. Compared to an adjacent landmass, a body of water does not warm as much during the day (or in summer) and does not cool as much at night (or in winter). In other words, a large body of water exhibits a greater resistance to temperature change, called **thermal inertia**, than does a landmass. Whereas the specific heat of water versus that of land is the major reason for this contrast in thermal inertia, differences in heat transport also contribute. Sunlight penetrates water to some depth and is absorbed (converted to heat) through a significant volume of water (Chapter 3). But sunlight cannot penetrate the opaque land surface and is therefore absorbed only at the surface. Furthermore, circulation of ocean and lake waters transports heat through great volumes of water, whereas heat is conducted only very slowly into soil. The input (or output) of equal amounts of heat energy causes a land surface to warm (or cool) more than the equivalent surface area of a body of water.

Air temperature is regulated to a considerable extent by the temperature of the surface over which the air resides or travels. Air over a large body of water tends to take on similar temperature characteristics as the surface water. Hence, places immediately downwind of the ocean experience much less contrast between average winter and summer temperature, with the climate described as *maritime*. Places at the same latitude, but well inland, experience a much greater contrast between winter and summer temperature, with the climate described as *continental*. That is, at the same latitude, summers are cooler and winters are milder in maritime climates than in continental climates.

Consider an example of the temperature contrast between continental and maritime locations (Figure 4.10).

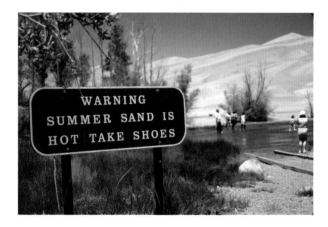

FIGURE 4.9
A sign near an entrance to the Great Sand Dunes National Monument in southern Colorado. The contrast in specific heat is one reason why the sand is hotter than the water.

FIGURE 4.10
Variation in the march of monthly mean temperature for (A) maritime San Francisco, CA and (B) continental St. Louis, MO. The two cities are located at about the same latitude.

The latitude of San Francisco, CA (37.8 degrees N) is almost the same as that of St. Louis, MO (38.8 degrees N) so that the seasonal variation in the amount of solar radiation striking Earth's atmosphere (due to astronomical factors) is about the same at both places. St. Louis is situated far from the moderating influence of the ocean and its climate is continental. St. Louis' average summer (June, July, and August) temperature is 25.6 °C (78.0 °F) and its average winter (December, January, and February) temperature is 0.6 °C (33.0 °F), giving an average summer-to-winter seasonal temperature contrast of 25 Celsius degrees (45 Fahrenheit degrees). San Francisco, on the other hand, is located on the West Coast, immediately downwind of the Pacific Ocean; its climate is distinctly maritime. The average summer temperature at San Francisco is 17.0 °C (62.6 °F) and the average winter temperature is 10.2 °C (50.4 °F), giving an average seasonal temperature contrast of only 6.8 Celsius degrees (12.2 Fahrenheit degrees).

Heat Imbalance: Atmosphere versus Earth's Surface

Weather is not a capricious act of nature. Ultimately, weather is a response to unequal rates of radiational heating and radiational cooling within the Earth-atmosphere system. Imbalances in rates of radiational heating and cooling from one place to another produce temperature gradients. In response to temperature gradients, the atmosphere circulates and thereby redistributes heat.

Figure 4.11 shows how solar radiation intercepted by planet Earth interacts with the atmosphere and Earth's surface. Numbers are global and annual averages. For every 100 units of solar radiation that enters the upper atmosphere, the Earth-atmosphere system scatters or reflects 31 units (31%) to space, the atmosphere absorbs 20 units (20%), and Earth's surface (principally the ocean) absorbs 49 units (49%). In response to radiational heating, Earth's surface emits 114 units of infrared radiation. Atmospheric gases and clouds absorb 105 units of terrestrial infrared radiation and emit 95 units toward the Earth's surface (the *greenhouse effect*). A total of 69 units of IR radiation is emitted out the top of the atmosphere to space, equal to the amount of solar radiation absorbed by the Earth-atmosphere system (*global radiative equilibrium*).

The global annual distribution of incoming solar radiation and outgoing infrared radiation implies net warming of Earth's surface, but a net cooling of the atmosphere (Table 4.4). At Earth's surface, absorption of solar radiation is greater than emission of terrestrial infrared radiation. In the atmosphere, on the other hand, emission of terrestrial infrared radiation to space is greater than absorption of solar radiation. That is, on a global average annual basis, Earth's surface undergoes net radiational heating while the atmosphere undergoes net radiational cooling.

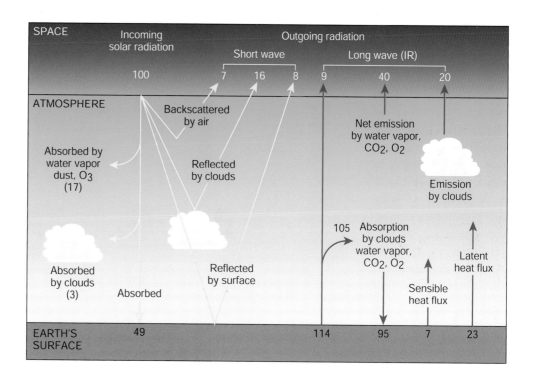

FIGURE 4.11
Globally and annually averaged disposition of 100 units of solar radiation entering the atmosphere. Solar radiation fluxes are depicted at the left, infrared radiation fluxes in the middle, and latent and sensible heat fluxes at the right.

TABLE 4.4
Global Radiation Balance

Solar radiation intercepted by Earth	100 units
Solar radiation budget	
Scattered and reflected to space (7 + 16 + 8)	31
Absorbed by the atmosphere (17 + 3)	20
Absorbed at the Earth's surface	49
Total	100 units
Radiation budget at the Earth's surface	
Infrared cooling (95 − 114)	−19
Solar heating	+49
Net heating	+30 units
Radiation budget of the atmosphere	
Infrared cooling (− 40 − 20 + 105 − 95)	−50
Solar heating	+20
Net cooling	−30 units
Non-radiative heat transfer: Earth's surface to atmosphere	
Sensible heating (conduction plus convection)	7
Latent heating (phase changes of water)	23
Net transfer	30 units

the atmosphere: 23 units (about 77% of the total) by latent heating and 7 units (about 23%) by sensible heating.

LATENT HEATING

Earth's surface absorbs radiation (both solar and infrared) and some of the heat energy is used to vaporize water from the ocean, lakes, rivers, soil, and vegetation without an attendant increase in surface temperature. The latent heat required for vaporization is supplied at the Earth's surface, and that same heat is subsequently released to the atmosphere during cloud development. Within the troposphere, clouds form as some of the water vapor condenses into liquid water droplets or deposits as ice crystals. During cloud formation, water changes phase and latent heat is released to the atmosphere. Through latent heating, then, heat is transferred from Earth's surface into the troposphere. In fact, latent heating is more important than either radiational cooling or sensible heating in cooling Earth's surface (Figure 4.12).

Unusually large quantities of heat are required to bring about phase changes of water as compared to phase changes of other naturally occurring substances. Consider, for example, the quantity of heat involved in changing the phase of a one-gram ice cube at sea-level as it is heated from an initial temperature of −20 °C (−4 °F) to a final temperature of 100 °C (212 °F)

The atmosphere is not actually cooling relative to Earth's surface. In response to the radiationally induced temperature gradient between Earth's surface and atmosphere, heat is transferred from Earth's surface to the atmosphere by non-radiative processes. A combination of latent heating and sensible heating (conduction and convection) is responsible for this transfer of heat. As shown in Figure 4.11, on a global annual average basis, 30 units of heat energy are transferred from Earth's surface to

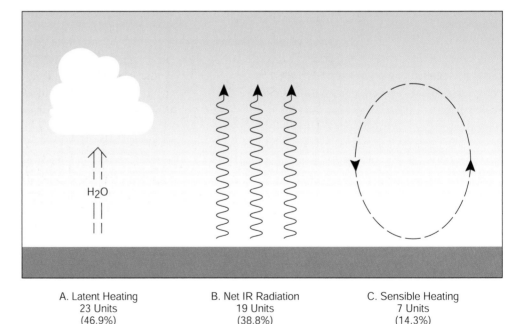

A. Latent Heating	B. Net IR Radiation	C. Sensible Heating
23 Units	19 Units	7 Units
(46.9%)	(38.8%)	(14.3%)

FIGURE 4.12
Earth's surface is cooled via (A) vaporization of water, (B) net emission of infrared radiation, and (C) conduction plus convection. Numbers are global annual averages.

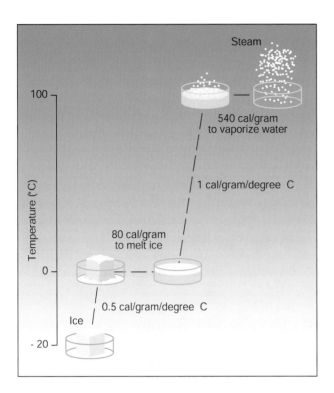

FIGURE 4.13
Heating a 1-gram ice cube causes a rise in temperature plus phase changes.

(Figure 4.13). The specific heat of ice is about 0.5 cal per gram per Celsius degree, which means that 0.5 cal of heat must be supplied for every 1 Celsius degree rise in temperature. Hence, warming our ice cube from −20 °C to 0 °C (−4 °F to 32 °F) requires an input of 10 cal of heat. Once the melting (or freezing) point is reached, an additional 80 cal of heat, called **latent heat of fusion**, must be supplied per gram to break the forces that bind water molecules in the ice phase. The temperature of the water and ice mixture remains at 0 °C until all the ice melts.

Once the ice cube completely melts, additional heating of the water causes the temperature of the liquid water to increase. The specific heat of liquid water is 1 cal per gram per Celsius degree so that 1 cal is needed for every 1 Celsius degree rise in water temperature. While evaporation can occur at any temperature, suppose that no evaporation takes place until the temperature of the system reaches the normal boiling point of 100 °C (212 °F). This 100 Celsius degree rise in temperature requires the addition of 100 calories—much more heat than the phase change from ice to liquid water. The **latent heat of vaporization** varies from about 600 cal per gram at 0 °C (32 °F) to 540 cal per gram at 100 °C (212 °F). When the water boils at sea-level, the temperature of the water will remain

at 100 °C (212 °F) until all the liquid is vaporized. Any additional heating will cause the temperature of the vapor to increase. For our 1-gram ice cube to vaporize directly without melting first (*sublimation*), the latent heat of fusion plus the latent heat of vaporization must be supplied to the ice cube. This amounts to 680 cal per gram at 0 °C.

If the process just described is reversed, that is, if the water vapor is cooled until it becomes liquid (*condensation*) and then ice (*freezing*), the water temperature drops and phase changes take place as equivalent amounts of latent heat are released to the environment. When water vapor becomes liquid, the latent heat of vaporization is released to the environment, and when water freezes, the latent heat of fusion is released. If water vapor changes to ice without first becoming liquid (*deposition*), the latent heats of vaporization plus fusion are released to the environment.

SENSIBLE HEATING

Heat transfer via conduction and convection can be monitored (*sensed*) by temperature change; hence, **sensible heating** encompasses both of these processes. Heat is conducted from the relatively warm surface of the Earth to the cooler overlying air. Heating reduces the density of that air, which is forced to rise by cooler denser air replacing it at the surface (Figure 4.6). In this way, convection transports heat from Earth's surface into the troposphere. Because air is a relatively poor conductor of heat, convection is much more important than conduction as a heat transfer mechanism within the troposphere.

Often sensible heating combines with latent heating to channel heat from Earth's surface into the troposphere. This happens during thunderstorm development. Updrafts (ascending branches) of vapor-laden air in convection currents often produce **cumulus clouds**, which resemble puffs of cotton floating in the sky (Figure 4.14). These clouds are sometimes referred to as *fair-weather cumulus* because they seldom produce rain or snow. On the other hand, if atmospheric conditions are favorable (described in Chapter 11), convection currents can surge to great altitudes with cumulus clouds merging and billowing upward to form towering **cumulonimbus clouds**, also known as thunderstorm clouds (Figure 4.15). In retrospect, two important heat transfer processes (a combination of latent heating and sensible heating) took place last summer when that thunderstorm washed out your ball game or sent you scurrying for shelter at the beach.

At times and places, heat transfer is directed from the troposphere to the Earth's surface, the reverse of the global average annual situation. This reversal in

FIGURE 4.14
Cumulus clouds form in the ascending branch of a convective circulation.

direction of heat transport occurs, for example, when mild winds blow over cold, snow-covered ground or when warm air moves over a relatively cool ocean surface. Heat transport from the atmosphere to Earth's surface is the usual situation at night (especially with clear skies) when

FIGURE 4.15
A cumulonimbus (thunderstorm) cloud forms when atmospheric conditions favor deep convection.

radiational cooling causes Earth's land surface to become colder than the overlying air.

As noted in Chapter 2, nearly all weather is confined to the troposphere, implying that heat transport by sensible and latent heating operates primarily within the lower atmosphere. Radiational processes dominate heat and temperature distribution above the troposphere.

BOWEN RATIO

The **Bowen ratio** describes how the heat energy received at the Earth surface (by absorption of solar and infrared radiation) is partitioned between sensible heating and latent heating. That is,

Bowen ratio = [(sensible heating)/(latent heating)]

At the global scale,

Bowen ratio = [(7 units)/(23 units)] = 0.3

As shown in Table 4.5, the Bowen ratio varies depending on the amount of surface moisture. The moister the surface, the less important is sensible heating and the more important is latent heating. The Bowen ratio ranges from about 0.1 (one-tenth as much sensible as latent heating) for the ocean to about 5.0 (five times as much sensible as latent heating) in deserts. Ocean waters cover much of Earth's surface so it is not surprising that the global Bowen ratio is relatively low (0.3).

TABLE 4.5	
Bowen Ratio[a] of Various Geographical Areas	
All Oceans	0.11
Atlantic Ocean	0.11
Pacific Ocean	0.10
Indian Ocean	0.09
All Land	0.96
North America	0.74
South America	0.56
Europe	0.62
Asia	1.14
Africa	1.61
Australia	2.18
Globe	0.30

[a]Ratio of sensible heating to latent heating.

Heat Imbalance: Tropics versus Middle and High Latitudes

On a global scale, imbalances in radiational heating and radiational cooling occur not only between Earth's surface and atmosphere, but also between the tropics and higher latitudes. Because the planet is nearly a sphere, parallel beams of incoming solar radiation strike the tropics more directly than higher latitudes. That is, solar altitudes are higher in the tropics, but lower at higher latitudes. At higher latitudes, solar radiation spreads over a greater area and is less intense per unit surface area than at lower latitudes.

Emission of infrared radiation (IR) by the Earth-atmosphere system also varies with latitude but less than solar radiation. Because air temperatures are generally lower at higher latitudes, IR emission also declines with increasing latitude. (Recall from Chapter 3 that radiation emission is temperature dependent.) Consequently, over the period of a year at higher latitudes, the rate of infrared cooling to space exceeds the rate of warming caused by absorption of solar radiation (Figure 4.16). At lower latitudes the reverse is true, that is, over the course of a year, the rate of solar radiational heating is greater than the rate of infrared radiational cooling. Averaged over the globe, incoming energy (absorbed solar radiation) must equal outgoing energy (infrared radiation emitted to space) as the planetary average temperature remains nearly constant. That is, the areas under the two curves in Figure 4.16 are equal. This global radiative equilibrium illustrates the *law of energy conservation.*

Measurements by instruments onboard Earth-orbiting satellites indicate that the division between regions of net radiational cooling and regions of net radiational warming is close to the 35-degree latitude circle in both hemispheres. By implication, latitudes poleward of about 35 degrees N and 35 degrees S should experience net cooling over the course of a year, while tropical latitudes are sites of net warming. In fact, lower latitudes do not become progressively warmer nor do higher latitudes become cooler because heat is transported poleward from the tropics into middle and high latitudes. This **poleward heat transport** is brought about by (1) air mass exchange, (2) storm systems, and (3) ocean currents. According to research conducted at the National Center for Atmospheric Research (NCAR) at Boulder, CO, atmospheric processes account for 78% of total poleward heat transport in the Northern Hemisphere and 92% in the Southern Hemisphere.

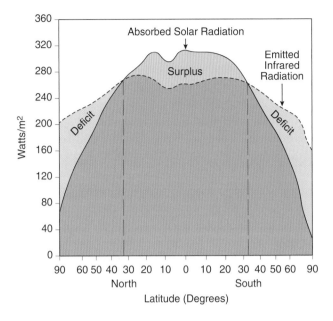

FIGURE 4.16
Variation by latitude of absorbed solar radiation and outgoing infrared radiation based on measurements by sensors flown onboard Earth-orbiting satellites. [NOAA/NESDIS]

An **air mass** is a huge volume of air covering thousands of square kilometers that is relatively uniform horizontally in temperature and humidity (water vapor concentration). The properties of an air mass largely depend on the characteristics of the surface over which the air mass forms (its *source region*) or travels. Air masses that form at high latitudes over cold, often snow- or ice-covered surfaces are relatively cold. Air masses that form at low latitudes are relatively warm. Air masses that develop over the ocean are humid and those that form over land are relatively dry. Hence, there are four basic types of air masses: cold and humid, cold and dry, warm and humid, and warm and dry. Warm air masses that form in lower latitudes flow toward the poles and are replaced by cold air masses that flow toward the equator from source regions at high latitudes. In this exchange of air masses, sensible heat is transported poleward.

Release of latent heat in storm systems (cyclones) plays an important role in the poleward transport of heat. At low latitudes, water that evaporates from the warm ocean surface is drawn into the circulation of a developing storm system. As the storm travels into higher latitudes, some of that water vapor condenses into clouds, thereby releasing latent heat to the troposphere. Latent heat of vaporization acquired at low latitudes is thereby delivered to middle and high latitudes. In general, tropical cyclones (e.g., hurricanes) are greater contributors to poleward heat transport than ordinary middle latitude (extra-tropical) cyclones because they entrain much more water vapor and latent heat. This mechanism of poleward heat transport is readily apparent in water vapor satellite imagery (Chapters 1 and 6).

The ocean's contribution to poleward heat transport is primarily via wind-driven surface currents and deeper conveyor-belt-like currents that traverse the lengths of the ocean basins. Surface water that is cooler than the overlying air is a *heat sink* for the atmosphere; that is, heat is conducted from air to sea. Surface water that is warmer than the overlying air is a *heat source* for the atmosphere; that is, heat is conducted from sea to air. Cold surface currents, such as the California Current, flow from high to low latitudes, absorbing heat from the relatively warm tropical troposphere and greater solar radiation. Warm surface currents, such as the Gulf Stream, flow from the tropics into middle latitudes, supplying heat to the cooler middle-latitude troposphere (Figure 4.17).

FIGURE 4.17
A composite infrared satellite image showing sea-surface temperatures color-coded in °C. The Gulf Stream is clearly discernible as a ribbon of relatively warm water flowing along the East Coast from Florida north to off the Delaware coast. [NOAA, National Environmental Satellite, Data, and Information Service]

The driving force for the **ocean conveyor-belt system** is evident in the North Atlantic Ocean near Greenland and Iceland (Figure 4.18). Cold, dry winds blowing from northern Canada chill surface waters. This cooling combined with evaporation and sea-ice formation produces a cold, salty water mass known as *North Atlantic Deep Water (NADW)*. The relatively dense NADW sinks and then flows southward along the continental slope of North and South America to near Antarctica. There the bottom current is warmer (and less dense) than the surface waters so that the current wells up to the surface where it is chilled and sinks again. Branches of the cold bottom current then spread northward into the Atlantic, Indian, and Pacific Ocean basins.

Flowing northward, the bottom current gradually warms and mixes with the overlying waters. The current rises to the surface in the Pacific, flows into the Indian Ocean basin, and then flows around southern Africa into the Atlantic. Intense solar radiation in the tropical Atlantic heats the surface current. The warm Atlantic surface current continues its flow northward eventually reaching the Labrador and Greenland seas, thereby completing the ocean conveyor-belt circulation.

The importance of the ocean conveyor-belt system in poleward heat transport is illustrated by the temperature contrast between surface and deep currents in the far North Atlantic. Surface waters approaching Greenland are some 8 Celsius degrees (14 Fahrenheit degrees) warmer than the bottom current (NADW) that flows southward. The difference in temperature between the surface and deep water is a measure of the magnitude of heat transport from the ocean surface to the overlying troposphere.

Why Weather?

As we have seen, imbalances in rates of radiational heating and radiational cooling give rise to temperature gradients between (1) Earth's surface and troposphere and (2) low and high latitudes. In response, heat is transported within the Earth-atmosphere system via conduction, convection, cloud development, air mass exchange, and storms. That is, the atmosphere circulates, bringing about changes in the state of the atmosphere (weather). A cause-and-effect chain thus operates in the Earth-atmosphere system, starting with the sun as the prime energy source and resulting in weather.

We have also seen that within the Earth-atmosphere system, some solar radiation is absorbed,

FIGURE 4.18
The ocean conveyor-belt system contributes to the transport of heat from low latitudes to high latitudes.

that is, converted to heat, and eventually all of this heat is emitted to space as infrared radiation. Some solar energy is also converted to kinetic energy, the energy of motion, in the circulation of the atmosphere. Kinetic energy is manifested in winds, convection currents, and the north-south exchange of air masses. Circulation (weather) systems do not last indefinitely, however. The kinetic energy of atmospheric circulation ultimately is dissipated as frictional heat as winds blow against Earth's surface. This heat, in turn, is emitted to space as infrared radiation. In summary, the sun drives the atmosphere: imbalances in solar heating spur atmospheric circulation, which redistributes heat. Hence, solar energy is the ultimate source of kinetic energy in weather systems.

The rate of heat redistribution within the Earth-atmosphere system varies seasonally so that atmospheric circulation and weather also change through the year. When steep temperature gradients prevail across North America, the weather tends to be more dynamic. Storm systems are large and intense, winds are stronger, and the weather is changeable. Such weather is typical of winter, when it is not unusual for daily temperatures in the southern United States to be more than 30 Celsius degrees (54 Fahrenheit degrees) higher than temperatures

across southern Canada. When air temperature varies little across the continent, as in summer, the weather tends to be more tranquil, and large-scale weather systems are generally weak and ill-defined. Nevertheless, summer weather is sometimes very active. Intense heating of the ground by the summer sun coupled with lifting processes often triggers deep convection and development of thunderstorms. Some of these weather systems spawn destructive hail, strong and gusty winds, and heavy rains. However, these systems are usually shorter lived and more localized than winter storms.

Variation of Air Temperature

Air temperature is variable, fluctuating from hour to hour, from one day to the next, with the seasons, and from one place to another. Our discussion of the basic reasons for atmospheric circulation and weather provides some insight as to why air temperature is variable. The radiation budget plus movements of air masses regulate air temperature locally. Although these two factors actually work in concert, for purpose of study, we initially consider them separately.

RADIATIONAL CONTROLS

Many factors govern the local radiation budget and air temperature, including the following: (1) time of day and day of the year, which determine the solar altitude and the intensity and duration of solar radiation striking Earth's surface; (2) cloud cover, because cloudiness affects the flux of both incoming solar and outgoing terrestrial radiation; and (3) surface characteristics, which determine the albedo and the percentage of absorbed radiation (heat) used for sensible heating and latent heating. Hence, air temperature is generally higher in July than in January (in the Northern Hemisphere), during the day than at night, under clear rather than overcast daytime skies, when the ground is bare instead of snow-covered, and when the ground is dry rather than wet.

The annual temperature cycle (also called the march of mean monthly temperature) reflects the systematic variation in incoming solar radiation over the course of a year (Figure 4.19). In the latitude belt between the Tropics of Cancer and Capricorn, incoming solar radiation varies little through the course of a year so that average monthly air temperatures exhibit minimal seasonal contrast. In fact, in the tropics, the temperature difference between night and day often is greater than the winter-to-summer temperature contrast. At middle latitudes, solar radiation features a pronounced annual maximum and minimum. At high latitudes, poleward of the Arctic and Antarctic circles, the seasonal difference in solar radiation is extreme, varying from zero in fall and winter to a maximum in spring and summer. This marked periodicity of solar radiation outside of the tropics accounts for the distinct winter-to-summer temperature contrasts observed in middle and high latitudes.

At middle and high latitudes, the march of mean monthly temperature lags behind the monthly variation in solar radiation so that the warmest and coldest months of the year typically do not coincide with the times of maximum and minimum solar radiation, respectively. The troposphere's temperature profile takes time to adjust to seasonal changes in solar energy input. Typically, the warmest portion of the year is about a month after the summer solstice, and the coldest part of the year usually occurs about a month after the winter solstice. In the United States, the temperature cycle lags the solar cycle by an average of 27 days. However, in coastal localities with a strong maritime influence (e.g., Florida, the shoreline of New England, and coastal California), the average lag time is up to 36 days. In addition, as we saw earlier in this chapter, the maritime influence reduces the amplitude of the annual march of mean monthly temperature; that is, the winter-to-summer temperature contrast is less in maritime climates.

Over the course of a 24-hour day, surface air temperature responds to regular variations in the flux of radiation. Typically, the day's lowest (minimum) temperature occurs shortly after sunrise as solar radiation just begins to heat the ground. The day's highest temperature is usually recorded in early or mid-afternoon, even though solar radiation peaks around the local solar noon. Air temperature depends on the relative magnitudes of the incoming solar radiation and outgoing terrestrial infrared radiation (Figure 4.20). Beginning shortly after sunrise, solar radiation exceeds emission of terrestrial IR and the air temperature rises. By early to mid-afternoon, solar radiation balances terrestrial radiation and air temperature reaches a maximum. Subsequently, terrestrial

FIGURE 4.19

March of monthly mean temperature at Manaus, Brazil, Kansas City, MO, and Yellowknife, Canada.

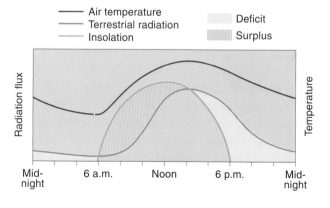

FIGURE 4.20

The variation in air temperature through the course of a 24-hour day depends upon the relative fluxes of incoming solar radiation (insolation) and outgoing infrared radiation.

radiation exceeds solar radiation and the air temperature falls as the solar radiation decreases with the decline in solar altitude. Overnight, the only radiational flux is outgoing terrestrial radiation, further cooling the surface and air above.

The diurnal lag between solar radiation and air temperature explains why in summer the greatest risk of sunburn is around local solar noon (the time of peak solar altitude) and not during the warmest time of day. Incoming solar ultraviolet radiation, the cause of sunburn, is most intense near noon, but the air temperature does not reach a maximum until several hours later.

As a further illustration of local radiational controls of air temperature, consider the influence of ground characteristics. All other factors being equal, in response to the same intensity of solar radiation striking Earth's surface, air over a dry surface (e.g., bare soil) warms more than air over a moist or vegetated surface. When the surface is dry, absorbed radiation is used primarily for sensible heating of the air (conduction and convection of heat from the surface into the overlying air). Hence, the air temperature is higher (and so is the Bowen ratio). On the other hand, when the surface is moist, much of the absorbed radiation is used to evaporate water, the air temperature is lower (and so is the Bowen ratio).

Dry soil (and a relatively high Bowen ratio) helps explain why unusually high air temperatures often accompany *drought*, a lengthy period of moisture deficit. Soils dry out, crops wither and die, and lakes and other reservoirs shrink. Because less surface moisture is available for vaporization, more of the available heat is channeled into raising the air temperature through conduction and convection. Consider as an example the severe drought that gripped a ten-state area of the southeastern United States between December 1985 and July 1986. In most places, rainfall was less than 70% of the long-term average, and in the hardest hit areas, portions of the Carolinas, it was less than 40%. By July, many weather stations in the drought-stricken region were setting new high temperature records. Columbia, SC, Savannah, GA, and Raleigh-Durham, NC reported the warmest July on record. Also contributing to record heat was more intense solar radiation reaching the ground, a consequence of less than the usual daytime cloud cover. The same association between exceptionally dry surface conditions and unusually high air temperatures was observed during the severe drought that afflicted the Midwest and Great Plains during the summer of 1988. At many long-term weather stations, the summer of 1988 was one of the driest and hottest on record.

A city is an island of warmth surrounded by cooler air, a so-called **urban heat island**. Snow melts faster and flowers bloom earlier in a city than in the surrounding countryside. Reporting in 2004, Xiaoyang Zhang and colleagues at Boston University, investigated urban heat islands using data on land surface temperatures and vegetation from the Moderate Resolution Imaging Spectroradiometer flown onboard NASA's Terra satellite. The researchers found that in 70 urban areas in eastern North America, nonagricultural vegetation began to bud about 7 days earlier in spring and retained foliage about 8 days longer in autumn when compared to vegetation in non-urban areas.

The relative lack of moisture in cities is one of the reasons why the average annual surface temperature is a degree or two higher in a city than in nearby rural areas. City sewer systems efficiently carry off most runoff from rain and snowmelt whereas the countryside typically has considerable standing water (e.g., lakes, rivers, moist soils) and much more vegetative cover for transpiration (emission of water vapor to the air by plants). In a city more of the available heat from absorbed radiation is used to raise the temperature of surfaces (sensible heating) and less for evaporation of water (latent heating). In the moister countryside, heat from absorption of radiation is used less for sensible heating and more for latent heating. On average, the Bowen ration is about four times greater in a city than the countryside.

Other factors that contribute to an urban heat island include the greater concentration of heat sources in a city (e.g., motor vehicles, space heaters, air conditioners). On a cold winter day in New York City, heat from urban sources may approach 100 W/m^2, about 7% of the solar constant. City surfaces generally have a lower albedo than the vegetative cover of rural areas. A city's canyon-like terrain of narrow streets and tall buildings causes multiple reflections of sunlight increasing the amount of solar radiation that is absorbed. Urban building materials (e.g., concrete, asphalt, and brick) conduct heat more readily than the soil and vegetation of rural areas so that release of heat to the urban atmosphere from buildings and streets partially counters radiational cooling, especially at night.

An urban heat island is best developed at night when the air is calm and the sky is clear. Under those conditions, the nighttime temperature contrast between a city and its surroundings can be as great as 10 Celsius degrees (18 Fahrenheit degrees). When strong winds are present, the temperature contrast is greatly diminished as city and country air is mixed.

Snow has a relatively high albedo and substantially reduces the amount of solar radiation that is absorbed at the surface and converted to heat. Furthermore, snow-covered ground reduces sensible heating of the overlying air because some of the available heat is used to vaporize or melt snow. Consequently, a snow cover lowers the day's maximum air temperature. Because snow is also an excellent emitter of infrared radiation, nocturnal radiational cooling is extreme where the ground is snow-covered, especially when skies are clear (minimum greenhouse effect). Cooling near the Earth's surface is further enhanced if winds are very light or the air is calm. Light winds or calm conditions reduce vertical mixing of air. On such nights, the air temperature near the surface may be 10 Celsius degrees (18 Fahrenheit degrees) or more lower than if the ground were bare of snow. By reducing both the maximum and minimum daily air temperature, a snow cover significantly lowers the 24-hr average temperature.

COLD AND WARM AIR ADVECTION

Air mass advection refers to the movement of an air mass from one locality to another. With advection, one air mass replaces another air mass having different temperature (and/or humidity) characteristics. **Cold air advection** occurs when the wind transports colder air into a previously warmer area. On a weather map cold air advection is indicated by winds blowing across regional isotherms from a colder area to a warmer area (arrow A in Figure 4.21). Cold air advection occurs behind a cold front (Chapter 10). **Warm air advection** takes place when the wind blows across regional isotherms from a warmer area to a colder area (arrow B in Figure 4.21). Warm air advection occurs behind a warm front and ahead of a cold front (Chapter 10). **Isotherms** are lines drawn on a map through localities having the same air temperature and usually must be interpolated between reporting weather stations. Recall from earlier in this chapter that air mass exchange is a major contributor to poleward heat transport.

The significance of air mass advection for local temperature variations depends on (1) the initial temperature of the new air mass, and (2) the degree of modification the air mass undergoes as it travels over Earth's surface. For example, a surge of bitterly cold arctic air loses much of its punch when it travels over ground that is not snow covered, because the arctic air is warmed from below by sensible heating (conduction and convection). In contrast, modification of an arctic air mass by sensible heating is minimized when the air mass travels over a cold, snow-covered surface.

So far, we have been describing how horizontal movement of air (advection) might influence air temperature at some locality. However, as we saw in our discussion of convection currents, air also moves vertically. As air ascends and descends, its temperature changes; air cools as it rises but warms as it descends. The reasons for these temperature changes are given in Chapter 5.

Although we have considered local radiational controls and air mass advection separately, the two actually regulate air temperature together. Sometimes air mass advection compensates for, or even overwhelms, local radiational influences on air temperature. As noted earlier, in response to the local radiation budget, the air temperature usually climbs from a minimum near sunrise to a maximum in early or midafternoon. This typical pattern can change, however, if an influx of cold air occurs at the same time. Depending on how cold the incoming air is, air temperatures may climb more slowly than usual, remain steady, or even fall during daylight hours. If cold air advection is extreme, air temperatures may drop precipitously throughout the day, in spite of bright, sunny skies. In another example, air temperatures may climb through the evening hours as a consequence of strong warm air advection, so the day's high temperature occurs at night.

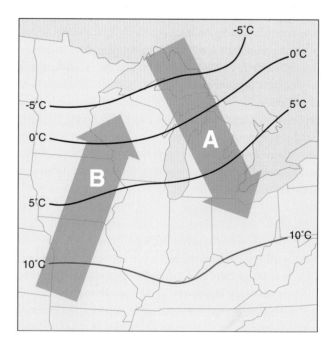

FIGURE 4.21
Cold air advection occurs when (A) horizontal winds blow across regional isotherms from colder areas toward warmer areas, and warm air advection occurs when (B) horizontal winds blow across regional isotherms from warmer areas toward colder areas. Solid lines are isotherms in °C.

Conclusions

Heat and temperature are distinct yet closely related quantities. Unequal rates of radiational heating and cooling give rise to temperature gradients within the Earth-atmosphere system. In response to these temperature gradients, heat is transferred from warmer to colder localities via radiation, conduction and convection, and latent heating. The temperature response of a substance to a gain or loss of heat depends primarily on its specific heat. Chiefly because of contrasts in specific heat, the temperature of a body of water is much less variable than that of land surfaces. This contrast in thermal inertia influences the temperature of the overlying air so that regions downwind of the ocean (or large lakes) exhibit less temperature contrast between summer and winter than locations far from large water bodies.

Imbalances in radiational heating and radiational cooling within the Earth-atmosphere system are ultimately responsible for the circulation of the atmosphere. These imbalances occur both vertically (between Earth's surface and the atmosphere) and horizontally (between tropical and higher latitudes). Through atmospheric circulation, heat is redistributed within the Earth-atmosphere system. This enables us to understand how air temperature is regulated by a combination of local radiational controls and air mass advection.

Another important consequence of atmospheric circulation is the formation of clouds that can produce rain, snow, and other forms of precipitation. Before examining cloud and precipitation forming processes in detail, we must first consider the behavior of gases, especially involving another important variable of the atmosphere, air pressure. This is the principal subject of the next chapter.

Basic Understandings

- Temperature is directly proportional to the average kinetic energy of the atoms or molecules composing a substance. Heat is the name given to energy transferred from a warmer object to a colder object.
- As a sample of air gains or loses heat, that heat may be used for some combination of changes in temperature, phase of water, or volume of the air sample.
- The Fahrenheit and Celsius temperature scales are based upon the reproducible phase changes in water. While the Fahrenheit temperature scale is still commonly used in the United States, the Celsius temperature scale is more convenient in that a 100-degree interval separates the freezing and boiling points of pure water at sea level. The Kelvin scale is based on absolute zero and is a more direct measure of average kinetic molecular activity than either the Fahrenheit or Celsius scale. An object at absolute zero (0 kelvin) emits no electromagnetic radiation. Heat energy is quantified as calories, joules, or British thermal units.

- Common types of thermometers are liquid-in-glass, bimetallic, and electronic. Another type of thermal sensor is a radiometer that measures radiation emitted from an object. Thermometers used for weather observations should be mounted where they are well ventilated but sheltered from precipitation and direct sunshine.

- In response to a temperature gradient, heat always flows from locations of higher temperature to locations of lower temperature. This is a consequence of the second law of thermodynamics. Heat transfer occurs via radiation, conduction, convection, as well as by phase changes of water (latent heating).

- All objects absorb and emit radiation, an energy transport mechanism that does not require a physical medium. If absorption exceeds emission (radiational heating), the temperature of an object rises, and if emission exceeds absorption (radiational cooling), the temperature of an object falls. At radiative equilibrium, absorption balances emission and the temperature of the object is constant.

- As a rule, solids (especially metals) are better conductors of heat than are liquids, and liquids are better conductors than gases. Motionless air is a very poor conductor of heat. Convection is the transport of heat within a fluid via motion of the fluid itself and is much more important than conduction in transporting heat within the troposphere.

- When water changes phase, heat is either absorbed from or released to the environment. Latent heat is absorbed during melting, evaporation, and sublimation. Latent heat is released during freezing, condensation, and deposition.

- The temperature response to an input or output

of heat differs from one substance to another depending primarily on the specific heat of each substance. Water bodies, such as the ocean or large lakes, exhibit less temperature variability from day to night and from summer to winter than do landmasses because the specific heat of water is higher than that of land, solar radiation penetrates water but soil is opaque to solar radiation, and water circulates. The winter-to-summer temperature contrast is greater in continental climates than in maritime climates. In addition, compared to continental locales, maritime locales experience a greater lag in the temperature response to seasonal variations in solar radiation.

- On a global average annual basis, radiational cooling is greater than radiational heating of the atmosphere. On the other hand, radiational heating is greater than radiational cooling of Earth's surface. In response, heat is transported from the warmer Earth's surface to the cooler troposphere via latent heating (vaporization of water followed by cloud development) and sensible heating (conduction plus convection).

- The ratio of sensible heating to latent heating, the Bowen ratio, depends on the amount of moisture at the Earth's surface. The Bowen ratio is relatively high for dry surfaces and relatively low for wet surfaces. The global Bowen ratio is 0.30.

- Poleward of about 35 degrees latitude, over the course of a year, the rate of cooling due to infrared emission to space is greater than the rate of warming due to absorption of incoming solar radiation. In tropical latitudes, on the other hand, the rate of warming due to absorption of solar radiation is greater than the rate of cooling due to emission of infrared radiation. Poleward heat transport within the Earth system is the consequence.

- Poleward heat transport is brought about chiefly by atmospheric processes (north-south exchange of air masses and release of latent heat in storm systems) and, to a lesser extent, by the circulation of warm and cold ocean waters.

- The sun drives the circulation of the atmosphere by causing heat imbalances within the Earth-atmosphere system. Some solar energy is converted to the kinetic energy of atmospheric circulation, which is ultimately dissipated as frictional heat that is radiated to space.

- The radiation budget plus air mass advection govern variations in local air temperature. The radiation budget varies with time of day, day of the year, cloud cover, and characteristics of the Earth's surface. Air mass advection occurs when the wind blows across regional isotherms. In some cases, cold or warm air advection compensates for or even overwhelms the influence of the local radiation budget on air temperature.

Review

1. Distinguish between *temperature* and *heat*.
2. What is the significance of *absolute zero* (0 K)?
3. Why is it a good idea to mount a thermometer inside an instrument shelter?
4. Identify and describe three processes whereby heat is transported in response to a temperature gradient. Present a common example of each process.
5. Why does a deep snow cover inhibit the freezing of underlying soil even though the temperature of the overlying air falls well below freezing?
6. Distinguish between *radiational heating* and *radiational cooling*.
7. Distinguish between *latent heating* and *sensible heating* of the atmosphere. Which is the more important on a global annual average basis?
8. Speculate on how the Bowen ratio might change as a drought progresses.
9. Why is the warmest time of day usually several hours after the day's peak solar radiation?
10. Under what conditions might the day's high temperature occur just before midnight?

Critical Thinking

1. Explain how a thermos bottle keeps hot beverages hot and cold beverages cold.
2. Explain why parks and other green space in a city help to reduce the urban heat island effect.
3. A Pennsylvania highway sign warns motorists that a bridge surface freezes before the road surface. Why does a bridge surface freeze first?
4. Design an experiment to determine the temperature response of samples of dry and wet sand to the same input of heat. Predict the outcome of such an experiment.
5. In winter, double-glazed windows or storm windows are used to cut heat loss from buildings. Speculate on how such windows cut conductive and convective heat flow.
6. What is the boiling point of pure water at sea level on the Kelvin scale?
7. An increment of 20 Celsius degrees corresponds to an increment of how many Fahrenheit degrees?
8. How much heat must be added to raise the temperature of 100 g of water from 20°C to 90°C?
9. Calculate the temperature change in Celsius degrees when...
   a. 5 cal of heat is added to 5 g of water.
   b. 5 cal of heat is added to 5 g of ice at –5°C.
   c. 1000 cal of heat is added to a brick with a mass of 1 kg.
   d. 100 cal of heat is added to a layer of dry sand with a mass of 100 g.
10. Compute the number of heating degree–days on a day when the...
   a. mean outdoor temperature is 45 °F.
   b. maximum temperature is 27 °F and the day's minimum temperature is 2 °F.
   c. maximum temperature is 10 °C and the day's minimum temperature is –2 °C.

ESSAY: Heating and Cooling Degree-Days

Television and newspaper weather summaries routinely report heating or cooling degree-day totals in addition to daily maximum and minimum temperature. Heating and cooling degree-days are indicators of household energy consumption for space heating and cooling, respectively.

In the United States, *heating degree-days* are based on the Fahrenheit temperature scale and are computed only for days when the average outdoor air temperature is lower than 65 °F (18 °C). Heating engineers who formulated this index early in the 20th century found that when the average outdoor temperature drops below 65 °F, space heating is required in most buildings to maintain an average indoor air temperature of 70 °F (21 °C). The average daily temperature is the simple arithmetic average of the 24-hr maximum and minimum air temperatures. Each degree of average temperature below 65 °F is counted as *one heating degree-day*. Subtracting the average daily temperature from 65 °F yields the number of heating degree-days for that day. Suppose, for example, that this morning's low temperature was 36 °F, and this afternoon's high temperature was 52 °F. Today's average temperature would then be 44 °F, for a total of 21 heating degree-days (65 − 44 = 21). It is usual to keep a running total of heating degree-days, that is, to add degree-days for successive days through the heating season (actually from 1 July of one year through 30 June of the next).

Fuel distributors and power companies closely monitor heating degree-days. Fuel oil dealers base fuel use rates on cumulative degree-days and schedule deliveries accordingly. Natural gas and electrical utilities anticipate power demands on the basis of degree-day totals, and implement priority use policies on the same basis when capacity fails to keep pace with demand.

The map in Figure 1 is a plot of the average annual heating degree-day totals over the coterminous United States. Outside of mountainous areas, regions of equal heating degree-day totals tend to parallel latitude circles with degree-day totals increasing poleward. As an example, the average annual space-heating requirement in Chicago (6100 heating degree-days) is about four times that of New Orleans (1500 heating degree-days). If per unit fuel costs are the same in both cities, then, in an average winter, Chicago homeowners can expect to pay four times as much for space heating as homeowners in New Orleans. This assumes that buildings in the two cities are comparable in structure and insulation.

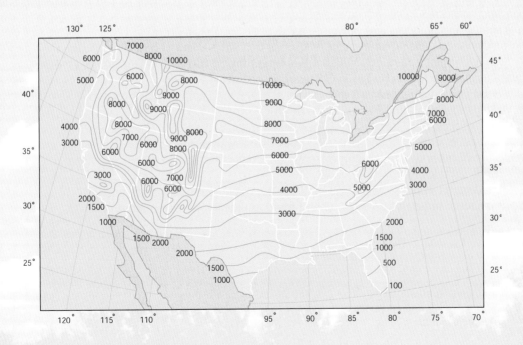

FIGURE 1
Average annual heating degree-day totals over the lower 48 states using a base of 65 °F.

Cooling degree-days are computed only for days when the average outdoor air temperature is higher than 65 °F (although higher base temperatures are sometimes used). Supplemental air conditioning may be needed on such days. Again, a cumulative total is maintained through the cooling season (1 January through 31 December). Across the United States, average annual cooling degree-day totals range from less than 500 in the northern tier states and along much of the Pacific coast to more than 4000 in South Texas, South Florida, and the Desert Southwest.

Indexes of heating and cooling requirements are based on outdoor air temperatures and do not take into account other weather elements, such as air circulation and humidity, which also influence human comfort and demands for space heating and cooling. Heating and cooling degree-days are therefore only approximations of residential fuel demands for heating and cooling.

ESSAY: Wind-chill

At low air temperature, the wind increases human discomfort outdoors and heightens the danger of *frostbite*, the freezing of body tissue, or *hypothermia,* a potentially lethal condition brought on by a drop in the temperature of the body's vital organs (e.g., heart, lungs). Air in motion is more effective than still air in transporting heat away from the body. To account for the effect of wind on human comfort and wellbeing, weather reports during winter in northern and mountainous regions include the *wind-chill equivalent temperature (WET)* along with the actual air temperature.

A very thin layer of motionless air (thickness measured in millimeters) next to the skin helps insulate the body from heat loss to the environment. Within this so-called *boundary layer*, heat loss is through the very slow process of conduction. (Recall that calm air is a poor conductor of heat.) The boundary layer is thickest and offers maximum insulation when the wind speed is under 0.5 mi per hr (0.2 m per sec). Because water vapor molecules diffuse slowly through the skin's boundary layer, the rate of evaporative cooling is also relatively slow. Hence, even at very low air temperatures, people who are appropriately clothed are comfortable as long as winds are light. As winds strengthen, the boundary layer becomes thinner and the rate of heat and water vapor transport from the skin surface increases. Thinning of the boundary layer (and accelerated heat loss) is most pronounced at low to moderate wind speeds. As wind speed increases above about 35 mi (55 km) per hour, incremental heat loss becomes relatively small as the boundary layer approaches its minimum thickness.

The *wind-chill equivalent temperature (WET)*, also called the *wind-chill index*, is a measure of the rate of body heat loss due to a combination of wind and low air temperature. The original index was based upon research conducted in Antarctica by P.A. Siple and C.F. Passel during the winter of 1941. Their original objective was to measure the time required for water to freeze under various weather conditions. Only later did the idea arise to develop a wind-chill index based upon this research. Their experiments using a small water-filled non-insulated plastic cylinder provide, at best, a rough approximation of the thermal response of a human body dressed appropriately for cold and windy weather. The wind-chill index also fails to account for the appreciable warming that occurs when the body absorbs solar radiation—Siple and Passel made their measurements in darkness.

In the winter of 2001-02, the National Weather Service (NWS) and the Meteorological Services of Canada (MSC) implemented a major revision of the wind-chill index (Figure 1). The new index incorporates recent advances

Wind (mph)

Temperature (°F) \ Calm	5	10	15	20	25	30	35	40	45	50	55	60
40	36	34	32	30	29	28	28	27	26	26	25	25
35	31	27	25	24	23	22	21	20	19	19	18	17
30	25	21	19	17	16	15	14	13	12	12	11	10
25	19	15	13	11	9	8	7	6	5	4	4	3
20	13	9	6	4	3	1	0	-1	-2	-3	-3	-4
15	7	3	0	-2	-4	-5	-7	-8	-9	-10	-11	-11
10	1	-4	-7	-9	-11	-12	-14	-15	-16	-17	-18	-19
5	-5	-10	-13	-15	-17	-19	-21	-22	-23	-24	-25	-26
0	-11	-16	-19	-22	-24	-26	-27	-29	-30	-31	-32	-33
-5	-16	-22	-26	-29	-31	-33	-34	-36	-37	-38	-39	-40
-10	-22	-28	-32	-35	-37	-39	-41	-43	-44	-45	-46	-48
-15	-28	-35	-39	-42	-44	-46	-48	-50	-51	-52	-54	-55
-20	-34	-41	-45	-48	-51	-53	-55	-57	-58	-60	-61	-62
-25	-40	-47	-51	-55	-58	-60	-62	-64	-65	-67	-68	-69
-30	-46	-53	-58	-61	-64	-67	-69	-71	-72	-74	-75	-76
-35	-52	-59	-64	-68	-71	-73	-76	-78	-79	-81	-82	-84
-40	-57	-66	-71	-74	-78	-80	-82	-84	-86	-88	-89	-91
-45	-63	-72	-77	-81	-84	-87	-89	-91	-93	-95	-97	-98

Temperature (°F)

Frostbite times (minutes)　　☐ 30　　▨ 10　　▧ 5

FIGURE 1
Wind-chill table introduced by the National Weather Service in the winter of 2001-02.

in science, technology, and computer modeling to provide a more accurate, understandable, and useful formula for representing the combined hazard of wind and low air temperatures. The new wind-chill index uses wind speed adjusted for the average height (1.5 m or 5 ft) of a human's face instead of standard anemometer height (10 m or 33 ft), applies modern heat transfer theory, and assumes the worst case scenario for solar radiation (clear night sky). The formula is

$$\text{WET (°F)} = 35.74 + 0.6215T - 35.75 \, (V^{0.16}) + 0.4275T \, (V^{0.16})$$

where T is the temperature in °F and V is the wind speed in miles per hour. This formula is the basis for the Wind-chill Table. (For computing wind-chill, calm is defined as 3 mi per hr or less.)

Suppose, for example, the air temperature is 35 °F and the air is calm; then the wind-chill equivalent temperature (35 °F) is the same as the actual air temperature. If the wind strengthens to 25 mi per hr with no change in actual air temperature, the WET drops to 23 °F. Contrary to popular opinion, this does not mean that the temperature of exposed skin actually drops to 23 °F. Skin temperature can drop no lower than the actual air temperature, which in this example is 35 °F. When skin temperature equals the air temperature, the temperature gradient between the skin surface and adjacent air is zero and no heat is exchanged between the skin and the air. Even though the WET may fall below the freezing point, skin will not freeze if the actual air temperature is above the freezing point.

On a cold and windy day, an exposed body part loses heat to the environment at the same rate that it would if the air were calm and the actual air temperature equaled the wind-chill equivalent temperature. In fact, many combinations of air temperature and wind speed produce about the same rate of heat loss. For instance, heat loss is essentially the same for air temperature/wind speed combinations of 15 °F/5 mi per hr and 25 °F/35 mi per hr. In both cases, the wind-chill equivalent temperature is 7 °F.

During cold and blustery weather, if the human body cannot supply heat to the skin at a rate sufficient to compensate for heat loss, skin temperature declines. Initially a person has a sense of discomfort. If the rate of heat loss from exposed skin causes skin temperature to fall to subfreezing levels, then frostbite may ensue. Particularly susceptible to frostbite are body parts that are usually exposed and have a relatively high surface-to-volume ratio, such as the ears, nose, and fingers. Frostbite may occur in 30 minutes or less at wind-chill values of −18 °F (−28 °C) or lower. In extreme circumstances, the rate of heat loss from the body may be great enough to cause life-threatening hypothermia.

CHAPTER 5

AIR PRESSURE

Mts. Makalu (left) and Everest (right) as seen from the International Space Station. At the elevation of these summits (over 8,400 meters) air pressure is only about one-third of its sea level value. [Courtesy NASA]

Case in Point

At 8850 m (29,035 ft) above sea level, the summit of Mount Everest is the highest mountain peak in the world. This massive glacier-encrusted mountain is located at the edge of the Tibetan Plateau on the border between Tibet and Nepal in the central Himalayas. In 1856, the mountain was named for Sir George Everest (1790-1866), surveyor general of India. For most Nepali people, however, the mountain is Sagarmatha ("forehead in the sky") whereas the Sherpa people of northern Nepal call it Chomolungma ("Goddess Mother of the World"). Local peoples revered the mountain as sacred and did not attempt to scale it prior to the 20th century. For many years, restrictions on foreign visitors, brutal weather, the threat of massive snow and ice avalanches on the mountain, plus the thin air at higher elevations were insurmountable barriers for climbers bent on conquering the peak. The summit of Mount Everest was not reached until 28 May 1953 when scaled by Sir Edmund Hillary of New Zealand and Sherpa Tenzing

Norgay of Nepal. Since then, more than 4000 people have attempted to climb to the summit of Mount Everest; 660 were successful but more than 140 died in the effort.

The latitude of Mount Everest (28 degrees N) is about the same as Tampa, FL but the rapid decline of air temperature with elevation means that the upper reaches of the mountain are perpetually at subfreezing temperatures. Estimated January mean temperature at the summit of Mount Everest is −36 °C (−33 °F). In July, the warmest month, the mean temperature is about −19 °C (−2 °F). From June through September, moist winds blowing inland from off the Indian Ocean (the wet monsoon) shroud the mountain in thick clouds and heavy snows. From November through February, the upper tropospheric jet stream dips down from the north, displacing the monsoon flow, and bringing to the mountain strong winds frequently blowing in excess of hurricane force. The combination of high winds and low temperatures make frostbite and hypothermia a constant threat for climbers. Because of high winds through April and the onset of heavy snows by June, most ascents of Mount Everest take place in May.

Air also becomes thinner with increasing elevation; that is, the number of air molecules per unit volume decreases. Although the ratio of nitrogen (N_2) to oxygen (O_2) remains constant at about 4 to 1, the decline in the amount of oxygen (coupled with the extreme weather) can quickly lead to life-threatening conditions. The decline in air density with altitude is accompanied by a decrease in air pressure (the weight per unit area of the overlying column of air). At the summit of Mount Everest, the pressure exerted by oxygen is only about one-third of its sea level value. Without a supplemental oxygen supply, people cannot survive for very long at the summit. Climbers attempt to cope with these extreme conditions by ascending gradually to higher altitudes—taking several weeks for their bodies to adjust to the thin air. But even with *acclimatization* (discussed in this chapter's first Essay), the summit of Mount Everest is so high and the air so thin that until recently experts considered survival near or at the summit to be impossible without a supplemental oxygen supply. The experts were proved wrong in 1978 when the Austrians Reinhold Messner and Peter Habeler ascended to the summit without a supplemental oxygen supply and survived. In spite of this remarkable feat, the extreme environment at the summit of Mount Everest remains very close to the physiological limits of human life.

Driving Question:
What is the significance of horizontal and vertical variations in air pressure?

In describing the state of the atmosphere, television and radio weathercasts usually cite the latest air pressure reading along with air temperature, relative humidity, and other weather elements. Although we are physically aware of changes in temperature and humidity, we do not sense changes in air pressure as readily. If we follow air pressure reports over a period of time, however, we quickly learn that important changes in weather can accompany relatively small variations in air pressure.

In this chapter, we examine the properties of air pressure, how air pressure is measured, and the reasons for spatial and temporal variations in air pressure. We also consider how air responds to changes in pressure when moving vertically through the atmosphere. In later chapters, we describe how variations in air pressure contribute to the circulation of the atmosphere and weather.

Defining Air Pressure

Because the atmosphere consists of molecules that have mass, air exerts a force on the surface of all objects that it contacts with air pressure representing a measure of that force per unit surface area. A **force** is defined as a push or pull on an object and is computed as mass times acceleration. Molecules composing air are always in rapid, random motion, and each molecule exerts a force as it collides with other molecules, including those on the surface of a solid (e.g., the ground) or liquid (e.g., the ocean). In one millionth of one second billions upon billions of gas molecules bombard every square centimeter of Earth's surface. The total air pressure is the cumulative force of a multitude of molecules colliding with a unit surface area of any object in contact with air.

Each gaseous component of air contributes to the total air pressure as described by Dalton's law of partial pressures, named for its discoverer the British scientist John Dalton (1766-1844). According to **Dalton's law**, the total pressure exerted by a mixture of gases equals the sum of the pressures produced by each constituent gas; that is, each gas species in the mixture acts independently of all the other molecules. Stated another way, each gas exerts a pressure as though it were the only gas present.

The pressure produced by the gas molecules composing air depends on (1) the mass of the molecules, and (2) the kinetic molecular activity. In the larger sense, we can think of **air pressure** at a given location on the Earth's surface as the weight per unit area of the column of air above that location. The pressure at any point within the atmosphere is equal to the weight per unit area of the atmosphere above that point. *Weight* is the force exerted by gravity on a mass, that is,

weight = (mass) × (acceleration of gravity)

The average air pressure at sea level is equivalent to the weight exerted by Earth's gravity on an area of one square cm by a mass of approximately 1.0 kg (or equivalently to 14.7 lb per square in.). A column of water about 10 m (33 ft) deep produces this same pressure at its base. Hence, the total weight of the atmosphere on the roof of a typical three-bedroom ranch-style house at sea level is about 2.1 million kg (4.6 million lb), equivalent to the combined weight of about 1500 full-size autos. Why doesn't the roof collapse? The reason is that air pressure at any point is the same in all directions (up, down, and sideways); that is, air is pushing up from under the roof with the same pressure. Air pressure within the house exactly counterbalances air pressure outside the house so that the net air pressure acting on the roof is zero. This pressure balance (or equilibrium) is a prevailing condition in the atmosphere because at any point in a gas or a mixture of gases, pressure is exerted equally in all directions.

Air Pressure Measurement

The **barometer** is the instrument used to measure air pressure and monitor its changes. The basic types are the mercury barometer and the aneroid barometer.

The more accurate, though cumbersome, of the two is the **mercury barometer**, invented in 1643 by Evangelista Torricelli (1608-1647), an Italian mathematician and student of Galileo. The instrument consists of a glass tube a little less than 1.0 m (39 in.) long, sealed at one end, open at the other end, and filled with mercury which is about 13 times denser than liquid water. The open end of the tube is inverted into a small open container of mercury, as shown in Figure 5.1. Mercury settles down the tube (and into the container) until the pressure of the mercury column exactly balances the pressure of the atmosphere acting on the surface of the mercury in the open container.

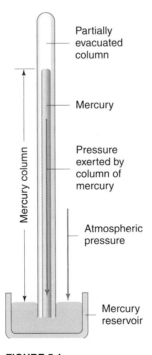

FIGURE 5.1
Schematic drawing of a mercury barometer indicating that the weight of the column of mercury is balanced by the weight of the air column.

The average air pressure at sea level will support the mercury column in the tube to a height of 760 mm (29.92 in.). The height of the mercury column changes as air pressure changes. Falling air pressure allows the mercury column to drop, whereas increasing air pressure forces the mercury column to rise with the height of the mercury column directly proportional to air pressure. This is the origin of the common practice of expressing air pressure in units of length of the mercury column. Air pressure readings by a mercury barometer require adjustments for (1) the expansion and contraction of mercury that accompanies changes in temperature, and (2) the slight variation of gravity with latitude and altitude that affect the weight of the mercury column. By convention, readings are adjusted to standard conditions of 0 °C (32 °F) and 45 degrees latitude at sea level.

An **aneroid** (nonliquid) **barometer** is more portable but less precise than a mercury barometer. It consists of a flexible chamber from which much of the air has been evacuated (Figure 5.2A). An internal spring prevents the chamber from collapsing. As air pressure changes, the chamber flexes, compressing when air pressure rises and expanding when air pressure drops. A series of gears and levers transmits these movements to a pointer on a dial, which is calibrated to read in equivalent millimeters (or inches) of mercury, or to read directly in units of air pressure (Figure 5.2B). The latest aneroid barometers provide direct digital readouts (and even have been incorporated into wristwatches). Increasingly, new aneroid barometers are *piezoelectric*, that is, they depend on the effect of air pressure on a crystalline substance. The barometric pressure sensors in the automated surface weather stations operated by the National Weather Service are digital pressure transducers.

Air pressure readings are typically taken indoors because the desire is to maintain a relatively constant temperature that is close to standard conditions. Indoor air pressure quickly adjusts to changes in outdoor air pressure. The instrument should be anchored to a sturdy wall not exposed to direct sunlight. Mercury barometers must be vertical and most aneroid barometers are designed to be read in a vertical orientation. In reading a dial-type aneroid barometer, it is a good idea to first gently tap the barometer because friction in the mechanism may cause the pointer to stick.

Aneroid barometers intended for home use typically have dials with legends, such as *fair*, *changeable*, and *stormy* corresponding to certain ranges of air pressure. These designations should not be taken literally because a

A

B

FIGURE 5.2
An aneroid barometer, a portable instrument used to monitor air pressure. Internal view (A) and external view (B). [Adapted from Snow, et al., "Basic Meteorological Observations for Schools: Atmospheric Pressure." *Bulletin of the American Meteorological Society* 73(1992):785]

FIGURE 5.3
A barograph provides a continuous trace of air pressure variations with time.

given air pressure reading does not always correspond to a specific type of weather. Much more useful than these legends for local weather forecasting is **air pressure tendency**, that is, the change in air pressure over a specific time interval, such as several hours. Rising air pressure usually means continued fair or clearing weather, whereas falling air pressure generally signals the approach of stormy weather. For determining pressure tendency, some aneroid barometers are equipped with a second pointer that serves as a reference marker. By turning the knob on the barometer face, the user sets the second pointer to correspond to the current air pressure reading. At a later time (perhaps in 2 or 3 hrs or less during changeable weather), the user can observe the new pressure reading and compare it with the earlier set reading to determine the air pressure tendency. An aneroid barometer may be linked to a pen that records on a clock-driven drum chart. This instrument, called a **barograph**, provides a continuous trace of air pressure variations with time, making it easier to determine pressure tendency (Figure 5.3).

Air Pressure Units

On television and radio weathercasts, air pressure readings are usually reported in units of length (millimeters or inches of mercury). A scientifically more appropriate practice is to express air pressure in the fundamental units of pressure. Physicists use the *pascal (Pa)* as the standard metric unit of pressure and have determined that the

TABLE 5.1
Conversion Factors for Units of Air Pressure

1 bar = 1000 millibars (mb)
1 mb = 0.02953 in. of mercury
1 inch of mercury = 33.86 mb
1 kilopascal (kPa) = 1000 pascals (Pa)
1 hectopascal (hPa) = 100 Pa
1 mb = 1 hPa
1 inch of mercury = 33.86 hPa
1 inch of mercury = 25.4 mm of mercury

average air pressure at sea level is 101,325 Pa, 1013.25 hectopascals (hPa), or 101.325 kilopascals (kPa). U.S. meteorologists, on the other hand, traditionally designate air pressure in *millibar (mb)* units, where 1 mb equals 1 hPa or 100 Pa. In turn, 1 mb is the equivalent of 0.02953 in. of mercury (Table 5.1). Average sea level air pressure is 1013.25 mb.

The usual worldwide range in sea-level air pressure is roughly 970 to 1040 mb (28.64 to 30.71 in. of mercury). The lowest sea-level air pressure ever recorded was 870 mb (25.69 in. of mercury), measured on 12 October 1979 in the eye of Typhoon Tip over the Pacific Ocean northwest of Guam. The air pressure no doubt has been lower than 870 mb in some tornadoes, but such low readings have never been confirmed directly because tornadic winds are so strong that they destroy barometers. The highest sea-level air pressure ever recorded was 1083.8 mb (32.01 in. of mercury) at Agata, Siberia on 31 December 1968 and was produced by an extremely cold, dense air mass.

Variation in Air Pressure with Altitude

We know from inflating an automobile or bicycle tire that air is compressible; that is, its volume and density are variable. The pull of gravity compresses the atmosphere so that the maximum **air density** (mass of molecules per unit volume) is at the Earth's surface. In other words, the atmosphere's gas molecules are most closely spaced at the Earth's surface, and the spacing between molecules increases with increasing altitude. The number of gas molecules per unit volume, the **number density** of air, thus decreases with altitude. Thinning of air is so rapid within the lower atmosphere that at an altitude of 6.5 km (4 mi), air density is about 50% of its average sea-level value and at 18 km (11 mi), it is about 10%.

Thinning of air with altitude is accompanied by a decline in air pressure (Figure 5.4). The French mathematician Blaise Pascal (1623-1662) was the first to propose that air pressure decreases with increasing altitude. Poor health prevented Pascal from verifying his hypothesis by actual field measurements, so he asked his brother-in-law, Florin Perier, for assistance. Perier agreed, and on 19 September 1648, Perier along with some clerics and laymen from his hometown set off with barometer in hand and climbed to the summit of Puy-de-Dôme (elevation, 1464 m or 4800 ft) in the Auvergene region of southern France. At a pre-arranged time, Pascal at the base of the mountain and Perier at the summit took barometer readings. Those readings confirmed Pascal's hypothesis of declining air pressure with altitude.

Because air is compressible, the rate of air pressure drop with altitude is not uniform; it is greatest in the lower troposphere and then becomes more gradual aloft. For example, air pressure decreases about 25% in the first 2500 m (8200 ft) of altitude, but a further ascent of 3000 m (9800 ft) is required for an additional 25% drop in air pressure. In the lower troposphere, air pressure usually drops by roughly one millibar for every 10 m of ascent. However, as we will see shortly, this rate depends on the air temperature and humidity.

FIGURE 5.4
Average variation in air pressure in millibars (mb) with altitude (km). The average air pressure at sea level is 1013.25 mb.

Vertical profiles of average air pressure (Figure 5.4) and temperature (Figure 2.12) are based on the standard atmosphere, a model of the real atmosphere which was initially used in assessing aircraft performance. The **standard atmosphere** is the state of the atmosphere averaged for all latitudes and seasons. It features a fixed sea-level air temperature (15 °C or 59 °F) and pressure (1013.25 mb) together with fixed vertical profiles of air temperature, air pressure, and air density (Table 5.2). However, the actual altitude of a specific air pressure (e.g., 500 mb) varies with time and from one place to another as the temperature and pressure vary from standard conditions. In fact, meteorologists routinely draw upper-air weather maps on which are plotted contours of elevation

TABLE 5.2
The Standard Atmosphere

Altitude (km)	Temperature (°C)	Pressure (mb)	P/P_o*	Density (kg/m³)	D/D_o*
30.00	−46.6	11.97	0.01	0.02	0.02
25.00	−51.6	25.49	0.03	0.04	0.03
20.00	−56.5	55.29	0.05	0.09	0.07
19.00	−56.5	64.67	0.06	0.10	0.08
18.00	−56.5	75.65	0.07	0.12	0.09
17.00	−56.5	88.49	0.09	0.14	0.12
16.00	−56.5	103.52	0.10	0.17	0.14
15.00	−56.5	121.11	0.12	0.20	0.16
14.00	−56.5	141.70	0.14	0.23	0.19
13.00	−56.5	165.79	0.16	0.27	0.22
12.00	−56.5	193.99	0.19	0.31	0.25
11.00	−56.4	226.99	0.22	0.37	0.30
10.00	−49.9	264.99	0.26	0.41	0.34
9.50	−46.7	285.84	0.28	0.44	0.36
9.00	−43.4	308.00	0.30	0.47	0.38
8.50	−40.2	331.54	0.33	0.50	0.40
8.00	−36.9	356.51	0.35	0.53	0.43
7.50	−33.7	382.99	0.38	0.56	0.45
7.00	−30.5	411.05	0.41	0.59	0.48
6.50	−27.2	440.75	0.43	0.62	0.50
6.00	−23.9	472.17	0.47	0.66	0.54
5.50	−20.7	505.39	0.50	0.70	0.57
5.00	−17.5	540.48	0.53	0.74	0.60
4.50	−14.2	577.52	0.57	0.78	0.63
4.00	−11.0	616.60	0.61	0.82	0.67
3.50	−7.7	657.80	0.65	0.86	0.70
3.00	−4.5	701.21	0.69	0.91	0.74
2.50	−1.2	746.91	0.74	0.96	0.78
2.00	2.0	795.01	0.78	1.01	0.82
1.50	5.3	845.59	0.83	1.06	0.86
1.00	8.5	898.76	0.89	1.11	0.91
0.50	11.8	954.61	0.94	1.17	0.95
0.00	15.0	1013.25	1.00	1.23	1.00

*P/P_o = ratio of air pressure to its sea-level value; D/D_o = ratio of air density to its sea-level value.

of an *isobaric surface*, that is, an imaginary surface where the air pressure is the same everywhere. For example, contour maps are constructed for the 300-mb, 500-mb, and 850-mb levels. Observational data for these maps are obtained primarily from radiosondes.

Although air pressure and air density drop with increasing altitude, it is impossible to specify an altitude where Earth's atmosphere definitely ends. That is, no one altitude can be clearly identified as the beginning of interplanetary space. At best, we can describe the vertical extent of the atmosphere in terms of the relative distribution of its mass with altitude. Half of the atmosphere's mass is between Earth's surface and an average altitude of about 5500 m (18,000 ft). About 99% of the atmosphere's mass is below 32 km (20 mi). Above 80 km (50 mi), that is, above the *homosphere*, the relative proportions of atmospheric gases change markedly, and by about 1000 km (620 mi), the atmosphere merges with the highly rarefied interplanetary gases, mainly hydrogen and helium.

If Earth's atmosphere had a uniform density throughout (a *homogeneous atmosphere*), it would have a well-defined top. Assuming a surface temperature of 0 °C (32 °F), a homogeneous atmosphere would have a thickness of only about 8000 m (26,000 ft). In such an atmosphere, the temperature would drop with altitude at a rate of 34 Celsius degrees per 1000 m, the *autoconvective lapse rate*. In the real atmosphere, an autoconvective lapse rate is possible in a thin layer of air overlying the intensely hot surface of a desert.

From a somewhat different perspective, at an altitude of only 32 km (20 mi), air pressure is less than 1% of its average sea-level value. The rapid vertical pressure drop in the lower reaches of the atmosphere means that appreciable variations in surface air pressure accompany relatively minor changes in land elevation. For example, the average air pressure at Denver, the *mile-high city*, is about 83% of the average air pressure at Boston, located just above sea level. As noted in this chapter's Case-in-Point, the expansion and thinning of air that accompany the fall in air pressure with altitude can cause discomfort and even serious illness for visitors to high altitudes. For more on this topic, refer to this chapter's first Essay, Human Responses to Changes in Air Pressure.

Very low air density at high altitudes also has interesting implications for air temperature and heat transfer. In the thermosphere, the highest thermal subdivision of the atmosphere (Figure 2.12), individual atoms and molecules move about with average kinetic energy indicative of very high temperatures. There are so few atoms and molecules per unit volume, however, that very little heat is transferred. In spite of temperatures that approach 1200 °C (2200 °F) in the thermosphere, heat is not readily conducted to cooler bodies. For example, satellites orbiting at these altitudes do not acquire such temperatures.

Because air pressure drops with increasing altitude at rates that can be readily determined, an aneroid barometer can be calibrated to monitor altitude. Such an instrument is a type of **altimeter**. For more on this, see this chapter's second Essay, Determining Altitude from Air Pressure.

Horizontal Variations in Air Pressure

Air pressure differs from one place to another, and these variations are not always due to differences in the elevation of the land. In fact, meteorologists are more interested in air pressure variations that arise from influences other than land elevation. Hence, weather observers determine an equivalent sea-level air pressure value; that is, for stations located above sea level, they adjust local air pressure readings to approximately what the air pressure would be if the station were actually located at sea level. The simplest adjustment assumes an imaginary column of air having the properties of the standard atmosphere extending from the station down to sea level. When this *reduction to sea level* is carried out everywhere, air pressure is observed to vary from one place to another (Figure 5.5) and fluctuate from day to day and even from hour to hour (Figure 5.6).

Air pressure readings, reduced to sea level, range in value from one place to another, but the magnitude of this variation is much less than the rate at which air pressure drops with altitude. Except in tornadoes or intense hurricanes, the horizontal pressure gradient at sea level rarely exceeds 3 mb per 200 km (125 mi), which is equivalent to the vertical change in air pressure experienced in the lowest 30 m (100 ft) of the troposphere. Nonetheless, these relatively small horizontal changes in air pressure can be accompanied by significant changes in weather.

In middle latitudes, a continuous procession of different air masses brings about changes in air pressure and weather. Recall that an *air mass* is a huge volume of air that is relatively uniform horizontally in temperature and water vapor concentration. As air masses move from place to place, surface air pressures fall or rise, and the weather changes. As a general rule, the weather becomes stormy when air pressure falls but clears or remains fair when air pressure rises.

FIGURE 5.5

A surface weather map shows spatial variations in air pressure (reduced to sea level). Dark lines are isobars (in mb) passing through localities having the same air pressure. *L* is plotted where air pressure is relatively low and *H* is plotted where air pressure is relatively high.

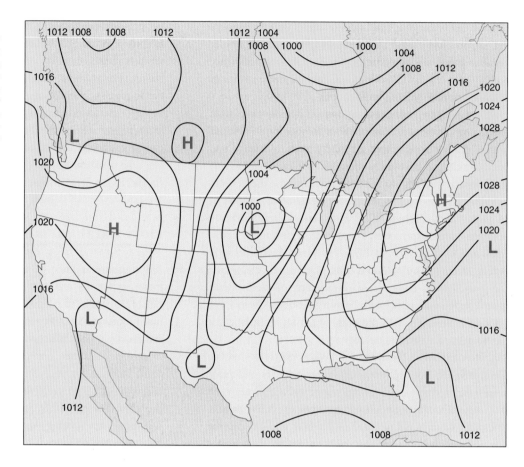

FIGURE 5.6

A trace from a barograph showing the variation in air pressure in millibars reduced to sea level at Green Bay, Wisconsin, from 30 March through 4 April 1982. During the period from 2 to 3 April, Green Bay was under the influence of a very intense low pressure system. Note that significant changes in air pressure occur from day to day and even from one hour to the next.

M = midnight on scale at top of record; time lines are in 2 hour increments

Why do some air masses exert greater pressure than other air masses? One reason is the contrast in air density that arises from differences in air temperature or water vapor concentration. As a rule, temperature has a much more important influence on air density and pressure than does water vapor concentration. Also, converging or diverging winds may bring about a change in air pressure as air either accumulates or is removed from a column of air.

INFLUENCE OF TEMPERATURE AND HUMIDITY

Recall from Chapter 4 that temperature is a measure of the average kinetic energy of individual molecules. Rising air temperature corresponds to an increase in average kinetic molecular activity. If air is heated within a closed container, such as a rigid metal can, we would expect the air pressure acting on the internal walls of the container to rise as the increasingly energetic molecules bombard the walls with greater force. Here we are considering pressure as the force exerted by the molecules colliding with a unit surface area of the container's walls. The air density inside the container does not change because no air is added to or removed from the container and the air volume is constant. By contrast, except for Earth's surface, walls do not confine the atmosphere, so air is free to expand and contract. That is, in the atmosphere, air density is variable.

Within the atmosphere, when air is heated (e.g., by absorption of radiation, conduction, convection, or phase changes of water), air density usually decreases because the greater activity of the heated molecules increases the spacing between neighboring molecules (Figure 5.7). As a column of air is heated, decreasing numbers of molecules exist per unit volume; that is, air density decreases. The lower total mass in the column will then exert less pressure on Earth's surface.

The greater density of cold air versus warm air at the same pressure affects the rate at which air pressure drops with increasing altitude. Air pressure drops more rapidly with altitude within a cold (denser) column of air than in a warm (less dense) column of air. Beginning with equal pressures at Earth's surface, equivalent pressure surfaces (e.g., the 500-mb level) occur at a lower altitude in a cold column of air than in a warm column of air. Within the troposphere, isobaric surfaces (surfaces of constant pressure) slope downward from the relatively warm tropics toward relatively cold high latitudes. As noted in this chapter's second Essay, the sloping of isobaric surfaces has important implications for altimetry.

Increasing humidity affects air density in the same way as rising air temperature; that is, the greater the concentration of water vapor, the less dense is the air. This statement is contrary to the popular perception that humid air feels "heavier" than dry air. Although hot, muggy air may weigh heavily on a person's disposition, humid air is, in fact, less dense than dry air at the same temperature and pressure. Water vapor reduces the density of air because the molecular weight of water is less than the average molecular weight of dry air.

Equal volumes of all gases (or mixtures of gases) measured under the same conditions of temperature and pressure contain the same number of molecules. This is **Avogadro's law**, first stated in 1811 by the Italian chemist Amedeo Avogadro (1776-1856). Avogadro's law implies that when water molecules enter the atmosphere as a vapor while the temperature and pressure of the air remains constant, they displace other gas molecules, principally nitrogen and oxygen. The molecular weight of water (H_2O) is 18 atomic mass units whereas the mass-weighted mean molecular weight of dry air (mostly N_2 and O_2) is about 29 atomic

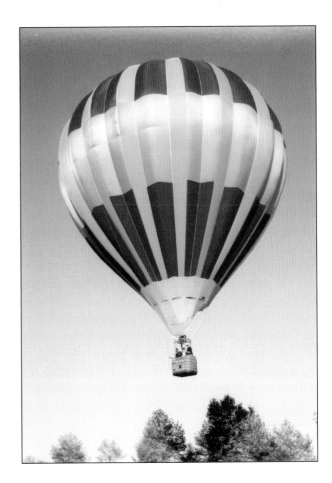

FIGURE 5.7
A hot air balloon ascends within the atmosphere because heated air within the balloon is less dense than the cooler air surrounding the balloon.

mass units. With all other factors equal, as the water vapor concentration in air increases (perhaps as the consequence of evaporation of water from Earth's surface), the net effect is for air density to decrease. For equal volumes at the same temperature, then, a column of humid air exerts less pressure than a column of relatively dry air.

Cold, dry air masses are denser and usually produce higher surface pressures than warm, humid air masses. Warm, dry air masses, in turn, often exert higher surface pressures than equally warm, but more humid, air masses. Hence, a change in surface air pressure usually accompanies the replacement of one air mass by another of different temperatures, that is, by *cold air advection* or *warm air advection*. *Air mass modification* (changes in air mass temperature and/or water vapor concentration) also can produce changes in surface air pressure. These modifications may occur when an air mass travels over a different surface type (e.g., from cold snow cover to mild bare ground) or, if the air mass is stationary, when the air is locally heated or cooled. In Chapter 4, we examined the regulation of air temperature by the local radiation budget plus air mass advection. The above discussion implies that local conditions and air mass advection can also influence surface air pressure.

INFLUENCE OF DIVERGING AND CONVERGING WINDS

In addition to variations in air temperature and (to a lesser extent) humidity, convergence or divergence of winds may also bring about changes in surface air pressure. Convergence or divergence is produced by a circulation pattern in which (1) horizontal winds blow toward or away from some location, or (2) wind speed changes in a downstream direction. We consider the first mechanism here and the second in Chapter 8.

Suppose that at Earth's surface, horizontal winds blow away from a column of air in all directions, as in Figure 5.8. This is an example of **diverging winds**. At the same time, horizontal winds aloft blow toward the air column; this is an example of **converging winds**. Within the air column, air descends from above and takes the place of air diverging at the surface. If more air diverges at the surface than converges aloft, the amount of air in the column decreases and the air density and surface air pressure decrease. On the other hand, if more air converges aloft than diverges at the surface, the amount of air in the column increases and the density of the air column and surface air pressure increase. In later chapters, we discuss in greater detail how divergence and convergence of air cause air pressure changes within weather systems.

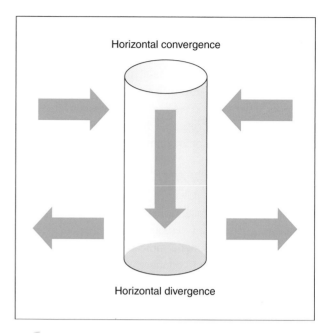

FIGURE 5.8
In this vertical cross section through the troposphere, horizontal winds diverging at the surface and converging aloft induce descending air motion.

Highs and Lows

We now have more insight into the meaning of those H (or High) and L (or Low) symbols plotted on surface weather maps (Figure 5.5). To locate Highs and Lows, a map is drawn to reveal the pattern of surface air pressure. First, simultaneous air pressure readings at all weather stations are adjusted to sea level, plotted on a weather map, and then isobars are drawn. An **isobar** is a line passing through locations having the same air pressure. Drawing isobars usually requires interpolation between reporting weather stations. By U.S. convention, isobars are drawn at 4-mb intervals (e.g., 996 mb, 1000 mb, 1004 mb) whereas in Europe the convention is to use 5-mb intervals.

A High or H symbol is used to designate places where sea-level air pressure is relatively high compared to the air pressure in surrounding areas. A High is also known as an *anticyclone*. A Low or L symbol signifies regions where sea-level air pressure is relatively low compared to surrounding areas. A Low is also known as a *cyclone*. For reasons presented in Chapter 8, usually a High is a fair weather system, and a Low is a stormy weather system. Viewed from above in the Northern Hemisphere, surface winds blow clockwise and diverge outward from the center of a High. Viewed from above in the Northern Hemisphere, surface winds blow counterclockwise and converge inward about the center of a Low. Winds are strong where isobars are closely spaced because of greater horizontal pressure differences, but are weak where isobars are widely spaced as the horizontal pressure differences are less. Isobars generally are more closely spaced near the center of a Low than near the center of a High.

The Gas Law

To this point, we have described the state of the atmosphere in terms of variations in temperature, pressure, and density. These important properties are known collectively as **variables of state**; their magnitudes change from one place to another across Earth's surface, with altitude above Earth's surface, and with time.

At typical temperatures and pressures encountered at sea level, the number density of a dry clean air is approximately 25 billion molecules per cubic centimeter. Equivalently, the mass density of dry clean air at mean sea level is approximately 1.29 kg per cubic meter (0.1 lb per cubic ft). As we saw in Chapter 4, the temperature of a substance is related to the average kinetic energy of the molecules. The kinetic energy is a function of both the mass and the speed of the moving object. At sea level, under normal temperatures and pressure, an average air molecule moves at an average speed of approximately 460 m per second (about 1000 mi per hr).

The three variables of state are interrelated through the **gas law**. Although the gas law was derived for a single ideal gas, the law provides a reasonably accurate description of the behavior of air, which is a mixture of many different gases. By definition, an **ideal gas** follows the *kinetic molecular theory* precisely. That is, an ideal gas is made up of a very large number of molecules that are in rapid and random motion. As they move about molecules experience perfectly elastic collisions, so they lose no momentum. Furthermore, molecules are so small that the attractive forces between them are negligible.

An ideal gas follows Charles' law and Boyle's law exactly, whereas a real gas behaves only approximately as these laws dictate. Named for the French scientist Jacques Charles (1746-1823), **Charles' law** holds that with constant pressure, the absolute temperature (in kelvins) of an ideal gas is inversely proportional to the density of the gas. As a sample of gas is heated, the gas expands and its density decreases. According to **Boyle's law**, named for the Irish physicist and chemist Robert Boyle (1627-91), when the temperature is held constant, the pressure and density of an ideal gas are directly proportional. As the pressure on an ideal gas increases, its volume decreases and its density increases. Charles' law and Boyle's law are combined as the *ideal gas law*.

Simply put, the ideal gas law states that the pressure exerted by a gas is directly proportional to the product of its density and temperature (expressed in kelvins). As a word equation, the ideal gas law becomes

pressure = (gas constant) × (density) × (temperature)

The *gas constant* is an experimentally derived number that converts a proportional relationship to an equation. The constant of proportionality varies depending on the specific gas. By specifying a certain value for the constant, this law describes approximately the behavior of dry air (air minus water vapor). With an additional adjustment, the gas law represents the behavior of the variables of state for humid air as long as no condensation or deposition takes place.

From the gas law equation, the following holds:

1. The density of air within a rigid closed container remains constant because the volume of the container and the mass of its contents are fixed. An increase in pressure exerted by the gas molecules on the interior walls of the container accompanies a rise in the temperature of the gas as the molecular speed increases. Hence, according to the gas law, the pressure and temperature are directly proportional at fixed density.

2. Consider an **air parcel**, an arbitrary amount of air useful for visualizing atmospheric processes, containing a fixed number of molecules. Its volume can change, but its mass remains the same meaning that the density changes. If the temperature is held constant, compressing the air parcel causes its density to increase because its volume decreases (while its mass remains constant). Hence, at a fixed temperature, pressure is directly proportional to density.

3. For the same air parcel at constant pressure, a rise in temperature is accompanied by a decrease in density. The density decreases because the more energetic molecules cause the parcel to expand, that is, its volume increases while its mass remains constant. Hence, at a fixed pressure, temperature is inversely proportional to density.

In the atmosphere, however, the situation is more complicated because all three variables of state may change simultaneously. Hence, as the air temperature rises (perhaps in response to radiational heating), air expands, air density decreases, and air pressure at the Earth's surface falls. On the other hand, in winter, it is usual for air temperature to drop (not rise) as the surface air pressure rises. The gas law is satisfied in the atmosphere because air density increases as the temperature drops.

Expansional Cooling and Compressional Warming

In this section, we explore how the variables of state respond when an air parcel moves vertically (up or down) within the atmosphere and experiences a change in pressure. As noted earlier in this chapter, air pressure decreases with increasing altitude within the atmosphere. One of the important consequences of the decline of atmospheric pressure with altitude is the expansion or compression of air parcels as they move up or down. As an air parcel ascends and expands, its temperature drops and as an air parcel descends and is compressed, its temperature rises. As discussed in Chapter 6, expansional cooling and compressional warming are major factors in the development and dissipation of clouds.

Whenever a gas (or mixture of gases) expands, the temperature of the gas drops; this process is known as **expansional cooling**. Expansional cooling explains why air released through the open valve of a bicycle tire is cool to the touch. Air pressure within the tire (perhaps 60 lb per square in.) is as much as four times greater than the atmospheric pressure outside the tire (around 14 lb per square in.) Air streaming through an open tire valve into the atmosphere does work as it pushes aside air that formerly occupied the volume into which it expands. Work requires energy, and the energy used in the work of expansion is drawn from the internal energy of the air so the temperature of the expanding air drops. Air that ascends within the atmosphere also undergoes expansional cooling in response to falling air pressure. As an air parcel ascends in the atmosphere, it expands in the same way as a helium-filled balloon does as it drifts skyward. Assuming that the parcel does not exchange heat with its environment, changes in volume translate into changes in the parcel's temperature. A rising air parcel expands due to lower pressure aloft and its temperature drops.

Conversely, as the pressure on an air parcel increases, the air parcel is compressed and its temperature rises, a process known as **compressional warming**. A familiar example is the warming of the cylinder wall of a tire pump as air is pumped (compressed) into a tire. The

work of compressing air is converted into heat. As an air parcel descends within the atmosphere, it is compressed because of higher pressure below and its temperature rises.

In a more general sense, imagine that upward or downward currents of air consist of continuous streams of individual air parcels. The temperature behavior of an air current is the same as that of its component air parcels. In summary, ascending currents of air (such as the updraft in a convective circulation) cool whereas descending currents of air (such as the downdraft in a convective circulation) warm.

CONSERVATION OF ENERGY

The *law of energy conservation* (also known as the *first law of thermodynamics*) applies to expansional cooling and compressional warming of air parcels moving vertically in the atmosphere. According to this law, we can account for all the original energy in any physical or biological system regardless of the energy transformations that take place. Heat energy gained by an air parcel is either added to the parcel's store of internal energy or is used to do work on the parcel. Conversely, heat energy that is released by an air parcel is either subtracted from the internal energy of the parcel or is the consequence of the parcel's work on its surroundings.

We explore this concept further by examining separately (1) internal energy and (2) work done on or by an air parcel. As noted in Chapter 4, *internal energy* encompasses all the energy in a substance, that is, the kinetic energy of atoms and molecules plus the potential energy arising from forces between atoms and molecules. A change in internal energy of an air parcel is directly proportional to a change in temperature of the parcel (with the specific heat being the constant of proportionality). A transfer of heat to the parcel raises its temperature whereas a transfer of heat from the parcel lowers its temperature.

Work done on or by an air parcel consists of compression or expansion of the air parcel. Consider, for example, a sealed cylindrical container of air equipped at one end with a piston that can compress the air sample or allow the air sample to expand. If we move the piston to compress the air, we use energy to do work on the air sample. If we then release the piston, the air sample expands and works against (pushes) the piston. When the air is compressed, work is done on it but when the air expands, the air does work on its surroundings. Energy is either supplied (during compression) or released (during expansion). Hence, according to the law of energy conservation, the heat flow into and out of an air parcel is accounted for by changes in internal energy (temperature), the work of expansion or compression of air, or both.

ADIABATIC PROCESS

With our application of the law of energy conservation to air parcels moving vertically within the atmosphere, we can now turn to the adiabatic assumption. During an **adiabatic process**, no heat is exchanged between an air parcel and its surroundings. That is, while ascending or descending within the atmosphere, an air parcel is neither heated nor cooled by radiation, conduction, phase changes of water, or mixing with the environment. The temperature of an ascending or descending unsaturated air parcel changes in response to expansion or compression only.

Adiabatic cooling of ascending unsaturated air amounts to 9.8 Celsius degrees per 1000 m (5.5 Fahrenheit degrees per 1000 ft) of ascent. This is the **dry adiabatic lapse rate** (Figure 5.9). The dry designation can be misleading because ascending and descending air parcels contain some water vapor. The dry adiabatic lapse rate applies to any parcel that is not saturated with water vapor (because no condensation or evaporation can take place during an adiabatic process). On the other hand,

the atmosphere compresses descending air, and the air temperature rises 9.8 Celsius degrees for every 1000 m (5.5 Fahrenheit degrees per 1000 ft) of descent. Thus, the dry adiabatic lapse rate describes the temperature change of unsaturated air as it moves vertically (up or down) within the atmosphere.

Should rising air parcels cool to the point that the relative humidity nears 100% (saturation) and condensation or deposition takes place, the ascending air no longer cools at the dry adiabatic rate (Figure 5.10). Latent heat that is released to the environment during condensation or deposition *partially* counters expansional cooling. Consequently, an ascending saturated (cloudy) air parcel cools more slowly than an ascending unsaturated (clear) air parcel. Rising saturated air parcels cool at the **moist adiabatic lapse rate**.

Although the magnitude of the dry adiabatic lapse rate is constant, the moist adiabatic lapse rate varies with temperature. Warm saturated air has more water vapor than cool saturated air. For the same temperature change, the greater condensation or deposition in warm saturated air releases more latent heat than condensation or deposition in cool saturated air. The greater the quantity of latent heat released, the more the expansional cooling is offset, and

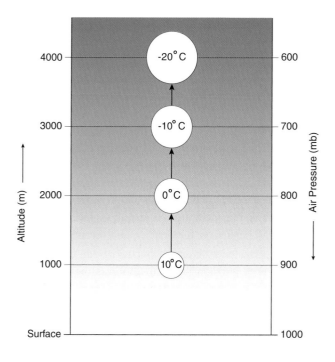

FIGURE 5.9
The dry adiabatic lapse rate describes the expansional cooling of ascending unsaturated (clear) air parcels. Here, the magnitude of the dry adiabatic lapse rate is rounded off to 10 Celsius degrees per 1000 m.

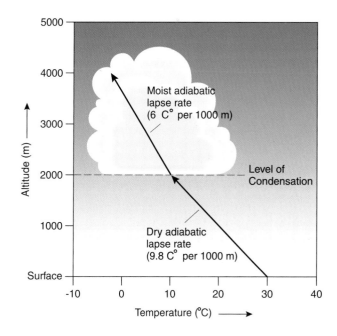

FIGURE 5.10
Ascending unsaturated (clear) air parcels cool at the dry adiabatic lapse rate whereas ascending saturated (cloudy) air parcels cool at the smaller moist adiabatic lapse rate.

the smaller is the magnitude of the moist adiabatic lapse rate. The moist adiabatic lapse rate ranges from about 4 Celsius degrees per 1000 m (2.2 Fahrenheit degrees per 1000 ft) for very warm saturated air to very near 9.8 Celsius degrees per 1000 m (5.5 Fahrenheit degrees per 1000 ft) for very cold saturated air. For convenience, we use an average value of 6 Celsius degrees per 1000 m (3.3 Fahrenheit degrees per 1000 ft) for the moist adiabatic lapse rate.

Conclusions

We now have a working definition of air pressure, and we have examined the causes of spatial and temporal variations in air pressure within the Earth-atmosphere system. Air pressure drops rapidly with altitude in the lower troposphere and then more gradually aloft. At great altitudes, the atmosphere gradually merges with the gases of interplanetary space so that the atmosphere has no clearly defined top. Adjusting a station's barometer readings to sea level eliminates the influence of weather station elevation on air pressure. Then, surface air pressure depends on air density, which in turn, is governed by air temperature and, to a lesser extent, by the concentration of water vapor in air. Diverging or converging winds may also affect air density and surface air pressure.

The range of air temperature and air pressure in the Earth-atmosphere system allows water to exist in all three phases. In Chapter 4, we saw how phase changes of water help transfer heat energy within the Earth-atmosphere system (latent heating). Changes in air temperature also trigger the phase changes of water that cause clouds to form or to dissipate. In the next chapter, we take a closer look at water within the atmosphere with emphasis on cloud-forming processes.

Basic Understandings

- The pressure (force per unit area) exerted by the atmosphere depends on the pull of gravity along with the mass and kinetic energy of the gas molecules that compose air. We can think of air pressure as the weight of a column of air acting on a unit area of Earth's surface. The air pressure at any specified altitude is equal to the weight per unit area of the air column above that altitude.

- At any specified point within the atmosphere, air pressure has the same magnitude in all directions.

- A barometer is the weather instrument that monitors changes in air pressure. A mercury barometer is more accurate but far less portable than an aneroid barometer. The aneroid barometer can be calibrated to measure altitude.

- Air pressure and air density decrease rapidly with increasing altitude in the lower atmosphere and then more gradually aloft. The atmosphere has no clearly defined upper boundary; rather, Earth's atmosphere gradually merges with the highly rarefied hydrogen/helium atmosphere of interplanetary space. About 50% of the mass of the atmosphere occurs below an altitude of 5.5 km (3.5 mi), and 99% below an altitude of 32 km (20 mi).

- Barometer readings are adjusted to sea level to permit a comparison of all simultaneous air pressure readings at the same elevation, that is, to remove the influence of station elevation on air pressure.

- Within the atmosphere, at constant pressure, air density is inversely proportional to air temperature. Hence, all other factors being equal, cold air masses are denser and exert higher pressure at Earth's surface than do warm air masses.

- Air pressure drops more rapidly with altitude in a column of cold air than in a column of warm air. Hence, an isobaric surface (e.g., the 500-mb level) usually slopes downward toward colder air.

- Within the atmosphere, air density is also inversely proportional to water vapor concentration. Hence, at equivalent temperatures, dry air masses are denser than humid air masses. As a rule, temperature has a much more significant influence on air density and air pressure than does humidity.

- Air pressure may fluctuate in response to divergence or convergence of air, which is produced by changes in wind speed or direction.

- Important changes in weather often accompany relatively small changes in air pressure at Earth's surface. As a rule, high or rising pressure signals clearing or continued fair weather, whereas low or falling pressure means stormy weather.

- Variables of state of the atmosphere (temperature, pressure, and density) are related through the gas law. Although the gas law was derived for a single ideal gas, the law provides a reasonably accurate description of the behavior of air, which is a mixture of many different gases. By definition, an ideal gas follows the *kinetic molecular theory* precisely.

- Charles' law holds that with constant pressure, the absolute temperature of an ideal gas is inversely proportional to the density of the gas. As a sample of gas is heated, the gas expands and its density decreases. According to Boyle's law, when the temperature is held constant, the pressure and density of an ideal gas are directly proportional. As the pressure on an ideal gas increases, its volume decreases and its density increases. Charles' law and Boyle's law are combined as the *ideal gas law*.

- Air pressure always declines with increasing altitude. Hence, as air ascends in the atmosphere, it expands and cools. Conversely, as air descends in the atmosphere, it is compressed and warms.

- The law of energy conservation applies to expansional cooling and compressional warming of air moving vertically in the atmosphere. Heat energy gained by an air parcel is either added to the parcel's store of internal energy or is used to do work on the parcel. Conversely, heat energy that is released by an air parcel is either subtracted from the internal energy of the parcel or is the consequence of the parcel's work on its surroundings.

- During an adiabatic process, no heat is exchanged between an air parcel and its environment. Adiabatic cooling of ascending unsaturated air amounts to 9.8 Celsius degrees per 1000 m (5.5 Fahrenheit degrees per 1000 ft) of ascent. This is the dry adiabatic lapse rate. Because of the release of latent heat accompanying phase changes of water vapor, an ascending saturated (cloudy) air parcel cools more slowly than an ascending unsaturated (clear) air parcel. Rising saturated air parcels cool at the moist adiabatic lapse rate averaging 6 Celsius degrees per 1000 m (3.3 Fahrenheit degrees per 1000 ft).

Review

1. Define air pressure.
2. Explain why air density is greatest at Earth's surface.
3. Does the atmosphere have a clearly defined top? Explain your answer.
4. How does air temperature influence the pressure exerted by a column of air on Earth's surface?
5. Describe how a mercury barometer works and explain how the height of the mercury column is a measure of air pressure.
6. At the same temperature, a humid air mass exerts less pressure than a dry air mass. Explain why.
7. In general terms, how does the weather change as air pressure at Earth's surface rises and falls?
8. Why is a barometer adaptable for use as an altimeter?
9. On a particularly hot and humid evening, a sportscaster comments that baseballs hit to the outfield will not carry far in the "heavy" air. How valid is this observation?
10. Explain how horizontal winds converging to and diverging from a column of air can bring about changes in the pressure exerted on the Earth's surface by the column.

Critical Thinking

1. If water is used instead of mercury in a glass-tube barometer, what is the required height for the tube? The density of mercury (Hg) is 13.6 g/cm^3 and the density of water is 1.0 g/cm^3.
2. A jet aircraft is cruising at the 400-mb level, that is, at the altitude where air pressure is 400 mb. What fraction of the atmosphere's mass is below the aircraft?
3. Design an experiment demonstrating that, at equal temperatures, relatively dry air exerts more pressure than relatively humid air?
4. What is an *ideal gas*? What assumptions are made in applying the gas law to the atmosphere?
5. With the same internal temperature would a hot air balloon rise faster through a layer of relatively cold air or a layer of relatively warm air? Explain your choice.
6. Why is it not necessary to mount a barometer outdoors in order to obtain an accurate measure of air pressure?
7. List the advantages and disadvantages of an aneroid barometer versus a mercury barometer for determining elevation above sea level.
8. Use the "standard atmosphere" to predict the actual air pressure at your location's elevation above sea level assuming that the air pressure at sea level is 1013.25 mb.
9. On a typical winter day, the air pressure drops more rapidly with increasing altitude over Minneapolis than over New Orleans. Explain why.
10. In general, how would you expect the altitude of the 500-mb surface to vary from south to north across North America during February? Justify your response.

ESSAY: Human Responses to Changes in Air Pressure

Visitors to mountain elevations above about 2500 m (8000 ft) may develop symptoms of *mountain sickness*: headache, shortness of breath, fatigue, insomnia, and nausea. Such illness is not uncommon—perhaps one of every four people who ascend to high elevations experiences one or more of these distressing symptoms. Some people who spend more than 36 to 72 hrs at elevations greater than about 2800 m (9000 ft) develop *high-altitude pulmonary edema*. Symptoms of this potentially life-threatening condition are somewhat similar to those of pneumonia, that is, severe cough, shortness of breath, lethargy, mild fever, and a buildup of fluid (edema) in the lungs. Onset of high-altitude pulmonary edema requires prompt medical attention.

Breathing air that does not supply adequate oxygen (O_2) can bring on altitude sickness. Thinning of air that accompanies the fall in air pressure with altitude also means a rapid decrease in the *number density* of the atmosphere's principal gases; that is, a decline in the number of nitrogen (N_2) and oxygen (O_2) molecules per unit volume of air. At altitudes of 2450 m to 2750 m (8000 ft to 10,000 ft), oxygen's number density is only about 71% to 74% of its value at sea level. Less oxygen per unit volume of air may lead to *hypoxia,* a deficiency of oxygen in the body. Symptoms of mild hypoxia are commonly known as mountain sickness, whereas symptoms of more severe (acute) hypoxia constitute high altitude pulmonary edema.

As a person ascends to high altitudes, the body attempts to compensate for the decline in O_2 by altering breathing. The breathing rate accelerates and breathing becomes deeper to increase the amount of oxygen entering the lungs per unit time. Accelerated and deeper breathing provides no relief from hypoxia unless adequate oxygen delivered to the lungs is quickly transported to body tissues. Hence, the heart rate and stroke volume (the quantity of blood pumped out of the heart during each contraction) also increase. Although the quantity of oxygen per unit volume of blood remains essentially constant, the heart propels more blood (and hence, more oxygen) per unit time to body tissue.

The easiest way to alleviate acute mountain sickness is to descend to and remain at a lower altitude, especially at night. The altitude at which a person sleeps is more important than the altitude reached during the day. If a person remains at a high altitude, emergency adjustments by the heart and the muscles that control breathing reduce the symptoms of hypoxia while other longer-term changes take place in the body. Symptoms of acute mountain sickness gradually subside after several days as additional hemoglobin (molecules that pick up oxygen from air in the lungs) and red blood cells (cells that transport hemoglobin molecules in the bloodstream) are manufactured in the bone marrow. Although increased cardiac output generally tapers off within a week or so, accelerated breathing persists as long as a person remains at high altitude. The body thus adjusts to low oxygen levels that otherwise could cause serious health problems; this is an example of *acclimatization.*

A person can hasten acclimatization to high altitudes. Although a person may be eager to put in a full day of skiing or backpacking upon arrival in the mountains, he or she is well advised to minimize physical activity the first day or two. Here the old adage *the impatient becomes the patient* applies. Overexertion often results in more severe and persistent symptoms. Because alcohol aggravates mountain sickness, its use should be avoided, particularly during the first 48 hours at high altitudes.

Some people are better able to acclimatize than others because of differences in their genetic makeup and general health. Nonetheless, there is a limit to acclimatization. Long-term residence at high altitude cannot fully restore the body's capacity to perform work at the level that is possible at sea level. At altitudes above about 5200 m (17,000 ft), without supplementary oxygen, nothing can be done to prevent a continual decline in all bodily functions. Hence, as described in this chapter's Case-in-Point, the summit of Mount Everest, which at 8850 m (29,035 ft) is the world's highest peak, is very close to (if not beyond) the limits of human survival.

Symptoms of hypoxia become more severe as the air thins; hence, an aircraft cabin must be pressurized at altitudes above 4600 m (15,000 ft) unless a supplemental oxygen supply is available to the flight crew and passengers. In actual practice, commercial aircraft cabins are pressurized beginning at takeoff and remain pressurized throughout the flight. A cabin is typically pressurized to about 75% of average sea-level air pressure. Although the aircraft cabin is pressurized, people commonly feel the effects of changing air pressure in a rapidly ascending or descending aircraft by a popping sensation in their ears. Rapid ascent or descent in an elevator or in a car on mountain roads of the UN Environmental Programme, reported that about 60% of cloud forests are in Asia (mostly in Indonesia and Papua New Guinea), 25% in Central and South America (from Honduras, Panama, and Costa Rica to as far south as northern Argentina), and the remaining 15% in Africa. They are also found at lower elevations (as low as 500 m or 1600 ft) on humid portions of Caribbean and Hawaiian Islands. Worldwide, based on satellite monitoring, cloud forests cover about 380,000 square km (147,000 square miles).

The prevailing onshore and upslope flow of warm, humid air is responsible for the low clouds, fog, and mist that characterize cloud forests. The air is initially unsaturated but in flowing up the mountain slopes, it expands and cools. Expansional cooling raises the relative humidity to saturation (100%) and water vapor condenses into low clouds and fog. By trapping tiny cloud droplets and promoting their coalescence into larger drops, the tree canopy strips moisture from the windblown clouds and this water drips to the forest floor. The volume of water provided in this way is equivalent to 20% to 60% of the local rainfall. Hence, the cloud forest is a steady source of water for mountain streams that in turn supply water to downstream cities and towns. Persistent cloud cover also shapes the cloud forest environment by reducing incoming solar radiation and suppressing evapotranspiration (the combination of direct evaporation and transpiration by plants.) Cloud forests provide unique habitats for lichens, tree firns, orchids, and numerous species of birds and mammals.

Clearing forests reduces the amount of available moisture and raises the air temperature. Clouds form less readily and those that do form do so at higher elevations. Satellite imagery of the Monteverde cloud forest of Costa Rica shows considerably more cloudiness over forested highlands than over deforested lowlands.

If global climate change translates into higher sea surface temperatures (SST) in the tropics, the cloud forests could be affected. Higher SST would have two opposing impacts on the properties of the air flowing onshore and upslope. For one, the air would be warmer so that greater ascent (i.e., more expansional cooling) would be required to produce clouds. Clouds would form at higher elevations and perhaps lift off some mountaintops entirely. The original cloud forest would become drier, dramatically altering plant and animal habitats. However, higher SST would also increase the rate of evaporation of ocean water and result in a more humid onshore and upslope airflow. More humid air would condense into clouds at lower elevations. Using a numerical climate model to simulate the effects of higher SST on tropical airflow, Stephen Schneider and his colleagues at Stanford University concluded that higher air temperatures would be the more important factor in controlling the elevation of cloud forests. Cloud forests appear to be particularly sensitive to climate and may be among the early indicators of the environmental effects of global climate change.

Driving Question:
How does the cycling of water in the Earth-atmosphere system help maintain a habitable planet?

Water occurs in all three phases in the atmosphere: as water vapor (an invisible gas) and as aggregates of tiny ice crystals and water droplets, visible as clouds. The total amount of water in the atmosphere is relatively small and most of that is confined to the lower portion of the troposphere. If all the water vapor were removed from the atmosphere as rain and distributed uniformly over the globe, this water would cover Earth's surface to a depth of only about 2.5 cm (1.0 in.). Water continually cycles into the atmosphere as vapor from reservoirs of water at the Earth's surface (e.g., ocean, lakes, soil, vegetation) while water continually leaves the atmosphere, returning to Earth's surface as rain, snow, and other forms of

precipitation. On average, the residence time of a water molecule is about 10 days in the atmosphere and on the order of hours in a cloud. This cycling is an essential component of the global water cycle.

In this chapter, we consider how the global water cycle functions, particularly as it relates to the transfer of water between Earth's surface and atmosphere. We learn how to quantify the water vapor component of air, how air becomes saturated through uplift and expansional cooling, and how atmospheric stability influences the ascent of air. All this is important because as air nears saturation, cloud development becomes more and more likely and clouds are prerequisites to precipitation.

CHAPTER 6

HUMIDITY, SATURATION, AND STABILITY

Early morning fog on a southern lake. [Courtesy NOAA]

Case in Point

About 2.5% of the world's tropical forests are perpetually shrouded in clouds and mist. These so-called **cloud forests** are an important source of clean fresh water for millions of people living in surrounding lowlands and are home to thousands of rare plants and animals, most of which have yet to be studied by scientists. However, pressure from land developers (i.e., clearing forests for cattle grazing, coca plantations, logging, and mining), perhaps exacerbated by climate change, make cloud forests one of the world's most threatened ecosystems. So far efforts by conservationists to halt the loss of cloud forests by establishing nature reserves have had little success.

Cloud forests are confined to mountainous areas of the tropics and subtropics generally at elevations from 2000 to 3000 m (6500 to 9800 ft) above sea level. In 2004, the World Conservation Monitoring Centre, a component of the UN Environmental Programme, reported that about 60% of cloud forests are in Asia (mostly in Indonesia and Papua New Guinea), 25% in Central and South America (from Honduras, Panama, and Costa Rica to as far south as northern Argentina), and the remaining 15% in Africa. They are also found at lower elevations (as low as 500 m or 1600 ft) on humid portions of Caribbean and Hawaiian Islands. Worldwide, based on satellite monitoring, cloud forests cover about 380,000 square km (147,000 square miles).

The prevailing onshore and upslope flow of warm, humid air is responsible for the low clouds, fog, and mist that characterize cloud forests. The air is initially unsaturated but in flowing up the mountain slopes, it expands and cools. Expansional cooling raises the relative humidity to saturation (100%) and water vapor condenses into low clouds and fog. By trapping tiny cloud droplets and promoting their coalescence into larger drops, the tree canopy strips moisture from the windblown clouds and this water drips to the forest floor. The volume of water provided in this way is equivalent to 20% to 60% of the local rainfall. Hence, the cloud forest is a steady source of water for mountain streams that in turn supply water to downstream cities and towns. Persistent cloud cover also shapes the cloud forest environment by reducing incoming solar radiation and suppressing evapotranspiration (the combination of direct evaporation and transpiration by plants.) Cloud forests provide unique habitats for lichens, tree firns, orchids, and numerous species of birds and mammals.

Clearing forests reduces the amount of available moisture and raises the air temperature. Clouds form less readily and those that do form do so at higher elevations. Satellite imagery of the Monteverde cloud forest of Costa Rica shows considerably more cloudiness over forested highlands than over deforested lowlands.

If global climate change translates into higher sea surface temperatures (SST) in the tropics, the cloud forests could be affected. Higher SST would have two opposing impacts on the properties of the air flowing onshore and upslope. For one, the air would be warmer so that greater ascent (i.e., more expansional cooling) would be required to produce clouds. Clouds would form at higher elevations and perhaps lift off some mountaintops entirely. The original cloud forest would become drier, dramatically altering plant and animal habitats. However, higher SST would also increase the rate of evaporation of ocean water and result in a more humid onshore and upslope airflow. More humid air would condense into clouds at lower elevations. Using a numerical climate model to simulate the effects of higher SST on tropical airflow, Stephen Schneider and his colleagues at Stanford University concluded that higher air temperatures would be the more important factor in controlling the elevation of cloud forests. Cloud forests appear to be particularly sensitive to climate and may be among the early indicators of the environmental effects of global climate change.

Driving Question:
How does the cycling of water in the Earth-atmosphere system help maintain a habitable planet?

Water occurs in all three phases in the atmosphere: as water vapor (an invisible gas) and as aggregates of tiny ice crystals and water droplets, visible as clouds. The total amount of water in the atmosphere is relatively small and most of that is confined to the lower portion of the troposphere. If all the water vapor were removed from the atmosphere as rain and distributed uniformly over the globe, this water would cover Earth's surface to a depth of only about 2.5 cm (1.0 in.). Water continually cycles into the atmosphere as vapor from reservoirs of water at the Earth's surface (e.g., ocean, lakes, soil, vegetation) while water continually leaves the atmosphere, returning to Earth's surface as rain, snow, and other forms of precipitation. On average, the residence time of a water molecule is about 10 days in the atmosphere and on the order of hours in a cloud. This cycling is an essential component of the global water cycle.

In this chapter, we consider how the global water cycle functions, particularly as it relates to the transfer of water between Earth's surface and atmosphere. We learn how to quantify the water vapor component of air, how air becomes saturated through uplift and expansional cooling, and how atmospheric stability influences the ascent of air. All this is important because as air nears saturation, cloud development becomes more and more likely and clouds are prerequisites to precipitation.

An alternative to a pressure altimeter is a *radio* (or *electronic*) *altimeter*, which is flown onboard most commercial aircraft. This instrument emits pulses of radio waves (or a continuous signal) from the plane to the ground, where the signal is reflected back to the aircraft. Altitude is calibrated in terms of the time elapsed between emission and reception of the signal. The longer the signal takes, the greater is the indicated altitude of the aircraft. Recent advances in GPS (Global Positioning System) technology, which provides accurate elevation information, have caused this system to be adopted as an alternative method of altitude determination.

ESSAY: Determining Altitude from Air Pressure

Altimetry is the determination of altitude above mean sea level. A *pressure altimeter* is an aneroid barometer that is graduated in increments of altitude. The graduation (that is, the calibration of altitude against air pressure) is prescribed by the *standard atmosphere*, described elsewhere in this chapter. At any time and place, however, the real atmosphere usually differs from the standard atmosphere so that an altimeter typically does not give the true altitude. The *indicated altitude* (the altimeter reading) is the same as the *true altitude* only when air pressure and temperature match the standard atmosphere. Unless adjustments are made, the discrepancy between indicated and true altitudes can pose serious problems, especially for private aircraft during the crucial takeoff and landing phases of flight or when flying over mountainous terrain.

Changes in surface air pressure en route are one cause of differences between indicated and true altitudes. For example, as an aircraft travels toward a destination reporting a lower surface air pressure than its departure point, the altimeter will read higher than the true altitude. Hence, aircraft altimeters are equipped with a movable scale that enables the pilot to adjust altimeter readings. The Federal Aviation Administration (FAA) requires all aircraft flying below an altitude of 5500 m (18,000 ft) to calibrate altimeters to surface air pressure radioed from flight service stations en route. (Above 5500 m, aircraft fly along an isobaric surface with the altimeter zeroed at the standard sea-level pressure of 1013.25 mb.)

In-flight adjustments of altimeters to surface conditions, however, do not correct for pressure variations that arise en route principally from temperature variations within the air column beneath the aircraft. Cold air is denser than warm air so that air pressure drops more rapidly with altitude in cold air than in warm air. Within a column of cold air, a given air pressure occurs at a lower altitude than does the same air pressure in a column of warm air (see Figure 1). This means, for example, that as an aircraft flies into a column of air that is warmer than specified by the standard atmosphere, the altitude indicated by the altimeter will be lower than the true altitude. On the other hand, the altimeter onboard an aircraft flying into air colder than specified by the standard atmosphere will read too high.

The danger, of course, is that an erroneous altimeter reading may impede a pilot's ability to clear an obstacle such as a mountain peak. In practice, this hazard can be greatly reduced by an onboard computer that measures air temperature at flight level and makes appropriate adjustments to the altimeter reading. Note that this correction should be based on the mean temperature of the air column so that the error is reduced but not eliminated.

In summary, differences between altimeter readings and true altitude arise from en route changes in surface air pressure and/or average temperature in the air column beneath the aircraft. Even with adjustments in altimeter readings, pilots are well advised to follow the adage *"cold or low, look out below."* Hence, pilots should always select a flight altitude that will allow for a margin of safety, especially when flying over mountainous terrain or during conditions of restricted visibility.

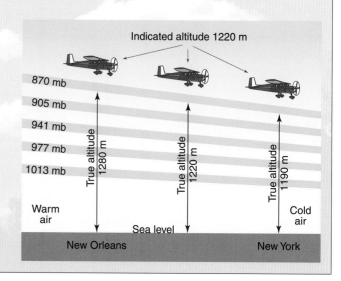

Figure 1
An aircraft *pressure altimeter* is initially calibrated based on the relationship between air pressure and altitude as specified by the standard atmosphere. But as the aircraft flies into colder or warmer air, the indicated altitude may differ from the true altitude because air pressure drops more rapidly with altitude in cold air than in warm air.

ESSAY: Human Responses to Changes in Air Pressure

Visitors to mountain elevations above about 2500 m (8000 ft) may develop symptoms of *mountain sickness*: headache, shortness of breath, fatigue, insomnia, and nausea. Such illness is not uncommon—perhaps one of every four people who ascend to high elevations experiences one or more of these distressing symptoms. Some people who spend more than 36 to 72 hrs at elevations greater than about 2800 m (9000 ft) develop *high-altitude pulmonary edema*. Symptoms of this potentially life-threatening condition are somewhat similar to those of pneumonia, that is, severe cough, shortness of breath, lethargy, mild fever, and a buildup of fluid (edema) in the lungs. Onset of high-altitude pulmonary edema requires prompt medical attention.

Breathing air that does not supply adequate oxygen (O_2) can bring on altitude sickness. Thinning of air that accompanies the fall in air pressure with altitude also means a rapid decrease in the *number density* of the atmosphere's principal gases; that is, a decline in the number of nitrogen (N_2) and oxygen (O_2) molecules per unit volume of air. At altitudes of 2450 m to 2750 m (8000 ft to 10,000 ft), oxygen's number density is only about 71% to 74% of its value at sea level. Less oxygen per unit volume of air may lead to *hypoxia,* a deficiency of oxygen in the body. Symptoms of mild hypoxia are commonly known as mountain sickness, whereas symptoms of more severe (acute) hypoxia constitute high altitude pulmonary edema.

As a person ascends to high altitudes, the body attempts to compensate for the decline in O_2 by altering breathing. The breathing rate accelerates and breathing becomes deeper to increase the amount of oxygen entering the lungs per unit time. Accelerated and deeper breathing provides no relief from hypoxia unless adequate oxygen delivered to the lungs is quickly transported to body tissues. Hence, the heart rate and stroke volume (the quantity of blood pumped out of the heart during each contraction) also increase. Although the quantity of oxygen per unit volume of blood remains essentially constant, the heart propels more blood (and hence, more oxygen) per unit time to body tissue.

The easiest way to alleviate acute mountain sickness is to descend to and remain at a lower altitude, especially at night. The altitude at which a person sleeps is more important than the altitude reached during the day. If a person remains at a high altitude, emergency adjustments by the heart and the muscles that control breathing reduce the symptoms of hypoxia while other longer-term changes take place in the body. Symptoms of acute mountain sickness gradually subside after several days as additional hemoglobin (molecules that pick up oxygen from air in the lungs) and red blood cells (cells that transport hemoglobin molecules in the bloodstream) are manufactured in the bone marrow. Although increased cardiac output generally tapers off within a week or so, accelerated breathing persists as long as a person remains at high altitude. The body thus adjusts to low oxygen levels that otherwise could cause serious health problems; this is an example of *acclimatization.*

A person can hasten acclimatization to high altitudes. Although a person may be eager to put in a full day of skiing or backpacking upon arrival in the mountains, he or she is well advised to minimize physical activity the first day or two. Here the old adage *the impatient becomes the patient* applies. Overexertion often results in more severe and persistent symptoms. Because alcohol aggravates mountain sickness, its use should be avoided, particularly during the first 48 hours at high altitudes.

Some people are better able to acclimatize than others because of differences in their genetic makeup and general health. Nonetheless, there is a limit to acclimatization. Long-term residence at high altitude cannot fully restore the body's capacity to perform work at the level that is possible at sea level. At altitudes above about 5200 m (17,000 ft), without supplementary oxygen, nothing can be done to prevent a continual decline in all bodily functions. Hence, as described in this chapter's Case-in-Point, the summit of Mount Everest, which at 8850 m (29,035 ft) is the world's highest peak, is very close to (if not beyond) the limits of human survival.

Symptoms of hypoxia become more severe as the air thins; hence, an aircraft cabin must be pressurized at altitudes above 4600 m (15,000 ft) unless a supplemental oxygen supply is available to the flight crew and passengers. In actual practice, commercial aircraft cabins are pressurized beginning at takeoff and remain pressurized throughout the flight. A cabin is typically pressurized to about 75% of average sea-level air pressure. Although the aircraft cabin is pressurized, people commonly feel the effects of changing air pressure in a rapidly ascending or descending aircraft by a popping sensation in their ears. Rapid ascent or descent in an elevator or in a car on mountain roads often produces the same sensation. Ear popping is symptomatic of a natural process that helps to protect the eardrum from damage.

The eardrum separates the outer ear from the middle ear chamber. As an aircraft takes off and cabin pressure drops, air pressure in the outer ear declines. As air pressure in the outer ear changes, the eardrum is distorted unless a compensating pressure change takes place in the middle ear. If the pressure does not equalize between the outer and middle ear, the eardrum bulges outward. On the other hand, when an aircraft descends and cabin pressure increases, air pressure in the outer ear increases. Without a compensating pressure change in the middle ear, the eardrum bulges inward. In both cases, deformation of the eardrum not only causes physical discomfort, but a bulging eardrum does not vibrate efficiently so that sounds are muffled. If the air pressure difference between the middle ear and outer ear continues to increase, the eardrum could rupture, perhaps causing permanent hearing loss.

Fortunately, the body has a natural mechanism that regulates air pressure in the middle ear. The *eustachian tube* connects the middle ear to the upper throat region which, in turn, leads to the outside via the oral and nasal cavities. Normally, the eustachian tube is closed where it enters the throat, but it opens if a sufficient air pressure difference develops between the middle ear and the throat. When the eustachian tube opens, air pressure in the middle ear quickly comes into equilibrium with the external air pressure and the eardrum pops back to its normal shape. Vibrations of the eardrum associated with its rapid change in shape are what we hear as *ear popping*, the body's way of preventing a permanent hearing loss when a person experiences a rapid change in air pressure. To reduce discomfort, yawning or swallowing hastens the opening of the eustachian tube. For this reason, travelers in aircraft or on mountain roads are advised to chew gum because the swallowing that accompanies gum chewing helps to open the eustachian tube.

Global Water Cycle

We can reasonably assume that the total amount of water in the Earth-atmosphere system is neither increasing nor decreasing although natural processes continually generate and breakdown water. Water vapor accounts for perhaps half of all gases emitted during a volcanic eruption; at least some of this water was originally sequestered in magma and solid rock. Volcanic activity is more or less continuous on Earth and adds to the supply of water. Also, a minute amount of water is added to Earth by meteorites and other extraterrestrial debris continually bombarding the upper atmosphere. At the same time, intense solar radiation entering the upper atmosphere, converts (*photodissociates*) a small amount of water vapor into its constituent hydrogen and oxygen atoms, which may escape to space. Also, water chemically reacts with other substances and is thereby locked up in various compounds. Annually, additions of water from volcanic eruptions and extraterrestrial sources roughly equal losses of water through photodissociation of water vapor and chemical reactions. This balance of give and take has prevailed on Earth for perhaps hundreds of millions of years.

The essentially fixed quantity of water in the Earth-atmosphere system is distributed in its three phases among various reservoirs (Table 6.1). The ocean is the largest of these reservoirs by far, accounting for 97.2% of all water on the planet; most of the rest is tied up as ice sheets up to 3 km (1.8 mi) thick that cover most of Antarctica and Greenland. Relatively small amounts of water occur in living organisms (plants and animals), rivers and lakes, and occupy the tiny pore spaces and fractures within soil, sediment, and bedrock (soil moisture and groundwater). Even smaller amounts of water occur in the atmosphere as clouds, precipitation, and invisible water vapor.

TABLE 6.1
Water Stored in Reservoirs of the Global Water Cycle

Reservoir	Percent of total water
Ocean	97.20
Ice sheets and glaciers	2.15
Groundwater	0.62
Lakes (freshwater)	0.009
Inland seas, saline lakes	0.008
Soil moisture	0.005
Atmosphere	0.001
Rivers and streams	0.0001

The ceaseless movement of water among the various reservoirs on a planetary scale is known as the **global water cycle** (Figure 6.1). In brief, water vaporizes from

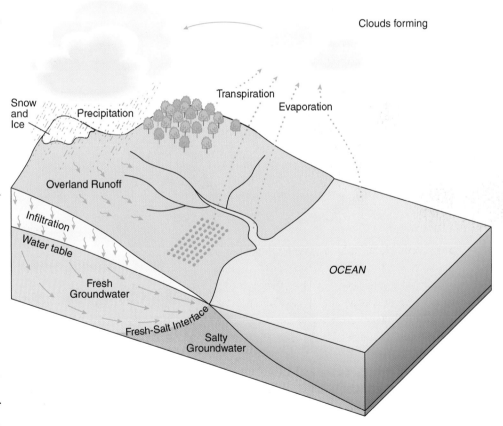

FIGURE 6.1
The global water cycle is a continuous flow of water and energy among oceanic, terrestrial (land-based), and atmospheric reservoirs.

ocean and land to the atmosphere where winds can transport water vapor to other locations, sometimes thousands of kilometers away. Clouds form and rain, snow and other forms of precipitation fall from clouds to Earth's surface, recharging the ocean and terrestrial (land-based) reservoirs of water. From terrestrial reservoirs, water flows into the ocean basins. The continuity of the global water cycle is captured in a verse from Ecclesiastes 1:7: "Every river flows into the sea, but the sea is not yet full. The waters return to where the rivers began and start all over again."

The sun drives the global water cycle. As we saw in Chapter 4, some of the radiation that strikes Earth's surface is absorbed, that is, converted to heat, and some of this heat evaporates water (or sublimates ice and snow). If water did not vaporize, there would be no clouds, no precipitation, and no global water cycle. While solar radiation powers the global water cycle, gravity is an important player in that this attractive force keeps water molecules from escaping to space, as well as causing water to fall from the sky as precipitation and to flow from the continents to the ocean. In this section, we focus on a critical link in the global water cycle—the link between the atmosphere and the oceanic and terrestrial reservoirs of water.

TRANSFER PROCESSES

As part of the global water cycle, water is transferred between Earth's surface and the atmosphere via phase changes (evaporation, condensation, transpiration, sublimation, and deposition) and precipitation. Within the ranges of air temperature and air pressure on Earth, all three phases of water can coexist naturally. At the interface between liquid water and air (e.g., lake or sea surface), water molecules continually change phase: some crossing the interface from water to air and others from air to water. If more water molecules enter the atmosphere as vapor than return as liquid, a net loss occurs in liquid water mass; this process is known as **evaporation**. Water evaporates from the surface of the ocean, lakes, and rivers as well as from soil and the damp surfaces of plant leaves and stems. About 85% of the total annual evaporation in the Earth-atmosphere system takes place at the ocean surface so that the ocean is the principal source of water in the atmosphere (Figure 6.2).

On the other hand, at the interface between liquid water and air, if more water molecules return to the water surface as liquid than enter the atmosphere as vapor, a net gain of liquid water mass results. This process is called

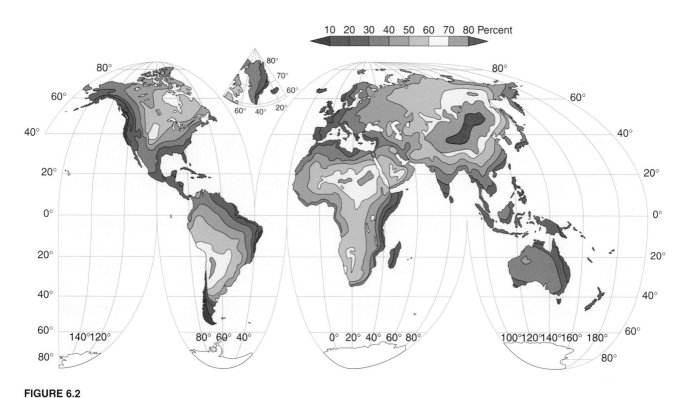

FIGURE 6.2
The percentage of annual precipitation that falls on land that originated as water that vaporized from the continents, averaged over 15 years. In many land areas, the principal source of water for precipitation is evaporation from the ocean. [World Climate Research Programme, Global Energy and Water Cycle Experiment]

condensation. Condensation of atmospheric water vapor can be observed when small droplets form on the cold surface of a glass of iced tea on a humid summer day.

Transpiration is the process whereby water that is taken up from the soil by plant roots eventually escapes as vapor through tiny pores on the surface of green leaves. On land during the growing season, transpiration is considerable and is often more important than direct evaporation of water in delivering water vapor to the atmosphere. For example, a single hectare (2.5 acres) of corn typically transpires about 34,000 liters (L) (8800 gal) of water per day. Annually, a mature oak tree may transpire more than 150,000 L (40,000 gal) of water. Measurements of direct evaporation from Earth's surface plus transpiration are often combined as **evapotranspiration**.

At the interface between ice and air (e.g., the surface of a snow cover), water molecules are also continually changing phase: from ice directly to vapor and from vapor directly to ice. If more water molecules enter the atmosphere as vapor than make the transition to ice, a net loss of ice mass occurs. **Sublimation** is the process whereby ice or snow becomes vapor without first becoming a liquid. Sublimation explains the gradual disappearance of snow and ice on sidewalks and roads even while the air temperature remains well below freezing. On the other hand, if more atmospheric water molecules transition to ice than move from ice to vapor, a net gain of ice mass results. **Deposition** is the process whereby water vapor becomes ice without first becoming a liquid. During a cold winter night, the formation of frost on automobile windows is an example of deposition. Condensation or deposition operating within the atmosphere produces clouds. **Precipitation** is water in liquid, frozen or freezing form (i.e., rain, drizzle, snow, ice pellets, hail, and freezing rain) that falls from clouds under the influence of gravity and reaches Earth surface, where most of it eventually vaporizes back into the atmosphere.

Evaporation (or sublimation) followed by condensation (or deposition) purifies water. As water vaporizes from the Earth's surface, all suspended and dissolved substances such as sea salts and other contaminants are left behind. Through this natural cleansing mechanism, ocean water that originally was too salty to drink is the source of much of what eventually falls as freshwater precipitation replenishing reservoirs on Earth's surface. Purification of water through phase changes is known as **distillation**.

GLOBAL WATER BUDGET

Return of water from the atmosphere to the land and ocean via condensation, deposition, and precipitation completes an essential subcycle in the global water cycle. To learn more about the atmosphere-Earth surface subcycle, compare the movement of water between the continents and the atmosphere with that between the ocean and the atmosphere. The balance sheet for the inputs and outputs of water to and from the various global reservoirs is called the **global water budget** (Table 6.2).

Over the course of a year, the volume of precipitation (rain plus melted snow) that falls on land exceeds the total volume of water that vaporizes (via evaporation, transpiration, and sublimation) from land by about one-third. (This imbalance occurs because landmasses favor certain precipitation-forming mechanisms.) Over the same period, the volume of precipitation falling on the ocean is less than the volume of water that evaporates from the ocean. (Evaporation is more important because the ocean surface is a nearly limitless source of water vapor.) The global water budget thus indicates an annual net gain of water mass on the continents and an annual net loss of water mass from the ocean. The annual excess of water on the continents essentially equals the deficit from the ocean. But year after year, the continents do not get any wetter and sea level is not changing appreciably because excess water on land drips, seeps and flows back to the sea thereby completing the global water cycle. The net flow of water from land to sea also implies a net flow of water within the atmosphere directed from sea to land.

TABLE 6.2
Global Water Budget

Source	*Cubic meters per year*	*Gallons per year*
Precipitation on the ocean	$+3.24 \times 10^{14}$	$+85.5 \times 10^{15}$
Evaporation from the ocean	-3.60×10^{14}	-95.2×10^{15}
Net loss from the ocean	-0.36×10^{14}	-9.7×10^{15}
Precipitation on land	$+0.98 \times 10^{14}$	$+26.1 \times 10^{15}$
Evapotranspiration from land	-0.62×10^{14}	-16.4×10^{15}
Net gain on land	$+0.36 \times 10^{14}$	$+9.7 \times 10^{15}$

Precipitation strikes the ground directly or it may be intercepted by vegetation and then evaporates or drips to the ground (Figure 6.3). Also, as described in this chapter's Case-in-Point, some trees collect moisture from drifting fog or low clouds and that water drips to the ground (known as *fog drip*). Once water reaches Earth's land surface, it follows various pathways. Some water vaporizes directly back into the atmosphere while some is temporarily stored in lakes, snow and ice fields, or glaciers. The remainder either flows on the surface as rivers or streams (*runoff component*) or seeps into the ground as soil moisture or groundwater (*infiltration component*). About one-third of the precipitation that falls on land runs off to the ocean. The ratio of the portion of water that infiltrates the ground to the portion that runs off depends on rainfall intensity, vegetation, topography, and physical properties of the land surface. For example, rain falling on frozen ground or city streets mostly runs off whereas rain falling on unfrozen sandy soil readily soaks into the ground.

Rivers and streams plus their tributaries drain a fixed geographical area known as a *drainage basin* (or *watershed*). The quantity and quality of water flowing in a river depends on the climate, vegetation, topography, geology, and land use in its drainage basin. For example,

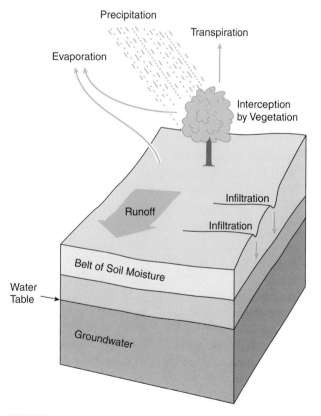

Precipitation

Transpiration

Evaporation

Interception by Vegetation

Infiltration

Runoff

Infiltration

Belt of Soil Moisture

Water Table

Groundwater

FIGURE 6.3
Various pathways taken by precipitation falling on land.

in places where the climate features distinct rainy and dry season, stream flow can vary considerably through the year. A drainage basin may also include lakes, wetlands, and glaciers, temporary impoundments of surface water.

How Humid Is It?

"It's not the heat, it's the humidity." This popular statement attributes the discomfort a person may feel on a hot, muggy day to the water vapor component of air. **Humidity** is the general term referring to any one of many different ways of describing the amount of water vapor in the air. Humidity is an important determinant of our physical comfort, as discussed in this chapter's first Essay, "Humidity and Human Comfort." Experience tells us that humidity varies with the time of year, from one day to the next, within a single day, and from one place to another. In most places summer days feel more humid than a typical winter day. In cold regions, dry winter air also causes some discomfort. This section covers the various quantitative measures of humidity.

VAPOR PRESSURE

When water enters the atmosphere as vapor, water molecules disperse in all directions and mix with the other gases composing air (mostly nitrogen and oxygen) thereby contributing to the total pressure exerted by the atmosphere. The amount of pressure produced by water vapor molecules is a measure of the humidity: the more water vapor, the greater the pressure exerted by water molecules. Water vapor's contribution to the total air pressure, as described by *Dalton's law* of partial pressures (Chapter 5), is known as **vapor pressure**.

As the water vapor content of the atmosphere increases, the vapor pressure also increases. Water vapor is a highly variable component of air but composes at most no more than about 4% of the atmosphere's mass in the lowest kilometer—even in the sultry air over the tropical ocean and rainforests. The total pressure exerted by all atmospheric gases at sea level averages about 1000 mb. This means that the vapor pressure is very unlikely anywhere to exceed 40 mb (4% × 1000 mb = 40 mb) at sea level, and in most places the vapor pressure is considerably less than 40 mb.

MIXING RATIO, SPECIFIC HUMIDITY, AND ABSOLUTE HUMIDITY

Other ways of quantifying humidity are the mixing ratio, specific humidity, and absolute humidity. **Mixing ratio** is defined as the mass of water vapor per mass of the remaining dry air, usually expressed as so many grams of water vapor per kilogram of dry air. Typically the mixing ratio at sea level is less than 40 grams per kilogram. **Specific humidity** is defined as the ratio of the mass of water vapor (in grams) to the mass (in kilograms) of the air including the water vapor (that is, the combined mass of dry air plus water vapor totals one kilogram). Values of specific humidity and mixing ratio are so close that they usually can be considered equivalent.

Absolute humidity is defined as the mass of water vapor per unit volume of humid air, typically expressed as grams of water vapor per cubic meter of air. In other words, absolute humidity is the density of the water vapor component of air. Although conceptually simple, absolute humidity has limited application in meteorology because the volume of a parcel of air may change causing its absolute humidity to vary even though no water vapor is gained or lost by the parcel. For example, an air parcel's volume increases when it is heated or lifted in the atmosphere. Even though no water vapor enters or leaves the air parcel, the amount of water vapor per unit volume decreases, that is, the absolute humidity decreases.

SATURATED AIR

Regardless of how humidity is quantified, at a specified temperature, the amount of water vapor in air has a practical upper limit. At its maximum humidity, air is described as *saturated* with respect to water vapor. Earlier in this chapter, we described a two-way exchange of water molecules at the interface between water and air (or between ice and air). Water molecules are in a continual state of flux between the liquid and vapor phases. During evaporation, more water molecules become vapor than return to the liquid phase, and during condensation, more water molecules return to the liquid phase than enter the vapor phase. Eventually, a dynamic equilibrium may develop such that the flux of water molecules is the same in both directions; that is, liquid water becomes vapor at the same rate that water vapor becomes liquid. At equilibrium, above a plane surface of liquid water or ice, the air is saturated with water vapor. The vapor pressure at this equilibrium condition is called the **saturation vapor pressure**, the mixing ratio is the **saturation mixing ratio**, the specific humidity is the **saturation specific humidity**, and the absolute humidity is the **saturation absolute humidity**.

Altering the temperature disturbs this dynamic equilibrium at least temporarily. Heating water causes the average kinetic energy of individual water molecules to increase and water molecules more readily escape the water surface as vapor. Initially, evaporation prevails. If the supply of water is sufficient and as long as water vapor is not continually carried away by the wind, eventually a new dynamic equilibrium is established. That is, the flux of water molecules becoming liquid once again balances the flux of water molecules becoming vapor. This new equilibrium is achieved with more water vapor in the air (above the water surface) at a higher temperature. Raising the temperature increases the saturation vapor pressure, saturation mixing ratio, saturation specific humidity, and saturation absolute humidity.

Conversely, with a drop in water temperature, the average kinetic energy of individual water molecules decreases and molecules less readily escape the water surface as vapor. Initially, condensation prevails but eventually a new equilibrium is established; that is, the flux of water molecules becoming vapor again balances the flux of water molecules becoming liquid. This new equilibrium is achieved with less water vapor in the air (above the water surface) at a lower temperature. Dropping the temperature reduces the saturation vapor pressure, saturation mixing ratio, saturation specific humidity, and saturation absolute humidity.

Ultimately, the water vapor component of air depends on the rate of vaporization of water, which is regulated chiefly by temperature, and on the presence of a water supply. The dependence of the saturation vapor pressure on temperature is shown in Figure 6.4 and Table 6.3. The variation of the saturation mixing ratio with temperature is shown in Figure 6.5 and Table 6.4. Because the mixing ratio depends on the mass of the air, the saturation mixing ratio also varies with pressure. Extensive laboratory work by 19th century steam engineers and scientists is the source of these data. For both measures of humidity, the relationship is non-linear. Note that for temperatures below freezing, two different values are given: one over supercooled water and the other over ice. Supercooled water remains liquid at subfreezing temperatures. As a general rule, the saturation vapor pressure and saturation mixing ratio approximately double in value for every 10 Celsius degree (20 Fahrenheit degree) rise in temperature. At 100 °C (212 °F) at sea level, the saturation vapor pressure is 1013.25 mb, the same as the standard sea level air pressure. Water boils when the saturation vapor pressure and ambient air pressure are equal.

The relationship between temperature and saturation vapor pressure (or saturation mixing ratio) is popularly interpreted to mean that warm air can "hold" more water vapor than can cold air. That is, air is likened to a sponge that can soak up only so much water depending on the temperature. While intuitively

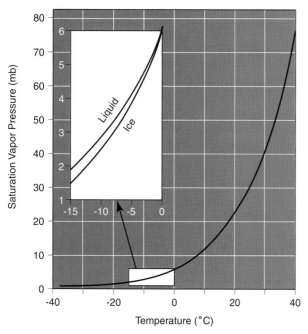

FIGURE 6.4
Variation in saturation vapor pressure with changing air temperature. Note that at subfreezing temperatures, the saturation vapor pressure is greater over supercooled water than over ice.

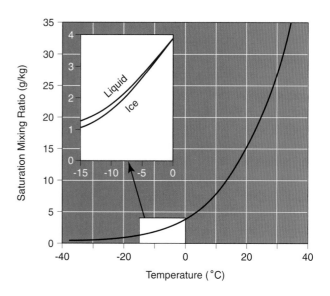

FIGURE 6.5
Variation in saturation mixing ratio with changing air temperature (at a pressure of 1000 mb). Note that at subfreezing temperatures, the saturation mixing ratio is greater over supercooled water than over ice.

TABLE 6.3
Variation of Saturation Vapor Pressure with Temperature

Temperature °C (°F)	Saturation Vapor Pressure (mb)	
	Over water	Over ice
50 (122)	123.40	
45 (113)	95.86	
40 (104)	73.78	
35 (95)	56.24	
30 (86)	42.43	
25 (77)	31.67	
20 (68)	23.37	
15 (59)	17.04	
10 (50)	12.27	
5 (41)	8.72	
0 (32)	6.11	6.11
−5 (23)	4.21	4.02
−10 (14)	2.86	2.60
−15 (5)	1.91	1.65
−20 (−4)	1.25	1.03
−25 (−13)	0.80	0.63
−30 (−22)	0.51	0.38
−35 (−31)	0.31	0.22
−40 (−40)	0.19	0.13
−45 (−49)	0.11	0.07

TABLE 6.4
Variation of Saturation Mixing Ratio with Temperature (at 1000 mb pressure)

Temperature °C (°F)	Saturation mixing ratio (g/kg)	
	Over water	Over ice
50 (122)	88.12	
45 (113)	66.33	
40 (104)	49.81	
35 (95)	37.25	
30 (86)	27.69	
25 (77)	20.44	
20 (68)	14.95	
15 (59)	10.83	
10 (50)	7.76	
5 (41)	5.50	
0 (32)	3.84	3.84
−5 (23)	2.64	2.52
−10 (14)	1.79	1.63
−15 (5)	1.20	1.03
−20 (−4)	0.78	0.65
−25 (−13)	0.50	0.40
−30 (−22)	0.32	0.24
−35 (−31)	0.20	0.14
−40 (−40)	0.12	0.08
−45 (−49)	0.07	0.05

appealing, this analogy can be misleading. Air does not literally hold water vapor like a sponge; rather, water vapor coexists with the other gases that form the mixture known as air. Recall from Dalton's law that each gas in a mixture of gases exerts a pressure as though it were the only gas present. Water vapor is just one of the many gases that compose air. If water vapor is introduced into an air parcel with the pressure and temperature remaining constant, it follows that water vapor displaces some of the other gaseous components of air. Because temperature largely governs the rate of vaporization of water, the saturation vapor pressure (or saturation mixing ratio) is actually a measure of water's vaporization rate. At any specified temperature, the saturation vapor pressure (or saturation mixing ratio) would have the same value even if water vapor were the only gas in the atmosphere.

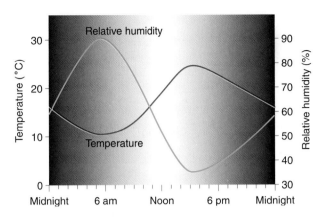

FIGURE 6.6
Variation in relative humidity and air temperature on a day when the air is calm and there is essentially no variation in vapor pressure. The relative humidity is highest when the temperature is lowest (near sunrise) and the relative humidity is lowest when the temperature is highest (early to mid afternoon).

RELATIVE HUMIDITY

Relative humidity is the water vapor measure frequently reported by television and radio weathercasters and is probably the most familiar for most of us. **Relative humidity** compares the actual amount of water vapor in the air with the amount of water vapor that would be present if that same air were saturated. Relative humidity (RH) is expressed as a percentage and can be computed from either the vapor pressure or mixing ratio. That is,

RH = [(vapor pressure)/(saturation vapor pressure)] × 100%

or

RH = [(mixing ratio)/(saturation mixing ratio)] × 100%

When the actual concentration of water vapor in air equals the water vapor concentration at saturation, the relative humidity is 100%; that is, the air is saturated with respect to water vapor.

Consider an example of how relative humidity is computed. Suppose that the air temperature is 10 °C (50 °F) and the vapor pressure is 6.1 mb. From Table 6.3, we determine that the saturation vapor pressure of air at 10 °C is 12.27 mb. Using the formula above, we compute the relative humidity to be 49.7%, that is,

RH = [(6.1 mb)/(12.27 mb)] × 100% = 49.7%

At constant temperature and pressure, the relative humidity varies directly with the vapor pressure (or mixing ratio); that is, the relative humidity increases as water vapor is added to air as long as the air temperature and pressure do not change. Because the saturation vapor pressure varies directly with temperature, the relative humidity varies

inversely with temperature. If no water vapor is added to or removed from unsaturated air, the relative humidity increases as the temperature drops and decreases as the temperature rises. Consider a common example.

On a clear day with no wind, the air temperature usually rises from a minimum near sunrise to a maximum during early to mid-afternoon and then falls through the evening hours and overnight (Chapter 4). If the amount of water vapor in air remains constant throughout the day, then the relative humidity will vary inversely with air temperature. As shown in Figure 6.6, the relative humidity is highest when the air temperature is lowest and the relative humidity is lowest when the temperature is highest. After sunrise, as the air warms, the relative humidity drops, but not because the amount of water vapor is decreasing. The relative humidity drops because the saturation vapor pressure increases as the air temperature rises.

In the previous example, the relative humidity responded only to variations in local air temperature; the air was calm so there was no cold or warm air advection. The situation is made more complicated by air mass advection, which can influence both local air temperature and vapor pressure. For example, when a warm and humid air mass replaces a cool and dry air mass, both rising temperatures and increasing vapor pressure affect the local relative humidity.

DEWPOINT

Dewpoint, cited on some television and radio weathercasts, is another useful measure of humidity. **Dewpoint** is the temperature to which air must be cooled at constant pressure to achieve saturation of air relative to liquid water. The higher the dewpoint, the greater is the concentration of water vapor in air. Cooling unsaturated air at constant pressure increases its relative humidity. When the relative humidity reaches 100%, the air is saturated and the air temperature becomes the same as the dewpoint. Conversely, warming the air without adding water vapor via evaporation lowers the relative humidity and increases the difference between the actual air temperature and the dewpoint.

Dew consists of tiny droplets of water formed when water vapor condenses on a cold surface such as blades of grass on a clear, calm night. As discussed in Chapter 7, dew forms as a consequence of radiational cooling. (Dew that freezes after forming is known as *white dew* because it appears as white beads of ice.) Dew is not a form of precipitation because it does not fall from clouds to Earth's surface. For water vapor to condense as dew on the surface of an object, the temperature of that surface must cool below the dewpoint. When cooling at constant pressure produces saturation at an air temperature below freezing, water vapor deposits as **frost**, ice crystals that form on exposed surfaces such as blades of grass. The air temperature at which further cooling will cause frost to form is known as the **frost point**.

Summer dewpoints are usually highest in locations bordering the Gulf of Mexico where the July mean dewpoint typically ranges between 21 °C and 24 °C (70 °F and 75 °F). During the oppressive heat waves that sometimes sweep over the continent east of the Rocky Mountains, the dewpoint may top the low 20s Celsius (low 70s Fahrenheit) even in the northern states. On 30 July 1999, during a particularly humid heat wave, the dewpoint at Milwaukee, WI tied a record high of 27.8 °C (82 °F). Summer dewpoints are lowest in the Rocky Mountain States and the American Southwest. From New Mexico northward into western Montana, the July mean dewpoint generally ranges between −1 °C and 7 °C (30 °F and 45 °F). The dewpoint (actually frost point) is exceptionally low in polar and arctic air masses that invade broad regions of the United States in winter.

PRECIPITABLE WATER

Precipitable water is another way of describing the amount of water vapor in the atmosphere. Unlike the other humidity measures that represent the amount of water vapor at a specific place (usually near the Earth's surface), **precipitable water** is the depth of water that would be produced if all the water vapor in a vertical column of air were condensed into liquid water. The air column is usually taken to extend from Earth's surface to the top of the troposphere, the portion of the atmosphere where most water vapor occurs. A reasonably good measure of precipitable water is obtained from in situ measurements by radiosonde soundings or remotely by orbiting satellites operating in the sounding mode.

Precipitable water is not always indicative of the amount of precipitation that might fall at a particular location. Numerous other factors, including horizontal advection of water vapor to or from the air column along with recycling of water locally, ultimately determine the amount of precipitation.

Condensing all the water vapor in the global atmosphere would produce a layer of water covering the entire Earth's surface to a depth of 2.5 cm (1.0 in.). Average precipitable water varies with latitude in response to the poleward decline in air temperature. This geographical distribution of precipitable water is usually evident on any given day as illustrated by Figure 6.7. Evaporation and precipitable water are less in cold regions. In fact, average annual precipitable water depths vary from more than 4.0 cm (1.6 in.) in the humid tropics to less than 0.5 cm (0.2 in.)

FIGURE 6.7
GOES satellite-determined precipitable water amounts are shown across the coterminous US and adjacent Pacific using the lower color scale in inches. Browns and blues are lowest values and purples and greens are highest. Gray is cloud cover.

at high latitudes. Seasonal variations in precipitable water also occur in middle latitudes, with the highest values generally occurring in summer as the troposphere warms.

Monitoring Water Vapor

A variety of techniques are used to monitor atmospheric water vapor both directly and remotely (by satellite). For information on measuring evapotranspiration, see this chapter's second Essay.

HUMIDITY INSTRUMENTS

In about 1450, Cardinal Nicholas of Cusa (*ca.* 1400-1464) conceived of the first known design in western civilization for an instrument to gauge the water vapor content of air. Later, Leonardo da Vinci (1452-1519), a creative genius of the 15th century, improved on the original design using a simple balance to measure water vapor in air. A small wad of dry cotton on one side of a scale exactly balanced a weight on the other side of the scale. As the cotton absorbed water vapor from the air, an imbalance developed and the amount of imbalance was an approximate measure of humidity.

The **hygrometer** is an instrument that measures the water vapor concentration of air; several different designs are available. The National Weather Service employs a **dewpoint hygrometer** as a component of its Automated Surface Observing System (Figure 6.8). With this instrument, air passes over the surface of a metallic mirror that is cooled electronically. An electronic sensor continually monitors the temperature of the mirror at the

FIGURE 6.8
The temperature/dewpoint sensor (hygrothermometer) that is a component of the National Weather Service's Automated Surface Observing System (ASOS).

same time that an infrared beam is pointed at the mirror. With sufficient cooling, a thin film of water condenses on the mirror changing its reflectivity and altering the reflection of the infrared beam. The mirror temperature is then automatically recorded as the dewpoint. The mirror is warmed electronically to evaporate the dew to prepare for the next measurement.

Some hygrometers take advantage of the sensitivity of organic materials to changes in humidity. One common design, called a **hair hygrometer**, uses human hair as the sensing element. Cells in the hair adsorb (collect on the surface) water and swell causing the hair to lengthen slightly as the relative humidity increases. Typically, hair changes length by about 2.5% over the full range of relative humidity from 0% to 100%. Usually, a sheaf of blond hair is linked mechanically to a pointer on a dial that is calibrated to read in percent relative humidity. A hair hygrometer may be designed to move a pen on a clock-driven drum. This instrument, called a **hygrograph**, provides a continuous trace of fluctuations in relative humidity with time. Unfortunately, hair hygrometers do not measure extremes in relative humidity accurately nor do they respond quickly to rapid changes in humidity.

An **electronic hygrometer** is based on changes in the electrical resistance of certain chemicals as they adsorb water vapor from the air. The adsorbing element may be a thin carbon coating on a glass or plastic strip. The more humid the air, the more water adsorbed, and the lower is the resistance to an electric current passing through the sensing element. Variations in electrical resistance are calibrated in terms of percent relative humidity or dewpoint. An electronic hygrometer is flown onboard radiosondes (Chapter 2).

For more than a century, most meteorological observations of water vapor utilized a psychrometer, an instrument that provides a less direct measure of relative humidity. A **psychrometer** consists of two identical liquid-in-glass thermometers mounted side by side with the bulb of one thermometer wrapped in a muslin wick. To take a reading, the wick-covered bulb is first soaked in water (preferably distilled) and then the instrument is ventilated. A *sling psychrometer* has an attached handle that allows it to be whirled about with ease (Figure 6.9), whereas a small fan is used to ventilate an *aspirated psychrometer*. The *dry-bulb thermometer* of the instrument measures the actual air temperature. Water vaporizes from the muslin wick into the air streaming past the *wet-bulb thermometer* and evaporative cooling lowers the reading on this thermometer to the **wet-bulb temperature**. As ventilation continues by whirling or

FIGURE 6.9
When whirled about, a sling psychrometer measures the actual air temperature (dry-bulb reading) and the wet-bulb temperature. The relative humidity and dewpoint can then be determined from psychrometric tables (Tables 6.5 and 6.6).

aspiration, the reading on the wet-bulb thermometer eventually steadies. The drier the air, the greater the evaporation, and the lower is the wet-bulb temperature compared to the dry-bulb temperature. The difference between the dry-bulb temperature and the wet-bulb temperature, known as the **wet-bulb depression**, is calibrated in terms of percent relative humidity on a psychrometric table (Table 6.5). This table was developed more than a century ago using a combination of theoretical considerations and extensive field experiments.

Consider an example of how relative humidity is determined using a psychrometer. Suppose that the air temperature (dry-bulb thermometer reading) is 20 °C (68 °F) and the wet-bulb temperature is 15 °C (59 °F) resulting in a wet-bulb depression (dry-bulb reading minus wet-bulb reading) of 5 Celsius degrees (9 Fahrenheit degrees). From Table 6.5, the relative humidity is 58%. When the wet-bulb depression is zero, the air is saturated; that is, the relative humidity is 100%.

A major drawback of a psychrometer is the difficulty of taking measurements at low and subfreezing temperatures. At low air temperatures, small differences in the wet-bulb depression correspond to greater increments in relative humidity than is the case at high temperatures. This situation requires greater precision in reading the

instrument at low air temperatures. At freezing, ice forms on the wick inhibiting evaporative cooling. For this reason, an electronic or hair hygrometer is more desirable when the air temperature falls below 0 °C (32 °F). Furthermore, in very dry air the wick may dry out prior to reaching the full depression value.

The wet-bulb temperature should not be confused with the dewpoint; they are not the same. The wet-bulb temperature is determined by inducing evaporative cooling. Adding water vapor to the air raises the temperature at which dew will form so that, except at saturation, the wet-bulb temperature is higher than the dewpoint. At saturation, the dewpoint, wet-bulb, and actual air temperatures are the same. The dewpoint also can be obtained from measurements of the dry-bulb temperature and the wet-bulb depression (Table 6.6). For example, if the dry-bulb temperature is 20 °C (68 °F) and the wet-bulb depression is 5 Celsius degrees (9 Fahrenheit degrees), then the dewpoint is 11.6 °C (53 °F). In this case, the wet-bulb temperature is 15 °C (59 °F), some 3.4 Celsius degrees (6 Fahrenheit degrees) higher than the dewpoint.

WATER VAPOR SATELLITE IMAGERY

Water vapor satellite imagery is a valuable remote sensing product for tracking the broad scale distribution and movement of water vapor within the atmosphere (Figure 6.10). Water vapor is invisible and does not appear on visible satellite images. But water vapor efficiently absorbs and emits certain wavelength ranges of infrared radiation that are readily detected by a special infrared sensor onboard a weather satellite. The sensor that produces conventional infrared (thermal) satellite images is sensitive to infrared radiation emitted by the Earth-atmosphere system at wavelengths within atmospheric windows, that is, within wavelength bands from 10.5 to 12.6 micrometers. Recall from Chapter 3 that *atmospheric windows* refer to wavelengths of upwelling infrared radiation not absorbed by the atmosphere. On the other hand, the satellite water vapor sensor detects infrared radiation at a wavelength of 6.7 micrometers, which is strongly absorbed and emitted by water in the atmosphere.

Water vapor imagery displays only water vapor and clouds occurring at altitudes above about 3000 m (10,000 ft). Although this type of satellite imagery does not show water vapor (or clouds) at lower altitudes, it does detect otherwise transparent water vapor in the middle troposphere and can show moisture gathering in broad scale circulation patterns prior to the development of extensive cloudiness in an incipient storm system. Water vapor imagery typically utilizes a gray scale. At one

Table 6.5
Psychrometric Table: Relative Humidity (Percent)

Dry-bulb Temp (°C)	Wet-bulb Depression (C°)														
	0.5	1.0	1.5	2.0	2.5	3.0	3.5	4.0	4.5	5.0	7.5	10.0	12.5	15.0	17.5
−10.0	85	69	54	39	24	10	—	—	—	—	—	—	—	—	—
−7.5	87	73	60	48	35	22	10	—	—	—	—	—	—	—	—
−5.0	88	77	66	54	43	32	21	11	1	—	—	—	—	—	—
−2.5	90	80	70	60	50	41	37	22	12	3	—	—	—	—	—
0.0	91	82	73	65	56	47	39	31	23	15	—	—	—	—	—
2.5	92	84	76	68	61	53	46	38	31	24	—	—	—	—	—
5.0	93	86	78	71	65	58	51	45	38	32	1	—	—	—	—
7.5	93	87	80	74	68	62	56	50	44	38	11	—	—	—	—
10.0	94	88	82	76	71	65	60	54	49	44	19	—	—	—	—
12.5	94	89	84	78	73	68	63	58	53	48	25	4	—	—	—
15.0	95	90	85	80	75	70	66	61	57	52	31	12	—	—	—
17.5	95	90	86	81	77	72	68	64	60	55	36	18	2	—	—
20.0	95	91	87	82	78	74	70	66	62	58	40	24	8	—	—
22.5	96	92	87	83	80	76	72	68	64	61	44	28	14	1	—
25.0	96	92	88	84	81	77	73	70	66	63	47	32	19	7	—
27.5	96	92	89	85	82	78	75	71	68	65	50	36	23	12	1
30.0	96	93	89	86	82	79	76	73	70	67	52	39	27	16	6
32.5	97	93	90	86	83	80	77	74	71	68	54	42	30	20	11
35.0	97	93	90	87	84	81	78	75	72	69	56	44	33	23	14
37.5	97	94	91	87	85	82	79	76	73	70	58	46	36	26	18
40.0	97	94	91	88	85	82	79	77	74	72	59	48	38	29	21

Table 6.6
Psychrometric Table: Dewpoint Temperature (°C)

Dry-bulb Temp (°C)	Wet-bulb Depression (C°)														
	0.5	1.0	1.5	2.0	2.5	3.0	3.5	4.0	4.5	5.0	7.5	10.0	12.5	15.0	17.5
−10.0	−12.1	−14.5	−17.5	−21.3	−26.6	−36.3	—	—	—	—	—	—	—	—	—
−7.5	−9.3	−11.4	−13.8	−16.7	−20.4	−25.5	−34.4	—	—	—	—	—	—	—	—
−5.0	−6.6	−8.4	−10.4	−12.8	−15.6	−19.0	−23.7	−31.3	−78.6	—	—	—	—	—	—
−2.5	−3.9	−5.5	−7.3	−9.2	−11.4	−14.1	−17.3	−21.5	−27.7	−41.3	—	—	—	—	—
0.0	−1.3	−2.7	−4.2	−5.9	−7.7	−9.8	−12.3	−15.2	−18.9	−23.9	—	—	—	—	—
2.5	1.3	0.1	−1.3	−2.7	−4.3	−6.1	−8.0	−10.3	−12.9	−16.1	—	—	—	—	—
5.0	3.9	2.8	1.6	0.3	−1.1	−2.6	−4.2	−6.1	−8.1	−10.4	−47.7	—	—	—	—
7.5	6.5	5.5	4.4	3.2	2.0	0.7	−0.8	−2.3	−4.0	−5.8	−21.6	—	—	—	—
10.0	9.1	8.1	7.1	6.0	4.9	3.8	2.5	1.2	−0.2	−1.8	−12.8	—	—	—	—
12.5	11.6	10.7	9.8	8.8	7.8	6.7	5.6	4.5	3.2	1.9	−6.8	−28.2	—	—	—
15.0	14.2	13.3	12.5	11.6	10.6	9.6	8.6	7.6	6.5	5.3	−1.9	−14.5	—	—	—
17.5	16.7	15.9	15.1	14.3	13.4	12.5	11.5	10.6	9.6	8.5	2.3	−7.0	−35.1	—	—
20.0	19.3	18.5	17.7	16.9	16.1	15.3	14.4	13.5	12.6	11.6	6.1	−1.4	−14.9	—	—
22.5	21.8	21.1	20.3	19.6	18.8	18.0	17.2	16.3	15.5	14.6	9.6	3.2	−6.3	−37.5	—
25.0	24.3	23.6	22.9	22.2	21.4	20.7	19.9	19.1	18.3	17.5	12.9	7.3	−0.2	−13.7	—
27.5	26.8	26.2	25.5	24.8	24.1	23.3	22.6	21.9	21.1	20.3	16.1	11.1	4.7	−4.7	−31.7
30.0	29.4	28.7	28.0	27.4	26.7	26.0	25.3	24.6	23.8	23.1	19.1	14.5	9.0	1.6	−11.1
32.5	31.9	31.2	30.6	29.9	29.3	28.6	27.9	27.2	26.5	25.8	22.1	17.8	12.8	6.6	−2.4
35.0	34.4	33.8	33.1	32.5	31.9	31.2	30.6	29.9	29.2	28.5	24.9	21.0	16.4	11.0	3.9
37.5	36.9	36.3	35.7	35.1	34.4	33.8	33.2	32.5	31.9	31.2	27.7	24.0	19.8	14.9	8.9
40.0	39.4	38.8	38.2	37.6	37.0	36.4	35.8	35.1	34.5	33.9	30.5	26.9	23.0	18.5	13.3

FIGURE 6.10
Water vapor imagery from satellites portrays atmospheric moisture at altitudes above 3000 m (10,000 ft) as in this October 2005 image of Hurricane Wilma. Milky white indicates relatively high concentrations of water vapor; black signals little or no water vapor; and bright white blotches are clouds.

extreme, black indicates little or no water vapor, whereas at the other extreme, milky white signals a relatively high concentration of water vapor. Clouds appear as bright white blotches.

Sequential water vapor images viewed in rapid succession to detect motion show water vapor being transported horizontally as huge swirling plumes, often originating over tropical seas. A typical **water vapor**

plume can be several hundred kilometers wide and thousands of kilometers in length (Figure 6.11). Plumes supply moisture to hurricanes, thunderstorm clusters, and winter storms. Water vapor imagery also reveals something about the vertical (up and down) motion of air. Most water vapor originates at the surface of the Earth so that air is moving upward in humid regions (appearing milky white) and downward in dry regions (appearing black).

FIGURE 6.11
A water vapor image portraying long-distance transport of water vapor in two plumes, one in Central US off the Pacific and through Mexico, feeding thunderstorms along a cold front, and another in Southeastern US with Tropical Storm Tammy (October 2005) off the Gulf of Mexico and the Atlantic Ocean.

How Air Becomes Saturated

As the relative humidity nears 100%, condensation or deposition of water vapor becomes more and more likely. Condensation or deposition within the atmosphere produces clouds so the probability of cloud development increases as the relative humidity nears saturation. A **cloud** is a visible aggregate of tiny water droplets and/or ice crystals suspended in the atmosphere. (Under special circumstances, the relative humidity can rise slightly higher than 100% without water vapor changing phase; in that case air is *supersaturated*.)

What causes the relative humidity to increase? This is an important question because clouds are required for precipitation and without precipitation, the global water cycle would not exist (and neither would we). The relative humidity of unsaturated air increases: (1) When air is cooled; the saturation vapor pressure decreases while the actual vapor pressure remains constant (or equivalently, the air temperature falls to the dewpoint). (2) When water vapor is added to the air at constant temperature; the vapor pressure increases while the saturation vapor pressure remains constant. In this chapter, we focus on the first process in which expansional cooling of air results in saturation.

Expansional cooling is the principal means whereby clouds form in the atmosphere. Recall from Chapter 5 that ascending air expands and cools whereas descending air is compressed and warms. As ascending currents of unsaturated (clear) air cool, the relative humidity increases and approaches saturation. At or near saturation, clouds form. On the other hand, descending currents of air warm and the relative humidity decreases. Clouds vaporize or fail to develop. Within the atmosphere, expansional cooling and compressional warming of unsaturated air are essentially *adiabatic processes*. This enables us to accurately predict the change in temperature of unsaturated air parcels as they ascend or descend within the atmosphere. Recall from Chapter 5 that the dry adiabatic lapse rate is 9.8 Celsius degrees per 1000 m (5.5 Fahrenheit degrees per 1000 ft) whereas the average moist adiabatic lapse rate is 6 Celsius degrees per 1000 m (3.3 Fahrenheit degrees per 1000 ft).

Regardless of temperature, the relative humidity of ascending saturated (cloudy) air remains constant at about 100%. As saturated air expands and cools, however, its saturation mixing ratio declines and so does its actual mixing ratio. That is, some water vapor is converted to water droplets (condensation) or ice crystals (deposition).

Consider an example. Saturated air at 10 °C (50 °F) has a mixing ratio of about 7.8 g/kg (Table 6.4). If that air is lifted 1000 m, it cools moist adiabatically to 4 °C (39 °F). At that temperature, the saturation mixing ratio is about 5.1 g/kg. Because the relative humidity remains at 100%, the mixing ratio must drop from 7.8 g/kg to about 5.1 g/kg. This means that 2.7 g/kg of water vapor condensed to cloud droplets. Some of these cloud droplets may grow into raindrops and fall out of the cloud (Chapter 7).

As long as an air parcel continues ascending and expanding, its temperature drops. Forces arising from density differences between a rising air parcel and the surrounding (ambient) air may either enhance or suppress vertical motion of air. The net effect depends on the stability of the atmosphere.

Atmospheric Stability

At constant pressure, the higher the temperature of an air parcel, the lower is its density. Parcels that are warmer (less dense) than the ambient air are buoyed upward by the denser surrounding air, whereas parcels that are cooler (denser) than the ambient air tend to sink. An air parcel continues to rise or sink until it reaches ambient air of the same density (i.e., the same temperature).

Meteorologists determine **atmospheric stability** by comparing the temperature change of an ascending or descending air parcel with the temperature profile, or *sounding*, of the ambient air through which the parcel ascends or descends. As we have seen, the cooling rate of a rising air parcel depends on whether the parcel is saturated (moist adiabatic lapse rate) or unsaturated (dry adiabatic lapse rate), whereas the warming rate of any descending air parcel is essentially 9.8 Celsius degrees per 1000 m. Recall from Chapter 2 that balloon-borne radiosondes routinely monitor the vertical temperature profile (sounding) of the ambient air up to an altitude of about 30,000 m (100,000 ft) where the balloon bursts.

Within a **stable air layer**, an ascending air parcel becomes cooler (denser) than the ambient air, and a descending air parcel becomes warmer (less dense) than the ambient air (Figure 6.12). Any upward or downward displacement of an air parcel in stable air gives rise to forces that will tend to return the parcel to its original altitude. Within an **unstable air layer**, on the other hand, an ascending air parcel remains warmer (less dense) than the ambient air and continues to ascend, whereas a descending air parcel remains cooler (denser) than the ambient air and continues to descend (Figure 6.13).

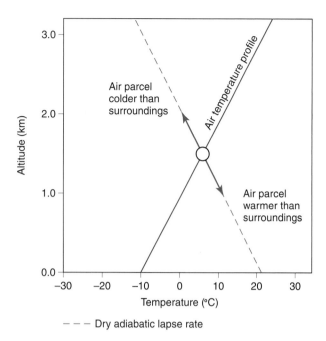

FIGURE 6.12
Upward and downward displacements of an unsaturated air parcel within a stable air layer. The displaced parcel is subject to a force that restores it to its original altitude; that is, stable air inhibits vertical motion.

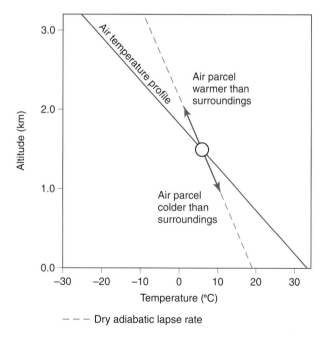

FIGURE 6.13
Upward and downward displacements of an unsaturated air parcel within an unstable air layer. The displaced parcel accelerates away from its original altitude; that is, unstable air enhances vertical motion.

SOUNDINGS

Although lapse rates for both unsaturated and saturated air parcels moving vertically within the atmosphere are essentially fixed, the actual temperature profile (sounding) of the ambient air changes significantly, sometimes even from one hour to the next. Changes in the sounding often translate into changes in atmospheric stability. Soundings (and stability) can change as a consequence of (1) local radiational heating or cooling, (2) air mass advection, or (3) large-scale ascent or descent of air.

On a clear and calm night, radiational cooling chills the ground, which in turn, cools and stabilizes the air immediately above the surface. On the other hand, during the day, intense solar radiation heats the ground, which in turn, heats and destabilizes the overlying air. An air mass is stabilized as it travels over a colder surface (snow-covered ground, for example), but is destabilized as it flows over a warmer surface. Through radiation or advection, atmospheric stability changes because the temperature profile (i.e., the sounding) changes. Air is stabilized when cooling from below reduces the temperature lapse rate (the rate at which air temperature varies with increasing altitude), and air is destabilized when heating from below increases the temperature lapse rate.

Generally, an air layer becomes more stable when it descends (subsides) but less stable when it ascends. When an air layer subsides, the upper portion undergoes more compressional warming than does the lower portion so that the lapse rate within the air layer decreases and stability increases. On the other hand, the lower portion of an ascending air layer is usually more humid than the upper portion and so achieves saturation sooner. Consequent release of latent heat in the lower portion of the air layer increases the lapse rate and stability decreases. Further complicating matters, stability can change with altitude. For example, a stable air layer may be sandwiched between unstable air layers. Different types of air mass advection occurring at different altitudes within the troposphere are often responsible for such variations in stability.

Figure 6.14 summarizes atmospheric stability conditions for a variety of soundings, along with the dry adiabatic and average moist adiabatic lapse rates. If the sounding indicates that the temperature of the ambient air is dropping more rapidly with altitude than the dry adiabatic lapse rate (that is, more than 9.8 Celsius degrees per 1000 m), then the ambient air is unstable for both saturated and unsaturated air parcels. This situation is called **absolute instability**. If the sounding lies between the dry adiabatic and moist adiabatic lapse rates, **conditional stability**

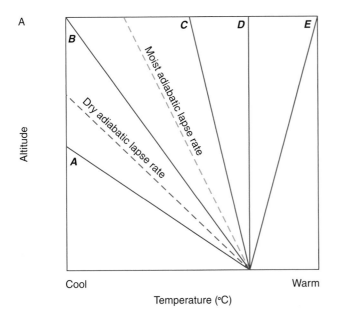

A

B

Sounding	Clear air	Cloudy air	Category	
A	Unstable	Unstable	Absolute instability	
B	Stable	Unstable	Conditional stability	
C	Stable	Stable	Lapse	Absolute stability
D	Stable	Stable	Isothermal	
E	Stable	Stable	Inversion	

FIGURE 6.14
Air stability is determined by comparing the temperature (density) of an ascending or descending air parcel with the temperature (density) of the surrounding air (sounding). (A) An air parcel at the Earth's surface initially has the same temperature as its surroundings. If the parcel is lifted, its temperature drops either dry adiabatically if it is unsaturated (clear air), or moist adiabatically if it is saturated (cloudy air). The temperature of the surrounding air is determined by radiosonde measurements. Depending on the specific sounding (*A* through *E*), the atmosphere is either stable or unstable. Stability conditions for each of the five sample soundings are summarized in B.

prevails. That is, the air layer is stable for unsaturated air parcels and unstable for saturated air parcels. This situation is relatively common. Conditional stability means that unsaturated air must be forced upward in order to reach saturation. But once saturation is achieved, the now cloudy air cools at the moist adiabatic lapse rate.

An air layer is stable for both saturated and unsaturated air parcels when the sounding indicates any of the following conditions: (1) The temperature of the ambient air drops more slowly with altitude than the moist adiabatic lapse rate. (2) The temperature does not change

with altitude (*isothermal*). (3) The temperature increases with altitude (*temperature inversion*). Any one of these three types of temperature profiles indicates **absolute stability**.

What happens when a sounding coincides with either the dry or moist adiabatic lapse rate? A sounding that equals the dry adiabatic lapse rate is neutral for unsaturated air parcels and unstable for saturated air parcels. A sounding that is the same as the moist adiabatic lapse rate is neutral for saturated air parcels but stable for unsaturated air parcels. Within a **neutral air layer**, a rising or descending air parcel always has the same temperature (and density) as its surroundings. Hence, a neutral air layer neither impedes nor spurs upward or downward motion of air parcels.

Atmospheric stability influences weather by affecting the vertical motion of air. Stable air suppresses vertical motion whereas unstable air enhances vertical motion, convection, expansional cooling, and cloud development. Because stability also affects the rate at which polluted air mixes with clean air, stability is an important factor in assessing air pollution potential. We examine this issue in this chapter's third Essay, Atmospheric Stability and Air Quality.

STÜVE DIAGRAM
Soundings and adiabatic processes in the atmosphere can be displayed graphically on a thermodynamic diagram. Although several types are available, in this book we use the **Stüve thermodynamic diagram**.

The Stüve diagram is designed to permit evaluation of various atmospheric processes using graphical techniques (Figure 6.15). Coordinates on this diagram consist of temperature in °C and °F (horizontal axis), increasing from left to right, and pressure in millibars (vertical axis), decreasing upward. Also marked on some diagrams are altitudes (in km and ft) that correspond to pressure levels, based on the standard atmosphere (Chapter 5). The dry adiabatic lapse rate is represented by a family of straight red lines slanting from lower right toward upper left. Often these lines are called *dry adiabats*. An ascending unsaturated air parcel follows a dry adiabat (either along one of the drawn adiabats or one that parallels the printed lines) from its initial temperature and pressure to its final temperature and pressure. Consider an example.

Suppose that the temperature of an unsaturated air parcel is 20 °C (68 °F) and the air pressure is 1000 mb. These initial conditions plot as point A on the Stüve

FIGURE 6.15
A Stüve thermodynamic
diagram.

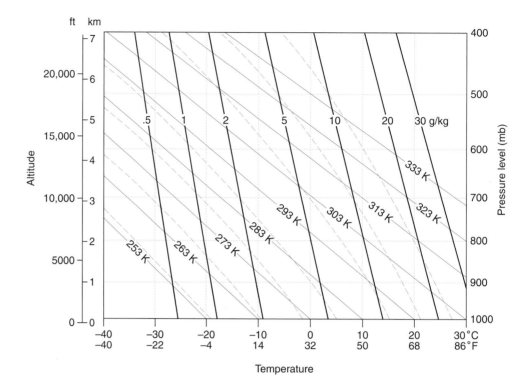

diagram in Figure 6.16. Now simulate expansional cooling by lifting the air parcel to the 850-mb level by moving along a dry adiabat. The temperature of the parcel at 850 mb is about 8 °C (46 °F) (point B in Figure 6.16). Now continue along the dry adiabat to a pressure of 700 mb where the air parcel temperature is about −8 °C (18 °F) (point C in Figure 6.16). Finally, move back along the same dry

adiabat to 1000 mb to simulate descent of the air parcel and compressional warming. Because it warms during descent at the same rate as it cooled during ascent, the temperature of the parcel is now at its original value of 20 °C (68 °F). In this case, the parcel remained unsaturated; water vapor did not change phase so that latent heat was not a factor in altering the parcel's temperature.

FIGURE 6.16
On a Stüve thermodynamic
diagram, an unsaturated air
parcel at point A is subject to
a dry adiabatic expansion to
point B (850 mb) and then to
point C (700 mb).

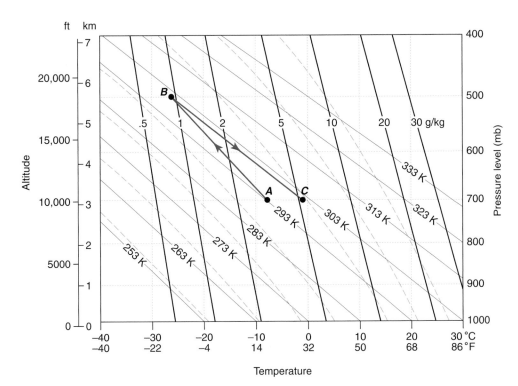

FIGURE 6.17
On a Stüve thermodynamic diagram, a saturated air parcel at point A (700 mb) is subject to a moist adiabatic expansion to point B (500 mb). The parcel is then subject to a dry adiabatic compression to point C (700 mb).

Moist adiabatic lapse rates appear on a Stüve diagram as a set of gently curving dashed lines, also known as *moist adiabats*. Moist adiabats become nearly indistinguishable from dry adiabats at very low pressure and low temperature—where very little water vapor exists and latent heat release is minimal. An ascending saturated air parcel follows a moist adiabat (either along one of the drawn moist adiabats or one that parallels the printed lines) from its initial temperature and pressure to its final temperature and pressure. Consider an example.

Suppose that a parcel of saturated air at the base of a cloud has a temperature of −8 °C (18 °F) at a pressure of 700 mb (point A in Figure 6.17). As the parcel ascends along a moist adiabat to 500 mb, its temperature drops to −27 °C (−17 °F) (point B in Figure 6.17). Assume that the water that condensed during the ascent immediately fell out of the parcel (as precipitation). If the parcel then descends back to the 700-mb level, it follows a dry adiabat and is compressionally warmed to −1 °C (30 °F) (point C in Figure 6.17). The parcel is now some 7 Celsius degrees (12 Fahrenheit degrees) warmer than it was when it started its ascent because of the release of latent heat due to phase changes of water vapor during its ascent.

Plotting a sounding on a Stüve diagram enables meteorologists to determine the stability of various layers within the atmosphere and assess the potential for deep convection and cloud development. Meteorologists also use plotted values of saturation mixing ratio (slanted black lines labeled in gm per kg) to determine relative humidity and saturation levels of rising air parcels.

Lifting Processes

Ascending unsaturated air cools and its relative humidity increases. With sufficient ascent and expansional cooling, the relative humidity nears 100% and condensation or deposition begins; that is, clouds form. What causes air to rise? Air rises (1) as the ascending branch of a convection current, (2) along the surface of a front, (3) up the slopes of a hill or mountain, or (4) where surface winds converge.

As we saw in Chapter 4, sensible heating (conduction and convection) is a means of heat transfer between Earth's surface and atmosphere. The sun heats Earth's surface, which then heats the overlying air by conduction. The heated air expands and its density decreases. Cool, dense air sinks toward Earth's surface and displaces the less dense heated air. The heated air rises, expands, and cools. Cumulus clouds may form where convection currents ascend and the sky is generally cloud-free where convection currents descend (Figure 6.18). The higher the altitude reached by ascending convection currents, the greater the amount of expansional cooling, and the more likely it is that clouds (and precipitation)

FIGURE 6.18
A convection current consists of (A) an updraft and a downdraft; (B) cumulus clouds form where air ascends while the surrounding sky is cloud-free where the air descends.

will form. Convection currents that soar to great altitudes within the troposphere typically spawn thunderstorms (*cumulonimbus clouds*).

Clouds and precipitation are often triggered by **frontal uplift**, which occurs where contrasting air masses meet. Recall that a *front* is a narrow zone of transition between two air masses that differ in temperature and/or humidity (Chapter 1). A warm and humid air mass is less dense than a cold and dry air mass and hence, as a cold air mass retreats, the warm air advances by riding up

and over the cold air (Figure 1.6A). The leading edge of the advancing warm air at Earth's surface is known as a *warm front*. In contrast, cold and dry air displaces warm and humid air by sliding under it and forcing the warm air upward (Figure 1.6B). The leading edge of advancing cold air at Earth's surface is known as a *cold front*. The net effect of the replacement of one air mass by another air mass is uplift and expansional cooling of air, cloud development, and perhaps rain or snow. Hence, clouds and precipitation are often (but not always) associated with fronts. Chapter 10 has much more about fronts and associated weather.

Orographic lifting occurs where air is forced upward by topography, the physical relief of the land. Horizontal winds sweeping across the landscape alternately ascend hills and descend into valleys. If relief is sufficiently great, the resulting expansional cooling and compressional warming of air affects cloud and precipitation development.

A mountain range that intercepts the prevailing winds forms a natural barrier that is responsible for a cloudier, wetter climate on one side of the range than on the other side (Figure 6.19). Air that is forced to ascend the *windward slopes* (facing the oncoming wind) expands and cools, which increases its relative humidity. With sufficient cooling, clouds and precipitation develop. The altitude at which the rising air becomes saturated and clouds form is known as the **lifting condensation level (LCL)** and usually corresponds to the base of the clouds. Meanwhile, air that descends the *leeward slopes* (downwind side) is compressed and warms, raising its saturation vapor pressure. The

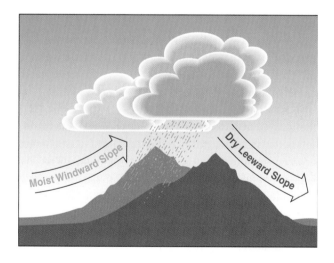

FIGURE 6.19
Winds ascend along the windward slopes of a mountain range and descend along the leeward slopes. The climate is wetter along the windward slopes than the leeward slopes.

relative humidity of descending air decreases and existing clouds vaporize so that precipitation is less likely. In this way, mountain ranges induce contrasting climates: moist climates on the windward slopes and dry climates on the leeward slopes. Dry conditions often extend many hundreds of kilometers downwind of a prominent mountain range; this region is known as a **rain shadow**. The Rocky Mountain rain shadow, for example, extends eastward from the Continental Divide to about the 100th meridian (100 degrees W longitude), traditionally considered to be the boundary between dry land or irrigated agriculture to the west and rain-fed agriculture to the east.

An orographically induced contrast in precipitation is apparent in the Pacific Northwest, where the north-south trending Coastal and Cascade Mountain Ranges intercept the prevailing west-to-east flow of humid air from off the Pacific Ocean. Exceptionally rainy conditions prevail in western Washington and Oregon, whereas semiarid conditions characterize much of the eastern portion of those states. For example, the average annual precipitation (rain plus melted snow) at Astoria, OR on the Pacific coast is 172 cm (67.7 in.) but only 20.8 cm (8.2 in.) at Yakima, WA in the rain shadow of the Cascade Mountains. This climate contrast affects the indigenous plant and animal communities, domestic water supply, demand for irrigation water, types of crops that can be grown, and requirements for human shelter.

The influence of topography on precipitation patterns is also impressive on the mountainous islands of Hawaii, where a few volcanic peaks top 4000 m (13,000 ft). Over the ocean waters surrounding the islands, estimated mean annual rainfall is uniformly between about 560 mm (22 in.) and 700 mm (28 in.). On the islands, however, mean annual precipitation is much more variable ranging from only 190 mm (7.5 in.) leeward of the Kohala Mountains on the Big Island of Hawaii to 11,990 mm (39.3 ft) on the windward slopes of Mount Waialeale on the island of Kauai.

Another mechanism that leads to uplift and cloud formation is convergence of surface winds. Associated upward motion means expansional cooling, increasing relative humidity, and eventually cloud and perhaps precipitation formation. In later chapters, we describe weather systems in which convergence of surface winds plays an important role in triggering stormy weather. For example, converging surface winds are largely responsible for cloudiness and precipitation in a low-pressure system (cyclone). Also, converging sea breezes is a major factor in the relatively high frequency of thunderstorms in central Florida (Chapter 11).

Fronts, topography, or converging winds can force stable unsaturated air upward to the point that clouds develop. If the air is conditionally stable, clouds will surge upward and precipitation may be heavy. On the other hand, if air is absolutely stable, clouds will show little vertical development and precipitation is likely to be light if it occurs at all.

Conclusions

The atmosphere is one of many reservoirs of water in the global water cycle. Water vapor enters the atmosphere from Earth's surface via evaporation of liquid water, transpiration by plants, and sublimation of ice and snow. Water moves from the atmosphere to Earth's surface via precipitation, condensation (dew), and deposition (frost). The amount of water vapor in air (humidity) can be expressed as vapor pressure, mixing ratio, specific humidity, absolute humidity, relative humidity, dewpoint, or precipitable water. The saturation vapor pressure and saturation mixing ratio increase with rising air temperature so that the water vapor component is greater in saturated warm air than in saturated cold air. On the other hand, the relative humidity of an unsaturated air parcel varies inversely with temperature.

Expansional cooling is the principal means whereby air becomes saturated with respect to water and clouds form. Ascending air expands and cools, its relative humidity nears 100%, and water vapor condenses (or deposits) as aggregates of tiny water droplets (or ice crystals) that are visible as clouds. Conversely, descending air is compressed and warms, its relative humidity drops, and clouds vaporize or fail to develop in the first place.

Ascending air parcels cool at the dry adiabatic lapse rate if unsaturated and at the moist adiabatic lapse rate if saturated. Atmospheric stability influences vertical motion in the atmosphere such that stable ambient air suppresses convection and the associated ascent of air parcels and cloud development, whereas unstable ambient air enhances ascent of air parcels and favors cloud development. Atmospheric stability can be determined by comparing the cooling rate of ascending air parcels with the temperature profile (sounding) of the ambient air through which air parcels ascend. Air ascends in convection currents, along fronts, up the slopes of mountain ranges, and in response to converging surface winds.

We continue our study of moisture in the atmosphere in the next chapter with a focus on cloud and precipitation forming processes.

Basic Understandings

- The global water cycle is the ceaseless circulation of a fixed quantity of water among Earth's oceanic, atmospheric, and terrestrial reservoirs. Powered by solar radiation and influenced by gravity, water and heat energy move between Earth's surface and the atmosphere via evaporation, condensation, transpiration, sublimation, deposition, and precipitation.

- The global water budget indicates an annual surplus of water on the land (more precipitation than evapotranspiration) and a deficit of water at sea (more evaporation than precipitation), implying a net flow of water from land to sea. Precipitation falling on land vaporizes, infiltrates the ground, is taken up by plant roots and transpired to the atmosphere, and/or runs off into rivers or streams.

- Vapor pressure, mixing ratio, specific humidity, and absolute humidity are direct measures of the water vapor component of air. At a specific temperature, relative humidity compares the actual amount of water vapor in air to the amount of water vapor at saturation.

- Saturation vapor pressure and saturation mixing ratio signal an equilibrium in the flux of water molecules entering and leaving the vapor phase. Both parameters increase with rising temperature because temperature largely regulates the rate of vaporization of water.

- When the water vapor concentration of air equals the water vapor concentration at saturation, the relative humidity is 100%. For the same unsaturated air, the relative humidity varies inversely with air temperature. On a calm day, the relative humidity is highest when the air temperature is lowest (near sunrise), and the relative humidity is lowest when the air temperature is highest (early to mid-afternoon).

- Dewpoint is the temperature to which air is cooled at constant pressure to achieve saturation. Dew consists of tiny droplets of water that condense onto cold surfaces from air that has been chilled to its dewpoint and below. When cooling at constant pressure produces saturation at air temperatures below freezing, water vapor deposits on cold surfaces as frost, ice crystals that form on the exposed surfaces of objects. The

air temperature at which frost begins forming is called the frost point.

- Precipitable water is the depth of water that would be produced if all the water vapor in a vertical column of air, extending from Earth's surface to the tropopause, were condensed into liquid water. Generally, the amount of precipitable water decreases with increasing latitude in response to lower average temperatures and reduced evaporation.

- Hygrometers are instruments that directly measure the water vapor concentration of air. They include dewpoint hygrometers, hair hygrometers, and electronic hygrometers. A less direct measure of humidity is provided by a psychrometer consisting of dry-bulb and wet-bulb thermometers mounted side-by-side. The greater the wet-bulb temperature depression, the lower is the relative humidity. When the wet-bulb and dry-bulb temperatures are equal, the relative humidity is 100%.

- Water vapor imagery obtained by sensors onboard satellites portrays water vapor (and clouds) at altitudes above about 3000 m (10,000 ft) and is derived from infrared radiation emitted by atmospheric water at a wavelength of 6.7 micrometers. Water vapor plumes revealed in water vapor images are particularly valuable for tracking the long-distance transport of moisture plumes within the atmosphere.

- The relative humidity of unsaturated air increases when the air is cooled (lowering the saturation vapor pressure) or when water vapor is added to the air (increasing the vapor pressure) at constant temperature. As the relative humidity nears 100%, clouds are increasingly likely to form.

- Expansional cooling is the principal means whereby clouds form in the atmosphere. As ascending currents of unsaturated (clear) air cool, the relative humidity increases and approaches saturation. At or near saturation, clouds form.

- Meteorologists determine atmospheric stability by comparing the temperature (or density) of an air parcel moving vertically (up or down) within the atmosphere with the temperature (or density) of the ambient air. Radiosondes and satellite sensors monitor the variation of ambient air temperature with altitude (a sounding).

- Stable air inhibits vertical motion, convection, and cloud formation. Unstable air enhances vertical motion, convection, and cloud formation. Local radiational heating or cooling, air mass advection, or large-scale ascent or subsidence can change the stability of an air mass.

- Expansional cooling and cloud development occur through uplift of air in convection currents, along fronts or mountain slopes, or where surface winds converge. Clouds form in the updraft of convection currents but dissipate or fail to develop in the downdraft. The ascent of warmer, less dense air along a front may give rise to clouds and precipitation.

- Winds ascend along the windward slopes of a mountain range and descend along the leeward slopes. For this reason, the windward slopes tend to be cloudier and wetter than the leeward slopes. A rain shadow may extend hundreds of kilometers downwind of a prominent mountain range.

Questions for Review

1. Distinguish among evaporation, transpiration, condensation, deposition, and sublimation.
2. Explain how and why heat energy is involved in phase change of water.
3. Distinguish between air pressure and vapor pressure. How do they compare in magnitude near Earth's surface?
4. Under what atmospheric condition is the actual mixing ratio equal to the saturation mixing ratio?
5. On a clear and calm day, why does the relative humidity usually fall from near sunrise to early afternoon?
6. Ascending parcels of saturated (cloudy) air cool more slowly than ascending parcels of unsaturated (clear) air. Explain why.
7. How does atmospheric stability influence the upward and downward motions of air parcels?
8. Why are clouds and precipitation often generated along fronts?
9. Explain how mountain ranges influence the development of clouds.
10. Is it possible for thunderstorms to form if the lower troposphere is conditionally stable? Explain your answer.

Critical Thinking Questions

1. Does a relative humidity of 25% measured on a cold day in January indicate the same water vapor presence as a relative humidity of 25% measured on a hot day in July? Explain your response.
2. With intense radiational cooling during the early morning hours, the air temperature is observed to fall rapidly until frost forms. Thereafter, until sunrise, the air temperature either remains steady or falls slowly. Why the change in air temperature behavior?
3. In early winter, cold air flows from snow-covered land out over the ice-free waters of Lake Ontario. Describe how and why the stability of the air mass changes.
4. Would you expect convective clouds (e.g., cumulus) to form over Antarctica? Explain your response.
5. Two otherwise identical air parcels, the first having a lower water vapor content than the second, are lifted from the same altitude. Which parcel would first experience condensation or deposition of water vapor? Why?
6. In winter at middle latitudes, the *relative humidity* is typically lower within a house than outside whereas the *absolute humidity* is usually higher within a house than outside. Explain this observation.
7. Determine the mixing ratio if the....
   a. relative humidity is 25% and the saturation mixing ratio is 24 g/kg.
   b. relative humidity is 100% and the air temperature is 30°C (86 °F).
   c. relative humidity is 80% and the saturation mixing ratio is 15 g/kg.
8. Outdoor air at 0 °C (32 °F) and relative humidity of 90% is brought indoors and heated to 20 °C (68 °F). Compute the relative humidity of the indoor air.
9. An unsaturated air parcel initially has a temperature of 0 °C (32 °F). Assuming that the relative humidity remains less than 100%, predict the temperature of the parcel after it is lifted 2500 m (8200 ft).
10. Determine whether the following soundings are stable, unstable, or neutral for both saturated and unsaturated air parcels.
a. +10 C°/1000 m	b. −5 C°/1000 m	c. −8 C°/1000 m
d. −10 F°/1000 ft	e. +1 F°/1000 ft	f. −13 C°/1000 m

ESSAY: Humidity and Human Comfort

The relationship between the vapor pressure of ambient air and evaporative cooling helps explain why people usually are more uncomfortable when the weather is both hot and humid. At air temperatures above about 25 °C (77 °F), perspiring and consequent evaporative cooling enhance heat loss from the body. But if the air is also humid, the evaporation rate is reduced, hampering the body's ability to maintain a nearly constant core temperature of approximately 37 °C (98.6 °F). The body's *core* refers to vital organs such as the heart and lungs. In contrast, drier air promotes evaporative cooling. At air temperatures above about 25 °C (77 °F), most people feel more comfortable when the air is dry rather than humid.

A combination of high temperature and high humidity adversely affects everyone to some extent. People generally are more irritable and less able to perform physical and mental tasks. During hot and humid weather, the efficiency of factory workers declines and students do not concentrate as well on their studies. Extreme heat and humidity are a potentially lethal combination when these weather conditions overtax the body's capacity to maintain a constant core temperature. Heat and humidity can also exacerbate other health problems leading to premature death.

In mid-July 1995, high air temperature combined with unusually high humidity pushed the so-called *heat index* to record high levels over the Midwest and in many cities along the East Coast. More than 1000 people lost their lives—more than the average annual number of fatalities in the U.S. from floods, hurricanes, and tornadoes. Chicago was particularly hard hit. Public safety officials estimate the number of deaths from the heat and humidity based on the *excess death rate*, that is, the number of reported deaths minus the typical number of deaths over a specified period. During the week of 14-20 July 1995, 739 Chicagoans above the norm died. According to the U.S. Centers for Disease Control and Prevention, individuals most vulnerable to the hazard of heat and humidity are elderly people who live alone, do not leave home daily, lack access to transportation, are sick or bedridden, do not have social contacts nearby, and have no air conditioning. Although the July 1995 heat wave was an extreme weather event with an unusually high mortality, National Weather Service scientists estimate that episodes of extreme heat (usually accompanied by high humidity) on average take the lives of almost 150 people annually in the U.S. (based on records from 1985 to 2003). Consequently, extreme heat has been the nation's most deadly weather hazard.

In the summer of 2003, extreme heat rather than a combination of heat and humidity was to blame for one of Europe's deadliest heat waves in a century. The World Meteorological Organization (WMO) placed the total heat-related death toll at more than 21,000. Based on the *excess death rate* method, the estimated mortality for individual nations was: France, 14,802; Germany, 7000; Spain, 4230; Italy, 4175; England and Wales, 2045.

Persistent episodes of hot, dry weather began in late spring and in some parts of Europe persisted until early October. From Spain to Hungary, the June mean temperature was 3 to 5 Celsius degrees (5.4 to 9 Fahrenheit degrees) above the long-term average. The heat wave during the first half of August was particularly severe with some localities establishing all-time maximum temperature records. During July-August from southern Spain to central France, the daily maximum temperature topped 34 °C (93 °F) on 30 to 50 days, some 20 days more than normal. Most Europeans are not accustomed to such extreme heat. Furthermore, the accompanying dry weather contributed to wildfires and significantly cut crop yields.

Scientists have experimented with a variety of indexes that attempt to gauge the combined influence of temperature and humidity on human wellbeing and advise people of the potential hazards of heat stress. Since the summer of 1984, the National Weather Service has regularly reported the *heat index*, or *apparent temperature index*, which was developed by R.G. Steadman in 1979. The heat index accounts for the increasing inability of the human body to dissipate heat to the environment as the relative humidity rises. As illustrated in Table 1, at an air temperature of 90 °F (32 °C) and a relative humidity of 60%, the body loses heat to the environment at the same rate as if the air temperature were 105 °F (41 °C) with a relative humidity of 10%. In both cases, the *apparent temperature* is 100 °F (38 °C). Examination of Table 1 reveals that various combinations of air temperature and relative humidity produce the same apparent temperature, implying that all these temperature/relative-humidity combinations have the same impact on human comfort and wellbeing.

The heat index is divided into four categories based on the severity of potential health impacts; these categories and associated symptoms of heat stress are listed in Table 2. Apparent temperatures in category IV pose the least hazard.

TABLE 1
Apparent Temperature Index

Air Temp. (°F)	Relative Humidity (%)																				
	0	5	10	15	20	25	30	35	40	45	50	55	60	65	70	75	80	85	90	95	100
120	107	111	116	123	130	139	148														
115	103	107	111	115	120	127	135	143	151												
110	99	102	105	108	112	117	123	130	137	143	150										
105	95	97	100	102	105	109	113	118	123	129	135	142	149								
100	91	93	95	97	99	101	104	107	110	115	120	126	132	138	144						
95	87	88	90	91	93	94	96	98	101	104	107	110	114	119	124	130	136				
90	83	84	85	86	87	88	90	91	93	95	96	98	100	102	106	109	113	117	122		
85	76	79	80	81	82	83	84	85	86	87	88	89	90	91	93	95	97	99	102	105	108
80	73	74	75	76	77	77	78	79	79	80	81	81	82	83	85	86	86	87	88	89	91
75	69	69	70	71	72	72	73	73	74	74	75	75	76	76	77	77	78	78	79	79	80
70	64	64	65	65	66	66	67	67	68	68	69	69	70	70	70	70	71	71	71	71	72

TABLE 2
Hazards Posed by Heat Stress by Range of Apparent Temperature[a]

Category	Apparent temperature	Heat syndrome
I	130 °F (54 °C) or higher	Extreme danger; heat stroke imminent.
II	105 to 130 °F (41 to 54 °C)	Danger; heat cramps or heat exhaustion likely. Heat stroke possible with prolonged exposure and physical activity.
III	90 to 105 °F (32 to 41 °C)	Heat cramps or heat exhaustion possible with prolonged exposure and physical activity.
IV	80 to 90 °F (27 to 32 °C)	Fatigue possible with prolonged exposure and physical activity.

Source: NOAA, National Weather Service
[a]Apparent temperature combines the effects of heat and humidity on human comfort.

When the apparent temperature is between 80 °F and 90 °F (27 °C and 32 °C), physical activity is more fatiguing than usual and caution is advised. At the opposite end of the scale, apparent temperatures in category I pose the greatest health risk. When the apparent temperature is 130 °F (53 °C) or higher, the danger is extreme and heatstroke (*hyperthermia*) may be imminent. During the heat wave of 10-16 July 1995, the highest heat index values were in the range of 115 °F to 120 °F (46 °C to 49 °C) (Figure 1).

The significance of a specific apparent temperature for personal wellbeing depends upon (1) the assumptions that form the basis of Steadman's index, and (2) age, general health, and body characteristics. Steadman's heat index assumes a person at rest in the shade with light winds. Personal experience tells us that exercise and exposure to the direct

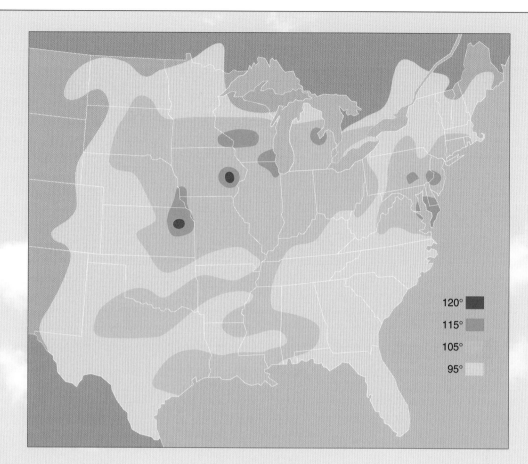

FIGURE 1
Maximum apparent temperature (in °F) recorded during the heat wave of 10-16 July 1995. [NOAA, Climate Prediction Center]

rays of the sun add considerably to the heat load that the body must dissipate to maintain a normal core temperature. For example, the apparent temperature may be as much as 8 Celsius degrees (14 Fahrenheit degrees) higher in direct sunlight than the shade. Furthermore, if the ambient air temperature is higher than skin temperature, the wind will convey more heat to the body than away from the body. Any combination of physical activity, exposure to direct sunlight, or hot winds elevates the danger of high temperature and high humidity than suggested by the apparent temperature.

Where do people experience the most uncomfortable (and potentially life-threatening) summer weather? In view of the adverse impact of high humidity on evaporative cooling, many of us would probably point to locales bordering the Gulf of Mexico where high temperature and high humidity are the norm. For example, during a summer heat wave, a typical temperature/relative humidity combination in New Orleans is 90 °F (32 °C)/60%. According to Tables 1 and 2, these conditions translate into an apparent temperature of 100 °F (38 °C), a category III hazard. During such weather conditions, most people would experience some discomfort and everyone is well advised to closely monitor his or her level of physical activity.

Perhaps surprisingly, North America's most stressful summer weather typically does not occur near the Gulf of Mexico, but instead in the deserts of Arizona and California. Although the relative humidity is considerably lower, much higher ambient air temperatures translate into greater heat stress than along the Gulf Coast. For example, residents of Phoenix, AZ experience summer afternoon temperatures that often approach 110 °F (43 °C) with a relative humidity of 20%. This combination of heat and humidity gives an apparent temperature of 112 °F (44 °C), a category II hazard. In general, residents of the eastern half of North America associate greater discomfort with the muggy days of summer whereas residents of the American Southwest ascribe their days of greatest discomfort to the very hot, albeit dry, conditions of the desert in summer.

Low humidity also influences human comfort. As the relative humidity declines, the vapor pressure gradient between the skin and the surrounding air increases, and the evaporative cooling rate rises. The lower the relative humidity, the greater the vapor pressure gradient, and consequently, the higher the rate of heat loss from the body via evaporative cooling. As shown in Table 1, for a specified ambient air temperature and successively lower values of relative humidity, the difference between apparent temperature and ambient air temperature decreases. Below some threshold value of relative humidity, the apparent temperature is actually lower than the ambient air temperature. At low relative humidity, people experience the apparent temperature as lower than the ambient air temperature because the higher rate of evaporation causes an excessive loss of heat. That is, enhanced evaporative cooling of the skin at low relative humidity gives the sensation that the air is cooler than it actually is.

ESSAY: Measuring Evaporation

The simplest and least expensive instrument for measuring evaporation is a *pan evaporimeter*, a large cylindrical metal pan filled with fresh water and equipped with a water height gauge, rain gauge, and floating thermometer (that monitors temperature at the air/water interface). Use of these devices for measuring evaporation dates back to the 19th century but the instrument was not standardized until 1951. The standard National Weather Service evaporation pan (often found at agricultural experiment stations) measures 121.9 cm (48 in.) in diameter and is 25.4 cm (10 in.) deep (Figure 1). Changes in water level are recorded as long as temperatures remain high enough that the water surface stays ice-free. The drop in water level from one day to the next (plus any rainfall) is recorded as evaporation.

A more sophisticated instrument for estimating direct evaporation plus transpiration (evapotranspiration) is the lysimeter. A *lysimeter* consists of an enclosed block of soil with a natural vegetation cover (usually grass) that is seated on a scale. Continuous measurements are made of rainfall and water percolating through the soil. Day-to-day changes in the weight of the soil block that are not accounted for by rainfall, runoff, or percolation are attributed to evapotranspiration.

A lysimeter can also be used to measure potential evapotranspiration, a useful parameter in arid and semiarid localities. *Potential evapotranspiration* refers to the maximum possible water loss (to vapor) given the available heat energy (required for latent heating). Potential evapotranspiration is measured in the same way as evapotranspiration except that the soil/vegetation surface of the lysimeter is continually irrigated. Under these conditions, evapotranspiration proceeds at the maximum possible rate. Lysimeters are even sunk into a snow pack to monitor sublimation and evaporation (of meltwater).

Numerical models are used to compute evapotranspiration based on direct measurements or estimates of selected environmental factors that influence the rate of vaporization of water. Evapotranspiration increases with rising temperature, increasing wind speed, and as the difference in vapor pressure between a water surface and the overlying air increases. Transpiration also varies with dewpoint, intensity of incident solar radiation, length of daylight, type of vegetation, stage in a plant's life cycle, and soil moisture.

FIGURE 1
Standard National Weather Service evaporation pan.

ESSAY: Atmospheric Stability and Air Quality

On the morning of 26 October 1948, a fog blanket reeking of pungent sulfur dioxide (SO_2) fumes spread over the town of Donora in southwestern Pennsylvania's Monongahela River Valley. Before the fog lifted some five days later, almost half of the area's 14,000 inhabitants had fallen ill and 20 had died. That killer fog resulted from a combination of mountainous topography and weather conditions that trapped and concentrated deadly effluents from the community's steel mill, zinc smelter, and sulfuric acid plant.

Air pollutants are especially dangerous when atmospheric conditions inhibit their dilution. Once pollutants enter the atmosphere through smokestacks or exhaust pipes, their concentrations usually begin to decline as they mix with cleaner air. The more thorough the mixing, the more rapid is the rate of dilution. When conditions in the atmosphere favor rapid dilution, the impact of air pollution is usually minor. On other occasions, called *air pollution episodes*, conditions in the atmosphere minimize dilution, and the impact can be severe, especially on human health. The two weather factors that most influence the rate of dilution are wind speed and atmospheric stability.

Intuitively, we know that air is likely to mix more thoroughly on a windy day than on a calm one. When it is windy, turbulent eddies accelerate dilution by mixing polluted air and cleaner air. But when the air is calm, dilution is by the much slower process of *molecular diffusion*, that is, dispersal at the molecular level. As a general rule, doubling the wind speed cuts the concentration of air pollutants in half (Figure 1). Some weather systems favor light winds and thus inhibit dispersal of contaminants. Over a broad region about the center of an *anticyclone* (a high pressure system), for example, winds are light or the air is calm, and pollutants do not disperse readily. On the other hand, within a *cyclone* (a low pressure system), stronger winds mean more rapid dilution of air pollution. In addition, rain or snow associated with a cyclone cleans the air by washing pollutants to the Earth's surface.

Atmospheric stability is a second factor that influences the rate at which polluted air mixes with clean air. Stability affects vertical motion within the atmosphere so that convection and turbulence are enhanced when the air is unstable but inhibited when the air is stable. A parcel of polluted air emitted into an unstable air environment undergoes more mixing than does the same parcel of polluted air emitted into a stable air environment. Stable air inhibits the vertical transport of air pollutants, and a layer of stable air aloft may act as a lid over the lower troposphere, trapping air pollutants near Earth's surface. Steady emission of contaminants into stable air results in the accumulation of pollutants.

Mixing depth is the vertical distance between Earth's surface and the altitude to which convection currents (i.e., mixing) reach. When mixing depths are great (many kilometers, for example), pollutants readily mix with the abundant volume of clean air and dilution is enhanced. When mixing depths are shallow (less than 1000 m, for example), air pollutants are restricted to a smaller volume of air, and concentrations may build to unhealthy levels. When air is stable, convection and turbulence are suppressed and mixing depths are shallow. When air is unstable, convection and turbulence are enhanced and mixing depths increase. Because solar heating triggers convection, mixing depths tend to be

FIGURE 1
Doubling the wind speed from 1 m per sec to 2 m per sec increases the spacing between puffs of smoke by a factor of two, thereby reducing pollutant concentrations by one half.

greater in the afternoon than in the morning, during the day than at night, and in summer than in winter.

We can sometimes estimate the stability of air layers by observing the behavior of a plume of smoke belching from a smokestack. If the smoke enters an unstable air layer, the plume undulates. In general, this plume behavior indicates that polluted air is mixing readily with the surrounding cleaner air and being diluted. The net effect is improved air quality (except where the plume may temporarily loop to the ground). On the other hand, a plume of smoke that flattens and spreads slowly downwind indicates very stable conditions and minimal dilution.

An air pollution episode is most likely when a persistent *temperature inversion* develops. Within an air layer characterized by a temperature inversion, air temperature increases with altitude; that is, warmer, lighter air overlies cooler, denser air. (A temperature inversion is the *inverse* of the usual temperature profile of the troposphere.) This extremely stable stratification strongly inhibits mixing and dilution of pollutants. A temperature inversion can form by (1) subsidence (sinking) of air, (2) extreme radiational cooling, or (3) some cases of air mass advection. The inversion may occur aloft or near Earth's surface.

A *subsidence temperature inversion* forms a lid over a broad area, often encompassing several states at once (Figure 2). It develops during a period of fair weather when a warm anticyclone (high pressure system) stalls. An anticyclone produces subsiding air that is warmed by compression. Subsiding warm air is prevented from reaching Earth's surface by the *mixing layer*, the portion of the troposphere in which convection thoroughly mixes the air. The air temperature within the mixing layer drops with altitude, but air just above the mixing layer, having been warmed by sinking and compression, is warmer than air at the top of the mixing layer. A temperature inversion marks a transition between the mixing layer below and the compressionally warmed air above. During these atmospheric conditions, air pollutants are distributed throughout the mixing layer, but no higher than the temperature inversion. Pollutants are confined to a relatively small volume of air, and continual emission will elevate concentrations.

A *radiational temperature inversion* is usually more localized than a subsidence temperature inversion (Figure 3). With clear night skies, radiational cooling chills both the ground and the air above the ground. However, the ground is a better emitter of infrared radiation than is the overlying air, so the ground surface cools faster than the air above it. Heat is conducted from the warmer

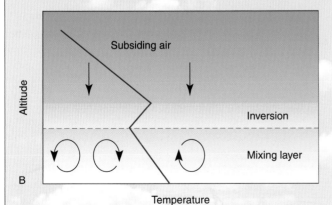

FIGURE 2
A temperature inversion can develop aloft through subsidence of air. Compare a sounding prior to subsidence (A) with a sounding during subsidence (B). The temperature inversion acts as lid over the lower atmosphere, trapping air pollutants.

FIGURE 3
A low-level temperature inversion caused by nocturnal radiational cooling.

overlying air to the cooler ground. Chilling of the air from below means that the coldest air is next to the ground and the air temperature increases with altitude; that is, a low-level temperature inversion forms. This process requires light winds or calm conditions because stronger winds would mix the air and prevent the stratification of warm air over cold air. A fresh snow cover often strengthens the inversion and hence, the stability.

A radiational temperature inversion usually disappears within a few hours after sunrise as the sun heats the ground and the wind strengthens. The ground heats the overlying air and eventually reestablishes a normal sounding in which air temperature decreases with altitude. In winter, however, where the sun's rays are relatively weak and a highly reflective layer of snow covers the ground, a radiational temperature inversion may persist for days or even weeks.

Advection of air masses can also give rise to temperature inversions and affect air quality. This sometimes happens at the base of the Rocky Mountains (Figure 4). A west wind is compressionally warmed as it descends the leeward slopes of the mountain range but along the foot of the mountains surface winds from the north advect a shallow layer of cold air southward. Hence, a temperature inversion aloft separates the relatively warm air above from the surface layer of cold air. Although temperature inversions also characterize warm and cold fronts, these inversions have little adverse effect on air quality because fronts are in motion and the accompanying precipitation washes pollutants from the air.

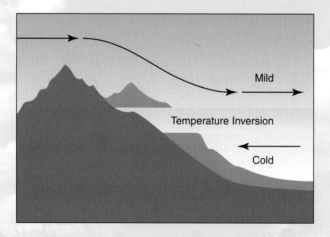

FIGURE 4
A temperature inversion develops aloft adjacent to the leeward slopes of the Rocky Mountains. A west-to-east air flow descends the leeward slopes, is warmed by compression, and overlies a layer of colder air advected southward by north winds.

CHAPTER 7

CLOUDS, PRECIPITATION, AND WEATHER RADAR

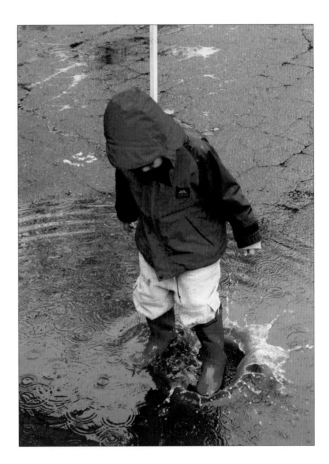

Youngster conducting a "splash test" in Seattle, Washington, after the city received 25 straight days of rain. The streak finally ended on 15 January 2006, at 27 straight days. [Photo by John Y. Geer]

Case in Point

A familiar sight in the daytime sky almost anywhere is *contrails*, bright white streamers of ice crystals that form in the exhaust of jet aircraft (Figure 7.1). Contrails are modifying the cloud cover along heavily traveled air corridors between major urban areas with possible implications for weather and climate. According to some studies, contrails already cover about 5% of the sky in some portions of the eastern United States. A contrail, short for *con*densation *trail*, develops when

FIGURE 7.1
Contrails form when the hot, humid exhaust from jet aircraft engines mixes with the cold, drier ambient air.

the hot humid air in jet engine exhaust mixes with the cold, drier air at high altitudes. Turbulence in the exhaust causes the mixing. A similar process enables us to "see our breath" when we exhale on a cold winter day. For details on this process, see this chapter's first Essay, "Clouds by Mixing."

Depending on atmospheric conditions, contrails may dissipate (sublimate) within minutes or hours or they may spread laterally forming wispy cirrus clouds that persist for a day or so. Atmospheric scientists hypothesized that increased cloud cover caused by contrails would affect the local radiation budget in two ways: During daylight hours, contrails and their cirrus byproducts reflect to space incoming solar radiation thereby cooling Earth's surface. At night, contrails and associated cirrus clouds absorb and emit infrared radiation welling up from below thereby enhancing the greenhouse effect and elevating Earth's surface temperature. Cooler days and warmer nights reduces the *diurnal temperature range (DTR)*, the difference between the day's maximum and minimum temperatures. Furthermore, contrails may stimulate precipitation locally by supplying ice crystal nuclei for lower clouds.

Scientists had an opportunity to test their hypothesis regarding the impact of contrails on the radiation budget immediately after the terrorist attacks of 11 September 2001 when the Federal Aviation Administration (FAA) ordered a three-day shutdown of all commercial air traffic in the United States. Almost immediately, contrails began to dissipate. David J. Travis, a climate scientist at the University of Wisconsin-Whitewater, and colleagues at Pennsylvania State University analyzed the effects of a contrail-free sky on surface temperatures at 4000 U.S. weather stations. They found that the DTR during the three-day period was about 1.1 Celsius degree (2 Fahrenheit degrees) higher than the long-term (30-year) average. Furthermore, the DTR for the three-day periods preceding and following the shutdown was below the long-term average.

These observations support the hypothesis that contrails may contribute to climate change by making days cooler and nights warmer. With the expected future increase in global aircraft traffic, some scientists expect the contribution of contrails to climate change to become more significant; the average contrail sky coverage expected to more than double by 2050. At this point, it is not known whether more contrails will have a net warming or cooling effect on global climate.

Driving Question:
How do clouds and precipitation form?

Clouds whisk across the sky in ever-changing patterns of white and gray; fog lends an eerie silence to a dreary day. Clouds and fog are products of condensation or deposition of water vapor within the atmosphere. Most clouds are the consequence of saturation brought about by uplift and expansional cooling of air. Fog is a cloud that forms near or in contact with Earth's surface; most fogs develop when the lowest layer of air is chilled to saturation via radiational or advective cooling.

Cloud formation is an essential part of the global water cycle because without clouds there would be no rain or snow. And yet most clouds—even those associated with large storm systems—do not produce precipitation. The principal subjects of this chapter are the development and classification of clouds and fog, plus the formation and types of precipitation. We also examine weather radar, a valuable tool for locating and tracking areas of precipitation and for monitoring air motion within weather systems. This chapter closes with a summary of the various direct and remote methods for measuring precipitation.

Cloud Formation

Water vapor is an invisible component of air, but its condensation and deposition products (water droplets and ice crystals) are visible. A **cloud** is the visible product of condensation or deposition of water vapor within the atmosphere; it consists of an aggregate of minute water droplets and/or ice crystals suspended in the atmosphere. This section covers the process of cloud development.

Clouds are increasingly likely to form as air nears saturation. But when scientists try to simulate this process in the laboratory using a clean-air chamber, a cloud does not form even if the relative humidity is elevated well above 100%, that is, to supersaturation values. A clean-air chamber is an enclosed container of air from which all solid and liquid particles (aerosols) have been filtered out. Introducing water vapor into the chamber raises the relative humidity but even if the relative humidity is elevated to as high as 200%, no cloud forms. How is that possible?

We expect that once air becomes saturated (relative to a flat-water surface), condensation would initially produce extremely small droplets and those droplets would eventually grow into cloud droplets through additional condensation. However, droplets will not form in the first place unless the relative humidity rises to extraordinarily high levels of supersaturation.

THE CURVATURE EFFECT

Tiny droplets cannot form in a cloud chamber without a supersaturated environment because of the so-called **curvature effect**. The curvature of a water surface affects the ability of water molecules to escape (vaporize) from the water surface. The smaller the droplet, the greater is the concentration of surrounding water vapor that is necessary for the droplet to grow. The curvature of the surface of a spherical water droplet increases as the radius of the droplet decreases; that is, the surface of a small droplet has a greater curvature than the surface of a large droplet. (At the limit, a flat-water surface has no curvature.) With increasing curvature, molecules that form the surface of a droplet have fewer neighboring molecules and are more weakly bonded. Molecules composing a flat-water surface have the most neighboring molecules and are most strongly bonded. Bond strength affects the

flux of water molecules from the liquid to vapor phase. For this reason, water molecules more readily escape a water droplet than a flat-water surface and water molecules more readily escape a small water droplet than a large water droplet. Consequently, at the same temperature, the saturation vapor pressure surrounding a small water droplet is greater than that surrounding a large droplet.

Values of saturation vapor pressure listed in Table 6.3 are defined for air over a flat surface of fresh water and are the basis for computing relative humidity (Chapter 6). The saturation vapor pressure increases with increasing curvature (and decreasing droplet size). For droplets having a radius of 0.001 micrometer, the saturation vapor pressure at a given temperature is about 3.4 times that specified in Table 6.3, which computes to a relative humidity of 340%. On the other hand, for droplets having a radius greater than 1.0 micrometer, the difference between the saturation vapor pressure surrounding the droplet and the values listed in Table 6.3 is minimal and computes to a relative humidity only slightly higher than 100%.

The bottom line: In clean air, water vapor will not condense into tiny water droplets unless the air is supersaturated to very high levels. In the real atmosphere, the relative humidity never even approaches such great supersaturation values, so tiny droplets cannot form or grow. What then makes cloud formation possible?

ROLE OF NUCLEI

The clean-air chamber experiment described above failed to produce a cloud because the air was not sufficiently supersaturated. In the real atmosphere, supersaturated air is not needed for clouds to develop; in fact, cloud droplets readily form as the relative humidity nears 100%. And clouds are abundant; at any given time, about 60% of the planet is shrouded in clouds. How then do cloud droplets form? The answer: they have a head start. Suspended in air are solid and liquid particles that provide relatively large surface areas on which condensation or deposition initially takes place. These naturally occurring particles that promote condensation or deposition in the atmosphere are known as **nuclei**. Nuclei have radii greater than 1.0 micrometer and favor condensation (or deposition) of water vapor. Once condensation (or deposition) starts, they become comparably sized cloud droplets (or ice crystals). Additional growth of these droplets (or ice crystals) by condensation (or deposition) is more likely because they can grow in an environment with a relative humidity that exceeds 100% by only 1% or so. Most cloud particles have radii of 2 to 10 micrometers.

Nuclei, essential for cloud formation, are abundant in the atmosphere and are continually cycled into the atmosphere from Earth's surface. Sources of nuclei include volcanic eruptions, wind erosion of soil, forest fires, and ocean spray. When sea waves break, drops of salt water enter the atmosphere and the water evaporates leaving behind tiny sea-salt crystals that function as nuclei (Figure 7.2). Emissions from domestic and industrial chimneys also contribute nuclei to the atmosphere.

Depending on the product (liquid water droplets or ice crystals), a distinction is made between cloud condensation nuclei and ice-forming nuclei. **Cloud condensation nuclei (CCN)** promote condensation of water vapor at temperatures both above and below the freezing point of water. Within the atmosphere, water vapor can condense into cloud droplets that remain liquid even at temperatures well below 0 °C (32 °F). Droplets at such temperatures are described as *supercooled* (discussed below). **Ice-forming nuclei (IN)** are much less common than CCNs and promote formation of ice crystals only at temperatures well below freezing. The most efficient ice-forming nuclei are substances having a crystal structure similar to that of ice and most are almost insoluble in water. Clayey soil particles are excellent ice-forming nuclei. The two types of ice-forming nuclei are freezing nuclei and deposition nuclei. *Freezing nuclei* are particles on which water vapor condenses and subsequently freezes; they are active at temperatures below about −9 °C (16 °F). *Deposition nuclei* are particles on which water vapor deposits directly as ice (without first becoming a liquid) and are not fully active until the temperature drops below about −20 °C (−4 °F).

FIGURE 7.2
Breaking sea waves are a source of salt crystals that serve as hygroscopic nuclei for cloud development.

Hygroscopic nuclei are a special category of cloud condensation nuclei because they possess a chemical attraction for water molecules. Condensation begins on hygroscopic nuclei at a relative humidity under 100%. Magnesium chloride ($MgCl_2$), a salt in sea-spray, can promote condensation at a relative humidity as low as 70%! Clouds form more efficiently where hygroscopic nuclei are abundant. Many sources of hygroscopic nuclei exist in urban-industrial areas and this helps explain why localities downwind of large cities tend to be somewhat cloudier and rainier than upwind localities. The *Metropolitan Meteorological Experiment (METROMEX)* conducted in the 1970s demonstrated that the average summer rainfall was 5% to 25% greater within and up to 50 to 75 km (31 to 47 mi) downwind of St. Louis, MO than upwind of the city. In more recent years, similar urban effects on precipitation were detected in Tokyo, Phoenix, and other cities. Besides being a source of hygroscopic nuclei, cities also spur cloud and precipitation development by contributing water vapor (raising the relative humidity) and heat (adding to the buoyancy of air). Furthermore, the relative roughness of a city surface induces convergence of horizontal winds, uplift of air, and expansional cooling (Chapter 8).

Interestingly, not all ice crystals form on the traditional nuclei described above. While sampling ice crystals in cold clouds from aircraft, scientists discovered that the concentration of ice crystals is highly variable within the cloud and ice crystals are 10 to 1000 times more numerous than nuclei. This discrepancy is likely explained by the presence of fragments of ice crystals that break off during midair collisions. These ice fragments then function as additional nuclei.

SUPERCOOLED WATER

About 1783, the Swiss naturalist Horace de Saussure (1740-1799) demonstrated **supercooling** of water; that is, he was able to cool fresh water below its normal freezing point of 0 °C (32 °F) and the water remained liquid. Sixty-seven years later while on a balloon ascent the French chemist Jean Barrel confirmed the existence of supercooled cloud droplets in the free atmosphere. Cloud condensation nuclei promote condensation of water vapor at temperatures both above and below 0 °C. How can cloud droplets remain liquid even at temperatures well below freezing?

Freezing of fresh water in the absence of already existing ice begins with the linking of water molecules to form a tiny ice structure known as an *ice embryo*. Once an ice embryo grows larger than a certain critical size, its growth continues and freezing begins. Within the very small droplets composing clouds, kinetic molecular activity is sufficient to inhibit growth of ice embryos to a critical size so that water droplets remain liquid even at temperatures well below freezing. As the droplet temperature falls, however, the average kinetic molecular activity diminishes, the number of ice embryos increases, and the probability of an ice embryo growing to critical size increases. The formation of ice embryos of critical size due to the chance aggregation of water molecules is known as *homogeneous* (or *spontaneous*) *nucleation*. If no foreign particles are present that would act as ice-forming nuclei, a cloud droplet can cool to as low as -39 °C (-38.2 °F) without freezing. Any additional cooling, however, always leads to homogeneous nucleation. This threshold temperature is called the *Schaefer point*, named for Vincent J. Schaefer (1906-1993), a pioneer in cloud physics research at the General Electric Research Laboratory in Schenectady, NY.

If a supercooled water droplet contains (or comes in contact with) foreign particles that are ice-forming nuclei, the cloud droplet will freeze at a temperature below freezing but well above the Schaefer point. Water molecules collect on the surface of a foreign particle and form an ice embryo. The ice embryo is the same size as the particle and may be close to critical size so that any additional growth of the embryo causes the droplet to freeze. This process is referred to as *heterogeneous nucleation*.

Cloud Classification

Clouds come in a variety of sizes and shapes, something that is obvious from even a cursory glance at the sky. Characteristics that are common to different clouds form the basis for their classification. Cloud classification is desirable because different types of clouds tell us something about atmospheric processes responsible

for their formation and may provide clues as to future weather. British naturalist Luke Howard (1772-1864) was among the first to devise a classification of cloud types. Formulated in 1802-03, the essentials of Howard's scheme are still used today.

Clouds are classified on the basis of (1) general appearance (texture) from the ground, (2) altitude of cloud base, (3) temperature, or (4) composition (Table 7.1). Based on a cloud's general appearance, the simplest distinction is among cirriform, stratiform, and cumuliform clouds. A **cirriform cloud** is wispy or fibrous, a **stratiform cloud** is layered, and a **cumuliform cloud** is heaped or puffy. On the basis of altitude of cloud base, a distinction is made among high, middle, and low clouds, and clouds having significant vertical development. The altitude of a cloud is important in that it affects its temperature and ultimately its composition. High, middle, and low clouds generally occur in layers and are produced by gentle uplift of air (typically less than 5 cm per sec or 0.1 mi per hr) over a broad geographical area. Clouds having significant vertical development usually cover smaller areas but are associated with much more vigorous uplift (sometimes in excess of 30 m per sec or 70 mi per hr).

Clouds can be described as warm or cold. The temperature in a **warm cloud** is above 0 °C (32 °F) whereas the temperature in a **cold cloud** is at or below 0 °C (32 °F). Average air temperature decreases from sea level to the tropopause and ascending cloudy air expands and cools so that high clouds are colder than low clouds. Vertically developed clouds that surge to great altitudes, such as thunderstorm clouds (cumulonimbus), may be warm near their base but cold aloft. To a large extent, temperature dictates the composition and appearance of clouds. Cold clouds are made up of ice crystals and/or supercooled water droplets; ice crystal clouds appear wispy especially at their edges. Warm clouds are made up of water droplets and their boundaries are more sharply defined.

TABLE 7.1
Summary of Cloud Classification Schemes

Temperature	Composition	Altitude	
		Stratiform	Cumuliform
Cold	ice crystals	high	clouds with
	supercooled droplets	middle	vertical
Warm	water droplets	low	development

TABLE 7.2
Cloud Classification

Cloud group	Altitude of base (m)[a]
High clouds	
Cirrus (Ci)	5000-13,000
Cirrostratus (Cs)	5000-13,000
Cirrocumulus (Cc)	5000-13,000
Middle clouds	
Altostratus (As)	2000-5000
Altocumulus (Ac)	2000-5000
Low clouds	
Stratus (St)	surface-2000
Stratocumulus (Sc)	surface-2000
Nimbostratus (Ns)	surface-2000
Clouds with vertical development	
Cumulus (Cu)	to 3000
Cumulonimbus (Cb)	to 3000

[a]Average for middle latitudes.

Over the last 200 years, meteorologists have identified ten fundamental cloud types. Here we present brief descriptions of these most common cloud types, organized by altitude of cloud base in middle latitudes (Table 7.2). The actual altitude of cloud base varies seasonally and with latitude. For example, the base of high clouds may be as low as 3000 m (10,000 ft) in polar latitudes and as high as 18,000 m (60,000 ft) in the tropics. Furthermore, certain qualifying terms are applied to clouds having special characteristics; some of these are listed in Table 7.3.

HIGH CLOUDS

High clouds have bases at altitudes above 5000 m (16,000 ft) where average temperatures are typically below −25 °C (−13 °F). At such low temperatures, clouds are almost exclusively composed of ice crystals, a composition that helps explain their fibrous appearance in the presence of sunlight. Their names include the prefix *cirro* from the Latin meaning "a curl of hair."

Cirrus (Ci) clouds are nearly transparent and occur as delicate silky strands, sometimes called mares' tails (Figure 7.3A). Strands are actually streaks of falling ice crystals blown laterally by strong winds. Like cirrus clouds, **cirrostratus (Cs) clouds** are also nearly transparent, so the sun or moon readily shines through them. They form a thin, white veil or sheet that partially or totally covers the sky (Figure 7.3B). **Cirrocumulus (Cc) clouds** consist of small, white, rounded patches arranged in a wavelike or mackerel (resembling fish scales) pattern (Figure 7.3C).

TABLE 7.3
Special Characteristics of Cloud Types

Characteristic	Meaning	Applied to
Castellanus	Tower-like vertical development	Cirrocumulus, altocumulus
Congestus	Crowded in heaps	Cumulus
Fractus	Broken, ragged, torn	Stratus, cumulus
Humilis	Little vertical development, flat base	Cumulus
Incus	Anvil-shape	Cumulonimbus
Lenticularis	Lens-shaped	Cirrostratus, altocumulus, Stratocumulus
Mammatus	Hanging protuberances	Cumulonimbus
Pileus	Cap-shaped cloud above	Cumuliform
Uncinus	Hook-shaped	Cirrus

FIGURE 7.3

High stratiform clouds are composed of mostly ice crystals: (A) cirrus, (B) cirrostratus, and (C) cirrocumulus.

Rarely do these clouds cover the entire sky. As a rule, no high cloud is thick enough to prevent objects on the ground from casting shadows during daylight hours.

These high clouds, especially cirrostratus, are often the first clouds to appear in advance of an approaching middle latitude storm system. Cirrus clouds sometimes develop in association with the vertical motions around the

upper tropospheric jet stream. At times, cirriform clouds blow off the tops of thunderstorm cells, particularly the anvils of cumulonimbus clouds.

MIDDLE CLOUDS

The base of middle clouds is typically at altitudes between 2000 and 5000 m (6600 and 16,000 ft). These clouds feature temperatures generally between 0 °C and −25 °C (32 °F and −13 °F) and are composed of supercooled water droplets or a mixture of supercooled water droplets and ice crystals. Their names include the prefix *alto*. **Altostratus (As) clouds** occur as uniformly gray or bluish white layers that totally or partially cover the sky (Figure 7.4A). They are usually so thick that the sun is only dimly visible, as if viewed through frosted glass. (As a rule, clouds must have a thickness of at least 50 m or about 150 ft to completely block out the sun.) **Altocumulus (Ac) clouds** consist of roll-like patches or puffs that often form waves or parallel bands (Figure 7.4B). They are distinguished from cirrocumulus by the larger size of the cloud patches and by sharper edges indicating the presence

FIGURE 7.4

Middle stratiform clouds are composed of ice crystals, water droplets, or a combination of the two: (A) altostratus, (B) altocumulus.

of water droplets rather than ice crystals. Altocumulus may occur in several distinct layers simultaneously and rarely produce precipitation that reaches the ground. If they appear early on a warm, humid summer day, there is a chance of an afternoon thunderstorm.

LOW CLOUDS

Low clouds have bases ranging from Earth's surface (fog) up to an altitude of perhaps 2000 m (6600 ft). Low clouds that form at temperatures above −5 °C (23 °F) are composed of mostly water droplets. **Stratocumulus (Sc) clouds** consist of large, irregular puffs or rolls separated by areas of clear sky (Figure 7.5A). Seldom does significant precipitation fall from stratocumulus clouds. **Stratus (St) clouds** appear as a uniform gray layer stretching from horizon to horizon (Figure 7.5B). Fog occurs where stratus meets the ground, and when fog lifts, the stratus cloud deck may break up into stratocumulus.

Usually only drizzle falls from stratus clouds, but significant amounts of rain or snow may fall from the much thicker **nimbostratus (Ns) clouds**. Nimbostratus resemble

FIGURE 7.5
Low stratiform clouds: (A) stratocumulus, (B) stratus.

stratus except that they are darker gray and have a less uniform, more ragged base. Precipitation from nimbostratus tends to be light to moderate and continuous for 12 hrs or longer. By contrast, relatively brief but heavy precipitation is often associated with a cumulonimbus (thunderstorm) cloud. Gentle rainfall from nimbostratus more readily infiltrates the soil, whereas the intense downpour of a thunderstorm quickly saturates the upper soil and then mostly runs off, perhaps causing flash flooding (Chapter 11).

Stratus and nimbostratus clouds often are found close to an approaching warm front, where warm and humid air is lifted over a dome of cooler air ahead of the front. Stratocumulus clouds may represent either eroding stratus clouds or are caused by unstable atmospheric conditions in the lower troposphere as cold air moves over relatively warm ground in the wake of a departing low pressure system.

CLOUDS HAVING VERTICAL DEVELOPMENT

Clouds having significant vertical development form in the updrafts of convection currents that can surge to great altitudes in the troposphere. The altitude at which condensation begins to occur through convection is known as the **convective condensation level (CCL)** and coincides with the altitude of cumuliform cloud base, typically between 1000 and 2000 m (3600 and 6600 ft). **Cumulus (Cu) clouds** are relatively small puffy clouds that resemble balls of cotton floating in the sky on a fair weather day (Figure 7.6A). Solar heating drives convection so that cumulus cloud development often follows the daily variation of incoming solar radiation. On a fair day, cumulus clouds begin forming by middle to late morning after the sun has warmed the ground and initiated convection. Cumulus sky cover is most extensive by mid afternoon, usually the warmest time of day. If cumulus clouds show some vertical growth, these normally fair-weather clouds may produce a brief, light shower of rain or snow. As sunset approaches, convection weakens, and cumulus clouds begin dissipating (that is, they vaporize).

Where convection is suppressed, so too is the development of cumulus clouds. Relatively cold surfaces chill and stabilize the overlying air and inhibit convection so that cumulus clouds do not readily form over snow-covered surfaces. Cold water also suppresses convection. This effect is sometimes observed along the shores of the Great Lakes during late spring and early summer afternoons when, on average, lake surface temperatures are lower than temperatures of the adjacent land surface. Fair-weather cumulus clouds develop over the warm land but not over the relatively cold lake

FIGURE 7.6
Cumuliform clouds: (A) cumulus, (B) cumulus congestus, (C) cumulonimbus.

FIGURE 7.7
In this visible satellite image, clusters of cumulus clouds develop over the relatively warm land surface but not over the adjacent cold surfaces of the Great Lakes.

surface (Figure 7.7). In fact, rows of cumulus clouds may form a distinct boundary along the shoreline.

Once cumulus clouds form, the stability profile of the troposphere determines the extent of vertical cloud development and whether cumulus clouds build into more ominous thunderstorm clouds. If ambient air aloft is stable, vertical motion is inhibited and cumulus clouds exhibit little vertical growth. Under these conditions, the weather is likely to remain fair. On the other hand, if ambient air aloft is unstable for saturated (cloudy) air, then vertical motion is enhanced, and the tops of cumulus clouds surge upward. If the ambient air is unstable to great altitudes, the entire cloud mass takes on a cauliflower appearance as it builds into a towering **cumulus congestus cloud** (Figure 7.6B) or perhaps a **cumulonimbus (Cb) cloud** (Figure 7.6C). Cumulonimbus clouds have tops that sometimes reach altitudes of 20,000 m (60,000 ft) or higher. The upper portion of a cumulonimbus cloud, with its familiar anvil shape, is typically composed of mostly ice crystals, the middle portion may be supercooled water droplets or a mixture of supercooled water droplets and ice crystals, while the lower portion of the cloud consists of ordinary water droplets.

Although this cloud classification category is usually reserved for cumuliform clouds, altostratus and nimbostratus may also be considered to be clouds having vertical development. Normally classified as middle and low clouds, respectively, because of cloud-base altitude, altostratus and nimbostratus often are so thick that they extend through more than one level.

SKY WATCHING

Cumuliform and stratiform clouds are often observed in the sky at the same time. For example, a layer of high cirrus may overlie low-level cumulus clouds. The cirrus may have developed in advance of an approaching surface warm front and is too thin to significantly weaken the incoming solar radiation. The sun heats the ground, triggering convection and development of cumulus clouds.

When more than one cloud layer appears in the sky at the same time, it can be instructive to visually track the direction of movement of each cloud layer. Often clouds at different altitudes move in different directions at different speeds. Because most clouds move with the wind, this observation indicates that, at least within the troposphere (where most clouds are found), the horizontal wind changes direction and speed with altitude. Any change in wind direction or wind speed with distance is known as **wind shear**. Strong vertical shear in horizontal wind speed or direction may cause clouds (or cloud elements) to line up into rows that often extend for hundreds of kilometers. These so-called **cloud streets** are observed in cumulus, stratocumulus, and cirrocumulus clouds. They develop where the air is humid and the axes of convective cells align with the average wind direction.

Other sky features to watch for are well-defined holes or canals in an otherwise uniform cloud layer. Holes in clouds are not unusual; numerous published reports and photographs of them have appeared over the years. P.V. Hobbs of the University of Washington attributes at least some holes in clouds to aircraft flying through thin cloud layers composed of supercooled water droplets (probably altocumulus). Turbulence produced in the wake of an aircraft induces expansional cooling of air; water droplets freeze to ice crystals that fall out of the cloud, thereby leaving a hole in the cloud. Aircraft ascending or descending through a cloud may produce nearly circular holes, whereas aircraft flying horizontally through a cloud layer may create cloud-free canals.

UNUSUAL CLOUDS

Chances are that all of us have seen most of the clouds described above because the circumstances leading to their formation are quite common. Other, more unusual clouds are formed by special atmospheric conditions that in some cases arise from orographic effects.

Many people have reported certain disk-shaped clouds as UFOs (*Unidentified Flying Objects*). Observing such clouds over a period of time reveals an intriguing characteristic besides their shape: They are almost motionless and differ from many other types of clouds that are carried along by winds aloft. These disk or lens-shaped middle level couds are **altocumulus lenticularis clouds** generated when a mountain range disturbs large-scale horizontal winds. As strong horizontal winds encounter a mountain range, the wind is deflected up the windward slopes and down the leeward slopes. This occurs as the prevailing westerlies, blowing from west to east, cross the Sierra Nevada Mountains of California or the Front Range of the Rocky Mountains. If the air ascending the windward slopes is stable, then the wind is deflected into a wave-like pattern that can extend hundreds of kilometers downwind of the mountain crest (Figure 7.8).

If air is sufficiently humid, lenticular clouds form at the crests of the waves and are absent in the troughs. Where air ascends within a wave, expansional cooling leads to condensation (or deposition) and clouds form. Where air descends within a wave, compressional warming leads to evaporation (or sublimation) and clouds dissipate. Clouds formed in this way directly over the mountain are known as **mountain-wave clouds**. (If these clouds extend just downwind of the mountain peak, they are referred to as *banner clouds*.) Lenticular clouds formed in the wave crests downwind of the mountain are known as **lee-wave clouds**.

Mountain-wave and lee-wave clouds are stationary because the wave itself is stationary, even though winds passing through the waves are strong. A stationary wave within the atmosphere is known as a *standing wave*. A waterfall on a river is a good analogy. In the plunge pool at the base of the waterfall, the water

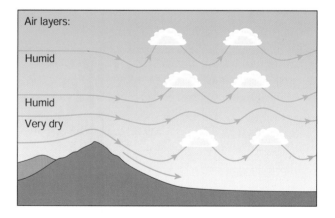

FIGURE 7.8

A mountain range deflects the horizontal wind into a wave-like pattern that extends downwind of the summit. If the air is sufficiently humid, clouds develop in the wave crests where ascending air expands and cools but clouds are absent in wave troughs where descending air is compressed and warms.

is very turbulent, but if we follow the river downstream, we quickly leave the turbulent region behind. The river water flows ceaselessly, but the turbulent segment remains stationary at the foot of the waterfall, just as a standing wave in the atmosphere remains stationary to the lee of a mountain range.

In some cases, a rotor-like circulation develops under the crest of a standing wave. Air rotates about a horizontal axis that roughly parallels the mountain range and sometimes a cloud (known as a *rotor cloud*) forms in the ascending branch. Turbulence associated with the rotor can be a major hazard to aviation.

In a stable atmosphere, waves and wave-type clouds also can develop along the interface between two layers of air that are moving horizontally at different speeds. In Figure 7.9, a layer of relatively warm air overlies a layer of colder, denser air. The warm air is moving horizontally more rapidly than the cold air. This vertical shear in the horizontal wind gives rise to *Kelvin-Helmholz waves* along the boundary between the two air layers. (Waves formed in this way are analogous to wind-driven water waves that form along the boundary between the ocean and atmosphere). Clouds that develop at the crests of Kelvin-Helmholz waves consist of a train of regularly spaced curls and are know as *billow clouds*.

Waves traveling horizontally within the atmosphere are also responsible for patterns exhibited by stratocumulus and cirrocumulus (as well as by varieties of altocumulus in addition to lenticularis). These waves are not linked to mountain ranges and propagate at different altitudes within the troposphere. Such waves produce bands of clouds that are aligned either parallel or perpendicular to the wind direction.

Almost all water vapor is confined to the troposphere, so it is not surprising that most clouds occur below the tropopause. Mountain-wave clouds sometimes develop in the stratosphere above high mountain crests

and occasionally the top of an intense cumulonimbus cloud surges through the tropopause and into the lower stratosphere. Other examples of clouds in the upper atmosphere are noctilucent and nacreous clouds.

Somewhat mysterious are cirrostratus-like **noctilucent clouds** that form in the upper mesosphere above an altitude of about 80 km (50 mi). They are seldom observed, and then only at high latitudes (mostly above 50 degrees in both hemispheres) in summer. They are too thin to be visible during the day and only show up at night. From well below the horizon, the sun illuminates noctilucent (*night-shining*) clouds, imparting to them a luminous blue-white or silvery white appearance that stands out against the black night sky (Figure 7.10). They are likely composed of tiny water-ice crystals formed on meteoric dust particles.

How is it possible for ice clouds to form in the upper atmosphere where there is so little water vapor (about 10 parts per million by volume)? The key is the exceptionally low air temperature in the upper mesosphere. As noted in Chapter 2, atmospheric temperatures are lowest at the mesopause. January temperatures generally range from −53 °C (−64 °F) to −43 °C (−46 °F) and July temperatures may drop as low as −173 °C (−279 °F). At such low temperatures, ice clouds can form at extremely low vapor pressures.

Nonetheless, this begs the question of where the water vapor comes from. Some is ejected into the upper atmosphere during violent volcanic eruptions. In fact, noctilucent clouds were first observed (in Germany and Russia) about two years after the violent 1883 eruption of the Indonesian volcano Krakatoa that blasted gases and ash to altitudes as great as 80 km (50 mi). The most important source of water vapor in the mesosphere may be the flux of water vapor from the lower atmosphere to the mesosphere associated with the meridional (north/south) summer circulation. Yet another source of water vapor may be chemical reactions involving methane (CH_4). Atmospheric circulation transports methane from the troposphere into the stratosphere where it is broken down by solar ultraviolet radiation, releasing hydrogen that is oxidized to water vapor through complex chemical reactions. Some of that water vapor is transported to the upper mesosphere and deposited as ice crystals on meteoric dust particles to form noctilucent clouds.

Curiously, the frequency of sightings of noctilucent clouds has been increasing since they were first reported in 1885. They are also being sighted at lower latitudes (as far south as Colorado). During the same period, the concentration of atmospheric methane

FIGURE 7.9
Formation of Kelvin-Helmholtz waves along the interface between two layers of air that contrast in density. Billow clouds may form in the wave crests.

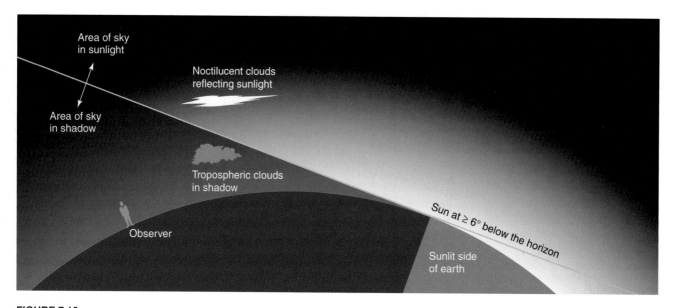

FIGURE 7.10
Noctilucent clouds are visible after sunset or prior to sunrise. These unusual clouds occur at such great altitudes (in the upper mesosphere) that they are illuminated by the rays of the sun below the horizon.

has also been increasing. G.E. Thomas of the University of Colorado's Laboratory for Atmospheric and Space Physics, suspects that a connection may exist between the present upward trend in atmospheric methane and sightings of noctilucent clouds.

Nacreous clouds (also called *polar stratospheric clouds*) occur in the stratosphere at altitudes of about 20 to 30 km (12 to 19 mi) where temperatures favor water in either the solid or supercooled state. These cirrus or altocumulus lenticularis clouds form on sulfuric acid nuclei possibly of volcanic origin. Because of their soft, pearly luster, these rarely seen clouds are also known as *mother-of-pearl clouds*. They are best viewed at high latitudes (e.g., Antarctica, Alaska, Scotland, Scandinavia) in winter when illuminated by the setting sun. As noted in Chapter 3, these clouds probably play a major role in the formation of the Antarctic ozone hole.

Fog

Fog is a visibility-restricting suspension of tiny water droplets or ice crystals (called *ice fog*) in an air layer next to Earth's surface. Simply put, fog is a cloud in contact with the ground. By international convention, fog is defined as restricting visibility to 1000 m (3250 ft) or less; otherwise the suspension is called **mist**. (The popular definition of mist is *light drizzle*.) *Dense fog* reduces visibility to 100 m (330 ft) or less. Fog may develop when air becomes saturated through radiational cooling, advective cooling, addition of water vapor, or expansional cooling.

In restricting visibility, fog adversely affects travel by motor vehicle, ship, and aircraft. Fog tends to be a major problem in some coastal areas. The world's foggiest place is Argentia, Newfoundland which reports roughly 205 days of fog per year. One of the foggiest places in the United States is Cape Disappointment, Washington at the mouth of the Columbia River, where dense fog occurs on average about 2556 hours annually (30% of the time). Moose Peak Lighthouse on Maine's Mistake Island has about 1560 hours of dense fog per year.

With a clear night sky, light winds, and an air mass that is humid near the ground and relatively dry aloft, radiational cooling may cause the air near the ground to approach saturation. When this condition occurs, a ground-level cloud forms and is called **radiation fog** (Figure 7.11). High humidity at low levels within the air mass is usually due to evaporation of water from a moist surface. Hence, radiation fog is most common over marshy areas or where the soil has been saturated by a recent period of heavy rainfall or snowmelt.

Light winds, rather than calm air, favor development of radiation fog. Light winds produce a slight mixing that more effectively transfers heat from throughout the layer of humid air to the relatively cold ground. Consequently, the entire air layer is chilled below the dewpoint (Chapter 6). If air were calm, however, the lack of mixing would mean heat transfer by conduction alone. Because motionless air

FIGURE 7.11
Radiation fog seen here in the distance develops as a consequence of radiational cooling on a night when there is some air movement and the atmosphere is humid at low levels.

is a poor conductor of heat, only a very thin layer of air immediately in contact with the ground would be cooled to saturation. Hence, calm conditions favor dew or frost rather than radiation fog. On the other hand, if winds become too strong, the humid air at low levels mixes with the drier air aloft, the relative humidity drops, and radiation fog disperses or fails to develop. Air that is chilled by radiational cooling is relatively dense and, in hilly terrain, drains downslope and settles in low-lying areas such as river valleys and wetlands. This air movement is known as *cold-air drainage*. Hilltops may be clear of fog while fog is thick and persistent in deep valleys (Figure 7.12).

Once a fog bank forms at night, radiational cooling becomes a little more complicated. The top surface of the fog bank very efficiently emits infrared (IR) radiation skyward. The fog droplets absorb some of the IR emitted by the ground and the droplets, in turn, emit IR to the ground so that the ground cools more slowly. The maximum cooling rate shifts to the top of the fog bank, the fog layer thickens, and visibility continues to drop.

Often radiation fog persists for only a few hours after sunrise. Fog gradually thins and disperses as saturated air at low altitudes mixes with drier air above the fog bank; the relative humidity drops and fog droplets vaporize. Mixing may be caused by convection triggered by solar heating of the ground or by strengthening of regional winds. In winter, however, the upper surface of a fog layer readily reflects the weak rays of the sun and radiation fog may be persistent. For example, in the valleys of the Great Basin and in California's San Joaquin Valley, winter radiation fogs may persist for many days to weeks at a time.

Fog sometimes accompanies air mass advection. The temperature and the water vapor concentration of an air mass depend on the nature of the surface over which the air mass forms and travels. As an air mass moves from one place to another, termed *air mass advection*, those characteristics change, partly because of the modifying influence of the surfaces over which the air mass travels. When the advecting air passes over a relatively cold surface, the air mass may be chilled to saturation in its lowest layers. This type of cooling is known as *advective cooling* and occurs, for example, in

FIGURE 7.12
NOAA visible satellite image showing morning fog in river valleys in parts of Pennsylvania and upstate New York (between the yellow arrows). [NOAA]

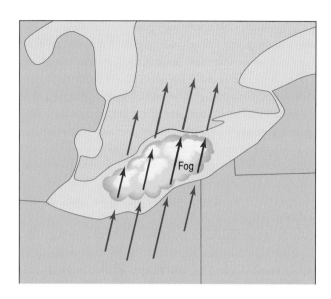

FIGURE 7.13
In summer, fog forms over the Great Lakes when relatively warm and humid air passes over the cold water surface and is chilled to its dewpoint.

early spring in the northern states when mild, humid air flows over relatively cold, snow-covered ground. Snow on the ground may chill the overlying air to the dewpoint and fog develops. Fog formed by advective cooling is known as **advection fog**.

Advection fog also develops when warm and humid air streams over the relatively cold surface of a lake or the ocean. Persistent, dense fogs develop in this way over the Great Lakes in summer (Figure 7.13). Thick sea fog forms when mild maritime air from over the warm Gulf Stream flows northward and encounters the frigid waters of the Grand Banks off Newfoundland.

Nocturnal radiational cooling sometimes combines with air mass advection to produce fog. An initially dry air mass becomes more humid in its lower levels following a long trajectory over the open water of a lake or the ocean. Over land areas, downwind from the water body, if the night sky is clear, the modified air mass is subjected to extreme radiational cooling and fog develops. San Francisco's famous fog forms in this way. Onshore winds transport cool, humid air into the city and nocturnal radiational cooling chills the air to saturation.

Steam fog (sometimes called *Arctic sea smoke*) is fog that develops in late fall or winter when extremely cold and dry air flows over a large unfrozen body of water. Evaporation and sensible heating cause the lower portion of the air mass to become more humid and warmer than the air above. Heating from below destabilizes the air and

the consequent mixing of mild, humid air with cold, dry air brings the air to saturation and fog forms. Because the air is destabilized, fog appears as rising filaments or streamers that resemble smoke or steam. Steam fog also develops on a cold day over a heated outdoor swimming pool or hot tub and sometimes over a wet highway or field when the sun comes out after a rain shower.

Another perspective on the origin of steam fog considers the distribution of vapor pressure over the water surface. Within about 1 to 2 m (3 to 7 ft) of the water surface, the vapor pressure is relatively high because of evaporation of water into the heated air. Above this shallow humid air layer, the air is colder and the vapor pressure is relatively low. A vertical vapor pressure gradient develops over the water body and, in response, water molecules stream (diffuse) upward. (As we will see in Chapter 8, gases move from high toward low pressure in response to a pressure gradient.) As the humid air streams upward, it expands and cools and the water vapor condenses into tiny droplets that we see as steam fog. Rising streamers encounter drier air and evaporate perhaps 5 to 10 m (15 to 35 ft) above the water surface.

Fog also develops on hillsides or mountain slopes as a consequence of the upslope movement of humid air. Ascending humid air undergoes expansional cooling and eventually reaches saturation. Any further ascent of the saturated air produces fog. Fog formed in this way is called **upslope fog** (Figure 7.14). In the coastal mountain ranges of California, upslope fog sometimes overtops the range crest and spreads as stratus clouds over the leeward valleys. A cloud layer formed in this way is known as *high fog*.

FIGURE 7.14
Upslope fog formed when humid air is forced to ascend the windward slopes of a hill or mountain. Expansional cooling brings the air to saturation.

Precipitation Processes

Appearance of clouds is no guarantee that it will rain or snow. Nimbostratus and cumulonimbus clouds produce the bulk of precipitation, but most clouds do not yield any significant rain or snow. This is because a special combination of circumstances is required for precipitation to develop. **Precipitation** is water in solid or liquid form that falls from clouds to Earth's surface under the influence of gravity. Key to understanding the mechanisms of precipitation formation is the concept of terminal velocity, the speed of a falling particle. We begin this section by examining terminal velocity and then cover the two mechanisms of precipitation formation: the collision-coalescence process and the Bergeron-Findeisen process.

TERMINAL VELOCITY

The speed of a falling cloud droplet or ice crystal (or any other particle) in calm air depends on (1) **gravity**, the force that accelerates the particle directly downward toward Earth's surface, and (2) the resistance offered by the air through which the particle falls. A downward accelerating particle meets increasing air resistance while gravity remains essentially constant. The magnitude of the resisting force eventually equals gravity; that is, the forces come into balance. If the forces

become balanced, then according to Newton's first law of motion, the downward moving particle attains a constant speed. **Newton's first law of motion** states that an object in constant straight-line motion or at rest remains that way unless acted upon by an unbalanced force. In this case, air resistance (directed upward) balances gravity (acting downward) and the particle continues downward at constant speed. That speed is the particle's **terminal velocity**.

Terminal velocity helps explain why the tiny particles that compose clouds (water droplets and ice crystals) will not fall to Earth's surface as precipitation unless they undergo considerable growth. Generally, terminal velocity increases with the size of the particle (Figure 7.15). For a particle to descend from a cloud to Earth's surface as precipitation, the particle's terminal velocity must be greater than the rising motion of air within the cloud (updrafts). Cloud water droplets and ice crystals are so small (typically 10 to 20 micrometers in diameter) that their terminal velocities are very low (usually only 0.3 to 1.2 cm per sec). Hence, even weak updrafts will keep them suspended in clouds. If droplets or ice crystals fall through the base of a cloud, their terminal velocity is so slow that it would take 24 hrs or longer for the cloud particles to reach Earth's surface. Long before that happens, the particles would vaporize in the unsaturated air under the cloud. (The relative humidity of the air below a cloud is typically less than 100%.)

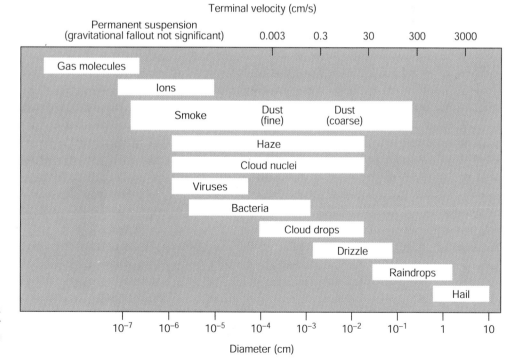

FIGURE 7.15
The terminal velocity of a particle falling through air increases with the size of the particle.

For clouds to precipitate, cloud particles must grow large enough that their terminal velocities overwhelm the updrafts. This is no minor task! It takes the water content of about 1 million cloud droplets (having diameters of 10 to 20 micrometers) to form a single raindrop (about 2 mm in diameter). Condensation or deposition alone cannot account for the formation of raindrop-sized particles. Cloud droplets grow into raindrops through collision-coalescence of cloud droplets in warm clouds whereas a combination of the Bergeron-Findeisen process and collision-coalescence causes ice crystals in cold clouds to grow into snowflakes.

WARM-CLOUD PRECIPITATION

In the 1940s, radar analysis of thunderstorms revealed that plentiful rain could fall from clouds that were too warm to contain ice. In a warm cloud (at temperatures above 0 °C), droplets may grow by colliding and coalescing (merging) with one another, the so-called **collision-coalescence process**. The collision-coalescence process takes place in a cloud composed of a mixture of droplets of different sizes, ideally with some droplets having diameters of at least 20 micrometers. Cloud droplets of unequal diameters have different terminal velocities, greatly increasing the likelihood that faster falling (larger) droplets will overtake, and then collide and coalesce with slower falling (smaller) droplets in their paths. Through repeated collisions and coalescence, droplets grow in size (Figure 7.16). On the other hand, cloud droplets of uniform diameter have essentially the same terminal velocities so that collisions are infrequent. Through collision-coalescence, a warm cloud droplet may grow so large that it becomes unstable and splits into smaller droplets that go on to coalesce with other droplets in a kind of chain reaction. Eventually some droplets become sufficiently large that they survive a fall from clouds to Earth's surface as raindrops.

A key factor in precipitation formation through collision-coalescence is collision efficiency. *Collision efficiency* refers to the fraction of all droplets in the path of a falling larger droplet that comes in contact with the larger droplet. Collision efficiency varies with the size of the larger droplet and is minimal (less than 10%) for droplets less than 40 micrometers in diameter but approaches 100% for droplets greater than 80 micrometers in diameter. Laboratory simulations demonstrate that colliding droplets will not coalesce unless they are significantly different sizes. Larger droplets form initially on larger nuclei (e.g., sea salt particles), through random collisions between smaller droplets, or via mixing between cloud droplets and the surrounding drier air.

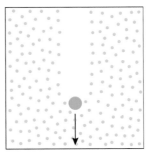

· Cloud droplets
● Rain drop

FIGURE 7.16
Within a warm cloud, a relatively large droplet falls through a cloud of much smaller droplets. The larger droplet falls faster and collides with the smaller droplets in its path and grows by coalescence. This is the collision-coalescence process of precipitation formation.

COLD-CLOUD PRECIPITATION

Although precipitation formation through the collision-coalescence process in warm clouds is important, especially in the tropics, most precipitation in middle and high latitudes originates in cold clouds (clouds or portions of clouds at temperatures below 0 °C) that have some ice crystals. At middle and high latitudes, clouds routinely reach altitudes where the temperature is below freezing regardless of season. Precipitation is most likely to fall from a cloud initially composed of a mixture of supercooled water droplets and ice crystals. In 1911, the German meteorologist Alfred Wegener (1880-1930), one of the original proponents of *continental drift*, first proposed that ice crystals grow at the expense of the surrounding supercooled water droplets in response to differences in saturation vapor pressure between water and ice surfaces. Around 1930, the Swedish meteorologist Tor Bergeron (1891-1977) contributed to an understanding of this process and the German physicist Walter Findeisen subsequently elaborated on the concept. For this reason, the mechanism of precipitation formation in cold clouds is called the **Bergeron-Findeisen process**, also known as the *ice-crystal process*.

As noted above, cloud condensation nuclei are much more abundant than ice-forming nuclei so that a mixed cloud (at least initially) consists of far more supercooled water droplets than ice crystals. Supercooled water droplets quickly vaporize as ice crystals grow. At subfreezing temperatures, water molecules more readily vaporize from a liquid (supercooled) water surface than from an ice surface because water molecules are more strongly bonded in the solid phase than the liquid phase. At the same subfreezing temperature, the saturation vapor pressure is greater over supercooled water than over ice. For temperatures below 0 °C (32 °F), two values of the saturation vapor pressure are given in Table 6.3: one over supercooled water, the other over ice.

Within a cloud composed of a mixture of ice crystals and supercooled water droplets, a vapor pressure that is saturated for water droplets is actually supersaturated for ice crystals at the same temperature. Suppose, for example, that a cloud of supercooled water droplets at −15 °C (5 °F) is saturated relative to water (relative humidity = 100%). According to Table 6.3, the saturation vapor pressure is 1.91 mb. Imagine the sudden appearance of an ice crystal in the same region of the cloud. Table 6.3 indicates that the saturation vapor pressure over ice at −15 °C (5 °F) is 1.65 mb so that air surrounding the ice crystals is supersaturated (relative humidity = 116%). Water vapor deposits on the ice crystals and the crystals grow. Deposition lowers the vapor pressure surrounding the water droplets to unsaturated conditions, causing water droplets to evaporate. Also, a lower vapor pressure in the air surrounding the ice crystals produces a pressure gradient such that water vapor molecules diffuse toward the ice. Through the Bergeron-Findeisen process, ice crystals grow at the expense of supercooled water droplets.

Growth of ice crystals is accompanied by an increase in their terminal velocities. Larger, faster falling ice crystals overtake, collide and agglomerate with smaller, slower falling ice crystals and supercooled water droplets (Figure 7.17). Ice crystals grow still larger and may fall out of the cloud base. If air temperatures are below freezing at least much of the way to the ground, ice crystals reach Earth's surface as snowflakes. If air temperatures are above freezing in the lower reaches of the cloud or between the cloud and Earth's surface, snowflakes melt into raindrops.

FIGURE 7.17
Within a cold cloud, ice crystals grow at the expense of supercooled water droplets. As they grow larger, ice crystals fall faster and collide with droplets and other ice crystals in their paths. Eventually, they may grow large enough to fall out of the cloud as snowflakes. This is the Bergeron-Findeisen process of precipitation formation.

. Supercooled cloud droplets
❄ Ice crystals

Regardless of the formation mechanism, once a falling raindrop or a snowflake leaves the base of a cloud, it enters unsaturated air and begins to vaporize. The longer the distance to the Earth's surface, (i.e., the higher the cloud base) and the lower the relative humidity of air beneath the clouds, the greater is the quantity of rain or snow that vaporizes. This is one of the reasons why highlands, being closer to the base of clouds, usually receive more precipitation than nearby lowlands.

Viewed from a distance, a shaft of raindrops, ice particles, or snowflakes falling from a cloud may appear as dark curtains or streaks against a bright background (Figure 7.18). **Virga** is the name given to such streaks when the water or ice particles vaporize before reaching Earth's surface. This is a common sight in the Great Basin of the American West where much potential precipitation vaporizes while falling through the very dry air beneath cloud base.

For a discussion of efforts to increase precipitation by stimulating natural precipitation processes, refer to this chapter's second Essay, Rainmaking.

FIGURE 7.18
Much of the rain falling from the base of a distant thunderstorm evaporates in the relatively dry air beneath the cloud. The shaft of falling precipitation is known as virga.

Forms of Precipitation

Within the atmosphere, some water vapor condenses or deposits forming clouds, and through the collision-coalescence and Bergeron-Findeisen processes, some clouds precipitate. Depending upon environmental conditions, precipitation occurs in many forms. Included are liquid precipitation (rain, drizzle), freezing precipitation (freezing rain, freezing drizzle), and frozen precipitation (snow, snow pellets, snow grains, ice pellets, hail).

Rain consists of liquid water drops that fall mostly from nimbostratus and cumulonimbus clouds. Air resistance causes raindrops to fall as slightly flattened spheres (not teardrops as popularly portrayed) with diameters generally in the range of 0.5 to 6 mm (0.02 to 0.2 in.). At greater diameters, drops are unstable and break up into smaller drops. (Imagine what life would be like if raindrops grew to the size of basketballs!) Water's surface tension keeps small drops together, but once a critical size is reached, surface tension is incapable of maintaining the drop. (*Surface tension* is the attraction between molecules at or near the surface of a liquid.) Research meteorologists sampling warm-cloud raindrops over Hilo, HI discovered an exception to this rule. They reported raindrops as large as 8 mm (0.3 in.) in diameter (about the size of a pea). In this case, strong updrafts in convective clouds prolonged the period of collision-coalescence, thereby enabling warm drops to grow to extraordinary sizes. At middle and high latitudes, raindrops usually begin as snowflakes (or sometimes would-be hailstones) that melt and coalesce as they descend through air at temperatures above 0 °C (32 °F).

Drizzle consists of liquid water drops having diameters between 0.2 and 0.5 mm (0.01 and 0.02 in.) that drift very slowly toward Earth's surface. Drizzle originates mostly in stratus clouds that are so low and thin that droplets undergo only limited growth by collision-coalescence. Drizzle often occurs with fog and contributes to poor visibility.

Snow is an agglomeration of ice crystals in the form of flakes. Although constituent ice crystals are hexagonal (six-sided), snowflakes vary in shape and size depending on water vapor concentration and temperature in the portion of the cloud where they form and grow. Crystals may consist of needles, dendrites, plates, or columns (Figure 7.19). Snowflake size depends in part on the availability of water vapor during crystal growth. At very low air temperatures, water vapor concentration is relatively low, and snowflakes are small. Snowflake size also depends on collision efficiency as flakes fall through the atmosphere. At air temperatures near or slightly above freezing, snowflakes more readily stick together (agglomerate) after colliding and their aggregate diameters have been known to reach 5 to 10 cm (2 to 4 in.). Appearance of such large flakes may indicate that snow is about to turn to rain.

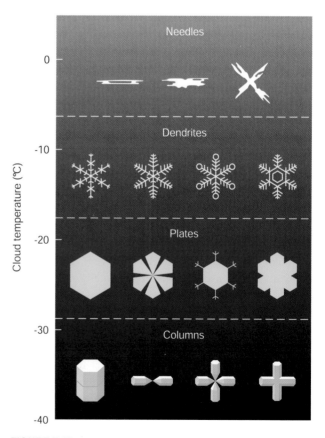

FIGURE 7.19
Snowflakes take on a variety of forms depending to a certain extent on cloud temperature.

Snow pellets and snow grains are related to snow-flakes. **Snow pellets** (formerly called *soft hail* or *graupel*) are soft conical or spherical white particles of ice having diameters of 2 to 5 mm (0.08 to 0.2 in.). They form when supercooled cloud droplets collide and freeze on an ice crystal. **Snow grains** (also known as *granular snow*) are flat or elongated opaque white particles of ice, usually less than 1.0 mm (0.04 in.) in diameter. They originate in much the same way as drizzle except that they freeze prior to reaching the ground. Is it ever too cold to snow? When is it too warm to snow? For answers to these questions, see this chapter's third Essay.

Ice pellets, commonly called **sleet**, are spherical or irregularly shaped transparent or translucent particles of ice that are 5 mm (0.2 in.) or less in diameter. Ice pellets form when snowflakes partially or completely melt as they fall through above-freezing air beneath cloud base (Figure 7.20).

These raindrops or partially melted snowflakes then fall into a relatively thick layer of subfreezing air where they refreeze into ice particles prior to striking the ground.

Freezing rain (or *freezing drizzle*) consists of rain (or drizzle) drops that become supercooled and at least partially freeze on contact with cold surfaces (at subfreezing temperatures), forming a coating of ice (*glaze*) on roads, tree branches, and other exposed surfaces. Even a thin coating of ice can create hazardous driving and walking conditions. Sometimes glaze grows so thick that its weight brings down tree limbs and snaps power lines. Freezing rain develops in much the same way as sleet except that the layer of subfreezing air at Earth's surface is shallower (Figure 7.21). If surface temperatures are close to freezing, the supercooled drops partially freeze, producing a wet and very slippery surface. We can readily distinguish ice pellets from freezing rain: Ice pellets bounce when striking the ground whereas freezing raindrops do not bounce. Whereas the ground must be at or below freezing for freezing rain to occur, snow and ice pellets may accumulate on surfaces at temperatures above 0 °C.

Freezing rain usually occurs during a relatively brief interval (several hours) between episodes of snow and ordinary rain. There have been some exceptionally long periods of freezing rain, however. In January 1998, a freezing rain event in Quebec and northern sections of New York State and New England persisted for almost five days. In many areas, liquid precipitation totaled

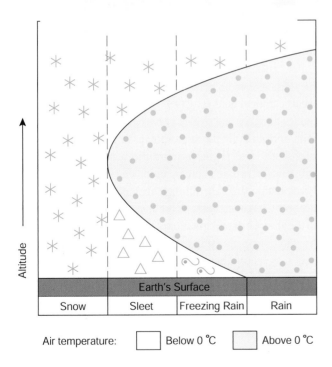

FIGURE 7.20
Schematic cross-section of the lower atmosphere showing temperature conditions required for formation of frozen, freezing, and liquid forms of precipitation.

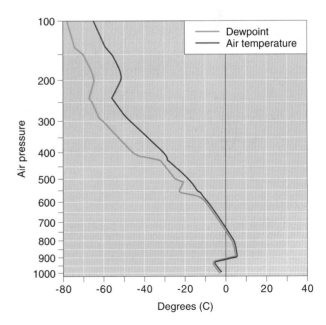

FIGURE 7.21
Radiosonde soundings of temperature and dewpoint indicating conditions favorable for freezing rain.

about 10 cm (4 in.) and turned to ice. Thick coatings of ice brought down trees and utility poles blocking roads and cutting off power for about 4 million people (1 million in the U.S. and 3 million in Canada). For Canada, this was the nation's most costly natural disaster with insurance companies paying out about $1 billion.

Freezing rain events can be highly localized and persistent where the terrain is hilly or mountainous such as the Appalachians of Pennsylvania and West Virginia. Cold, dense air drains into valley bottoms. Rain that falls from warm air aloft into this shallow layer of subfreezing air becomes supercooled and forms a glaze on cold surfaces. This situation often persists until the wind shifts and flushes the subfreezing air out of the valley bottom.

Glaze can develop on a road surface even without supercooling of raindrops. A prolonged period of extremely cold winter weather will chill a road surface to temperatures well below freezing. A sudden shift in weather pattern causes the air temperature to rise above the freezing point while the road surface temperature remains below freezing. Rain (not supercooled) freezes on the road surface forming a glaze that is just as hazardous as if it were produced by freezing rain or drizzle.

Hail consists of balls or jagged lumps of ice, often characterized by concentric internal layering resembling the structure of an onion (Figure 7.22). Layering is related to the various moisture collection environments that the hail encounters as it travels through the cloud. Hail forms within intense thunderstorms (cumulonimbus clouds) characterized by vigorous updrafts, an abundant supply of supercooled water droplets, and great vertical cloud development. Updrafts transport ice pellets into the middle and upper portions of the cumulonimbus cloud. Along the way, ice pellets grow by collecting supercooled water droplets, and eventually become too heavy to be supported by updrafts. Ice pellets then descend through the cloud, exit the cloud base, and enter air that is typically above the freezing point. Pellets begin melting, but if large enough initially, some ice will survive the journey to Earth's surface as *hailstones*.

Most hailstones are harmless granules of ice less than 1 cm in diameter, but violent thunderstorms may spawn destructive hailstones the size of golf balls or larger. In fact, large hail having a diameter of 0.75 in. (1.9 cm) or greater is one of the criteria whereby the National Weather Service designates a thunderstorm as severe. Hail is usually a spring or summer phenomenon that is particularly devastating to crops. There is more about hail in Chapter 11.

Acid Deposition

As described in Chapter 6, the atmospheric sub-cycle of the global water cycle purifies water. That is, when water evaporates (or ice sublimates), dissolved and suspended materials are left behind. As raindrops and snowflakes fall from clouds to the Earth's surface, however, they dissolve gases and wash pollutants from the air, changing the chemistry of the precipitation.

Rain and snow are naturally slightly acidic because they dissolve some atmospheric carbon dioxide, producing weak carbonic acid (H_2CO_3). Where air is polluted with oxides of sulfur and oxides of nitrogen, these gases interact with moisture in the atmosphere to form tiny droplets of sulfuric acid (H_2SO_4) and nitric acid (HNO_3). These substances dissolve in precipitation and increase its acidity. Precipitation that falls through such contaminated air may become 200 times more acidic than normal. Furthermore, in the absence of precipitation, sulfuric acid droplets convert to acidic aerosols (sulfate particles) that reduce visibility and may cause human health problems when inhaled. Eventually, acidic (and other) aerosols settle to the ground as *dry deposition*. The combination of acid precipitation and dry deposition is known as **acid deposition**.

An *acid* is a hydrogen-containing compound that releases hydrogen ions (H^+) when it dissolves in water. Strong acids more readily release hydrogen ions than weak acids. An alkaline substance releases hydroxyl ions (OH^-) when dissolved in water and may be weak or strong. Pure water has properties of both acidic and alkaline materials as

FIGURE 7.22
A hailstone consists of internal concentric layers of clear and opaque ice as shown in this cross section photographed in polarized light. [National Center for Atmospheric Research/ University Corporation for Atmospheric Research/National Science Foundation]

water molecules (H_2O) continually break up (into hydrogen and hydroxyl ions) and reform. The acidity and alkalinity of water or any other substance is expressed as pH, a measure of the hydrogen ion concentration. As shown on the **pH scale** in Figure 7.23, pH ranges from 0 to 14 as the hydrogen ion concentration decreases. Pure water has a pH of 7, which is considered neutral; a pH at values above 7 is increasingly alkaline whereas a pH below 7 is increasingly acidic.

The normal pH of rainwater is 5.6, that is, the pH of distilled water that is saturated with CO_2. Rain that is more acidic than normal (a pH lower than 5.6) is considered to be **acid rain**. Note that the pH scale is logarithmic; that is, each unit increment corresponds to a tenfold change in acidity or alkalinity. Hence, a two-unit drop in pH (e.g., from 5.6 to 3.6) represents a hundredfold (10×10) increase in acidity.

Gene E. Likens of the Institute of Ecosystem Studies was one of the first scientists to sound the alarm regarding acid precipitation more than three decades ago. Likens and his colleagues reported an increase in the acidity of rainfall over the eastern United States between 1955 and 1973. Their findings were later confirmed and updated by measurements made by the National Atmospheric Deposition Program in the United States and by the Canadian Network for Sampling Precipitation. In general, the mean annual pH of precipitation is under 5 in localities east of the Mississippi River and over 5 west of the Mississippi. Rain and snow tend to be most acidic in the northeastern United States and adjacent portions of Canada.

Where soils are thin and the bedrock is non-carbonate (neither limestone nor dolostone), acid rains and snowmelt are not usually neutralized and may adversely impact waterways. Acid drainage lowers the pH of lakes and streams to levels that disrupt the reproductive cycles of fish. Furthermore, acid rains leach metals (e.g., aluminum) from the soil, washing them into lakes and streams where they may harm fish, microorganisms, and aquatic plants. Increased acidity has caused the decline or elimination of fish populations in some lakes and streams in Norway, Sweden, eastern Canada, and the northeastern United States.

In addition to threatening aquatic systems, acid rains and fogs have been implicated along with other air pollutants (especially ozone) in the decline and dieback of coniferous forests in West Germany and in the Appalachian Mountains from North Carolina to New England. Another costly impact of acid precipitation is accelerated weathering of building materials, especially limestone, marble, and concrete. Metals, too, corrode faster than normal when exposed to acidic moisture.

FIGURE 7.23

Acidity and alkalinity are expressed in terms of pH, a measure of the hydrogen ion concentration in water. The pH increases from 0 to 14 as the hydrogen ion concentration decreases. On the pH scale, pure water has a pH of 7, which is considered neutral; a pH above 7 is increasingly alkaline and a pH below 7 is increasingly acidic. Normal rain water (in equilibrium with atmospheric carbon dioxide) has a pH of 5.6.

Acid precipitation is attributed to gaseous precursors emitted as byproducts of fossil fuel combustion for electric power, industry, and motor vehicles. Coal burning for electric power generation is the principal source of sulfur oxides, whereas high-temperature industrial processes and internal combustion engines (in motor vehicles) produce nitrogen oxides. According to the U.S. Environmental Protection Agency, the electric power industry accounts for about 67% of annual sulfur dioxide emissions and 22% of total annual nitrogen oxides released to the atmosphere.

In response to the acid deposition problem, the U.S. Congress created the Acid Rain Program as part of the 1990 Clean Air Act Amendments. The goals of this legislation were to lower the electric power industry's emissions of sulfur dioxide and nitrogen oxides. As of 2003, the industry had achieved nearly 100% compliance with the provisions of the Acid Rain Program. The electric power industry had reduced annual SO_2 emissions by 38% from 1980 levels and significant reductions in nitrogen oxide emissions were also reported. Over the last decade, ambient levels of sulfur dioxide and sulfates in the eastern U.S. are down more than 40% and 30% respectively. And there are indications of recovery in acidified lakes and streams in the Adirondack Mountains of New York, the northern Appalachian Plateau, and the upper Midwest.

Weather Radar: Locating Precipitation

As noted in Chapter 2, **radar** (acronym for *ra*dio *d*etection *a*nd *r*anging) is a valuable remote sensing tool for determining the location, movement, and intensity of areas of precipitation. Radar emits microwave signals and receives reflected signals from targets as it continually scans a large volume of the lower atmosphere. Today's weather radar can detect a tornado's circulation as it develops within its parent thunderstorm cloud, the spiral bands of a hurricane before they sweep onshore, and microbursts that can be hazardous to aircraft. Weather radar also monitors rainfall rates and provides cumulative rainfall totals that may forewarn of flash flooding.

As of this writing a network of 113 *WSR-88D* weather radar units monitors much of the nation. The *WSR-88D* radar operates in either the reflectivity or velocity mode. In the *reflectivity mode*, the radar signal detects areas of precipitation whereas in the *velocity mode*, the radar determines air motions directly toward or away from the radar associated with the circulation within a weather system.

REFLECTIVITY MODE

The *WSR-88D* weather radar emits short pulses of microwave energy having wavelengths of 10.0 to 11.1 cm (Figure 7.24). At these wavelengths, radar signals are reflected (or more precisely, scattered) by rain, snow, or hail but not significantly by the tiny water droplets or ice crystals that compose clouds. That is, weather radar is designed to detect (*see*) precipitation-size particles but not the parent clouds. Falling precipitation particles reflect some of the radar signal back to a receiving unit where it is electronically processed and displayed on a computer screen as a **radar echo** (electrical pulse).

Even when no precipitation is falling, the *WSR-88D* weather radar can detect boundaries within the atmosphere. Operating in the very sensitive *clear-air mode*, radar signals detect dust particles or swarms of insects that tend to collect along boundaries within air masses (e.g., an outflow boundary from a distant thunderstorm). Birds feeding on the insects also produce radar echoes and thereby enhance boundaries. These boundaries may be important because they are potential sites for future development of thunderstorms (Chapter 11).

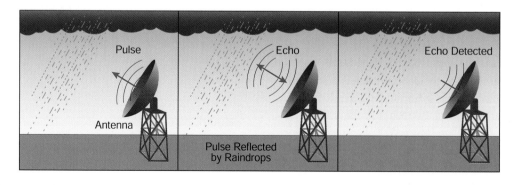

FIGURE 7.24
Operating in the reflectivity mode, weather radar continually sends out pulses of microwave energy that are scattered by raindrops, hailstones, and snowflakes back to a receiving unit that processes and displays radar echoes on a television-type screen.

FIGURE 7.25
This radome for a *WSR-88D* radar unit houses a rotating radar dish antenna.

The weather radar sending and receiving unit is a dish-type antenna housed in a radome (Figure 7.25). A *radome* is a spherical structure composed of fiberglass that protects the radar antenna from wind and weather but is transparent to radar signals. Pulsed radar signals are sent out and received hundreds of times each second as the antenna sweeps out a spiraling volume scan of the sky every 5 minutes. The radar combines several single elevation scans (ranging from 0.5° to 19.5° above the horizon) with a 360-degree sweep in the horizontal direction to complete one volume scan. The product is a map of radar echoes representing the precipitation distribution (if any) in the region surrounding the radar unit. The speed of the radar pulse is known so that the elapsed time between emission and reception of a radar signal can be calibrated to give the distance to the precipitation.

The strength (intensity) of a radar echo depends on the reflectivity of the targeted precipitation particle, with the greatest reflectivity for hailstones and large raindrops. The concentration of raindrops along the path of the radar beam also affects echo intensity but to a lesser extent. Echo intensity is an index of rainfall rate and can be used to identify severe thunderstorm cells, which often contain large hail. Radar systems electronically display echo intensity via a color scale. By one convention (often seen on televised weathercasts), red indicates very heavy rain (or hail) and, at the other end of the scale, light green (or sometimes blue) signifies very light rain (Figure 7.26). Other color schemes are sometimes used to portray snow (e.g., white) or a mixture of rain and snow (e.g., pink). As described in more detail later in this chapter, weather

FIGURE 7.26
A sample radar reflectivity product in which echo intensity is graduated by color.

radar can also produce maps of rainfall totals over a specified time period.

Not all radar echoes are caused by meteorological phenomena. Nearby objects fixed on the ground, such as buildings or smokestacks, also reflect radar signals; such radar echoes constitute **ground clutter**. A ground clutter pattern produced in this way is unique to a particular radar site, appears all the time, and hence is readily distinguished from precipitation echoes. Typically, this constant ground clutter echo pattern is electronically subtracted from reflectivity displays. On the other hand, special atmospheric conditions sometimes develop that give rise to ground clutter that may be mistaken for precipitation. For example, a strong temperature inversion may cause the outgoing radar signal to bend downward so that it strikes the ground. Such ground clutter differs from precipitation echoes in that it is stationary, stronger, and grainier in appearance. Often, these *anomalous propagation* patterns appear just prior to sunrise when a strong low-level temperature inversion is present.

Sometimes a radar screen shows a broad area of echoes, but weather stations located in the same area report no precipitation. In this case, the radar is detecting echoes from rain and/or snow that falls from clouds but vaporizes completely in the relatively dry air beneath cloud base. (Recall our earlier discussion of *virga*.)

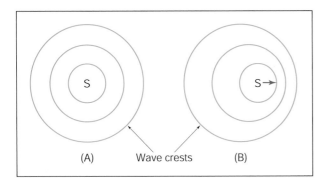

FIGURE 7.27
The Doppler Effect refers to the shift in the frequency of sound or electromagnetic waves that accompanies the motion of the wave source(s) or wave receiver. (A) A sound wave source (e.g., train whistle) is stationary and wave frequency is uniform everywhere. (B) The wave source is in motion so that wave frequency is greater ahead of the source than behind the source.

VELOCITY (DOPPLER) MODE

WSR-88D is the first weather radar to operate in both velocity and reflectivity modes. In the velocity mode, the radar system applies the Doppler Effect to determine horizontal air motions within a weather system based upon the detected motions of precipitation particles assumed to be tracers of the wind. The Doppler Effect is named for Johann Christian Doppler (1803-1853), the Austrian physicist who was the first to explain the phenomenon in 1842. For this reason, radar with velocity-detection capability is often referred to as a **Doppler radar**. The Doppler Effect is also employed in devices that measure the speed of a pitched ball or motor vehicle traffic.

The **Doppler Effect** refers to a shift in the frequency of sound waves or electromagnetic waves emanating from a moving source. For example, the pitch (frequency) of a train whistle sounds higher as a train approaches and drops off as the train pulls away. As shown schematically in Figure 7.27A, the crests of sound waves radiate outward from a stationary source as evenly spaced concentric circles; that is, the wave frequency is uniform. If the source is moving, however, as in Figure 7.27B, wave crests become more closely spaced in the direction in which the source is moving so that the frequency is higher ahead of the source but lower behind the source.

Doppler radar monitors the motion of precipitation particles moving directly toward or away from the radar antenna. The frequency of the radar signal shifts slightly between emission and the return signal (*echo*) and this frequency shift is calibrated in terms of the motion of the particle (Figure 7.28). No frequency shift occurs for components of particle motion that are perpendicular to the radar beam; that is, Doppler radar cannot detect air motion at right angles to the radar beam. When air is moving in directions other than directly toward or away from the path of the radar signal, only the component of motion toward or away from the radar is detectable. Doppler radar displays are color-coded so that greens and blues (cold colors) indicate motion directly toward the radar and reds and yellows (warm colors) indicate motion directly away from the radar (Figure 7.29).

Doppler radar enables meteorologists to provide the public with advance warning of hazardous weather including severe thunderstorms, tornadoes, and potentially flooding rains. The geographical range of radar is limited

FIGURE 7.28
Doppler radar operating in three different weather situations. (A) With a stationary rain shower, the frequency of the emitted signal is the same as that of the return echo. (B) If the rain shower approaches the radar, the frequency of the return echo is greater than that of the emitted signal. (C) If the rain shower moves away from the radar, the frequency of the return echo is less than that of the emitted signal. [Adapted from SAM, NOAA/Environmental Research Laboratories/Forecast Systems Laboratory]

FIGURE 7.29
A sample Doppler weather radar image. Greens and blues (cold colors) indicate motion directly toward the radar whereas reds and yellows (warm colors) indicate motion directly away from the radar.

by the curvature of the Earth; that is, radar signals travel along downward-bending paths somewhat less curved than Earth's surface. Radar sees well beyond the horizon but its beam gains altitude with increasing distance from the radar antenna so that when operating in the reflectivity mode, the radar's maximum range is about 460 km (285 mi). For other reasons when operating in the velocity (Doppler) mode, the radar's maximum range decreases to about 230 km (143 mi).

Measuring Precipitation

Rainfall and snowfall are routinely measured in terms of depth of accumulation over a specified interval of time, usually hourly and every 6 hrs and 24 hrs. Measurements are made directly by collecting a volume of rain or snow in a rain or snow gauge or estimated remotely by weather radar or satellite sensors.

RAIN AND SNOW GAUGES

Today precipitation is collected and measured using essentially the same instrument that was developed centuries ago: a container open to the sky. The first mention of a rain gauge in European literature appeared in 1639, although gauges were used in Asia much earlier.

About 400 B.C., the Indian author Kautilya described the first known rain gauge in his manuscript *Arthastra*. The gauge consisted of a 45-cm (20-in.) diameter bowl, and measurements were taken regularly as a way of estimating the annual crop to be sown.

A standard non-recording **rain gauge** design consists of a cylinder equipped with a cone-shaped funnel at the top (Figure 7.30). The funnel directs rainwater into a narrower cylinder seated inside the larger outer cylinder. The funnel and narrow cylinder magnify the scale of measurement so that the instrument can resolve rainfall into increments as small as 0.01 in. (0.25 mm). A simple graduated stick is used to measure the depth of water that accumulates in the inner cylinder. (The stick is graduated in inches in the U.S. but in millimeters in Canada and most other nations.) Rainfall of less than 0.005 in. (0.1 mm) is recorded as a *trace*. Rainfall is usually measured at some fixed time once every 24 hrs and the gauge is then emptied. This type of rain gauge must be read manually.

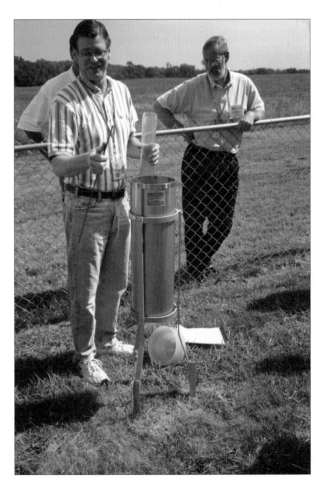

FIGURE 7.30
A standard National Weather Service non-recording rain gauge.

Continuous monitoring of rainfall is often useful, especially in flood-prone areas. Accordingly, some rain gauges are designed to provide a cumulative record of rainfall through time, thereby yielding rainfall rates, an indicator of precipitation intensity. Two common designs are the weighing-bucket and tipping-bucket rain gauges. These recording rain gauges can be used in remote locations. A **weighing-bucket rain gauge** calibrates the weight of accumulating rainwater in terms of water depth. This instrument has a device that marks a chart on a clock-driven drum or sends an electronic signal to a computer for processing. At subfreezing temperatures, antifreeze in the collection bucket or a heater melts snow or ice pellets producing a cumulative record of melt water.

A **tipping-bucket rain gauge** consists of a free-swinging container partitioned into two compartments, each of which can collect the equivalent of 0.01 in. of rainfall. Each compartment alternately fills with water, tips and spills its contents, and trips an electric switch that either marks a chart on a clock-driven drum or sends an electrical pulse to a computer for recording. Compared to a weighing-bucket rain gauge, a tipping-bucket rain gauge does not perform as well at subfreezing air temperatures or at very high rainfall rates. A heated tipping-bucket gauge has been a standard component of the NWS Automated Surface Observing System (ASOS) but it is to be replaced by a weighing-bucket precipitation gauge (Figure 7.31).

For snow, meteorologists are interested in (1) the depth of snow that falls during the period between observations, (2) the melt water equivalent of that snowfall, and (3) the depth of snow on the ground at observation time. New snowfall accumulates on a simple wooden board placed on top of the old snow cover. Using a ruler graduated in tenths of an inch (or a meter stick graduated in centimeters), snow depth is measured to the board. The board is then swept clean and moved to a new location. Snowfall measurements, reported to the nearest 0.1 in., are made at regularly scheduled times, typically once daily.

The melt water equivalent of new snowfall can be determined by measurements taken by a weighing-bucket gauge or by melting the snow collected in a non-recording gauge (with the funnel and inner cylinder removed). The average density of fresh snow is about 0.1 gram per cubic centimeter so that as a very general rule, 10 cm of fresh snow melts to 1 cm of water. However, the actual snow/melt-water ratio varies considerably depending on (1) the crystalline form of the snowflakes and (2) the temperature of the air through which the snow falls. Snow consisting of columnar crystals can be relatively dense whereas snow made up of dendritic (star-like) crystals (typical of

FIGURE 7.31
New weighing-bucket rain gauge to be used as a component of the National Weather Service Automated Surface Observing System.

lake-effect snow) has very low density with the ratio of snowfall depth to melt-water depth as great as 50 to 1. Wet snow falling at surface air temperatures at or above 0 °C (32 °F) has much greater water content than dry snow falling at very low surface air temperatures. The ratio of snowfall depth to melt-water depth may vary from 3 to 1 for very wet snow to 30 to 1 or higher for dry fluffy snow. As a snow cover ages, snow converts to tiny granules of ice, air-filled space is reduced, the snow settles, and snow density increases.

The depth of snow on the ground is usually determined using a graduated rule inserted vertically into the snow at several representative locations. These measurements are averaged, rounded to the nearest inch, and reported daily. Care must be taken to avoid areas where the wind whipped the snow into drifts. The snow depth may represent an accumulation of several snowfall events that have not melted or sublimated.

The amount of rainfall and snowfall can vary considerably from one place to another, especially when produced by convective showers and thunderstorms. Precipitation gauges are sited so that measurements are as accurate and representative as possible. Instruments must be sheltered from strong winds, which cut the collection efficiency of rain gauges. Winds tend to accelerate over the open top of a gauge, reducing the amount of rain that enters the instrument. One study found that winds blowing at 16 km (10 mi) per hr reduced the amount of rainwater collected by 10% compared to the amount that would enter the gauge if the air were calm. Gauges should not be placed in windswept locations, but must be sited well away from buildings and tall vegetation that might shield the instrument from precipitation. As a general rule, obstacles should be no closer to the gauge than four times the height of the obstacle.

Traditionally, meteorologists derive spatial patterns of atmospheric variables from measurements made by instruments at discrete points, that is, at weather stations. This approach works reasonably well for variables such as air temperature and pressure that vary continuously from one place to another. Hence, the temperature is likely to be near 65 °F at a location half way between two weather stations, one reporting 60 °F and the other reporting 70 °F. Basing spatial patterns on measurements at discrete points does not work as well for discontinuous variables such as precipitation. Precipitation is typically highly variable spatially. Hence, it does not always follow that moderate amounts of rain fell at a location halfway between two weather stations, one reporting heavy rainfall and the other reporting light rainfall. Furthermore, regular precipitation measurements are missing from vast stretches of the ocean where significant amounts of precipitation fall. To help remedy this situation, scientists developed radar technologies and satellite-borne instruments that provide more continuous coverage of precipitation over broad areas.

REMOTE SENSING OF PRECIPITATION

The *WSR-88D* weather radar determines not only the location and intensity of rainfall but also provides estimates of the total amount of rainfall. Whereas networks of precipitation gauges measure rainfall at discrete locations often more than 100 km (60 mi) apart, radar measures rainfall within continuous volume scans of the atmosphere centered on the unit. A special computer algorithm uses radar monitoring of rainfall rate to generate color-coded maps of rainfall totals over a specific period of time (Figure 7.32).

FIGURE 7.32
Cumulative rainfall as determined by computer analysis of radar echoes.

To estimate rainfall, the *WSR-88D* radar measures the reflectivity obtained from a volume scan that combines the lowest four tilt angles (0.5°, 1.5°, 2.5°, and 3.5° above the horizon) as frequently as every six minutes. Reflectivity is proportional to the *surface area* of raindrops whereas rainfall rate is proportional to the *volume* of the raindrops. Reflectivity data are converted to rainfall rates by estimating the raindrop size distribution and results are then checked against selected precipitation gauge measurements on the ground. If properly calibrated, radar can provide a better spatial representation of hourly precipitation amounts than networks of precipitation gauges. This guidance information is particularly valuable for flash flood forecasting (Chapter 11).

Satellite sensors are also valuable remote sensing tools for precipitation. The *Tropical Rainfall Measuring Mission (TRMM)* utilizes satellite technology primarily to measure rainfall over the area between 40 degrees N and 40 degrees S. Knowledge of tropical rainfall and the associated flow of heat energy promises to improve our understanding of the global climate system and make possible the development of more realistic global climate models. About two-thirds of all precipitation falls in the tropics and much of the planetary-scale heat transport originates in the tropics. This satellite mission is also helping scientists detect the onset and follow the evolution of El Niño and La Niña (Chapter 9). Launched in November 1997, TRMM is a joint venture of the National Aeronautics and Space Administration (NASA) and Japan's National Space Development Agency.

The TRMM satellite, in orbit about 350 km (215 mi) above Earth's surface, utilizes three sensors to measure rainfall remotely: radar, a microwave imager, and a visible/IR scanner. Satellite-based precipitation radar (PR) is similar to ground-based radar except that the signal has a much shorter wavelength. PR obtains vertical profiles of rain and snow from Earth's surface to an altitude of about 20,000 m (65,500 ft) and has a horizontal resolution on Earth's surface of 4 km (2.5 mi). The TRMM Microwave Imager (TMI) measures the minute flux of microwave energy emitted by the Earth-atmosphere system. The instrument can "see through" clouds and measure sea surface temperatures. Variations in the amount of energy received at different wavelengths are interpreted to measure water vapor, cloud water, and rainfall intensity. Similar sensors have been flown onboard polar-orbiting Defense Meteorological Satellites since 1987. The TRMM Visible and Infrared Scanner (VIRS) monitors five spectral channels from visible to infrared (between 0.63 and 12 micrometers). The height of convective clouds (determined from IR-derived cloud-top temperature) is the basis for rainfall estimates; that is, the higher the cloud, the greater is the rainfall. The same type of precipitation-measuring scanner is used routinely on Polar Orbiting Environmental Satellites (POES) and Geostationary Operational Satellites (GOES) for weather analysis and forecasting.

Meteorologists also measure snow cover remotely, information that is valuable for water resource managers and flood forecasters. In mountainous areas where snowfall is considerable, the melt water equivalent of snow can be determined remotely using snow pillows. A *snow pillow* is a device that is filled with antifreeze solution and fitted with a manometer (an instrument that measures pressure changes). The pressure of the enclosed antifreeze solution resulting from the weight of the overlying snow provides a measure of the snow's water equivalence. Data are radioed to a satellite and from there to a data center for downloading and analysis. The *Airborne Gamma Radiation Snow Survey Program* also provides remote sensing of the water content of snow packs. At designated times, low-flying aircraft measure terrestrial gamma ray emission along selected flight lines. Gamma radiation emitted by Earth materials attenuates as the snow pack thickens. Comparison of gamma emission over the same flight line with and without snow cover is calibrated in terms of the melt water equivalent of snow (or soil moisture).

Conclusions

As air nears saturation, water vapor begins condensing or depositing on airborne nuclei. With continued cooling, usually due to expansion of rising air, clouds form. Clouds are distinguished on the basis of appearance (cirriform, stratiform, cumuliform), altitude of their base (high, middle, low, having significant vertical development), temperature (cold, warm), and composition (water droplets, ice crystals). Fog is a cloud in contact with Earth's surface and forms when air becomes saturated at low levels through radiational cooling, chilling of warm humid air as it moves over a relatively cold surface, cold air advection over a relatively warm, wet surface, or expansional cooling that accompanies upslope motion of air in mountainous terrain.

Cloud droplets and ice crystals are much too small to fall to Earth's surface as precipitation. Through the collision-coalescence and Bergeron-Findeisen processes, cloud droplets and ice crystals grow large enough to survive the fall to Earth's surface as precipitation. Precipitation occurs as rain, drizzle, snow, ice pellets (sleet), freezing rain (or freezing drizzle), and hail. Precipitation type depends upon cloud conditions and the temperature of the air column through which the precipitation falls to Earth's surface.

A variety of direct and remote sensing techniques are employed by scientists to monitor and measure precipitation. Weather radar sends out pulses of microwave energy that locate areas of precipitation and determine the intensity of rainfall. Operating in the Doppler mode, weather radar can monitor air motions within weather systems, making it possible to provide the public with advance warning of the potential for severe weather. Instruments onboard Earth-orbiting satellites are also used to estimate rainfall over tropical and sub tropical latitudes.

Atmospheric circulation plays a key role in bringing air to saturation and triggering cloud development. The next five chapters cover the many atmospheric circulation systems and their associated weather. Chapter 8 begins with a discussion of the forces that drive and shape atmospheric circulation.

Basic Understandings

- Clouds, the visible product of condensation or deposition within the atmosphere, are composed of large numbers of tiny water droplets, ice crystals, or a combination of the two.

- As the relative humidity of air nears 100%, condensation and deposition occur on nuclei, tiny solid and liquid particles suspended in the atmosphere. Cloud condensation nuclei are much more abundant than ice-forming nuclei (i.e., freezing nuclei and deposition nuclei). Most ice-forming nuclei are active at temperatures well below the freezing point.

- Many condensation nuclei are hygroscopic; that is, they have a chemical affinity for water and induce condensation at a relative humidity less than 100%.

- Clouds are classified by general appearance (cirriform, stratiform, cumuliform), altitude of base (high, middle, low, significant vertical development), temperature (cold, warm), and composition (water droplets, ice crystals).

- High, middle, and low clouds are caused by relatively gentle uplift of air over a broad geographical area. These clouds are layered, that is, stratiform. Clouds having significant vertical development are the consequence of more vigorous uplift in more restricted geographical areas and are heaped or puffy in appearance, that is, cumuliform.

- High clouds are composed of mainly ice crystals, whereas middle and low clouds are mostly water droplets or a mixture of ice crystals and supercooled water droplets.

- Nimbostratus and cumulonimbus are the principal precipitation-producing clouds. Precipitation from nimbostratus clouds is typically lighter and is more persistent than showery precipitation from cumulonimbus clouds.

- Atmospheric stability determines whether cumulus clouds build vertically into cumulus congestus or cumulonimbus clouds. The convective condensation level corresponds to the base of cumuliform clouds.

- Lee-wave clouds develop downwind of a prominent mountain range and are nearly stationary. Noctilucent and nacreous clouds are among the very few clouds that occur above the troposphere. Noctilucent clouds develop in the upper mesosphere and may be composed of ice deposited on meteoric dust particles. Nacreous clouds form in the upper stratosphere where temperatures favor water in either the solid or supercooled state. They are cirrus or altocumulus lenticularis that form on sulfuric acid nuclei possibly of volcanic origin.

- Fog is a visibility-restricting suspension of tiny water droplets or ice crystals in an air layer in contact with Earth's surface. Based on mode of origin, fog is classified as radiation fog, advection fog, steam fog, or upslope fog.

- The relatively low terminal velocities of cloud droplets and ice crystals mean that they remain suspended in the atmosphere indefinitely unless they vaporize or undergo significant growth.

- The collision-coalescence process and Bergeron-Findeisen process describe mechanisms whereby cloud particles grow large enough to counter updrafts and fall to Earth's surface as precipitation under the influence of gravity.

- The collision-coalescence process occurs in warm clouds and requires the presence of relatively large cloud droplets that grow through collision and coalescence with smaller cloud droplets.

- The Bergeron-Findeisen process requires the coexistence of ice crystals, supercooled water droplets, and water vapor in cold clouds. At the same subfreezing temperature, the saturation vapor pressure surrounding a supercooled water droplet is higher than the saturation vapor pressure surrounding an ice crystal. Hence, air that is saturated for supercooled droplets is supersaturated for ice crystals. Ice crystals grow by deposition while water droplets vaporize.

- The bulk of precipitation that falls at middle and high latitudes originates in cold clouds composed of a mixture of ice crystals and supercooled water droplets. Once the precipitation process begins, collision and coalescence promote growth of precipitation particles.

- Principal forms of precipitation are rain, drizzle, snow, ice pellets (sleet), freezing rain, and hail. The form of precipitation depends on the source cloud and the temperature profile (sounding) of the air beneath the cloud.

- Most rain and snow fall from relatively thick clouds (nimbostratus or cumulonimbus) whereas drizzle falls from relatively thin clouds (stratus). Ice pellets are raindrops that freeze prior to reaching the ground, whereas freezing rain consists of supercooled drops that freeze on contact with surfaces at subfreezing temperatures. Hail is produced by intense thunderstorms having vigorous updrafts, an abundant supply of supercooled water droplets, and great vertical development.

- Rain and snow are normally slightly acidic because they dissolve some atmospheric carbon dioxide, producing weak carbonic acid (H_2CO_3). Where air is polluted with oxides of sulfur and oxides of nitrogen, these gases interact with moisture in the atmosphere to form tiny droplets of sulfuric acid (H_2SO_4) and nitric acid (HNO_3). These substances dissolve in precipitation and increase its acidity.
- Weather radar is used to determine the location and movement of areas of precipitation. Operating in the reflectivity mode, radar echo strength increases with precipitation intensity. Operating in the Doppler mode, weather radar can be used to determine the detailed motion of air within a weather system.
- Precipitation is measured directly by collecting a volume of rain or snow in a rain or snow gauge or estimated remotely using weather radar or sensors onboard Earth-orbiting satellites.

Review

1. List several sources of cloud condensation nuclei (CCN).
2. What is meant by "supercooled" cloud droplets?
3. What is the significance of *hygroscopic* nuclei for cloud development?
4. How are clouds classified?
5. How and why does the composition of cumuliform clouds vary with altitude?
6. Why is radiation fog usually short-lived? Under what conditions might radiation fog persist for many days or even weeks?
7. Under what conditions does freezing rain develop? Distinguish between freezing rain and ice pellets (sleet).
8. Explain how hail reaches the ground even when air temperatures are well above freezing.
9. What is the average density of fresh-fallen snow? What does this imply about the melt-water equivalent of snowfall?
10. Distinguish between radar operating in the reflectivity mode from radar operating in the velocity (Doppler) mode in terms of what is being displayed.

Critical Thinking

1. Is it possible for upslope fog, orographic rainfall, and wave clouds to form simultaneously on the same mountain range? Elaborate on your answer.
2. How is it possible for liquid water to become supercooled?
3. Speculate on what might cause a cumuliform cloud to tilt or lean with altitude.
4. How might the formation of advection fog affect a snow cover? Answer for air temperatures above and below freezing.
5. An automobile outside on a clear, calm night is observed to have a coating of frost on its hood, roof, and trunk lid. Interestingly, frost is absent along all sides of the vehicle. Why didn't frost form on the sides of the vehicle?
6. Speculate on why in some localities the exterior of a rain gauge is painted white. Also, why is it desirable to shield a rain or snow gauge from strong winds?
7. Why is the magnitude of the saturation vapor pressure surrounding supercooled water droplets greater than the magnitude of the saturation vapor pressure surrounding ice crystals at the same temperature?
8. Give two reasons why rainfall is likely to be heavier on top of a mountain than in a nearby valley.
9. The changeover from rain to snow is usually faster if precipitation is moderate to heavy rather than light. Explain why.
10. How many calories of heat are required per square centimeter to melt 10 cm of snow at 0°C? Assume the snow density to be 0.1 g/cm^3.

ESSAY: Clouds by Mixing

Outdoors on a cold winter day, you sometimes "see" your breath when you exhale. You're actually seeing a small cloud formed by the mixing of your warm, humid breath with the colder, drier ambient air. Mixing of air masses (or air layers within the same air mass) that differ in temperature and vapor pressure is another mechanism whereby clouds form. Surprisingly, a cloud may form even though the two air masses are initially unsaturated.

As emphasized in Chapter 6, the saturation vapor pressure increases rapidly with rising temperature. This relationship is depicted schematically in Figure 1 where temperature is plotted on the horizontal axis and vapor pressure is plotted on the vertical axis. The average temperature and average vapor pressure of a specific air mass plot as a single point on the diagram. An air mass that plots below the saturation vapor pressure curve is unsaturated, on the curve is saturated, and above the curve is supersaturated.

Suppose that two different unsaturated air masses plot as points A and B on the diagram. It is reasonable to assume that mixing the two air masses would produce a new air mass having properties (average temperature and vapor pressure) that would plot somewhere along a straight line connecting the points A and B. The precise location of that point (the mixture) along the line depends on the relative volumes of the two air masses. In any case, the mixture of the two air masses is unsaturated so that no cloud forms. Consider, however, two other unsaturated air masses, C and D, one cold and dry, the other warm and humid. In this case the straight line linking C and D intersects the saturation vapor pressure curve. The new air mass resulting from the mixing of equal volumes of air masses C and D is saturated and a cloud forms.

This description of cloud formation by mixing provides insight as to the cause of jet aircraft contrails (Figure 7.1). The exhaust from jet engines mixes with the ambient air and may form a *contrail* (i.e., condensation trail) behind the aircraft. Heat and water are among the combustion products of jet engines so that the exhaust is hot and humid. Turbulence in the wake of a jet engine promotes the mixing of the exhaust with ambient air. If the ambient air has the appropriate combination of vapor pressure and temperature, the mixture will be saturated and a contrail will form. Such conditions are most likely in the upper troposphere where commercial jetliners travel.

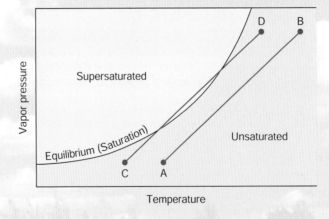

Figure 1
Variation of saturation vapor pressure with temperature. The properties of an air mass that plots as a point above the curve is supersaturated, on the curve is saturated, and below the curve is unsaturated.

ESSAY: Rainmaking

Since the mid-1940s, considerable research has gone into methods of enhancing precipitation by cloud seeding. *Cloud seeding* is an attempt to stimulate natural precipitation processes by injecting nucleating agents into clouds. Cloud seeding also has been used to reduce the size of hailstones, dissipate fog, and lessen the effects of lightning. Most cloud seeding is directed at cold clouds although in recent years warm cloud seeding has received significant interest.

Discovery of cloud seeding was serendipitous. In the 1940s, the Nobel Prize winning chemist Irving Langmuir (1881-1957) and his assistant Vincent Schaefer were conducting experiments at the General Electric Research Laboratory in Schenectady, NY on ways to prevent the build up of ice (rime) on the surfaces of airplane wings. One strategy that intrigued them was to somehow cause supercooled cloud droplets to freeze prior to fusing to the wing. On a hot summer day in 1946, Schaefer was working with supercooled water in a cold chamber (an open freezer). The day was hot and to get the chamber to cool down he added some dry ice (solid CO_2). To Schaefer's amazement, the supercooled water in the chamber turned to a cloud of ice crystals. He realized that this might be a way to stimulate the Bergeron-Findeisen precipitation process (described earlier in this chapter). On 13 November 1946, General Electric scientists confirmed this new technique of cloud seeding when they dumped dry ice particles from an aircraft into a stratus cloud composed of supercooled droplets. Immediately after seeding, the seeded area of the cloud converted to ice crystals.

The objective of seeding cold clouds is to stimulate the Bergeron-Findeisen process in clouds that are deficient in ice crystals. The seeding (nucleating) agent typically is either silver iodide (AgI), a substance with crystal properties similar to ice, or dry ice, which sublimates at a temperature of about $-80\ °C$ ($-112\ °F$). (Extremely cold liquid propane is also sometimes used.) The day after the test of dry ice by Langmuir and Schaefer, Bernard Vonnegut (1914-1997) discovered that microscopic silver iodide could be used as a nucleating agent. He conducted the first field test using silver iodide in 1948. Silver iodide crystals are freezing nuclei that are active at $-5\ °C$ ($23\ °F$) and below. Dry ice pellets are so cold that within a cloud they cause surrounding supercooled water droplets to freeze. Frozen droplets then grow into snowflakes through the Bergeron-Findeisen process followed by collision and agglomeration. Furthermore, latent heat released when supercooled water droplets freeze makes the cloud slightly warmer and more buoyant, stimulating additional cloud growth that can lead to more precipitation.

Clouds can be seeded via aircraft or from the ground. In either case, silver iodide is released into updrafts at cloud base from liquid fuel generators or pyrotechnic flares. Only one gram of silver iodide can produce as many as 10^{15} particles. Dry ice pellets are dropped through an opening in the aircraft floor directly into a cloud's updraft. Dry ice pellets are less efficient at producing ice crystals than silver iodide; as much as 2000 grams of dry ice are needed to match the output of just one gram of silver iodide. Of the two methods of seeding, cloud seeding from ground-based generators, while relatively inexpensive, can be less satisfactory than airborne seeding because the seeding agent may not diffuse adequately and reach sufficient altitudes to be effective. Nonetheless, both methods are used.

The traditional method of seeding warm clouds is to inject hygroscopic substances (e.g., sea salt crystals) into clouds to stimulate formation of relatively large cloud droplets that grow into raindrops by collision and coalescence. In the early 1990s, this technique was given a boost by the development of a new cloud-seeding flare (based on a U.S. Navy fog-producing flare) that when ignited releases large quantities of microscopic salt particles (mostly potassium chloride). A series of flares mounted on an aircraft wing releases salt particles. The plane flies just below cloud base so that updrafts carry salt particles into the (cumuliform) cloud. Initial results from experimental use of this technique in South Africa and Mexico suggest that flares are more effective than the old methods of dispensing hygroscopic nucleating agents in liquid sprays. In August 2000, Roelof Bruintjes and his colleagues at the National Center for Atmospheric Research (NCAR) reported statistically significant rainfall enhancement using this technique during a 3-year cloud seeding experiment carried out over drought-prone northern Mexico.

The Sierra Cooperative Pilot Project (SCPP) is an example of a long-term, ongoing study of cloud seeding. Scientists seed *orographic clouds* over the windward western slopes of California's Sierra Nevada Mountains with the goal of increasing snowfall and thereby thickening the mountain snow pack. The consequent increase in spring runoff is intended to help California meet its growing domestic and agricultural water demands. The American River Basin, just west of Lake Tahoe, is the principal SCPP study site, and January through March is the primary seeding season. Clouds targeted for seeding are rich in supercooled water droplets but deficient in ice crystals. To identify clouds best suited for seeding, SCPP scientists employ an aircraft that is outfitted with sophisticated instruments that measure the size and concentration of cloud and precipitation particles. Another aircraft seeds selected (cold) clouds with silver iodide or dry ice pellets. Meanwhile, on the ground, an array of precipitation gauges, weather radar, and other weather instruments monitor the effectiveness of seeding.

Does cloud seeding work? In the 1970s and early 1980s, NOAA scientists conducted a statistically rigorous experiment designed to test the effectiveness of cloud seeding. The experiment involved seeding cumulus clouds over southern Florida. The testing period was about evenly divided between days when clouds were seeded with silver iodide crystals and days when clouds were seeded with inert (chemically inactive) sand grains. Only after the experiment was completed and the results analyzed were participating scientists informed of the specific days when silver iodide was the seeding agent. This procedure was intended to ensure both an unbiased selection of clouds to be seeded and an unbiased interpretation of results.

The Florida seeding experiment was divided into two phases. Results from an initial *exploratory* phase were to be either verified or rejected by a later *confirmatory* phase when seeding was repeated. Results of the first phase were very encouraging, showing a 25% increase in rainfall on days when silver iodide was the seeding agent, compared to days when sand was the bogus seeding agent. This finding was statistically significant at the 90% level, meaning that there is only a 10% probability that the increased rainfall was a chance occurrence. However, the success of the initial phase was not replicated during the second phase when seeding brought no statistically significant increase in rainfall.

Although cloud seeding is successful in some instances, the actual amount of additional precipitation produced by cloud seeding and the advisability of large-scale seeding efforts are controversial. Some cloud seeders claim to increase precipitation by 15% to 20% or more, but the question remains as to whether the rain or snow that follows cloud seeding would have fallen anyway. Even if apparently successful, some people argue that cloud seeding may merely redistribute a fixed supply of precipitation, so that more precipitation in one area might mean a compensating reduction in another area. For example, rainmaking might benefit agricultural interests on the High Plains of eastern Colorado but also deprive wheat farmers of rain in the adjacent downwind states of Kansas and Nebraska. Such conflicts can erupt in legal battles between residents of adjacent counties, states, and provinces.

The potential for cloud seeding success is greatest in areas already receiving considerable precipitation, as in the SCPP effort described above. Unfortunately, the potential for successful cloud seeding in arid or drought-prone areas is less than promising because the necessary atmospheric conditions are usually not present either because of insufficient atmospheric moisture or lack of suitable lifting mechanism to produce clouds.

ESSAY: When Is It Too Cold or Too Warm to Snow?

During an episode of particularly frigid winter weather, some people will claim that it is too cold to snow. In fact, the coldest weather is often accompanied by fair skies associated with an arctic high pressure system, and the climate records of the northern United States and Canada indicate that snowfall totals decline with falling temperature. For some northern U.S. cities (e.g., Billings, MT, Huron, SD, and Minneapolis-St. Paul, MN), March on average is both the snowiest and the mildest of the winter months (December through March). In Canada, outside of the mountains, average annual snowfall declines from more than 400 cm (160 in.) in relatively mild parts of maritime Newfoundland to less than 100 cm (40 in.) along the frigid shores of the Arctic Ocean. But even though total snowfall decreases with falling temperature, snow is possible even at extremely low air temperatures. In bitter cold air, however, snowflakes are small and accumulations are usually meager.

The relatively small amount of water vapor in very cold air means that comparatively little water is available for precipitation (i.e., low amounts of *precipitable water*). Recall from Chapter 6 that the saturation vapor pressure drops rapidly as air temperature falls. For example, the water vapor concentration in saturated air at −30 °C (−22 °F) is only about 12% of the water vapor concentration in saturated air at −5 °C (23 °F). Hence, the amount of water potentially available for precipitation decreases with dropping air temperature.

Heaviest snowfalls typically occur when the temperature of the lower atmosphere is within a few degrees of the freezing point, because at that temperature, the potential amount of water that can precipitate in the solid form (as snow) is at a maximum. On the other hand, moderate or heavy snowfall is very unlikely when the temperature of the lower atmosphere falls below −20 °C (−4 °F). But even in the coldest regions of the globe where precipitable water amounts are lowest, some snow falls. For example, an estimated average annual 5 cm (2 in.) of snow falls on the high interior plateau of Greenland where average annual temperatures are below −30 °C (−22 °F).

When is it too warm to snow? Surprisingly, snow can fall even when the near-surface air temperature is as high as 10 °C (50 °F). The essential requirement is that the wet-bulb temperature remains below 0 °C (32 °F); that is, the relative humidity must be very low. For example, if the air temperature is 5 °C (41 °F), the relative humidity must be under 32% for the wet-bulb temperature to be subfreezing (see Table 6.5). The first snowflakes leaving the cloud vaporize or melt as they fall through relatively dry, above-freezing air and reach the ground as raindrops. Vaporization and melting of snowflakes tap heat from the ambient air; that is, sensible heat is converted to latent heat, and the air temperature drops. With sufficient vaporization and melting, the air eventually cools to the wet-bulb temperature, that is, below the freezing point. Hence, at the Earth's surface, what started out as rain (or a mixture of rain and snow) turns to snow. This is most likely to happen if the precipitation is moderate to heavy—more vaporizing and melting snowflakes means more cooling.

CHAPTER 8

WIND AND WEATHER

Wind damage from a tornado in March 1997. [Courtesy NWS/NOAA]

Case in Point

A popular ballad by Gordon Lightfoot memorialized the November 1975 sinking of the ore carrier *Edmund Fitzgerald* with the loss of its crew of 29 in the storm-tossed waters of Lake Superior. At the time, the 222-m (729-ft) long ship was the largest ore carrier on the Great Lakes. Early on the afternoon of 9 November, the ship was fully loaded with 26,116 tons of iron ore (taconite) pellets when it left the Duluth-Superior harbor at the far western end of Lake Superior on a northeast course at about 20 knots (23 mi per hr). The ship's destination was a steel plant on Zug Island in the Detroit River.

At 6 a.m. (CST) on 9 November, a cyclone (low-pressure system) began organizing over central Kansas. From there, the intensifying storm tracked toward the northeast and at 6 a.m. on 10 November passed near La Crosse, WI, and at noon was centered just west of Marquette, MI. By this time the storm's central pressure had dropped to 982 mb and gale-force northeast winds were sweeping the eastern end of Lake Superior. Winds gusted to 115 km per hr (71 mph) at Sault Ste. Marie, MI.

At 1 a.m. (CST) on 10 November, the *Edmund Fitzgerald* reported northeast winds at 97 km per hr (60 mph) with waves to 3 m (10 ft). At 7 a.m., the ship was about 73 km (45 mi) north of Copper Harbor, MI and reporting northeast winds at 65 km per hr (40 mph). With the storm bearing down on the *Edmund Fitzgerald*, the ship's captain, Ernest McSorley, changed course to the east and then southeast hugging the north shore of Lake Superior. McSorley chose a course that he thought would take the ship through waters that were sheltered from the strong northeast winds. That afternoon, the storm passed over the *Edmund Fitzgerald*. In the evening, as the storm center neared Moosonee, ON, near the southern shore of James Bay, winds on Lake Superior shifted from northeast to north and then northwest and west. The longer fetch of the northwest and west wind over the lake caused the waves to grow. (*Fetch* is the distance the wind blows over a continuous water surface.) Another ship within several kilometers of the *Edmund Fitzgerald* estimated wind speeds of 95 km per hr (58 mph) gusting to 137 km per hr (85 mph) with waves of 3.5 to 5 m (12 to 16 ft).

Sometime between 6:15 and 6:25 p.m. (CST), the *Edmund Fitzgerald* foundered and sank in 163 m (535 ft) of water about 27 km (17 mi) northwest of Whitefish Point, MI. More than 1000 ships have sunk in the Great Lakes and most of these wrecks were weather-related. The *Edmund Fitzgerald* was the largest ever to go down.

Driving Question:
What forces control the speed and direction of the wind?

Some weather systems are responsible for clear skies, light winds, and frosty mornings, whereas others bring ominous clouds, precipitation, and biting winds. Some weather systems trigger brief showers, and others are accompanied by persistent fog and drizzle. Certain weather systems dominate the weather over thousands of square kilometers for weeks at a time. Different weather systems bring different types of weather depending on the air circulation (wind) that characterizes each system.

Wind, the principal focus of this chapter, is the local motion of air measured relative to the rotating Earth. The atmosphere is coupled to the planet and rotates with it. Once every 24 hrs, all points on Earth's surface and in the atmosphere (except right at the poles) complete a circular path in space. The circumference of that path decreases with increasing latitude; hence, the speed at which fixed points on Earth progress eastward decreases with increasing latitude. The speed drops from 1670 km per hr (1035 mph) at the equator to 835 km per hr (517 mph) at 60 degrees N and S, and to zero at the poles. We are not aware of this rapid motion because we also move with the rotating planet and its atmosphere at the same speed. In meteorology, we are interested in air motion measured relative to Earth's continually moving surface (i.e., the wind).

In Chapter 4, we saw how unequal rates of radiational heating and cooling produce temperature gradients within the Earth-atmosphere system. In response to temperature gradients between Earth's surface and the troposphere as well as between the tropics and higher latitudes, the atmosphere (and ocean) circulates and heat is redistributed. This chapter covers the various forces that either initiate or modify atmospheric circulation, that is, the wind. First, each force is examined separately as if it acted independently of all the other forces. Forces are then combined to demonstrate how together they drive atmospheric circulation. We begin by learning how wind speed and direction are measured.

Monitoring Wind Speed and Direction

The velocity of the wind is a *vector* quantity, that is, it has both magnitude (speed) and direction. A distinction is usually made between *horizontal* (east-west and north-south) and *vertical* (up-down) components of the wind. Except in small, intense weather systems such as thunderstorms, the magnitude of vertical air motion is typically only 1% to 10% of the horizontal wind speed. Nonetheless, as demonstrated in Chapter 6, the vertical component of the wind plays the key role in cloud formation by promoting expansional cooling. Furthermore, as shown later in this chapter, vertical and horizontal components of the wind are linked so that a change in one may be accompanied by a change in the other.

The most common wind-monitoring instruments are designed to measure only the horizontal component of the wind. For some specialized research purposes, very sensitive instruments are available that measure vertical wind speeds or a combination of vertical and horizontal wind components. An ordinary **wind vane** consists of a free-swinging horizontal shaft with a vertical plate at one end and a counterweight (arrowhead) at the other end (Figure 1.7). The counterweight always points directly into the wind. Another design is the airport **windsock**, a cone-shaped cloth sleeve that is open at both ends (Figure 8.1). The larger end of the sock is held open by a metal ring that is attached to a pole and is free to rotate. Air enters the larger opening and stretches the sleeve downwind.

Wind direction is always designated as the direction *from which* the wind blows. A wind blowing from the east toward the west is described as an east wind whereas a wind blowing from the northwest to the southeast is a northwest wind. A wind vane may be linked electronically or mechanically to a dial that is calibrated to read in points of the compass or in degrees. Measured clockwise from true north, an east wind is specified as 90 degrees, a south wind as 180 degrees, a west wind as 270 degrees, and a north wind as 360 degrees. Wind direction is reported as 0 degrees only during calm conditions (when the wind speed is zero).

Wind speed can be estimated by observing the wind's effect on lake or ocean surfaces or on land-based flexible objects such as trees. Such observations are the basis of the **Beaufort scale**, which is a graduated sequence of wind strength ranging from 0 for calm air to 12 for hurricane-strength winds (Table 8.1). The scale bears the name of Sir Francis Beaufort (1774-1857), who developed it in the early 1800s while a ship's commander in the British Navy. Beaufort's goal was to standardize terms used by sailors to describe the state of the sea under various wind conditions. In 1838, after some revision, the British Navy adopted the Beaufort scale, and in 1853, it was sanctioned for international use by seafarers. Later, when the scale was extended from sea to land, it was necessary to develop wind speed equivalents for each Beaufort number. A uniform set of equivalents was adopted in 1926 and revised slightly in 1946. The Beaufort scale is still used today. Although crude by today's standards, some modern-day mariners prefer Beaufort numbers to onboard instrument measurements of wind speed at sea.

A **cup anemometer** consists of 3 or 4 open hemispheric cups mounted to spin horizontally on a vertical shaft (Figure 8.2). At least one open cup faces the wind at any time. The rotation rate of the cups is calibrated to read in m per sec, km per hr, or knots. (One *knot* = 1 nautical mi per hr = 0.515 m per sec = 1.15 statute mi per hr.) Several other types of anemometers are available, including the very sensitive **hot-wire anemometer**. In this instrument, the wind blows past a heated wire or wires and the heat lost to moving air is calibrated in terms of wind speed. Some wind sensors, called **aerovanes**, are designed to measure both wind speed and direction. This instrument has a three or four blade propeller that spins at a rate proportional to the wind speed and a fin on its back that causes it to turn into the wind, thereby indicating the wind direction. Electronic sensors in the instrument are connected to a recording computer or digital display.

Another wind measuring instrument is based on the effect of wind on the propagation of sound waves (Chapter 14). A **sonic anemometer** consists

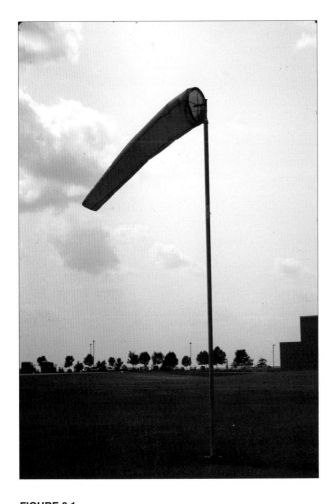

FIGURE 8.1

An airport windsock gives wind direction and a general indication of wind speed. The sock points downwind.

TABLE 8.1
Beaufort Scale of Wind Force

Beaufort Number	General description	Land and sea observations for estimating wind speed	Wind speed 10 m above ground (km/hr)
0	Calm	Smoke rises vertically; sea like mirror.	<1
1	Light air	Smoke but not wind vane shows direction of wind; slight ripples at sea.	1-5
2	Light breeze	Wind felt on face, leaves rustle, wind vane moves; small, short wavelets.	6-11
3	Gentle breeze	Leaves and small twigs move constantly, small flags extended; large wavelets, scattered whitecaps.	12-19
4	Moderate breeze	Dust and loose paper raised, small branches moved; small waves, frequent whitecaps.	20-28
5	Fresh breeze	Small leafy trees swayed; moderate waves.	29-38
6	Strong breeze	Large branches in motion, whistling heard in utility wires; large waves, some spray.	39-49
7	Near gale	Whole trees in motion; white foam from breaking waves.	50-61
8	Gale	Twigs break off trees; moderately high waves of great length.	62-74
9	Strong gale	Slight structural damage; crests of waves begin to roll over, spray may impede visibility.	75-88
10	Storm	Trees uprooted, considerable structural damage; sea white with foam, heavy tumbling of sea.	89-102
11	Violent storm	Very rare, widespread damage; unusually high waves.	103-118
12	Hurricane	Very rare, disastrous; much foam and spray greatly reduce visibility.	119 and over

FIGURE 8.2
A cup anemometer measures wind speed; the greater the wind speed, the faster the cups spin.

FIGURE 8.3
A sonic anemometer is based on the effect of wind on the propagation of sound waves. This instrument is scheduled to replace cup anemometers at NWS Automated Surface Observing Systems (ASOS).

of three arms that send and receive ultrasonic pulses (Figure 8.3). The travel times of sound waves with and against the wind are translated into wind speed and direction. Sonic anemometers are scheduled to replace cup anemometers as the standard wind sensor in the National Weather Service's Automated Surface Observing System (ASOS).

Recording a continuous trace of wind speed and direction can be informative. Wind vanes and anemometers can be linked to pens that record on a paper chart that is attached to a clock-driven drum. For example, the trace in Figure 8.4 indicates considerable variation in both wind direction and wind speed with time. Gusts and lulls in the wind speed, along with changes in wind direction, indicate turbulent air. More commonly today, a computer records the output from wind vanes and anemometers and readings are displayed digitally.

Ideally, a wind vane and anemometer system should be mounted on a tower so that the instruments monitor horizontal winds 10 m (33 ft) above the ground. (This is the standard height for National Weather Service anemometers.) Rooftop locations should be avoided because the wind tends to accelerate as it flows over buildings. In addition, the system should be sited well away from (1) structures that might shelter the instruments and (2) any obstacles that might channel (and thus accelerate) the wind or alter its direction.

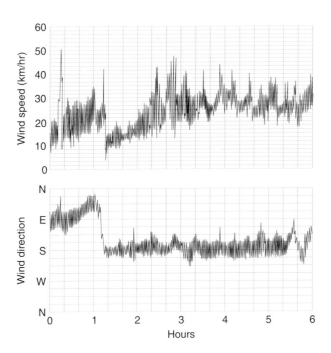

FIGURE 8.4

Continuous trace of time variations in wind speed and direction over a six-hour period.

Wind vanes and anemometers monitor winds near Earth's surface. How are winds measured aloft? In Chapter 2, we saw how meteorologists measure winds in the middle and upper troposphere by tracking the movements of a balloon-borne radiosonde (a *rawinsonde observation*). Beginning in the 1970s, sensors onboard geostationary satellites measure winds over the ocean and other regions where weather data are sparse. A sequence of satellite images formatted as an animated loop is used to determine the speed of individual recognizable cloud elements that are assumed to be carried by the wind. Since the early 1990s, the Doppler Effect has been used in a new technology designed to monitor winds up to an altitude of about 16,000 m (52,500 ft). For more on these *wind profilers*, refer to this chapter's first Essay. This chapter's second Essay, Wind Power, describes how modern technology is tapping the energy of air in motion.

Forces Governing the Wind

Several forces influence wind speed and direction. A **force** is defined as a push or pull that can cause an object at rest to move or that alters the movement of an object already in motion. Like the wind, a force has both direction and magnitude (a *vector* quantity).

In examining the various forces that govern the wind, it is useful to apply each force to a parcel that is a unit mass (e.g., single kilogram) of air. Imagine the wind to be a continuous stream of air consisting of discrete air parcels. Assume that any force acting on an air parcel has the same influence on a stream of air parcels, in other words, on the wind. Hence, in describing each force that affects air motion, we examine the force per unit mass of air.

In meteorology, *force* and *acceleration* are terms that sometimes are used interchangeably. This practice follows from **Newton's second law of motion**, where

$$\text{force} = (\text{mass}) \times (\text{acceleration}).$$

If the air parcel is a unit mass, a force per unit mass is numerically equivalent to acceleration. Although the terms are numerically equivalent, acceleration (a change in velocity) is actually a response to a force. A force acts on an air parcel to accelerate that parcel. Furthermore, acceleration involves a change in speed or direction or both. We have more on this later.

Forces acting on air parcels either initiate or modify motion and are the consequence of (1) an air pressure gradient, (2) the centripetal force, (3) the Coriolis Effect, (4) friction, and (5) gravity. Actually, the centripetal force is not an independent force but occurs as a consequence of other forces.

PRESSURE GRADIENT FORCE

A *gradient* is simply a change in some property over distance. An **air pressure gradient** exists whenever air pressure varies from one place to another. As noted in Chapter 5, spatial variations in air pressure can arise from contrasts in air temperature (principally), differences in water vapor concentration, or both. In addition, diverging or converging winds over a large region can bring about air pressure changes by redistributing the amount of air in a vertical column and thereby induce an air pressure gradient.

Air pressure gradients occur both horizontally and vertically within the atmosphere. A horizontal pressure gradient refers to air pressure changes along a surface of constant altitude (e.g., mean sea level). A vertical pressure gradient refers to the air pressure change directly above a point on Earth's surface; it is a permanent feature of the atmosphere because air pressure is greatest at the Earth's surface and always decreases with altitude. Horizontal air pressure gradients can be determined on weather maps from isobar patterns. An **isobar** is a line joining points having the same air pressure. But first, to eliminate the influence of station elevation on air pressure, the barometer reading at each weather station is adjusted to sea level (Chapter 5). By U.S. convention, isobars are drawn at 4-mb (4-hPa) intervals and interpolation between weather stations is always necessary.

An isobaric analysis is used to locate centers of high and low pressure on a weather map and to determine the magnitude of the horizontal air pressure gradient between weather systems. Where isobars are closely spaced (Figure 8.5A), air pressure changes rapidly with distance, and the pressure gradient is described as steep or strong. More widely spaced isobars (Figure 8.5B) indicate that air pressure changes more gradually with distance, and the pressure gradient is weaker. Note that air pressure gradients are always measured in the direction of greatest change, that is, *perpendicular* to isobars.

How do air pressure gradients influence the motion of air? Consider an analogous situation. Suppose a bathtub is partially filled with water, as shown in Figure 8.6. Sloshing the water back and forth from one end of the tub to the other creates rapidly changing water pressure gradients along the tub bottom. At any instant, the water surface is not horizontal. The bottom water pressure is high where

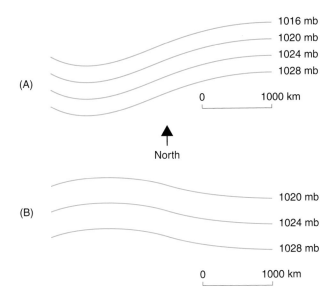

North

FIGURE 8.5
In this map view, the horizontal air pressure gradient is (A) relatively steep where isobars are closely spaced and (B) weaker where isobars are farther apart. Isobars are lines joining places of equal air pressure. Here the contour interval (difference between successive isobars) is 4 mb.

the water level is relatively high and low where the water level is relatively low. If we stop agitating the water, the sloshing back and forth dampens, and the undulating water surface returns to horizontal. The water pressure along the bottom is then the same from one end of the tub to the other. Hence, in response to a water pressure gradient, water flows from one end of the tub (where the water pressure is greater) to the other end (where the water pressure is less), thereby eliminating the pressure gradient.

FIGURE 8.6
Sloshing water back and forth from one end of a tub to the other end creates water pressure gradients along the bottom of the tub. The water pressure gradient along the tub bottom is analogous to a horizontal air pressure gradient in the atmosphere. In response to a pressure gradient, water (or air) flows from an area of higher pressure toward an area of lower pressure.

Similarly, when an air pressure gradient develops, air flows in a direction to eliminate the pressure gradient. The force that causes air parcels to move as the consequence of an air pressure gradient, known as the **pressure gradient force**, always acts directly across isobars and toward low pressure. The magnitude of the pressure gradient force is inversely related to isobar spacing. The wind is strong where the pressure gradient is great (closely spaced isobars), but light or calm where the pressure gradient is weak (widely spaced isobars).

CENTRIPETAL FORCE

Isobars plotted on a surface weather map are almost always curved, indicating that the pressure gradient force changes direction from one place to another. Consequently, the wind blows in curved paths. Curved motion indicates the influence of the centripetal force.

A simple demonstration illustrates the centripetal force. A rock is tied to a string and then whirled about so that the tethered rock describes a circular orbit of constant radius (Figure 8.7). The string exerts a net force on the rock by confining it to a curved (circular) path. At any instant, the net force is directed inward, perpendicular to the direction of motion, and toward the center of the circular orbit. For this reason, the net force is known as the **centripetal** (*center-seeking*) **force**. If we cut the string, the centripetal force no longer operates; that is, a net force no longer confines the rock to a curved path. The rock flies off in a straight line as described by **Newton's first law of motion**; that is, an object in straight-line, un-accelerated motion remains that way unless acted upon by an unbalanced force.

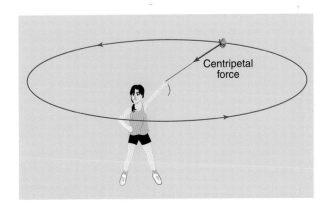

FIGURE 8.7
A rock tied to a string follows a circular path as it is whirled about. Centripetal (*center-seeking*) is the name of the force that confines an object to a curved path. If the string is cut, the centripetal force is eliminated, and the rock moves in a straight line (tangent to the circular path).

A net (i.e., unbalanced) force causes acceleration. We usually think of acceleration as a change in speed, as when an automobile speeds up. But velocity is a vector quantity; that is, it has both magnitude and direction. Acceleration is also a vector quantity and consists of a change in either speed or direction, or both. In our rock-on-a-string example, centripetal force is responsible only for a continual change in the direction of the rock (curved rather than straight-line path); the rock neither speeds up nor slows down. The acceleration imparted to a unit mass by the centripetal force is directed toward the center of curvature, with a magnitude directly proportional to the square of the speed and inversely proportional to the radius of curvature of the path. That is, increasing the rotation rate, which increases the instantaneous forward speed of the rock, requires a larger inward centripetal force, as would a shorter string (or radius of curvature).

The centripetal force is not an independent force; rather, it arises from the action of other forces and may be the consequence of imbalances in other forces. In our rock-on-a-string example, the tension of the string is responsible for the centripetal force. Consider another example. Suppose you are a passenger in an auto that rounds a curve at a high speed. You feel a force that pushes you outward from the turning auto. Actually, you experience the tendency for your body to continue moving in a straight path while the auto follows a curved path. In this case, the frictional resistance of the tires against the pavement provides the centripetal force.

A centripetal force operates whenever air parcels follow a curved path. As we will see later in this chapter, the centripetal force arises from an imbalance in other forces operating in the atmosphere.

CORIOLIS EFFECT

Imagine that you are located far away at some fixed point in space, looking back at Planet Earth. Over many hours, you follow the track of a storm, which is clearly identifiable by a mass of clouds slowly swirling about a central point. From your perspective, the storm center appears to move in a straight line at constant speed. (Note that a geostationary satellite does not provide this perspective because the satellite is in a coordinate system fixed with respect to the rotating Earth.) At the same time, an observer on Earth is tracking the storm using radar and surface weather observations. From that observer's perspective, the storm center appears to follow a curved path. Surprisingly, both descriptions of the storm's track are correct!

The two descriptions are correct because the two observers used different frames of reference in following the storm's movements. The Earthbound observer's frame of reference is the solid Earth to which the familiar north-south, east-west, and up-down coordinate system is attached. To the Earthbound observer, it is not obvious that this coordinate system is rotating because it and the observer rotate along with the turning Earth. Viewed from space, however, it is evident that the Earth-bound coordinate system actually shifts as Earth rotates (Figure 8.8). In fact, Earth and the coordinate system rotate under the storm (or any other object moving freely over Earth's surface). Meanwhile, from your location in space, you followed the storm's movement with respect to a non-rotating coordinate system, fixed in space with respect to the background stars. In summary, the difference in observed storm tracks (curved versus straight) arises from the differences in coordinate systems (rotating versus non-rotating).

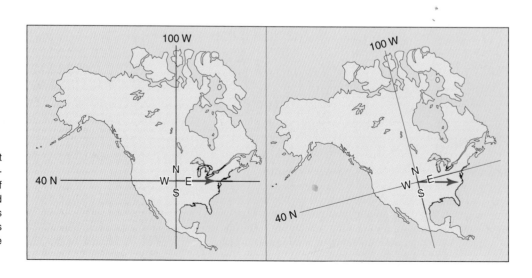

FIGURE 8.8
Viewed from a fixed point in space, the familiar north-south, east-west frame of reference rotates eastward in space as Earth rotates on its axis. Rotation of this coordinate system gives rise to the Coriolis Effect.

Recall our earlier discussion of *Newton's first law of motion* and the centripetal force. We saw that curved motion implies that a net (or unbalanced) force is operating, whereas unaccelerated, straight-line motion implies a balance of forces. Applying this law to our storm track example, we conclude that a net force operates when we use the Earthbound rotating coordinate system, whereas forces are balanced when we use the non-rotating coordinate system fixed in space. Hence, changing our frame of reference (coordinate system) from non-rotating to rotating introduces a net force responsible for curved motion. This apparent deflective force is known as the **Coriolis Effect**, named for Gaspard Gustave de Coriolis (1792-1843), the French mathematician who first described the phenomenon mathematically in 1835. Wind direction and speed are measured with respect to the north-south, east-west, and up-down frame of reference fixed to the rotating planet. Therefore, we must take the Coriolis Effect into account in any explanation of air circulation. The Coriolis Effect deflects the horizontal wind to the right of its initial direction in the Northern Hemisphere and to the left of its initial direction in the Southern Hemisphere (Figure 8.9).

Why does the Coriolis Effect reverse direction between the hemispheres so that large-scale winds in the Southern Hemisphere swerve to the left rather than to

the right? This reversal is related to the difference in an observer's sense of Earth's rotation in the two hemispheres. To an observer looking down from high above the North Pole, the planet rotates counterclockwise, whereas to an observer high above the South Pole, the planet rotates clockwise. For the observer measuring motion relative to a coordinate system anchored to the rotating Earth, this reversal in the apparent direction of rotation between the two hemispheres translates into a reversal in the direction of the Coriolis Effect.

Although the Coriolis Effect influences the wind regardless of its direction, the amount of deflection varies significantly with latitude (as the sine of the latitude). Earth's rotation on its axis imparts a rotation to our Earth-bound frame of reference that increases in magnitude from zero at the equator to a maximum at the poles. The latitudinal variation in the magnitude of the Coriolis Effect can be understood by visualizing the daily rotation of towers situated at different latitudes. In a 24-hr day, Earth makes one complete rotation, as would a tower if located at the North or South Pole. In the same period, a tower at the equator would not rotate about its vertical axis at all because of its orientation perpendicular to Earth's axis of rotation. At any latitude in between, some rotation of a tower occurs but not as much as at the poles. The Coriolis Effect is thus latitude-dependent: the Coriolis Effect is zero at the equator and increases with latitude to a maximum at the poles.

The magnitude of the Coriolis Effect also varies with wind speed and spatial scale of atmospheric circulation. The Coriolis deflection increases as the wind strengthens because, in the same period of time, faster air parcels cover greater distances than slower air parcels. The longer the trajectory, the greater is the shift of the rotating coordinate system with respect to a moving air parcel. For practical purposes, the Coriolis Effect significantly influences the wind only in large-scale weather systems, that is, systems larger than ordinary thunderstorms. Large-scale weather systems also have longer life expectancies than small-scale systems so that air parcels travel greater distances over longer periods of time, increasing the Coriolis deflection.

A rotational motion usually accompanies the draining of water from a sink or a bathtub. It is a popular misconception that the direction of this rotation (clockwise or counterclockwise) is consistently in one direction in the Northern Hemisphere and in the opposite direction in the Southern Hemisphere, presumably because of the Coriolis Effect. At the very small scale represented by the water in a sink or bathtub, the

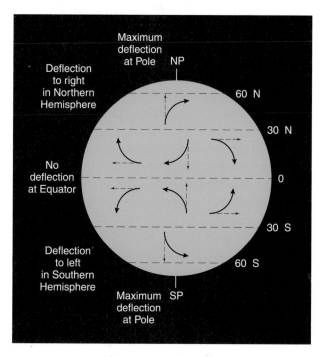

FIGURE 8.9
Large-scale winds are deflected to the right of their initial direction in the Northern Hemisphere and to the left of their initial direction in the Southern Hemisphere. This deflection, known as the Coriolis Effect, is maximum at the poles and zero at the equator.

magnitude of the Coriolis Effect is simply too small to significantly influence the direction of rotation. Drainage direction is more likely a consequence of some already present motion of the water or the shape of the sink or bathtub and may be either clockwise or counterclockwise regardless of hemisphere.

FRICTION

Friction is the resistance that an object or medium encounters as it moves in contact with another object or medium. We are all familiar with the friction associated with solid objects, as when we attempt to slide a heavy appliance across the floor. But friction also affects fluids, both liquids and gases. The friction of fluid flow, known as **viscosity**, is of two types: molecular viscosity and eddy viscosity. One source of fluid friction is the random motion of molecules composing a liquid or gas; this type of fluid friction is called **molecular viscosity**. Considerably more important, however, is fluid friction that arises from much larger irregular motions, called *eddies*, which develop within fluids; this type of fluid friction is known as **eddy viscosity**.

A swiftly flowing stream illustrates the effects of eddy viscosity. Rocks in the streambed obstruct the flow of water and cause the current to break into eddies immediately downstream of the rocks (Figure 8.10). Eddies, visible as swirls of water, tap some of the stream's kinetic energy so that the stream slows. In an analogous manner, obstacles on Earth's surface such as trees, houses, and telephone poles break the wind into eddies of various sizes to the lee of each obstacle. Consequently, the near surface wind slows.

FIGURE 8.10
Rocks in a riverbed are obstacles that break the current into turbulent eddies downstream from the rocks, slowing the stream flow. A similar frictional interaction takes place as wind encounters obstacles on Earth's surface.

FIGURE 8.11
A snow fence slows the wind, reducing its ability to transport snow in suspension. Hence, snow accumulates immediately downwind from the snow fence.

A snow fence provides a practical illustration of the frictional slowing of the wind (Figure 8.11). Snow fences are designed to trap wind-blown snow, in some instances to prevent snow from drifting onto a nearby highway and in others to keep the soil snow covered. (Snow that accumulates downwind of a snow fence ensures a supply of soil moisture and insulates the soil from freezing to great depths.) A snow fence taps some of the wind's kinetic energy by breaking the wind into small eddies. The wind speed diminishes, losing some of its snow-transporting ability, and snow accumulates on the downwind side of the fence.

The rougher the surface of the Earth, the greater is the eddy viscosity of the wind. A forest thus offers more frictional resistance to the wind than does the smoother surface of a freshly mowed lawn. Eddy viscosity diminishes rapidly with altitude above Earth's surface, away from obstacles mainly responsible for frictional resistance. Hence, horizontal wind speed increases with altitude. This explains the advantage of positioning a windmill at as high an elevation above surrounding land as possible. Above an average altitude of about 1000 m (3300 ft) above Earth's surface, friction is a minor force that has little impact on the smooth flow of air. The atmospheric zone to which frictional resistance (eddy viscosity) is essentially confined is called the **atmospheric boundary layer**.

Turbulence is fluid flow characterized by eddy motion. Various obstacles on Earth's surface exert a drag on the wind and are sources of eddies. Irregular fluid flow that originates in this way is known as *mechanical turbulence*.

In addition, eddies develop in air as a consequence of solar heating of the ground; irregular fluid flow that originates in this way is known as *thermal turbulence*. Convection is an example of thermal turbulence within the atmosphere. In actual practice, it is virtually impossible to distinguish between the two sources of turbulent eddies (mechanical or thermal). Regardless of source, we experience turbulent eddies as gusts of wind. The gustiness of the wind often varies with the time of day; that is, gusts tend to be strongest during the warmest hours of the day. Pilots of light aircraft are well aware of the changes in turbulence between day and night.

GRAVITY

Air parcels are subject to the same force that holds all objects on Earth's surface, that is, **gravity**. Gravity is the net result of two forces working together: gravitation and centripetal force. *Gravitation* is the force of attraction between Earth and some object; its magnitude is directly proportional to the product of the masses of Earth and the object, but inversely proportional to the square of the distance between their centers of mass. The much weaker centripetal force is imparted to all objects because of their rotation with Earth on its axis. Combined as gravity, the two forces accelerate a unit mass of any object directly downward toward Earth's surface at the rate of 9.8 m per sec each second.

Gravity always acts directly downward. For this reason, gravity, unlike the Coriolis Effect and friction, does not modify the horizontal wind. Gravity influences air that is ascending or descending, such as the updrafts and downdrafts in convection currents, and gravity is responsible for the downhill drainage of cold, dense air.

SUMMARY

We have now examined individually the various forces that influence horizontal and vertical air motion, and we can draw the following conclusions:

1. The horizontal pressure gradient force, which is responsible for initiating essentially all air motion, accelerates air parcels perpendicular to isobars away from regions of high air pressure and toward regions of low air pressure. Acceleration is directly proportional to the pressure gradient; that is, the closer the spacing of isobars, the steeper the pressure gradient, and the greater is the acceleration.

2. A centripetal force is an imbalance of actual forces and exists whenever the wind describes a curved path. It is responsible for a change in wind direction, but not wind speed. This force, which is always pointed inward toward the center of rotation, has a magnitude that is directly related to the parcel's speed, but inversely proportional to the radius of curvature.

3. The Coriolis Effect arises from the rotation of Earth on its axis and deflects large-scale winds to the right of their initial direction in the Northern Hemisphere, but to the left of their initial direction in the Southern Hemisphere. The Coriolis Effect increases with latitude from zero at the equator to a maximum at the poles and is directly proportional to wind speed.

4. Friction acts opposite to the wind direction and increases with increasing surface roughness. Friction slows horizontal winds blowing within about 1000 m (3300 ft) of Earth's surface.

5. Gravity accelerates air downward toward the Earth's surface but it does not modify the horizontal wind.

Joining Forces

To this point, we have examined forces operating in the atmosphere as if each force acted independently of all the others. In reality, these forces interact with one another in governing both the direction and speed of the wind. In some cases, two or more forces achieve a balance or equilibrium. From *Newton's first law of motion*, when the forces acting on an air parcel are balanced, no net force operates and the parcel either remains stationary or continues to move along a straight path at constant speed. When forces are balanced, the net acceleration is zero.

In this section, we build an increasingly sophisticated model of atmospheric motion by examining how forces interact in the atmosphere to control the vertical and horizontal motion of air, that is, the wind. These interactions result in (1) hydrostatic equilibrium, (2) the geostrophic wind, (3) the gradient wind, and (4) surface winds, horizontal winds within the atmospheric boundary layer.

HYDROSTATIC EQUILIBRIUM

In developing a realistic model of atmospheric motion, we will assume that the atmosphere is in a state of hydrostatic equilibrium. This assumption allows us to focus on horizontal motions of air.

Air pressure always declines with increasing altitude so that a vertical air pressure gradient is a permanent feature of the atmosphere. As shown schematically

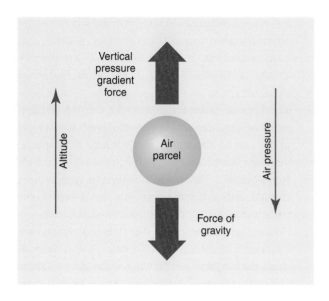

FIGURE 8.12
In the atmosphere, hydrostatic equilibrium is the balance between the upward-directed pressure gradient force and the downward-directed force of gravity

in Figure 8.12, the force due to this pressure gradient is directed upward from higher air pressures at Earth's surface toward lower air pressures aloft. If this force acted alone, the vertical pressure gradient force would accelerate air away from Earth, and we would be left gasping for breath. However, except for relatively brief periods in some small-scale violent weather systems (e.g., severe thunderstorms), the atmosphere's vertical pressure gradient force is almost balanced by the equal but oppositely directed force of gravity. An actual balance of these two forces is known as **hydrostatic equilibrium**.

Whenever forces are in balance, net acceleration is zero; that is, there is no change in speed or direction. Hydrostatic equilibrium, however, does not preclude vertical (up or down) motions of air. With balanced forces, ascending air parcels continue moving upward at constant velocity while descending air parcels continue moving downward at constant velocity. Slight deviations from hydrostatic equilibrium cause air parcels to change speed (accelerate) vertically.

GEOSTROPHIC WIND

The existence of air pressure differences in a horizontal direction would result in a wind blowing from high toward low pressure. Air moves in this direction on a local scale, such as during the evening when cold, dense air drains from near the top of a hill into a valley.

However, inspection of a weather map shows that winds blowing at a larger scale tend to parallel isobars with low pressure to the left in the Northern Hemisphere. In an attempt to explain this observation, we make a set of assumptions contained in the geostrophic wind model. The term *geostrophic* means "Earth turning." This frictionless model assumes that isobars are straight and parallel.

The **geostrophic wind** is an un-accelerated, horizontal movement of air that follows a straight path at altitudes above the atmospheric boundary layer. It results from a balance between the horizontal pressure gradient force and the Coriolis Effect. The Coriolis Effect is significant only in broad-scale circulations so that the geostrophic wind develops only in large-scale weather systems.

Consider the traditional description of the evolution of geostrophic equilibrium: An air parcel is placed in a preexisting horizontal pressure field where isobars are straight and parallel (Figure 8.13). In response to the horizontal pressure gradient force (P_H), the air parcel initially accelerates directly across isobars, away from high pressure and toward low pressure. As the air parcel accelerates, however, the Coriolis Effect (C) strengthens and causes the air parcel to turn gradually to the right of its initial flow direction (in the Northern Hemisphere). The Coriolis Effect changes direction as the parcel turns, always

FIGURE 8.13
This diagram approximates the evolution of geostrophic equilibrium, a balance between the horizontal pressure gradient force and the Coriolis Effect. The geostrophic wind blows parallel to straight isobars at altitudes above the atmospheric boundary layer.

remaining at right angles to the parcel's direction of motion. The two forces eventually act in opposite directions and attain a balance, known as *geostrophic equilibrium*, so that the geostrophic wind blows at a constant speed in a straight path parallel to isobars with the lowest air pressure to the left of the direction of air motion.

Numerical simulations of the interactions of the pressure gradient force and the Coriolis Effect conducted by J.A. Knox and his colleagues at NASA's Goddard Institute for Space Studies show that air parcels actually undergo an oscillatory motion along the curved path shown in Figure 8.13. The oscillatory motion gradually dampens as air parcels approach geostrophic equilibrium. This so-called *inertial oscillation* is an interaction of the pressure field with the motion of the air parcels and may be an important feature of some weather systems.

GRADIENT WIND

A less restrictive model of atmospheric flow is the **gradient wind** that shares many of the same characteristics as the geostrophic wind. It is also large-scale, horizontal, and frictionless, and blows parallel to isobars. However, the important distinction between the two models is that the geostrophic wind blows in a straight path, whereas the path of the gradient wind is curved. Forces are not balanced in the gradient wind because a net centripetal force constrains air parcels to a curved trajectory. Recall from earlier in this chapter that the centripetal force changes only the direction and not the speed of an air parcel. The horizontal pressure gradient force, the Coriolis Effect, and the centripetal force interact in the gradient wind.

.   A gradient wind develops at altitudes above the atmospheric boundary layer around a dome of high air pressure, called an **anticyclone** (or *High*), or around a center of low air pressure, called a **cyclone** (or *Low*). In an idealized anticyclone, isobars form a series of concentric circles about the location of highest air pressure, as shown in Figure 8.14. The horizontal pressure gradient force (P_H) is directed radially outward, away from the center of the high. The Coriolis Effect (C) is directed inward. The Coriolis Effect is slightly greater than the pressure gradient force, with the difference between the two forces giving rise to the inward-directed centripetal force (C_E). (This is what was meant earlier when we indicated that a centripetal force results from an imbalance of other forces.) Viewed from above in the Northern Hemisphere, the gradient wind in an anticyclone blows clockwise and parallel to isobars above the atmospheric boundary layer.

In an idealized cyclone, isobars form a series of concentric circles about the location of lowest air pressure. As indicated in Figure 8.15, the horizontal pressure gradient force (P_H) is directed inward toward the cyclone center, and the Coriolis Effect (C) is directed radially outward from the center of the low. The pressure gradient force is slightly greater than the Coriolis Effect, with the difference being equal to the net inward-directed centripetal force (C_E). Viewed from above the Northern Hemisphere, the gradient wind in a cyclone blows counterclockwise and parallel to isobars above the atmospheric boundary layer.

The geostrophic and gradient wind models only approximate the actual behavior of horizontal winds above the atmospheric boundary layer. These approximations are nonetheless quite useful, and meteorologists routinely rely on such approximations in analyzing weather maps.

FIGURE 8.14
Viewed from above in the Northern Hemisphere, the gradient wind blows clockwise and parallel to isobars in an anticyclone. In this idealized case, isobars form a pattern of concentric circles.

FIGURE 8.15
Viewed from above in the Northern Hemisphere, the gradient wind blows counterclockwise and parallel to isobars in a cyclone. In this idealized case, isobars form a pattern of concentric circles.

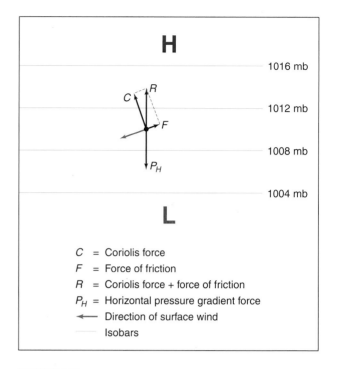

FIGURE 8.16
Within the atmospheric boundary layer, friction slows the wind and shifts the wind across isobars toward low pressure.

SURFACE WINDS

Geostrophic and gradient winds are frictionless; that is, they occur at altitudes where frictional resistance is insignificant. How does friction affect horizontal winds within the atmospheric boundary layer? Intuitively, we know that friction should slow the wind, but in addition, friction interacts with the other forces and alters the wind direction.

As shown in Figure 8.16, for large-scale air motion along a straight path, the frictional force (F) combines with the Coriolis Effect (C) to balance the horizontal pressure gradient force (P_H). Friction acts directly opposite (180 degrees) to the wind direction whereas the Coriolis Effect is always at a right angle (90 degrees) to the wind direction. Friction slows the wind and thereby weakens the Coriolis Effect so that the Coriolis no longer balances the horizontal pressure gradient force. The horizontal pressure gradient force (P_H) is balanced by the resultant (R) of the Coriolis (C) plus friction (F). Friction (due to the roughness of Earth's surface) slows the horizontal wind and shifts the wind direction across isobars and toward low pressure.

The angle between wind direction and isobars depends on friction, which in turn depends on the roughness of Earth's surface. That angle varies from 10 degrees or less over relatively smooth surfaces, where friction is minimal, to almost 45 degrees over rough terrain, where friction is greater. As we noted earlier, friction's influence on the horizontal wind diminishes with altitude and where it becomes negligibly small marks the top of the atmospheric boundary layer. Horizontal winds strengthen with altitude through the atmospheric boundary layer. Furthermore, the angle between wind direction and isobars is maximum near Earth's surface, decreases with altitude, and is essentially zero at the top of the atmospheric boundary layer (Figure 8.17). Above the atmospheric boundary layer, the horizontal wind is either geostrophic (where isobars are straight) or gradient (where isobars are curved).

How does surface roughness affect horizontal surface winds blowing in an anticyclone and cyclone? As with straight-line surface winds, friction slows anticyclonic and cyclonic winds and combines with the Coriolis Effect to shift winds so that they blow across isobars and toward low pressure. Viewed from above, surface winds in a

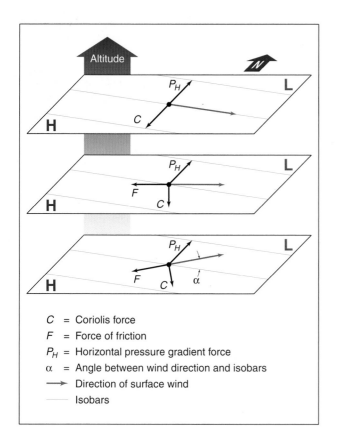

FIGURE 8.17
For the same horizontal air pressure gradient, the angle between the wind direction and isobars decreases with altitude within the atmospheric boundary layer.

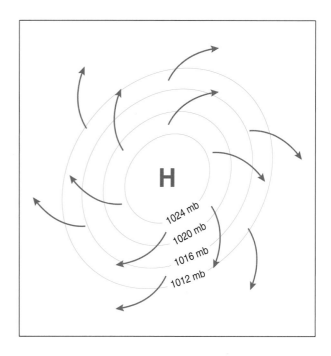

FIGURE 8.18
Viewed from above in the Northern Hemisphere, surface winds blow clockwise and outward in an anticyclone.

Northern Hemisphere anticyclone blow clockwise and spiral outward, as shown in Figure 8.18, and surface winds in a Northern Hemisphere cyclone blow counterclockwise and spiral inward, as shown in Figure 8.19.

Characteristic surface winds in a cyclone are the basis for a simple rule of thumb for locating cyclone centers. In a Northern Hemisphere location, if you stand with your back to the wind and then turn approximately 45 degrees to your right, the cyclone center will be located to your left. This rule is a modification of an observation first stated in 1857 by Dutch meteorologist Christopher H. D. Buys-Ballot (1817-1890). It must be applied with caution, however, because isobars are not always circular in cyclones and large-scale surface winds may be modified by local atmospheric circulation systems such as a sea breeze or a valley breeze.

In the Southern Hemisphere, anticyclonic and cyclonic winds are opposite their Northern Hemisphere counterparts. The difference is due to the Coriolis Effect acting to the left of the direction of motion in the Southern

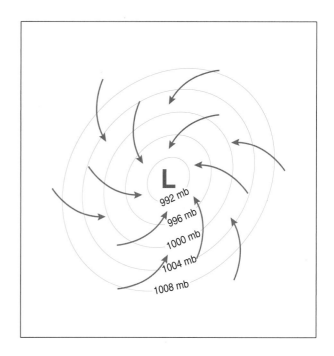

FIGURE 8.19
Viewed from above in the Northern Hemisphere, surface winds blow counterclockwise and inward in a cyclone.

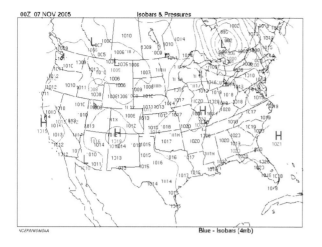

FIGURE 8.20
On a typical surface weather map, isobars exhibit clockwise curvature (*ridges*) and counterclockwise curvature (*troughs*).

Hemisphere, opposite to its effect in the Northern Hemisphere. Viewed from above in the Southern Hemisphere, surface winds in a cyclone blow clockwise and spiral inward, whereas surface winds in an anticyclone blow counterclockwise and spiral outward. Above the atmospheric boundary layer, Southern Hemisphere anticyclonic winds blow counterclockwise and parallel to isobars, whereas Southern Hemisphere cyclonic winds blow clockwise and parallel to isobars.

A glance at almost any national weather map reveals that isobars seldom describe lengthy straight segments or circular patterns (Figure 8.20). Isobars often form more complicated patterns of *ridges* (anticyclonic curves) and *troughs* (cyclonic curves). In ridges and troughs, winds tend to parallel isobars above the atmospheric boundary layer and cross isobars toward low pressure near Earth's surface. An additional consideration in analyzing isobaric patterns for wind is the spacing of isobars. As noted earlier, the greater the air pressure gradient, the faster is the wind. Where isobars are closely spaced, the geostrophic and gradient winds are relatively strong. Where isobars are widely spaced, these winds are weak. The same rule applies to surface winds.

Continuity of Wind

Like all fluids, air is continuous and this *continuity* implies a link between the horizontal and vertical components of the wind. For example, surface winds are forced to follow Earth's undulating topography, ascending hills

and descending into valleys. In addition, uplift occurs along frontal surfaces as one air mass advances and either overrides or pushes under another retreating air mass (Chapters 1 and 6). Having examined the horizontal circulation in anticyclones and cyclones, we can identify other important connections between the horizontal and vertical components of the wind.

As noted earlier in this chapter, surface winds in a Northern Hemisphere anticyclone spiral clockwise and outward from its high pressure center. Consequently, horizontal surface winds diverge from the center of the high. A vacuum does not develop at the center, however, because air slowly descends to Earth's surface and replaces the air that is diverging. Aloft, horizontal winds converge above the center of the surface high (Figure 8.21). Recall that adiabatic compression raises the temperature and saturation vapor pressure, causes existing clouds to vaporize, and lowers the relative humidity of descending air. Skies therefore tend to be clear within anticyclones, and anticyclones are appropriately described as fair weather systems. Furthermore, within an anticyclone, the horizontal air pressure gradient is typically very weak over a broad area around the center of the system. Light winds or calm air coupled with clear skies and low water vapor content favor intense nocturnal radiational cooling. Air adjacent to the ground may be chilled to saturation so that nighttime dew, frost, or radiation fog may develop (Chapter 7).

Surface winds in a Northern Hemisphere cyclone spiral counterclockwise and inward. Surface winds therefore converge toward the center of a low. Air does not simply pile up at the center; rather, air ascends

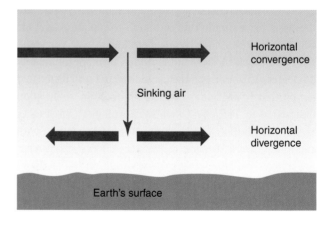

FIGURE 8.21
In this idealized vertical cross-section of an anticyclone, horizontal winds converge aloft, air descends, and surface winds diverge.

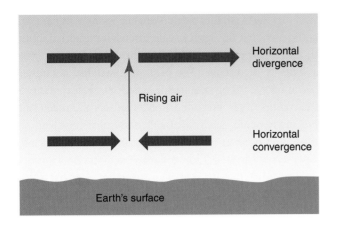

FIGURE 8.22
In this idealized vertical cross-section of a cyclone, surface winds converge, air ascends, and winds aloft diverge.

in response to converging surface winds and diverging winds aloft (Figure 8.22). Recall that adiabatic expansion of rising air lowers the temperature and saturation vapor pressure, thereby increasing the relative humidity. Clouds

and precipitation may eventually develop, so that cyclones are typically stormy weather systems.

Continuity of the wind also means that vertical motion can be induced by downwind changes in surface roughness. The rougher the Earth's surface, the greater the resistance it offers to horizontal winds. When the horizontal wind blows from a rough surface to a relatively smooth surface, as when it blows from land to sea, the wind accelerates. As shown in Figure 8.23, this acceleration causes the wind to diverge (stretch), thereby inducing downward motion of air (an example of *speed divergence*). In contrast, when the horizontal wind blows from a smooth to a rough surface, the wind slows and converges (piles up), thereby inducing upward air motion (an example of *speed convergence*). This is one reason why, along a coastline, cumuliform clouds (e.g., cumulus) tend to develop with an onshore wind (directed from sea to land) and tend to dissipate with an offshore wind (directed from land to sea). Frictionally-induced convergence of surface winds also plays an important role in the development of lake-effect snow, as discussed in this chapter's third Essay.

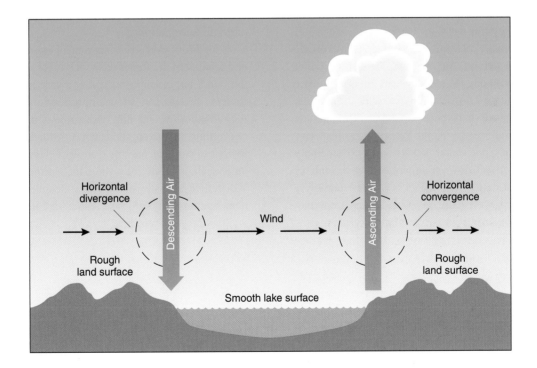

FIGURE 8.23
Surface winds accelerate and undergo horizontal divergence when blowing from a rough to a smooth surface (e.g., from land to water). Surface winds slow and undergo horizontal convergence when blowing form a smooth to a rough surface (e.g., from water to land). Divergence of surface winds causes air to descend whereas convergence of surface winds causes air to ascend.

Scales of Weather Systems

Although the atmosphere is a continuous fluid, for convenience of study we subdivide atmospheric circulation into discrete weather systems that operate at different spatial and temporal scales (Table 8.2). The large-scale wind belts encircling the planet (polar easterlies, midlatitude westerlies, and trade winds) are global or **planetary-scale systems**. **Synoptic-scale systems** are continental or oceanic in scale; migrating cyclones, hurricanes, and air masses are examples. **Mesoscale systems** include thunderstorms and sea and lake breezes, circulation systems that are so small that they may influence the weather in only a portion of a large city or county. A weather system covering a very small area such as several city blocks or a small town represents the smallest spatial subdivision of atmospheric motion, **microscale systems**. A weak tornado is an example of a microscale system.

Circulation systems not only differ in spatial scale, they also contrast in life expectancy. Essentially the same patterns in the planetary-scale circulation may persist for weeks or even months (Chapter 9). Synoptic-scale systems typically last for several days to a week or so. Mesoscale systems usually complete their life cycles in a matter of hours to perhaps a day, whereas microscale systems might persist for minutes or less. Other differences exist among the various scales of atmospheric circulation systems. At the micro- and meso-scale, vertical wind speeds may be comparable in magnitude to horizontal wind speeds. At the synoptic and planetary scales, however, horizontal winds are considerably stronger than vertical flow. Furthermore, at the micro- and meso-scale, the Coriolis Effect is usually negligibly small. By contrast, the Coriolis Effect is very important in synoptic- and planetary-scale circulation systems.

Each smaller scale weather system is part of, and dependent on, larger scale atmospheric circulation; that is, the various scales of atmospheric motion form a kind of hierarchy. For example, extreme nocturnal radiational cooling requires a synoptic weather pattern that favors clear skies and light winds or calm air. At the micro-scale, such weather conditions may lead to formation of frost or radiation fog in a river valley. In Chapters 9 through 12, we apply basic understandings of the atmosphere in examining weather systems at all scales.

Conclusions

Unequal rates of radiational heating and radiational cooling within the Earth-atmosphere system are responsible for gradients in temperature. In response to those temperature gradients, the atmosphere circulates and thereby, heat energy is converted to kinetic energy. In this chapter, we have examined the various forces that initiate and shape atmospheric circulation (the wind). Note that the pressure gradient force and gravity would exist even if air were not in motion, with the other forces (centripetal, Coriolis, and friction) coming into play only after air is in motion.

From everyday experience, we are aware of the end product of the forces described in this chapter, namely the wind, but we are not readily aware of the individual forces. In learning about atmospheric forces and how they interact, we see that each force is bound by certain constraints. For example, friction is important only in the lower troposphere, and the Coriolis Effect always deflects large-scale winds to the right in the Northern Hemisphere. We built a realistic model of atmospheric motion that demonstrates why and how winds circulate around high and low pressure systems.

TABLE 8.2
Scales of Atmospheric Circulation

Circulation	Space scale	Time scale
Planetary scale	10,000 to 40,000 km	weeks to months
Synoptic scale	100 to 10,000 km	days to a week
Mesoscale	1 to 100 km	hours to a day
Microscale	1 m to 1 km	seconds to an hour

In the following chapters, our awareness of these and other constraints will aid in understanding the characteristics of the various weather systems; for example, why hurricanes do not form at the equator and why winds in a tornado may blow in either a clockwise or counterclockwise direction. We are now ready to begin our discussion of the characteristics of the various circulation systems, beginning with those operating at the planetary scale.

Basic Understandings

- Wind is the movement of air measured relative to Earth's surface. Wind has both direction and magnitude and is usually divided into horizontal and vertical components. A wind vane and anemometer are the usual instruments for monitoring surface wind direction and speed. Winds aloft can be determined remotely by tracking rawinsondes, precipitation particles (by Doppler radar), and cloud elements (from sensors on Earth-orbiting satellites).

- The horizontal wind is governed by interactions of the pressure gradient force, Coriolis Effect, friction, and centripetal force.

- The pressure gradient force initiates air motion and arises in part from spatial variations in air temperature and, to a lesser extent, water vapor concentration. In response to air pressure gradients, air accelerates away from areas of relatively high air pressure, directly across isobars, and toward areas of relatively low air pressure.

- The centripetal force arises from an imbalance in other forces and operates whenever the wind follows a curved path. The centripetal force is responsible for changes in wind direction but not changes in wind speed.

- The Coriolis Effect arises from Earth's rotation on its axis. Wind is deflected to the right of its initial direction in the Northern Hemisphere, but to the left in the Southern Hemisphere. The force employed to describe this deflection is zero at the equator and increases with latitude to a maximum at the poles. The Coriolis Effect also increases as wind speed increases and is most important in large-scale (planetary- and synoptic-scale) circulation systems.

- Friction affects horizontal winds blowing within about 1000 m (3300 ft) of Earth's surface (the atmospheric boundary layer). Obstacles on Earth's surface slow the wind by breaking it into turbulent eddies.

- Gravity always accelerates objects directly downward and is important in the vertical motion of air (e.g., cold air drainage).

- Hydrostatic equilibrium is the balance between the upward-directed pressure gradient force resulting from the decrease of air pressure with altitude and the downward-directed force of gravity. Slight deviations from hydrostatic equilibrium cause air to accelerate upward or downward.

- The geostrophic wind is an un-accelerated, horizontal wind that blows in a straight path parallel to isobars at altitudes above the atmospheric boundary layer. The geostrophic wind results from a balance between the horizontal pressure gradient force and the Coriolis Effect.

- The gradient wind is a horizontal wind that parallels curved isobars at altitudes above the atmospheric boundary layer. The centripetal force operates in the gradient wind as the result of an imbalance between the horizontal pressure gradient force and the Coriolis Effect. Viewed from above in the Northern Hemisphere, the gradient wind blows clockwise in anticyclones (*Highs*) and counterclockwise in cyclones (*Lows*).

- In large-scale (synoptic- and planetary-scale) circulation systems, friction slows the near-surface wind and interacts with the Coriolis Effect to shift the wind direction across isobars and toward lower pressure.

- Within the atmospheric boundary layer, viewed from above, horizontal winds blow clockwise and spiral outward in Northern Hemisphere anticyclones but counterclockwise and inward in Northern Hemisphere cyclones.

- In an anticyclone, horizontal divergence of surface winds causes air above to descend and warm by compression. Hence, an anticyclone is generally a fair-weather system. In a cyclone, horizontal convergence of surface winds causes ascending air, which expands and cools. Hence, a cyclone is frequently a stormy weather system.

- Along a coastline, surface winds blowing offshore speed up and undergo horizontal divergence (inducing descending air), whereas onshore winds are slowed by friction and undergo horizontal convergence (inducing ascending air).

- Atmospheric circulation is typically divided into four spatial/temporal scales: planetary, synoptic, meso-scale, and micro-scale.

Review

1. How does the magnitude of the vertical component of the wind compare to the horizontal component in large-scale weather systems?
2. What is the primary cause of horizontal gradients in air pressure? How do air parcels respond to air pressure gradients?
3. What is the general relationship between the horizontal air pressure gradient and wind speed?
4. Explain why the direction of the Coriolis Effect in the Southern Hemisphere is opposite that in the Northern Hemisphere.
5. Give an example of how gravity influences air motion.
6. How does the gradient wind differ from the geostrophic wind?
7. How does the roughness of Earth's surface affect the direction and speed of the horizontal wind within the atmospheric boundary layer?
8. Demonstrate how downwind changes in surface roughness induce divergence and convergence of the horizontal wind.
9. Why is fair weather usually associated with anticyclones and stormy weather with cyclones?
10. Compare the magnitude of the horizontal pressure gradient at Earth's surface with the magnitude of the vertical pressure gradient within the troposphere.

Critical Thinking

1. Suppose that the magnitude of the horizontal pressure gradient changes with altitude. How would this change affect the horizontal wind at higher altitudes?
2. In view of Newton's first law of motion, is the gradient wind a consequence of *balanced forces*? Explain your response.
3. In the atmosphere, horizontal pressure gradients are usually much weaker than the vertical pressure gradient. Why then are horizontal winds usually much stronger than vertical winds?
4. Predict how wind direction and speed at your locality change as the center of a cyclone approaches. Do the same for an approaching anticyclone.
5. Suppose that a synoptic-scale cyclone is centered over central Kansas. Describe the air mass advection to the southeast, west, and northeast of the storm center.
6. Gravity is much weaker on Mars than on Earth. What does this difference imply about the relative magnitude of the vertical pressure gradient force on Mars?
7. The pattern of horizontal winds blowing about the center of a low-pressure system implies the existence of a centripetal force. Explain why.
8. How does the Coriolis Effect influence the direction of large-scale ocean currents in the Northern Hemisphere?
9. Why are horizontal winds associated with a sloping pressure surface (e.g., 700-mb surface)?
10. Suppose that the atmosphere were not a *continuous* fluid. Speculate on some of the consequences.

ESSAY: Wind Profilers

A special application of Doppler radar is providing meteorologists with much more detailed surveillance of winds aloft than is possible by tracking radiosondes (a *rawinsonde observation*). A *wind profiler* consists of a wire-mesh antenna about half the size of a tennis court that sends radar signals (having wavelengths of 33 cm to 6 m) upward into the atmosphere (Figure 1). The signal detects changes in atmospheric density caused by turbulent mixing of volumes of air that differ slightly in temperature and humidity. Fluctuations in the index of refraction are used as a tracer of both the horizontal and vertical components of the wind.

In May 1992, the National Oceanic and Atmospheric Administration (NOAA) announced that the nation's first wind profiler network was up and operating. The inaugural network consisted of 29 wind profilers in 15 Midwestern States. As of this writing, the wind profiler network is composed of 35 stations in 18 states including Alaska and New York. Each wind profiler monitors wind speed and direction at 72 different levels up to an altitude of 16,000 m (52,500 ft). Data are automatically collected every 6 minutes and transmitted to a quality-control hub in Boulder, CO. Wind data are then averaged over 1-hr periods and made available to National Weather Service Forecast Offices across the nation.

The principal advantage of a wind profiler over a radiosonde is the much greater frequency of wind observations. As noted in Chapter 2, radiosondes are launched once every 12 hrs. Winds aloft can change significantly in much shorter periods. Such changes could, for example, alter the track of a cyclone so that a city in the storm's path receives snow instead of rain. More detailed monitoring of winds aloft also permits commercial airlines to better plan flight routes that avoid strong headwinds and take advantage of tailwinds. And, in recent years, temperature profiling and moisture-sensing capabilities have been added to some wind profilers.

FIGURE 1
A wind profiler located in northwestern Missouri.

sub-Saharan Africa grew worse. Over North America, the winter storm track shifted hundreds of kilometers southeast of its usual location, bringing episodes of destructive high winds and heavy rains to portions of California. Flooding rains also caused havoc across the southeastern United States. Meanwhile ski resorts in the northern United States experienced a snow drought and considerable economic loss.

Just prior to these worldwide weather extremes, the ocean circulation off the northwest coast of South America changed drastically with dire implications for marine productivity. Along the coast of Ecuador and Peru, plankton populations plunged 20-fold. The decline in plankton reduced the numbers of anchovy, which feed on plankton, to a record low. Other fish dependent on anchovy, such as jack mackerel, suffered a similar fate. Commercial fisheries off the coast of Ecuador and Peru collapsed. With the decline in fish populations, marine birds (e.g., frigate birds and terns) and marine mammals (e.g., fur seals and sea lions) also experienced major population declines as insufficient food supplies caused breeding failures as well as starvation of adults.

The impact of these 1982-83 environmental changes was particularly severe on the ecology of the remote island of Kiritimati (Christmas Island) at 2 degrees N, 157 degrees W, in the central tropical Pacific.

An estimated 17 million seabirds, which feed on fish and squid, normally nest on the island. But scientists arriving on Kiritimati in November 1982 discovered that almost all adult birds had abandoned the island, leaving their young to starve. Apparently, sharp declines in food sources forced fish and squid to search for better feeding grounds, and the adult birds followed their prey. By July 1983, with the return of more typical ocean circulation and a resurgence in plankton populations, adult birds returned to Kiritimati, nesting began again, and sea bird populations started to recover.

What caused these drastic changes in atmospheric and oceanic conditions? Early on, some scientists attributed the weather extremes to the violent eruption of the Mexican volcano El Chichón during March-April 1982. But it quickly became apparent that the worldwide weather extremes were linked to large-scale atmosphere/ocean circulation changes in the tropical Pacific and soon a new scientific term was added to the public's vocabulary, *El Niño*. The 1982-83 El Niño spurred research on atmosphere-ocean interactions and the deployment of an array of direct and remote sensing instruments in the tropical Pacific to provide early warning of a developing El Niño. In the late 1990s, when El Niño returned in full fury, the global community was better prepared.

Driving Question:

What are the principal features of the planetary-scale atmospheric circulation and how does the circulation affect the weather and climate?

Ultimately, the planetary-scale atmospheric circulation is responsible for the development and displacement of smaller scale weather systems. Experience indicates that many of the weather systems, such as cyclones and anticyclones, which affect middle latitudes, travel from west to east whereas in the tropics, systems such as tropical cyclones (e.g., hurricanes, tropical storms) move from east to west. Appropriately, our description of atmospheric circulation systems begins with the global scale. This chapter covers the pressure systems and wind belts that operate at the planetary scale, with special emphasis on circulation patterns of the middle latitude westerlies. We also cover anomalous variations in the planetary circulation regime that result in El Niño and La

Niña, where atmosphere/ocean interactions in the tropical Pacific have ramifications for weather and climate in many other regions of the world.

Idealized Circulation Pattern

Planetary-scale atmospheric circulation is a complex pattern of winds and pressure systems. To understand how this circulation is shaped, we begin with an idealized model of planet Earth. Imagine Earth as a non-rotating sphere with a uniform solid surface. Also assume that the sun heats the equatorial regions more intensely than the poles as it does on the real Earth. A temperature gradient

CHAPTER 9

ATMOSPHERE'S PLANETARY CIRCULATION

Planet Earth, view from space, appears as a "Blue Marble" with its surface mostly ocean water and partially obscured by swirling cloud masses. [Courtesy of NASA, Goddard Space Flight Center.]

Case in Point

In 1982-83, the weather seemed to go wild in many parts of the world and after it was over the total worldwide impact included 2000 deaths and an estimated $13 billion in property damage. Excessive rains between mid-November 1982 and late January 1983 caused the worst flooding of the century in the usually arid portions of Ecuador. Strong winds and torrential rains associated with six tropical cyclones lashed French Polynesia in a span of only three months. At the other extreme, drought parched eastern Australia, Indonesia, and southern Africa. Huge drought-related wildfires broke out in Australia and Borneo. Australia's drought was the nation's worst in 200 years, causing $2 billion in crop losses and the deaths of millions of sheep and cattle. Meanwhile, drought in sub-Saharan Africa grew worse. Over North America, the winter storm track shifted hundreds of kilometers southeast of its usual location, bringing episodes of destructive high winds and heavy rains to portions of California. Flooding rains also caused havoc across the southeastern United States. Meanwhile ski resorts in the northern United States experienced a snow drought and considerable economic loss.

Just prior to these worldwide weather extremes, the ocean circulation off the northwest coast of South America changed drastically with dire implications for marine productivity. Along the coast of Ecuador and Peru, plankton populations plunged 20-fold. The decline in plankton reduced the numbers of anchovy, which feed on plankton, to a record low. Other fish dependent on anchovy, such as jack mackerel, suffered a similar fate. Commercial fisheries off the coast of Ecuador and Peru collapsed. With the decline in fish populations, marine birds (e.g., frigate birds and terns) and marine mammals (e.g., fur seals and sea lions) also experienced major population declines as insufficient food supplies caused breeding failures as well as starvation of adults.

The impact of these 1982-83 environmental changes was particularly severe on the ecology of the remote island of Kiritimati (Christmas Island) at 2 degrees N, 157 degrees W, in the central tropical Pacific.

An estimated 17 million seabirds, which feed on fish and squid, normally nest on the island. But scientists arriving on Kiritimati in November 1982 discovered that almost all adult birds had abandoned the island, leaving their young to starve. Apparently, sharp declines in food sources forced fish and squid to search for better feeding grounds, and the adult birds followed their prey. By July 1983, with the return of more typical ocean circulation and a resurgence in plankton populations, adult birds returned to Kiritimati, nesting began again, and sea bird populations started to recover.

What caused these drastic changes in atmospheric and oceanic conditions? Early on, some scientists attributed the weather extremes to the violent eruption of the Mexican volcano El Chichón during March-April 1982. But it quickly became apparent that the worldwide weather extremes were linked to large-scale atmosphere/ocean circulation changes in the tropical Pacific and soon a new scientific term was added to the public's vocabulary, *El Niño*. The 1982-83 El Niño spurred research on atmosphere-ocean interactions and the deployment of an array of direct and remote sensing instruments in the tropical Pacific to provide early warning of a developing El Niño. In the late 1990s, when El Niño returned in full fury, the global community was better prepared.

Driving Question:
What are the principal features of the planetary-scale atmospheric circulation and how does the circulation affect the weather and climate?

Ultimately, the planetary-scale atmospheric circulation is responsible for the development and displacement of smaller scale weather systems. Experience indicates that many of the weather systems, such as cyclones and anticyclones, which affect middle latitudes, travel from west to east whereas in the tropics, systems such as tropical cyclones (e.g., hurricanes, tropical storms) move from east to west. Appropriately, our description of atmospheric circulation systems begins with the global scale. This chapter covers the pressure systems and wind belts that operate at the planetary scale, with special emphasis on circulation patterns of the middle latitude westerlies. We also cover anomalous variations in the planetary circulation regime that result in El Niño and La

Niña, where atmosphere/ocean interactions in the tropical Pacific have ramifications for weather and climate in many other regions of the world.

Idealized Circulation Pattern

Planetary-scale atmospheric circulation is a complex pattern of winds and pressure systems. To understand how this circulation is shaped, we begin with an idealized model of planet Earth. Imagine Earth as a non-rotating sphere with a uniform solid surface. Also assume that the sun heats the equatorial regions more intensely than the poles as it does on the real Earth. A temperature gradient

In addition to the Great Lakes region, lake-effect snows also affect the valleys southeast of Utah's Great Salt Lake. Each year perhaps six significant lake-effect snowfalls occur in the Tooele and Salt Lake valleys, bowl-shaped depressions that slope up and away from Great Salt Lake. Both valleys parallel the northwest-southeast-trending long axis of the lake. Which of the two valleys receives the heavier snowfall depends on wind direction. Cold air on northwest winds is moderated by contact with the relatively warm lake surface, and downwind, the mountain valley topography forces horizontal convergence and uplift. Clouds billow upward and locally release bursts of heavy snow.

Great Salt Lake snows are generally less intense than their Great Lakes counterparts. Major reasons are the smaller area of the lake and the shorter fetch of winds blowing over the lake, so that air masses do not modify as much. The waters of Great Salt Lake cover an area that is only about 13% of that of Lake Ontario, the smallest of the five Great Lakes. Maximum fetch on Great Salt Lake is only about 120 km (75 mi), whereas maximum fetches on the Great Lakes are many hundreds of kilometers.

Similar localized snowfalls sometimes accompany onshore winds along Atlantic coastal localities. Cape Cod, for example, may experience this "ocean effect" snow with northerly winds. Rarely, north winds following the passage of a coastal low pressure system have even produced "bay-effect" snows over eastern Virginia off the Chesapeake Bay.

Occasionally, lake-effect snows develop on the western shores of the lakes which are normally upwind. For example, an early winter extra-tropical cyclone tracking through the lower Great Lakes region may produce strong northeast winds which blow onshore on the western shores. In this case, sometimes distinguished as *lake-enhanced snow*, the lake's snow-generating mechanism adds to the snowfall produced by the cyclone. This can mean paralyzing accumulations of snow for the Milwaukee-Chicago metropolitan areas, for example.

Strong cold winds blowing over the Great Lakes from the west and northwest produce lake-effect snow that falls from cloud bands that are oriented parallel to the wind direction. These *wind-parallel snow bands* are shown in the visible satellite image in Figure 2. Lake-effect snow can also develop with relatively weak regional winds. With a sufficient temperature contrast between water and land surfaces (more than 10 Celsius degrees or 18 Fahrenheit degrees), a horizontal air pressure gradient develops between the land and lake with higher pressure over the colder land surface and lower pressure over the warmer lake surface. In response to this pressure gradient, a cold wind develops that is directed offshore (called a *land breeze*). The leading edge of the land breeze is like a miniature cold front that forces upward the warmer air over the lake; clouds form and snow develops along bands that are oriented parallel to the shoreline. *Shore-parallel snow bands* are shown in the visible satellite image in Figure 3. Where shore-parallel snow bands drift onshore, they usually produce greater snowfalls than wind-parallel snow bands.

Figure 2
A visible satellite image showing wind-parallel snow bands.

Figure 3
A visible satellite image showing shore-parallel snow bands.

ESSAY: Lake-Effect Snow

A highly localized fall of snow immediately downwind of an open lake at middle latitudes of the Northern Hemisphere is known as *lake-effect snow*. Typically, such snows extend inland only a few tens of kilometers. In fact, the snowfall is often confined to such a small area that weather stations do not detect the event except by radar or local observer reports. Residents of the affected area, however, may be swamped by snow. On 21 January 1994, Adams, NY at the eastern end of Lake Ontario, received 152 cm (60 in.) of road-clogging snow in only 18 hrs. Such an extreme lake-effect snowfall is sometimes called a *snowburst*.

Lake-effect snow is most common in autumn and early winter when lake surface temperatures are still relatively mild. As an early season outbreak of cold (arctic) air streams over the lake, water readily evaporates and raises the vapor pressure of the lowest portion of the advecting air mass. (As described in Chapter 7, this same process may also produce *steam fog*.) In addition, the warmer lake water heats the advecting cold air from below, reducing its stability and enhancing convection and cloud development. Often this is all that is needed to trigger snowfall over the lake.

As the modified (milder, more humid, and less stable) air flows toward the lake's lee (downwind) shore, the contrast in surface roughness between the lake and land becomes important. The rougher land surface slows onshore winds, and the consequent horizontal speed convergence induces ascent of air, further development of clouds, and lake-effect snow. The topography of the downwind shore also affects the amount of precipitation: Hilly terrain forces greater uplift and enhances snowfall.

Ultimately, the frequency and intensity of lake-effect snows hinge on the degree of air mass modification, which in turn, depends on (1) the temperature contrast between the relatively warm lake surface and overlying cold air, and (2) the distance the wind travels over open water (*fetch*). Field studies conducted in the Great Lakes region indicate that lake-effect snow is most likely when the temperature difference between the lake-surface and an altitude of about 1500 m (5000 ft) is greater than 13 Celsius degrees (23 Fahrenheit degrees) and the temperature contrast between the lake-surface and the adjacent land surface exceeds 10 Celsius degrees (18 Fahrenheit degrees). Ideally, the fetch of the wind must be at least 160 km (100 mi) and the horizontal wind direction must exhibit very little shear with altitude (varying by less than 30 degrees between the lake-surface and an altitude of about 3000 m or 10,000 ft).

To the lee of the Great Lakes, the bulk of lake-effect snows falls between mid-November and mid-January, the period when the temperature contrast between lake-surface and overlying air is usually greatest. Cold air usually sweeps into the Great Lakes region on west and northwest winds. Considering the maximum possible fetch, the greatest potential for substantial lake-effect snows is along the downwind southern and eastern shores of the Great Lakes. In these so-called *snowbelts*, lake-effect snow accounts for a substantial portion of total seasonal snowfall (Figure 1).

Figure 1
Average annual snowfall in the Great Lakes region (in inches). Note that the greatest snowfall totals occur downwind of the lakes and are largely due to lake-effect snows. [NOAA data]

inherent variability of the wind. The electrical output of a wind turbine varies as a consequence. Hence, a wind power system must include a means of storing the energy generated during gusty periods for use when the wind is light or the air is calm. Banks of batteries may serve this purpose. Wind power has its greatest immediate potential in regions where average winds are relatively strong and consistent in direction. Favorable regions include the western High Plains, the Pacific Northwest coast, portions of coastal California, the Great Lakes region, the south coast of Texas, and exposed summits and passes in the Rockies and Appalachians.

Economy of scale favors centralized arrays of many wind turbines, called *windmill farms*, over individual household wind turbines. Windmill farms consist of a dozen or more super wind turbines, each capable of producing as much as 0.5 megawatt of electricity. Windmill farms currently operating in California supplement conventional sources by feeding electricity directly to power grids. Since 1981, more than 16,000 turbines have been installed in windy mountain passes in California. In 2004, California's wind turbines produced approximately 4.26 billion kilowatt-hours of electricity, about 1.5% of the state's total electrical demand.

ESSAY: Wind Profilers

A special application of Doppler radar is providing meteorologists with much more detailed surveillance of winds aloft than is possible by tracking radiosondes (a *rawinsonde observation*). A *wind profiler* consists of a wire-mesh antenna about half the size of a tennis court that sends radar signals (having wavelengths of 33 cm to 6 m) upward into the atmosphere (Figure 1). The signal detects changes in atmospheric density caused by turbulent mixing of volumes of air that differ slightly in temperature and humidity. Fluctuations in the index of refraction are used as a tracer of both the horizontal and vertical components of the wind.

In May 1992, the National Oceanic and Atmospheric Administration (NOAA) announced that the nation's first wind profiler network was up and operating. The inaugural network consisted of 29 wind profilers in 15 Midwestern States. As of this writing, the wind profiler network is composed of 35 stations in 18 states including Alaska and New York. Each wind profiler monitors wind speed and direction at 72 different levels up to an altitude of 16,000 m (52,500 ft). Data are automatically collected every 6 minutes and transmitted to a quality-control hub in Boulder, CO. Wind data are then averaged over 1-hr periods and made available to National Weather Service Forecast Offices across the nation.

The principal advantage of a wind profiler over a radiosonde is the much greater frequency of wind observations. As noted in Chapter 2, radiosondes are launched once every 12 hrs. Winds aloft can change significantly in much shorter periods. Such changes could, for example, alter the track of a cyclone so that a city in the storm's path receives snow instead of rain. More detailed monitoring of winds aloft also permits commercial airlines to better plan flight routes that avoid strong headwinds and take advantage of tailwinds. And, in recent years, temperature profiling and moisture-sensing capabilities have been added to some wind profilers.

FIGURE 1
A wind profiler located in northwestern Missouri.

ESSAY: Wind Power

Harnessing the kinetic energy of the wind is a technology that was established as early as the 12th century in portions of the Middle East where water power was not available. In North America, the energy crisis of the 1970s spurred renewed interest in this ancient technology. More recent efforts to reduce our nation's dependency on fossil fuels in view of concerns over possible global climate change have rekindled interest in *wind power*. Today, scientists and engineers employ modern aerodynamic principles and space-age materials in designing and constructing modern wind-driven turbines that convert some of the wind's kinetic energy into electricity.

In Chapter 4, we saw how the sun drives the atmosphere. Only about 2% of the solar energy that reaches Earth is ultimately converted to the kinetic energy of wind, but that is still a tremendous amount of energy. Theoretically, windmill blades can convert a maximum of about 60% of the wind's energy into mechanical energy. In practice, however, wind generators extract at best only about 25% of the wind's energy. Furthermore, minimum wind speeds must be at least 15 km (9 mi) per hour for most wind-powered electricity-generating systems to operate economically. The amount of power that a wind turbine can extract from air in motion varies directly with (1) the cube of the instantaneous wind speed at hub height (V^3), (2) the area swept out by the windmill blade, and (3) air density.

Wind speed is by far the most important consideration in evaluating a location's wind energy potential. Even small changes in wind speed translate into great variations in energy harvested. For example, doubling the wind speed (a common occurrence) multiplies the available wind power by a factor of eight ($2 \times 2 \times 2$). Wind speed usually increases with altitude above Earth's surface, especially within the lowest meters of the atmosphere, so that a wind turbine is mounted on the top of a tower to take advantage of the stronger winds at that elevation. As a general rule, a minimum of several years of detailed wind monitoring is needed for a preliminary evaluation of the wind power potential of any site. Also, the long-term climate record should be checked for the frequency of potentially destructive winds. Wind data from nearby weather stations can be very useful as long as care is taken in extrapolating wind data between localities and from one elevation to another. (Recall that standard National Weather Service anemometers are located 10 m or 33 ft above the ground.)

At ordinary speeds, wind is a relatively diffuse energy source, comparable in magnitude to incoming solar radiation. Hence, a wind turbine's power generation potential also depends on the area swept out by the windmill blades; larger windmill blades can harvest more energy. Until recent decades, design and strength-of-materials problems limited the size of wind turbines. Today, availability of stronger and lighter materials for blades is making possible larger wind turbines that can generate as much as 0.5 megawatt of electricity. One wind turbine design uses three 23-m (75-ft) blades (Figure 1).

Tapping the wind's energy for electric power generation faces several challenges. Both wind speed and direction vary with exposure of the site, roughness of the terrain, and season of the year. The most formidable obstacle to the development of wind power potential stems from the

FIGURE 1
This windmill farm in northeastern Wisconsin is designed to meet the electrical energy needs of about 3600 households.

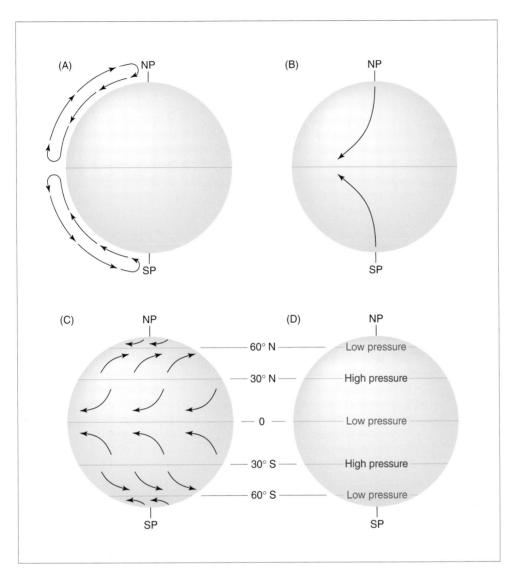

(A) NP SP

(B) NP SP

(C) NP SP

(D) NP

— 60° N — Low pressure

— 30° N — High pressure

— 0 — Low pressure

— 30° S — High pressure

— 60° S — Low pressure

SP

FIGURE 9.1

Planetary-scale air circulation on an idealized spherical model of Earth featuring a uniform solid surface. (A) If the sphere is initially non-rotating, huge convection currents develop on the sunlit portion of the planet's two hemispheres so that air circulates between the hot equator and cold poles. (B) With a rotating Earth, surface winds blow from the northeast in the Northern Hemisphere and from the southeast in the Southern Hemisphere owing to the Coriolis Effect. (C) In reality, surface winds divide into three belts in each hemisphere of the rotating planet. (D) Zones of converging and diverging surface winds give rise to east-west belts of low pressure and high pressure.

develops between the equator and poles. In response, two huge convection cells form, one in each hemisphere (Figure 9.1A). Cold, dense air sinks at the poles and flows at the surface toward the equator, where it forces warm, less dense air to rise. Aloft, the equatorial air flows toward the poles, completing the convective circulation.

If our idealized planet begins to rotate, the Coriolis Effect comes into play (Figure 9.1B). In the Northern Hemisphere, surface winds observed relative to Earth's surface shift to the right and blow toward the southwest, and in the Southern Hemisphere, surface winds shift to the left and blow toward the northwest. Hence, on our hypothetical planet, surface winds blow counter to the planet's direction of rotation, which is from west to east. Circulation is maintained in the atmosphere of our idealized Earth because the planetary-scale winds split into three belts in each hemisphere, so that some winds blow with and some winds blow against

the planet's rotational direction (Figure 9.1C). In the Northern Hemisphere, average surface winds are from the northeast between the equator and 30 degrees latitude, from the southwest between 30 and 60 degrees, and from the northeast between 60 degrees and the North Pole. In the Southern Hemisphere, surface winds blow from the southeast between the equator and 30 degrees, from the northwest between 30 and 60 degrees, and from the southeast between 60 degrees and the South Pole.

Surface winds converge along the equator and along the 60-degree latitude circles. Convergence leads to rising air, expansional cooling, cloud development, and precipitation. These convergence zones are belts of relatively low surface air pressure (Figure 9.1D). On the other hand, surface winds diverge at the poles and along the 30-degree latitude circles. In these regions, air descends, is compressed and warms, and the weather is generally fair. These divergence zones are belts of relatively high surface air pressure.

If the continents and ocean basins are added to our idealized Earth, the temperature characteristics of Earth's surface become more complicated, and so do the planetary-scale air pressure pattern and winds. Some of the pressure belts break into separate cells, and important contrasts in air pressure develop over land versus sea. Now our idealized model of planetary-scale atmospheric circulation more closely approximates the actual circulation pattern. In the next section, we describe the principal features of the planetary-scale atmospheric circulation.

Features of the Planetary-Scale Circulation

Maps of average air pressure at sea level for January and July reveal several areas of relatively high and low air pressure (Figure 9.2). These are **semi-permanent pressure systems**. Although these systems are persistent features of the planetary-scale circulation, they undergo important seasonal changes in both location and strength, hence the modifier *semi-permanent*. Pressure systems include subtropical

January

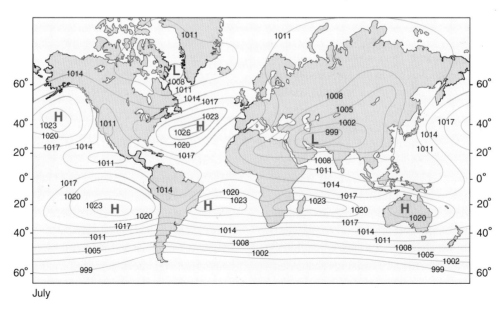

July

FIGURE 9.2
Mean sea-level air pressure during January and July. Contour lines are isobars in millibars (mb).

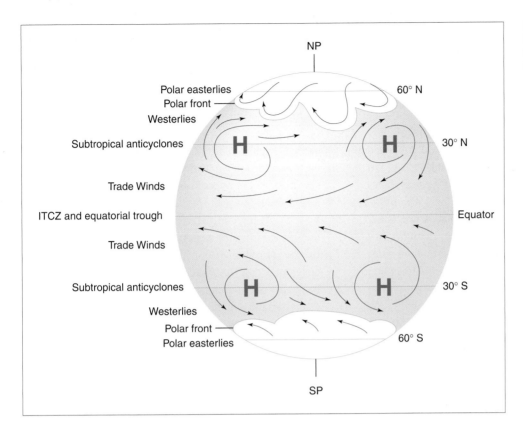

FIGURE 9.3
Schematic representation of the planetary-scale surface circulation of the atmosphere.

anticyclones, the intertropical convergence zone (ITCZ), subpolar lows, and polar highs. These pressure systems are in turn, linked by planetary-scale wind belts (Figure 9.3).

PRESSURE SYSTEMS AND WIND BELTS

Subtropical anticyclones are imposing features of the planetary-scale circulation that are centered over subtropical latitudes (on average, near 30 degrees N and S) of the North and South Atlantic, the North and South Pacific, and the Indian Ocean. These highs extend from the ocean surface up to the tropopause and exert a major influence on weather and climate over vast areas of the ocean and continents.

Stretching from the center of each subtropical high, outward over its eastern flank, are extensive areas of subsiding stable air. Subsiding air undergoes compressional warming, which produces low relative humidity and fair skies. The world's major subtropical deserts, including the Sahara of North Africa and the Sonora of Mexico and southwest United States, are located under the eastern flanks of subtropical anticyclones. On the far western portions of the subtropical highs, however, subsidence is less, the air is not as stable, and episodes of cloudy, stormy weather are more frequent. The contrast in climate between the eastern and western flanks of a subtropical high is apparent across southern North America. The

weather of the American Southwest (on the eastern side of the North Pacific high, also called the *Hawaiian high*) is considerably drier than the weather of the American Southeast (on the western side of the North Atlantic high, also called the *Bermuda-Azores high*).

As is typical of anticyclones, a subtropical high features a weak horizontal air pressure gradient over a broad area surrounding the system's center. Hence, surface winds are very light or the air is calm over extensive areas of the subtropical ocean. This situation played havoc with ancient sailing ships, which were becalmed for days or even weeks at a time. Ships setting sail from Spain to the New World were often caught in this predicament, and crews were forced to jettison their cargo of horses when supplies of water and food ran low. For this reason, early mariners referred to this region of calm air as the **horse latitudes**, a name now applied to all latitudes between about 30 and 35 degrees N and S under subtropical highs.

In the Northern Hemisphere, viewed from above, surface winds blow clockwise and outward, away from the centers of the subtropical highs, forming the westerlies and trade winds. Surface winds north of the horse latitudes constitute the highly variable **midlatitude westerlies** (which on average actually blow from the southwest). Surface winds blowing from the northeast out of the southern flanks of the anticyclones are known as the **trade winds**. The trades are the most persistent winds on the planet, in some regions blowing from the same direction more than 80% of the time. Analogous winds develop in the Southern Hemisphere, but recall that the Coriolis deflection is to the left in the Southern Hemisphere. A counterclockwise and outward surface airflow thus causes southeast trade winds on the northern flanks of the Southern Hemisphere subtropical highs and a belt of northwesterlies on the southern flanks.

Mariners were aware of the westerlies and trades of the North Atlantic at least as early as the 15th century. On his venture to find a route to India, Christopher Columbus (1451-1506) took advantage of what we now know is the circulation about the Bermuda-Azores subtropical high. In his westward voyage, Columbus first sailed southward from Spain along the northwest African coast into the northeast trade winds that eventually took his ships westward to the Caribbean. On his return trip to Spain, he sailed north into the westerlies.

Trade winds of the two hemispheres converge into a broad east-west equatorial belt of light and variable winds, called the **doldrums**. In that belt, ascending air induces cloudiness and rainfall. The most active weather develops along the **intertropical convergence zone (ITCZ)**, a discontinuous low-pressure belt with thunderstorms paralleling the equator. The average location of the ITCZ corresponds approximately to the latitude where Earth's mean annual surface temperature is highest, the **heat equator**. Primarily because more land is in the Northern Hemisphere than in the Southern Hemisphere, the world-wide average location of the heat equator is near 10 degrees N latitude.

On the poleward side of the subtropical highs, surface westerlies flow into regions of low pressure. In the Northern Hemisphere, there are two **subpolar lows**: the *Aleutian low* over the North Pacific Ocean and the *Icelandic low* over the North Atlantic. These pressure cells mark the convergence of the midlatitude southwesterlies with the polar northeasterlies. In contrast, in the Southern Hemisphere, the midlatitude northwesterlies and the polar southeasterlies converge along a nearly continuous belt of low pressure surrounding the Antarctic continent (the *Antarctic circumpolar vortex*).

Surface westerlies meet and override the polar easterlies along the **polar front**. Recall that a *front* is a narrow zone of transition between air masses that differ in temperature, humidity, or both. In this case, dense, cold air masses flowing toward the equator meet milder, less dense air masses moving toward the pole. The polar front is not continuous around the globe; rather, it is well-defined in

some areas and not in others, depending on the temperature contrast across the front. Where that temperature gradient is great, the front is well defined and is a potential site for development of extra-tropical cyclones (Chapter 10). On the other hand, where the air temperature contrast is minimal, the polar front is poorly defined and inactive or non-existent. The polar front is usually apparent on a surface weather map of North America, dividing colder air to the north from warmer air to the south. At any time, segments of the polar front may be stationary or moving northward as a warm front or southward as a cold front.

At high latitudes, air subsides and flows away at the surface from the centers of shallow, cold anticyclones. In the Northern Hemisphere, **polar highs** are well developed only in winter over the continental interiors. In the Southern Hemisphere, cold highs persist over the glacier-bound Antarctic continent year-round.

WINDS ALOFT

What is the pattern of the planetary-scale winds aloft, that is, in the middle and upper troposphere? As noted earlier, air subsides in subtropical anticyclones, sweeps toward the equator as the surface trade winds, and then ascends in the ITCZ. Aloft, in the middle and upper troposphere, winds blow poleward, away from the doldrums and into the subtropical highs. The Coriolis Effect shifts these upper-level winds toward the right in the Northern Hemisphere (southwest winds), and toward the left in the Southern Hemisphere (northwest winds). In the tropics, therefore, winds aloft blow in a direction opposite that of the surface trade winds.

The north-south vertical profile of this low-latitude circulation resembles a huge convection current (Figure 9.4). This circulation is known as the **Hadley**

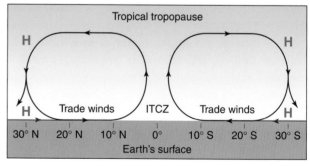

H = Subtropical anticyclones

FIGURE 9.4
Idealized north-south vertical cross-section of the Hadley cell circulation in tropical latitudes of the Northern and Southern Hemispheres. Air rises in the intertropical convergence zone (ITCZ) and sinks in the subtropical anticyclones.

cell, named for the English meteorologist George Hadley (1685-1768), who first proposed its existence in 1735. Hadley cells are situated on either side of the ITCZ and extend poleward to the subtropical highs. It was once proposed that separate cells, similar to Hadley cells, occurred in both middle and polar latitudes. But upper-air monitoring does not provide definitive evidence of such well-defined cells.

Aloft in middle latitudes, winds blow from west to east in a wavelike pattern of ridges and troughs, as shown in Figure 9.5. These winds are responsible for the development and movement of the synoptic-scale weather systems (highs, lows, air masses, and fronts) discussed in Chapter 10. Also, their north/south components contribute to poleward heat transport described in Chapter 4. Because the upper-air westerlies are so important for the weather of middle latitudes, we examine them more extensively in a separate section of this chapter.

Figure 9.6 is a vertical cross-sectional profile of prevailing winds in the troposphere from the North Pole to the equator. In this perspective, we are viewing only the north-south and vertical (up-down) components of the wind and are neglecting the west-east component. Note that the altitude of the tropopause does not steadily increase from pole to equator but occurs in discrete steps. The altitude of the tropopause is directly related to the mean air temperature of the troposphere; that is, the lower the mean temperature, the lower is the altitude of the tropopause. Thus, the polar tropopause is at a lower altitude than the midlatitude tropopause, which, in turn, is at a lower altitude than the tropical tropopause.

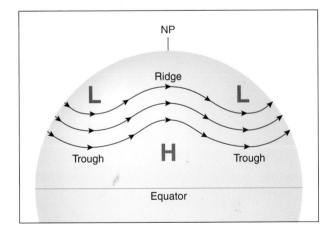

FIGURE 9.5
In the middle and upper troposphere, the Northern Hemisphere westerlies blow from west to east in a wave-like pattern of ridges (clockwise turns) and troughs (counterclockwise turns).

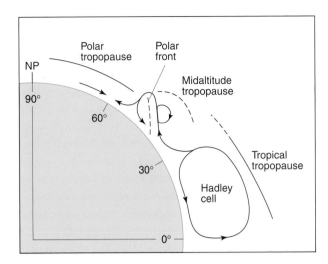

FIGURE 9.6
Vertical cross-section of the north-south (meridional) component of the atmospheric circulation of the Northern Hemisphere. Note that the tropopause occurs in three segments, occurring at highest altitudes in the tropics and lowest altitudes in the polar regions. The vertical scale is greatly exaggerated.

TRADE WIND INVERSION

The circulation on the eastern flank of subtropical anticyclones gives rise to the **trade wind inversion**, a persistent and climatically significant feature of the planetary-scale circulation over the eastern portions of tropical ocean basins. Key to formation of the trade wind inversion is the descending branch of the Hadley cell. As air subsides in the subtropical highs as part of the Hadley circulation, it is warmed by compression and its relative humidity decreases. Descending air encounters the *marine air layer*, a shallow layer of air that overlies the ocean surface. Where sea-surface temperatures are relatively low, the marine air layer is cool, humid, and stable. Where sea-surface temperatures are relatively high, the marine air layer is warm, more humid, less stable, and well mixed by convection.

Air subsiding from above is warmer (and much drier) than the upper portion of the marine air layer. The trade wind inversion forms at the altitude where air subsiding from above meets the top of the marine air layer. As noted in Chapter 6, the air temperature increases with increasing altitude within a temperature inversion. Air characterized by a temperature inversion is extremely stable and strongly inhibits vertical motion of air. The trade wind inversion is an elevated temperature inversion that essentially acts as a lid over the lower atmosphere.

As noted earlier in this chapter, most subsidence occurs on the eastern flank of a subtropical high. A trade wind inversion develops to the east and southeast of the center of a subtropical high, in the region dominated by the trade winds. The inversion is highest near the center of the high and gradually slopes downward toward the western coasts of the continents. For example, the trade wind inversion slopes downward from an average altitude of about 2000 m (6560 ft) over Hawaii to about 800 m (2400 ft) over coastal southern California.

Because of its extreme stability, the trade wind inversion acts as a cap on the vertical development of convective clouds and rainfall. As we will see in Chapter 12, this inhibits development of tropical storms and hurricanes. The inversion also limits orographic precipitation (Chapter 6). For example, some high volcanic peaks on the Hawaiian Islands poke through the trade wind inversion into the dry air above. Because of orographic lifting, rainfall generally increases with elevation along windward slopes of the volcanic mountains but only up to the trade wind inversion. Above the inversion, conditions are dry.

SEASONAL SHIFTS

Between winter and summer, important changes take place in the planetary-scale circulation. Pressure systems, the polar front, the planetary wind belts, and the ITCZ follow the sun, shifting toward the pole in spring and toward the equator in autumn. Because the seasons are reversed in the two hemispheres, the planetary-scale systems of both hemispheres move north and south in tandem. In addition, the strength of pressure cells varies seasonally. Subtropical anticyclones, such as the Bermuda-Azores high, exert higher surface pressures in summer than in winter. The Icelandic low deepens in winter and greatly weakens in summer, and, though well developed in winter, the Aleutian low disappears in summer.

Seasonal reversals in surface air pressure also occur over the continents. These pressure changes stem from the contrast in solar heating of land versus sea. For reasons presented in Chapter 4, the ocean surface exhibits smaller temperature variations over the course of a year than does Earth's land surface. Hence, continents at middle and high latitudes are dominated by relatively high pressure in winter and relatively low pressure in summer. In winter, in response to extreme radiational cooling, cold anticyclones develop over northwestern North America and over the interior of Asia, the most prominent of which is the massive Siberian high. In summer, in response to intense solar heating, a belt of low pressure forms across North Africa and from the Arabian Peninsula eastward into Southeast Asia. Warm low-pressure cells (called *thermal lows*) also develop in summer over arid and semi-arid regions of Mexico and the Southwestern United States.

Seasonal shifts in the planetary-scale wind belts, pressure systems, and the ITCZ leave their mark on the world's climates. Northward migration of the ITCZ triggers summer monsoon rains in Central America, North Africa, India, and Southeast Asia (discussed in the following section). As shown in Figure 9.7, north-south movements of the ITCZ are greater over continents than over the ocean. Over the ocean, the mean latitude of the ITCZ varies by only about 4 degrees through the year (between 4 degrees N in April and 8 degrees N in September). Anchoring of the ITCZ over the ocean is a consequence of the ocean's greater thermal inertia.

The influence of the subtropical anticyclones on precipitation regimes is illustrated by the contrast in the march of mean monthly precipitation between Charleston,

FIGURE 9.7
The Intertropical Convergence Zone (ITCZ) follows the sun, reaching its most northerly latitudes in July and its most southerly latitudes in January.

FIGURE 9.8
Mean monthly precipitation (rain plus melted snow) in centimeters and inches for (A) San Diego, CA, and (B) Charleston, SC for the period 1971-2000. San Diego has a distinct dry season (summer) when its weather is dominated by subsiding air on the eastern flank of the Hawaiian subtropical high.

SC and San Diego, CA (Figure 9.8). Although the two cities have about the same latitude, San Diego has a distinct rainy season (winter) and dry season (summer), whereas Charleston has abundant precipitation throughout the year. In summer, San Diego is under the dry eastern flank of the Hawaiian high, while Charleston is on the receiving end of the humid flow on the western flank of the Bermuda-Azores high. Consequently, San Diego is dry while Charleston has frequent episodes of convective showers. After the subtropical highs shift equatorward in autumn, the weather of both cities is influenced by widespread precipitation associated with west-to-east moving extra-tropical cyclones so that winters are wet in both places.

The wind-driven circulation regime in the surface layers of the ocean closely corresponds to the planetary-scale circulation pattern of the atmosphere. Early on, mariners took advantage of surface ocean currents. The long-term average pattern of ocean currents is plotted in Figure 9.9. Large-scale circulation regimes, called gyres, appear in each of the major ocean basins and are associated with the prevailing winds that help set up the currents. In the Northern Hemisphere, clockwise circulating gyres in the North Atlantic and North Pacific are associated with the clockwise circulation of winds around the semi-permanent subtropical highs centered over each basin. In the North Atlantic, the Gulf Stream is a warm current that moves northward along the East Coast of North America before turning east toward northwest Europe, while the cold southward flowing Canary Current moves along the African coast. Surface currents flow westward across the equatorial

Atlantic. In the North Pacific, the Kuroshio Current moves northward off Asia, then travels eastward across the Pacific before turning south as the cold California Current. Opposite circulation regimes due to a reversed Coriolis Effect occur in the Southern Hemisphere, with a counterclockwise gyre located in the South Pacific. Of significance is the cold northward flowing Peru Current, which then helps form a westward flowing equatorial current.

Monsoon Circulation

Monsoon is derived from the Arabic word (*mausim*) for season. A **monsoon circulation** characterizes regions where seasonal reversals in prevailing winds cause wet summers and relatively dry winters. Monsoon was first applied to winds over the Arabian Sea, which blow from the northeast for about six months and then from the southwest for about six months. In this section, we describe the vigorous monsoon circulation over portions of Africa and Asia, where more than 2 billion people depend on monsoon rains for their drinking water and agriculture. Over much of India, monsoon rains (falling mostly between June and September) account for 80% or more of total annual precipitation. We then discuss the weaker monsoon that affects the American Southwest.

What causes the Asian and African monsoons? As first proposed in 1686 by the English astronomer Edmund Halley (1656-1742), monsoons depend on seasonal contrasts in the heating of land and ocean. The ocean has a greater

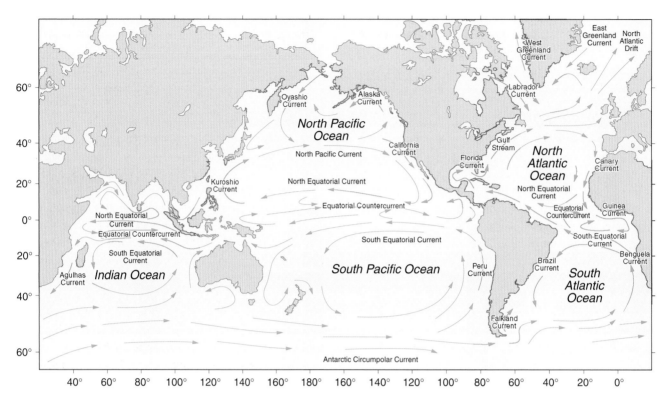

FIGURE 9.9
Long-term average pattern of wind-driven ocean-surface currents. Gyres in the ocean basin are driven by the planetary-scale atmospheric circulation.

thermal inertia than does the land (Chapter 4). Beginning in spring, relatively cool air over the ocean and relatively warm air over the land give rise to a horizontal air pressure gradient directed from sea to land, generating an onshore flow of humid air. Over the land, intense solar heating triggers convection. Hot, humid air rises, and consequent expansional cooling leads to condensation, clouds, and rain. Release of latent heat intensifies the buoyant uplift, triggering even more cloud development and rainfall. Aloft, the air spreads seaward and subsides over the relatively cool ocean surface, thus completing the monsoon circulation. Monsoon winds have sufficiently long trajectories and persist long enough to be influenced by the Coriolis Effect. Surface monsoon winds are deflected to the right in the Northern Hemisphere and to the left in the Southern Hemisphere.

By early autumn, radiational cooling chills the land more than the adjacent ocean surface, resulting in higher surface pressures over land and setting up a horizontal air pressure gradient directed from land to sea. Air subsides over the land, and dry surface winds sweep seaward. Air rises over the relatively warm ocean surface and aloft drifts landward, completing the winter monsoon circulation. Over land, therefore, the summer monsoon is wet whereas the winter monsoon is dry (Figure 9.10).

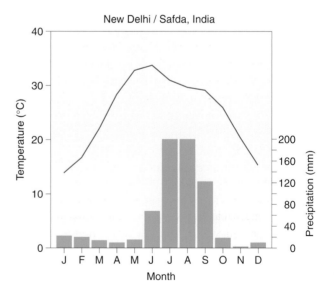

FIGURE 9.10
March of mean monthly temperature (in °C) and mean monthly precipitation (in millimeters) for New Dehli/Safda, India. Most precipitation occurs from June through September, the wet monsoon. Note that the highest mean monthly temperatures are in May and June. Cooler temperatures in July, August, and September are due to considerable cloudiness during that time of year. [GHCN data supplied by E. J. Hopkins]

Topography complicates the monsoon circulation and the geographical distribution of rainfall. For example, the massive Tibetan plateau strongly influences the Asian monsoon because its elevation tops 4000 m (13,000 ft) over a broad area. In winter, the westerly jet stream (a corridor of very strong winds in the westerlies) splits into two branches, one to the south and the other to the north of the plateau. The southerly branch steers cyclones that originate over the Mediterranean across northern India, bringing significant precipitation to that region. Meanwhile, the rest of India experiences the dry monsoon flow. In spring, the southern branch weakens and by late May shifts northward over the plateau. It is not until this happens that the moist monsoon flow begins over India.

Monsoon rainfall is neither uniform nor continual. On the contrary, the rainy season typically consists of a sequence of active and dormant phases. During a *monsoon active phase*, the weather is mostly cloudy with frequent deluges of rain, but during a *monsoon dormant phase*, the weather is sunny and hot. The monsoon shifts from active to dormant phases as bands of heavy rainfall surge inland. Heavy rains first strike coastal areas and soak the ground. As the soil becomes saturated with water, more solar radiation is used for evaporation and less is available for sensible heating. Coastal areas cool, uplift weakens, and skies partially clear (monsoon dormant phase). Meanwhile, the area of maximum heating, most vigorous uplift, and heavy rains shifts inland. Back in the coastal areas, however, the hot sun eventually dries the soil, sensible heating intensifies, uplift strengthens, and rains resume (monsoon active phase). This sequence of active and dormant phases is repeated about every 15 to 20 days during the wet monsoon.

Solar radiation, land and water distribution, and topography impose some regularity on the monsoon circulation; that is, summers are wet and winters are dry. The planetary-scale circulation (especially shifts of the ITCZ) and the strength and distribution of convective activity, however, vary from one year to the next. These variations mean that the intensity and duration of monsoon rains change from year to year. As a consequence, drought is always possible in monsoon climates. In this chapter's first Essay, "Drought in Sub-Saharan Africa," we consider a particularly tragic example of long-term monsoon failure and drought.

The *North American Monsoon System (NAMS)*, also called the **southwest monsoon**, affects the American Southwest including Arizona, New Mexico, and parts of southern Colorado. The monsoon brings a dramatic increase in rainfall to this region mainly during July and August. Many places in New Mexico, for example, receive 40% to 50% of their total annual precipitation during these two months.

The southwest monsoon originates over northern Mexico during May and June. In fact, the southwest monsoon is actually the northern extension of the Mexican monsoon which is responsible for up to 70% of annual precipitation in portions of Mexico. Intense solar radiational heating of the ground raises the temperature of the overlying air, reducing the air pressure at low levels of the troposphere over a broad area (a *thermal low*). Meanwhile a warm high pressure system (the *monsoon high*) develops aloft in the middle and upper troposphere. A horizontal pressure gradient develops at low levels, which is directed from high pressure over the waters of the Gulf of California and the Gulf of Mexico toward low pressure over interior Mexico. In response to this pressure gradient, warm humid air moves inland giving rise to considerable cloudiness and rainfall. Southerly winds on the western flank of the monsoon high advect moisture northward between the Sierra Madre Mountains to the east and smaller mountains in Baja California to the west.

The monsoon high shifts northward and by July is centered in New Mexico. Winds across the American Southwest shift from the dry westerlies to a humid flow from the south and southeast with some of the flow originating over the Gulf of California and some from the Gulf of Mexico. With this wind shift the southwest monsoon is underway. As a rough guide, the monsoon is considered to begin in Phoenix, AZ when the dewpoint reaches 13 °C (55 °F) or higher for three consecutive days. That date on average is 7 July. During the monsoon, rainfall across the American Southwest is not continuous but consists of isolated showers and thunderstorms (with heaviest rains in the mountains). Subsiding dry air associated with the monsoon high is responsible for frequent dry episodes. Nonetheless, the southwest monsoon (sometimes augmented by the remnants of tropical cyclones from the eastern Pacific) is responsible for 70% to 80% of total annual precipitation across Arizona and the Sonora Desert (Figure 9.11). The southwest monsoon usually ends in September with the return of the dry westerlies.

The southwest monsoon provides water for dryland farming, ranching, and wildfire control but the timing and strength of the monsoon vary from one year to the next. A weak monsoon leads to water shortages and greater susceptibility to forest and brush fires. Also, heavy rains cause flash flooding of waterways that are usually dry most of the year. In New Mexico, flash floods are most common in July and August.

Tucson, Arizona

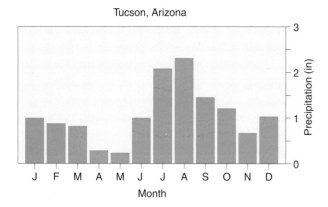

FIGURE 9.11
Mean monthly precipitation in inches (based on 1971-2000) at Tucson International Airport, AZ, showing the abrupt increase in rainfall from June to July signaling the onset of the southwest monsoon. [NOAA data]

Waves in the Westerlies

The middle latitude westerlies of the Northern Hemisphere merit special attention here because they govern the weather over much of North America. As noted earlier, in the middle and upper troposphere, the westerlies flow from west to east about the hemisphere in wavelike patterns of ridges and troughs. Winds exhibit a clockwise (anticyclonic) curvature in ridges, and a counterclockwise (cyclonic) curvature in troughs. Between two and five waves typically encircle the hemisphere at any one time. These long waves are called **Rossby waves**, after Carl-Gustav Rossby (1898-1957), the Swedish-American meteorologist who discovered them in the late 1930s. Rossby waves characterize the westerlies above the 500-mb level, that is, above the altitude where the pressure drops to 500 mb. At lower levels, waves are distorted somewhat by friction and topographic irregularities of the Earth's surface.

Meteorologists describe the upper-air westerlies in terms of (1) wavelength (distance between successive troughs or, equivalently, successive ridges), (2) amplitude (north-south extent), and (3) number of waves encircling the hemisphere. The westerlies exhibit changes in all three characteristics, and, as a direct consequence, the weather changes. The westerlies are more vigorous in winter than in summer. In winter, they strengthen and exhibit fewer waves of longer length and greater amplitude. These seasonal changes stem from variations in the north-south air pressure gradient, which is steeper in winter because of the greater temperature contrast between north and south at that time of year. In summer, north-south temperature differences are less, air pressure gradients are weaker, and so are the westerlies.

ZONAL AND MERIDIONAL FLOW PATTERNS

The weaving westerlies have two components of motion: a north-south wind superimposed on a west-to-east wind. The north-south airflow is the westerlies' *meridional component* and the west-to-east airflow is its *zonal component*. The meridional component of Rossby waves brings about a north-south exchange of air masses and poleward transport of heat. In the Northern Hemisphere, winds blowing from the southwest carry warm air masses toward the northeast, and winds blowing from the northwest transport cold air masses southeastward. Cold air is exchanged for warm air and heat is transported poleward. However, as Rossby waves change length, amplitude, and number, concurrent changes take place in the advection of air masses. Consider some examples.

Occasionally, the westerlies blow almost directly from west to east, nearly parallel to latitude circles, with only a weak meridional component (Figure 9.12). This is a **zonal flow pattern** in which the north-south exchange of air masses is minimal. Cold air masses stay to the north, and warm air masses remain in the south. At the same time, air that originated over the Pacific Ocean floods the coterminous United States and southern Canada. Pacific air dries out to some extent as it passes over the western mountain ranges, and is compressed and warmed as it descends onto the Great Plains, spreading relatively mild and generally fair weather east of the Rocky Mountains.

At other times, the westerlies exhibit considerable amplitude and flow in a pattern of deep troughs and sharp ridges (Figure 9.13). In this **meridional flow pattern**, masses of cold air surge southward and warm air streams northward. Greater temperature contrasts develop over the United States and southern Canada. Where contrasting air

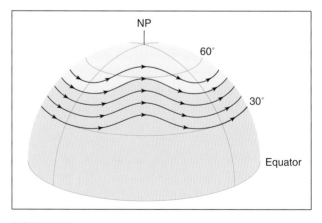

FIGURE 9.12
Midlatitude westerlies exhibit a zonal flow pattern when winds blow almost directly from west to east, with only a small meridional (north-south) component.

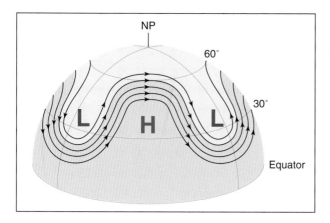

FIGURE 9.13
Midlatitude westerlies exhibit a meridional flow pattern when west to east winds have a strong meridional (north-south) component.

masses collide, warm air overrides cold air, and the stage is set for the development of extra-tropical cyclones that are then swept along by the westerlies.

These two illustrations of Rossby wave configurations are the opposite extremes of a wide range of possible westerly wind patterns, each featuring different components of meridional and zonal flow. More complicated is a **split flow pattern**, in which westerlies to the north have a wave configuration different from that of westerlies to the south. For example, winds may be zonal across central Canada while winds are meridional over much of the coterminous United States.

The westerly wind pattern typically shifts back and forth between dominantly zonal and dominantly meridional flow. For example, zonal flow might persist for a week and then give way to a more meridional flow that lasts for a few weeks, before returning to zonal flow. The transition from one wave pattern to another is usually abrupt and sometimes takes place within a single day. This abruptness poses a challenge to weather forecasters because a sudden shift in the upper-air winds may divert a cyclone toward or away from a locality or cause an unanticipated influx of colder air that could, for example, change rain to snow.

Unfortunately for the long-range weather forecaster, shifts in westerly wave patterns appear to have no regularity; that is, there is no predictable zonal/meridional cycle. The only observation useful to forecasters is that meridional patterns tend to persist for longer periods than zonal patterns. During the winter of 1976-77, for example, a strong meridional wave pattern persisted over North America from late October through mid-February. Northwesterly winds brought surge after surge of bitterly cold arctic air into the midsection of the

United States. The result was one of the coldest winters of the 20th century for that region. During the same period, southwesterly winds brought unseasonably mild air to far-western North America, including Alaska.

BLOCKING SYSTEMS AND WEATHER EXTREMES

For the continent as a whole, North American weather is more dramatic when the westerlies are strongly meridional. Sometimes undulations of the westerlies become so great that huge whirling masses of air actually separate from the main westerly air flow. This situation, shown schematically in Figure 9.14, is analogous to whirlpools that form in rapidly flowing rivers. In the atmosphere, cutoff masses of air whirl in either a cyclonic or an anticyclonic direction (viewed from above). A *cutoff low* or a *cutoff high* that prevents the usual west-to-east movement of weather systems is referred to as a **blocking system**. Because a blocking circulation pattern tends to persist for extended periods (often several weeks or longer), extremes of weather such as drought or flooding rains or excessive heat or cold can result. Consider some examples.

In the spring and early summer of 1986, an unusually severe and prolonged drought affected a ten-state region in the southeastern United States. (For a discussion of what constitutes a drought, refer to this chapter's second Essay.) In the hardest hit areas, precipitation totals for the eight months prior to August 1986 were less than 40% of the long-term average. The primary reason for the May-to-early-July episode of drought was a persistent westerly

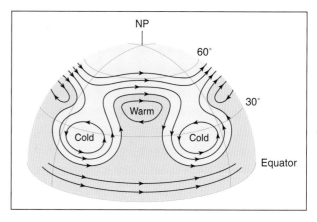

FIGURE 9.14
Blocking pattern in the middle latitude westerlies in which huge pools of rotating air are cut off from the main west to east air flow. The pool of relatively cool air rotating in a counterclockwise direction is a cutoff low, and the pool of relatively warm air rotating in a clockwise direction is a cutoff high. The latter system is sometimes referred to as an *omega block* because of its resemblance to the Greek letter.

long-wave pattern that featured a trough anchored off the East Coast near longitude 65 degrees W and, upstream (to the west), a ridge over the Southeast. In effect, the center of the Bermuda-Azores high extended its influence well west of its usual domain. This persistent circulation pattern brought day after day of subsiding stable air that suppressed the convective activity that normally brings the Southeast abundant spring and summer rainfall.

The drought that affected the Midwest and Great Plains during the spring and summer of 1988 is another example of the linkage between a weather extreme and a blocking weather pattern. In Figure 9.15, the major upper-air circulation features that dominated the summer of 1988 are contrasted with long-term average conditions. From early May through mid-August, the prevailing westerlies were more meridional than usual and featured a huge stationary, warm high-pressure system over the nation's midsection and troughs over the West Coast and East Coast. The belt of strongest westerlies was displaced north of its usual location so that moisture-bearing weather systems were diverted into central Canada, well north of their usual

paths. In the Corn Belt, the May through June period was the driest since 1895. By late July, drought was categorized as either severe or extreme over 43% of the land area of the coterminous United States. By the end of the growing season, the impact on the nation's grain harvest was severe: Corn production was down by 33%, soybeans by 20%, and spring wheat by more than 50%. The National Climatic Data Center (NCDC) estimated that the 1988 drought was one of the most costly weather-related disasters to hit the nation in the last twenty-five years, resulting in $61.6 billion (in 2002 dollars) in damage.

A blocking circulation pattern during the summer of 1993 was responsible for record flooding in the Midwest and drought over the Southeast (Figure 9.16). A cold upper-air trough stalled over the Pacific Northwest and northern Rocky Mountains, bringing unseasonably cool weather to those regions. Meanwhile, the Bermuda-Azores high shifted west of its usual location over the subtropical Atlantic, causing the worst drought since 1986 over the Carolinas and Virginia. Between the northwestern trough and the subtropical high to the southeast, the principal storm track and an unseasonably strong jet stream weaved over the Midwest. This circulation pattern persisted through June, July, and part of August, bringing a nearly continual procession of clusters of thunderstorms to that region. Across Iowa, Illinois, and Wisconsin, the June-July period was the wettest on record. Meanwhile over

A

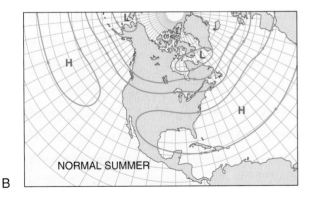

B

FIGURE 9.15
Prevailing circulation pattern in the mid to upper troposphere (A) during the summer of 1988 as compared to (B) the long-term average circulation pattern. The blocking warm anticyclone over the central U.S. contributed to severe drought.

FIGURE 9.16
Principal features of the prevailing atmospheric circulation pattern during the summer of 1993.

the Southeast, subsiding, stable air inhibited thunderstorm development so that hot and dry conditions prevailed through most of the summer.

Heavy rains falling on the drainage basins of the Missouri and Upper Mississippi River valleys saturated soils and triggered excessive runoff, all-time record river crests, and flooding that impacted all or part of nine states. Setting the stage for flooding in the upper Mississippi River valley was the wet autumn of 1992, heavy winter snowfall, and abundant spring snowmelt. The worst flooding occurred between Minneapolis, MN and Cairo, IL on the Mississippi River, and between Omaha, NE and St. Louis, MO on the Missouri River (Figure 9.17). Flooding was not only unprecedented in magnitude but also in persistence with some places reporting more than one record river crest. At St. Louis, the Mississippi River remained above the previous record crest for three weeks. Societal and economic impacts of the 1993 flood were devastating. In many cities (such as Des Moines, IA and St. Joseph, MO), the fresh water supply was cut off. Barge traffic was halted on the Upper Mississippi River and a portion of the Missouri River from late June to early August. At least 50,000 homes were damaged or destroyed; and more than 4 million hectares (10 million acres) of cropland were inundated. All told, property damage totaled $26.7 billion (in 2002 dollars), about one-third in crop losses. The death toll from flooding was 48.

In the summer of 1993, some parts of the Midwest received more than twice the long-term average seasonal rainfall while some localities in the Southeast received less than half of their long-term average seasonal rainfall (Figure 9.18). As a whole, the Southeast experienced

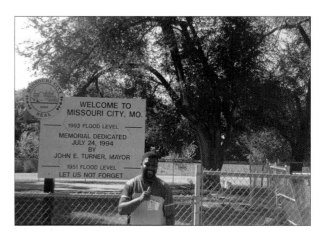

FIGURE 9.17
Sign marks the crest of floodwaters at Missouri City, MO during the unusually wet summer of 1993.

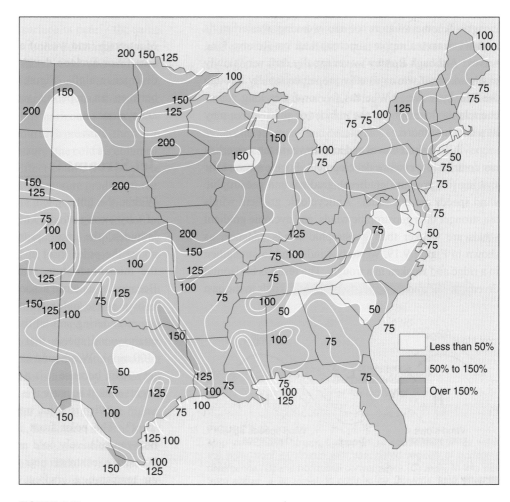

FIGURE 9.18
Total rainfall for the period June-August 1993, expressed as a percentage of the long-term average. [From NOAA, Climate Analysis Center]

front, and right-front. Horizontal divergence occurs in both the left-front and right-rear quadrants, and horizontal convergence takes place in both the right-front and the left-rear quadrants. In a cyclone, horizontal winds diverge aloft and converge at the surface (Chapter 8). A jet streak provides *upper-air support* for a cyclone by contributing horizontal divergence aloft. For an essentially straight jet streak, the strongest horizontal divergence is in the left-front quadrant, so it is under this sector of the jet streak that a cyclone typically has the best chance of developing. This rule also applies to a cyclonically curved jet streak; for an anticyclonically curved jet streak, the strongest divergence is in the right-rear quadrant.

Although the polar front jet stream weaves with the westerlies, a jet streak typically progresses from west to east at a faster pace than the west to east displacement of the troughs and ridges in the westerlies. The strongest divergence aloft occurs when a jet streak is situated on the east side of a trough. Hence, cyclone development is much more likely when a jet streak is in that position.

Like the polar front, the jet stream undergoes important seasonal shifts. The jet stream strengthens in winter, when the north-south air temperature contrast is greatest, and weakens in summer, when temperature contrasts are less. As shown in Figure 9.23, the average summer location of the polar front jet stream is across southern Canada, and the average winter position is across the southern United States. These locations represent long-term averages; the jet stream actually weaves over a considerable range of latitude from week to week, and even from one day to the next. As a general rule, when the polar front jet stream is south of your location, the weather tends to be relatively cold, and when the polar front jet stream is north of your location, the weather tends to be relatively warm.

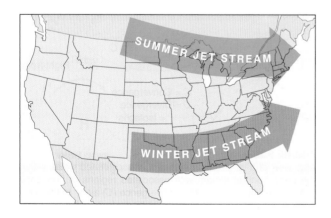

FIGURE 9.23
Approximate average location of the polar front jet stream in winter (December through March) and summer (June through October).

The polar front jet stream is not the only jet stream. The **subtropical jet stream** occurs near the break in the tropopause between tropical and middle latitudes, on the poleward side of the Hadley cell. It is strongest in winter and less variable with latitude than its northerly counterpart. Other jet streams include the *tropical easterly jet* that is a feature of the summer circulation at about 15 degrees N over North Africa, and south of India and Southeast Asia. In addition, in summer a *low-level jet*, perhaps several hundred meters above Earth's surface, surges up the Mississippi River Valley and contributes to the development of nocturnal thunderstorms (Chapter 11).

El Niño and La Niña

Some middle latitude weather extremes such as drought and episodes of unusually heavy rainfall are linked to episodic and sometimes significant changes in atmospheric and oceanic circulation in the tropics. One of the most extensively studied of these circulation anomalies occurs in the tropical Pacific and is known as **El Niño**. (Other atmosphere/ocean oscillations are described in this chapter's third Essay.) During El Niño, trade winds weaken, sea-surface temperatures (SST) rise well above long-term averages over the central and eastern tropical Pacific, and areas of heavy rainfall shift from the western into the central tropical Pacific. Sometimes (but not always) following El Niño is **La Niña**, an episode of exceptionally strong trade winds across the tropical Pacific with lower than usual SST in the central and eastern tropical Pacific. Based on changes in SST in the central and eastern tropical Pacific, some scientists refer to El Niño as the *warm phase* and La Niña as the *cold phase* of this tropical atmosphere/ocean interaction.

Broad-scale changes in sea-surface temperature patterns over the tropical Pacific that accompany El Niño and La Niña influence the prevailing circulation of the atmosphere in middle latitudes, especially in winter. Weather extremes that most often accompany El Niño are essentially opposite those that usually occur during La Niña.

HISTORICAL PERSPECTIVE

Originally, El Niño was the name given by fishermen to the seasonal occurrence of an unusually warm southward flowing ocean current and poor fishing off the coast of Peru and Ecuador often during the Christmas season. (*El Niño* is the Spanish reference to the Christ

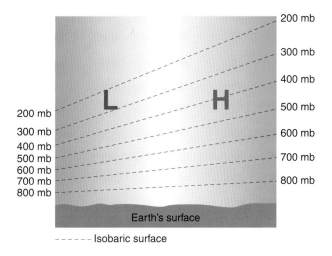

FIGURE 9.21
Air pressure drops more rapidly with altitude in cold air than in warm air giving rise to a horizontal pressure gradient directed from warm air toward cold air.

in a column of warm air (Figure 9.21). Hence, even if the air pressure at the Earth's surface is nearly the same everywhere, with increasing altitude a horizontal pressure gradient develops between adjacent cold and warm air masses. At any specified altitude within the troposphere, the pressure is higher in the warm air mass than in the cold air mass. In response to this horizontal air pressure gradient, air accelerates away from high pressure (the warm air column) and toward low pressure (the cold air column). Simultaneously, the Coriolis Effect comes into play and eventually balances the horizontal pressure gradient force. The net effect is for the wind to blow parallel to isotherms (that is, parallel to the front) with the cold air to the left of the direction of motion in the Northern Hemisphere. The pattern is reversed in the Southern Hemisphere due to the Coriolis Effect, with cold air on the right.

With the horizontal pressure gradient strengthening with increasing altitude, the horizontal wind speed increases with altitude. Wind speed is highest near the tropopause because at altitudes above the tropopause (in the stratosphere) the horizontal temperature gradient reverses direction as absorption of sunlight by ozone (O_3) heats the polar stratopause more continuously than in the tropics. In the troposphere, the coldest air is at higher latitudes, but in the stratosphere, the coldest air is at lower latitudes. In the stratosphere, the horizontal pressure gradient weakens with increasing altitude so that the horizontal wind speed also weakens with altitude above the tropopause. Hence, the maximum wind speed (the polar front jet stream) is located near the tropopause and above the polar front.

Like the front with which it is associated, the polar front jet stream is not uniformly well defined around the globe. Where the polar front is well defined, that is, where surface horizontal temperature gradients are particularly steep, jet stream winds are stronger. Such a segment, in which the wind may strengthen by as much as an additional 100 km per hr (62 mph), is known as a **jet streak**. The strongest jet streaks develop in winter along the east coasts of North America and Asia where the contrast in temperature between snow-covered land and ice-free sea surface is particularly great. Over those areas, jet streak wind speeds on rare occasions have exceeded 350 km per hr (217 mph). A typical jet streak is 160 km (100 mi) wide, 2 to 3 km (1 to 2 mi) thick, and several hundred kilometers in length.

A very important role is played by jet streaks in the generation and maintenance of extra-tropical cyclones. Air flowing through a jet streak changes speed and sometimes direction, and these changes induce a pattern of horizontal divergence and horizontal convergence aloft. As described in Chapter 8, patterns of divergence and convergence aloft are linked to vertical air motion and divergence and convergence of surface winds.

Consider for example Figure 9.22, a straight jet streak viewed from above. Blue lines are *isotachs*, lines of equal wind speed (in km per hr). Air accelerates as it enters the jet streak and decelerates as it exits the jet streak. Associated with these changes in wind speed is diverging and converging air. Viewed from above, a jet streak can be divided into four quadrants: left-rear, right-rear, left-

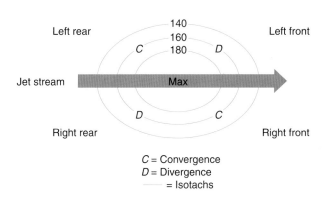

FIGURE 9.22
Map view of a jet streak, a segment of accelerated winds within the polar front jet stream with associated regions of horizontal divergence (*D*) and horizontal convergence (*C*) aloft. In this view from above, a jet streak is outlined by *isotachs*, lines of equal wind speed (in km per hr). In this case of a straight jet streak, the strongest horizontal divergence is in the left-front quadrant, supplying upper-air support for the development of an extra-tropical cyclone.

front, and right-front. Horizontal divergence occurs in both the left-front and right-rear quadrants, and horizontal convergence takes place in both the right-front and the left-rear quadrants. In a cyclone, horizontal winds diverge aloft and converge at the surface (Chapter 8). A jet streak provides *upper-air support* for a cyclone by contributing horizontal divergence aloft. For an essentially straight jet streak, the strongest horizontal divergence is in the left-front quadrant, so it is under this sector of the jet streak that a cyclone typically has the best chance of developing. This rule also applies to a cyclonically curved jet streak; for an anticyclonically curved jet streak, the strongest divergence is in the right-rear quadrant.

Although the polar front jet stream weaves with the westerlies, a jet streak typically progresses from west to east at a faster pace than the west to east displacement of the troughs and ridges in the westerlies. The strongest divergence aloft occurs when a jet streak is situated on the east side of a trough. Hence, cyclone development is much more likely when a jet streak is in that position.

Like the polar front, the jet stream undergoes important seasonal shifts. The jet stream strengthens in winter, when the north-south air temperature contrast is greatest, and weakens in summer, when temperature contrasts are less. As shown in Figure 9.23, the average summer location of the polar front jet stream is across southern Canada, and the average winter position is across the southern United States. These locations represent long-term averages; the jet stream actually weaves over a considerable range of latitude from week to week, and even from one day to the next. As a general rule, when the polar front jet stream is south of your location, the weather tends to be relatively cold, and when the polar front jet stream is north of your location, the weather tends to be relatively warm.

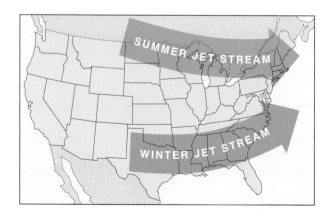

FIGURE 9.23
Approximate average location of the polar front jet stream in winter (December through March) and summer (June through October).

The polar front jet stream is not the only jet stream. The **subtropical jet stream** occurs near the break in the tropopause between tropical and middle latitudes, on the poleward side of the Hadley cell. It is strongest in winter and less variable with latitude than its northerly counterpart. Other jet streams include the *tropical easterly jet* that is a feature of the summer circulation at about 15 degrees N over North Africa, and south of India and Southeast Asia. In addition, in summer a *low-level jet*, perhaps several hundred meters above Earth's surface, surges up the Mississippi River Valley and contributes to the development of nocturnal thunderstorms (Chapter 11).

El Niño and La Niña

Some middle latitude weather extremes such as drought and episodes of unusually heavy rainfall are linked to episodic and sometimes significant changes in atmospheric and oceanic circulation in the tropics. One of the most extensively studied of these circulation anomalies occurs in the tropical Pacific and is known as **El Niño**. (Other atmosphere/ocean oscillations are described in this chapter's third Essay.) During El Niño, trade winds weaken, sea-surface temperatures (SST) rise well above long-term averages over the central and eastern tropical Pacific, and areas of heavy rainfall shift from the western into the central tropical Pacific. Sometimes (but not always) following El Niño is **La Niña**, an episode of exceptionally strong trade winds across the tropical Pacific with lower than usual SST in the central and eastern tropical Pacific. Based on changes in SST in the central and eastern tropical Pacific, some scientists refer to El Niño as the *warm phase* and La Niña as the *cold phase* of this tropical atmosphere/ocean interaction.

Broad-scale changes in sea-surface temperature patterns over the tropical Pacific that accompany El Niño and La Niña influence the prevailing circulation of the atmosphere in middle latitudes, especially in winter. Weather extremes that most often accompany El Niño are essentially opposite those that usually occur during La Niña.

HISTORICAL PERSPECTIVE

Originally, El Niño was the name given by fishermen to the seasonal occurrence of an unusually warm southward flowing ocean current and poor fishing off the coast of Peru and Ecuador often during the Christmas season. (*El Niño* is the Spanish reference to the Christ the Southeast, subsiding, stable air inhibited thunderstorm development so that hot and dry conditions prevailed through most of the summer.

Heavy rains falling on the drainage basins of the Missouri and Upper Mississippi River valleys saturated soils and triggered excessive runoff, all-time record river crests, and flooding that impacted all or part of nine states. Setting the stage for flooding in the upper Mississippi River valley was the wet autumn of 1992, heavy winter snowfall, and abundant spring snowmelt. The worst flooding occurred between Minneapolis, MN and Cairo, IL on the Mississippi River, and between Omaha, NE and St. Louis, MO on the Missouri River (Figure 9.17). Flooding was not only unprecedented in magnitude but also in persistence with some places reporting more than one record river crest. At St. Louis, the Mississippi River remained above the previous record crest for three weeks. Societal and economic impacts of the 1993 flood were devastating. In many cities (such as Des Moines, IA and St. Joseph, MO), the fresh water supply was cut off. Barge traffic was halted on the Upper Mississippi River and a portion of the Missouri River from late June to early August. At least 50,000 homes were damaged or destroyed; and more than 4 million hectares (10 million acres) of cropland were inundated. All told, property damage totaled $26.7 billion (in 2002 dollars), about one-third in crop losses. The death toll from flooding was 48.

In the summer of 1993, some parts of the Midwest received more than twice the long-term average seasonal rainfall while some localities in the Southeast received less than half of their long-term average seasonal rainfall (Figure 9.18). As a whole, the Southeast experienced

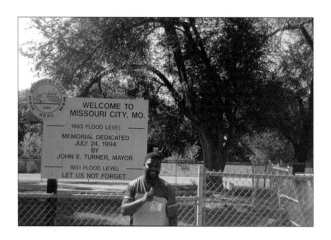

FIGURE 9.17
Sign marks the crest of floodwaters at Missouri City, MO during the unusually wet summer of 1993.

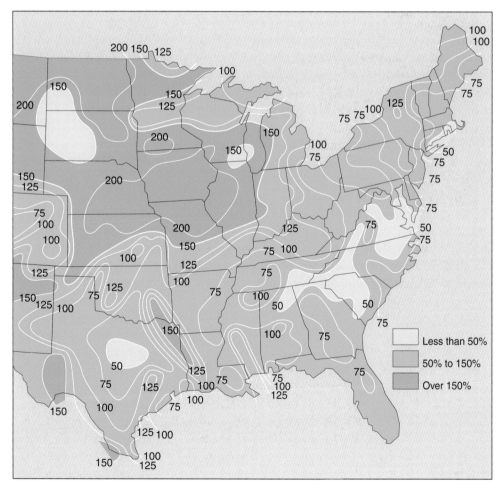

FIGURE 9.18
Total rainfall for the period June-August 1993, expressed as a percentage of the long-term average. [From NOAA, Climate Analysis Center]

its second driest July on record, and from Alabama and Georgia north to Tennessee and Virginia, July 1993 was the hottest on record. The combination of drought and heat stress caused severe crop damage, especially in South Carolina where over 95% of the corn crop and 70% of the soybean crop were lost. Total crop losses were estimated at $1.6 billion (in 2002 dollars). Deaths due to heat stress along the Eastern Seaboard topped 100.

As illustrated by weather events of the summers of 1986, 1988, and 1993, a persistent meridional flow pattern in the westerlies can block the usual movement of weather systems and cause weather extremes such as drought or flooding rains. In fact, any westerly wave pattern, meridional or zonal, can cause extremes in weather if the pattern persists for a sufficiently long period of time. A persistent westerly wave pattern means the same type of air mass advection, the same storm tracks, and basically the same weather type.

SHORT WAVES

Another feature of the weaving westerlies is a **short wave**, a ripple superimposed on Rossby long waves. Although Rossby waves usually drift very slowly eastward, short waves usually propagate rapidly through the Rossby waves. Whereas five or fewer long waves encircle the hemisphere, the number of short waves may be a dozen or more.

Both short waves and long waves in the westerlies can contribute to cyclone development. For the same isobar spacing (air pressure gradient), gradient and geostrophic wind speeds are not equal. Anticyclonic gradient winds are stronger than geostrophic winds, and cyclonic gradient winds are weaker than geostrophic winds. Hence, as shown in Figure 9.19, westerly winds tend to strengthen in a ridge and weaken in a trough. The result is horizontal divergence of mid- to upper-tropospheric winds to the east

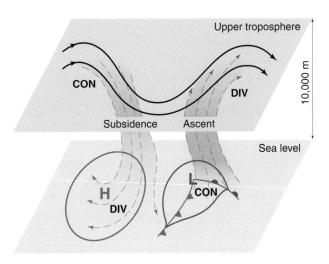

CON = Convergence
DIV = Divergence

FIGURE 9.20
Schematic representation of the relationship between waves in the westerlies and a surface high and low.

of a trough (and west of a ridge). Short and long waves thus favor cyclone development by inducing horizontal divergence aloft. Figure 9.20 portrays the relationship between an upper-air wave and surface cyclone and anticyclone.

Jet Streams

Within the atmosphere are relatively narrow corridors of very strong winds, known as *jet streams*. In middle latitudes, the most prominent jet stream is located above the polar front in the upper troposphere between the midlatitude tropopause and the polar tropopause. Because of its close association with the polar front, it is known as the **polar front jet stream**. This jet follows the meandering path of the planetary westerly waves and attains wind speeds that frequently top 160 km per hr (100 mph). Westbound aircraft understandably avoid this jet stream because it is a head wind, whereas eastbound flights seek it because it is a tail wind.

Why is a jet stream associated with the polar front? The polar front is a narrow zone of transition between relatively cold and warm air masses. The link between a jet stream near the tropopause and a horizontal air temperature gradient at the Earth's surface hinges on the influence of air temperature on air density. Cold air is denser than warm air, so air pressure drops more rapidly with altitude in a column of cold air than it does

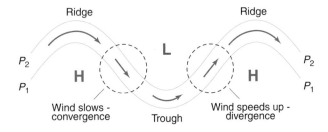

FIGURE 9.19
Westerlies accelerate in ridges and slow in troughs, inducing horizontal speed convergence aloft ahead of ridges and horizontal speed divergence aloft ahead of troughs. Solid lines are isobars; P_1 is greater than P_2.

child). Typically, these warm water episodes are relatively brief, lasting perhaps a month or two, before sea-surface temperatures and the fisheries return to normal levels. Every 3 to 7 years, however, El Niño persists for 12 to 18 months or even longer and is accompanied by significant changes in SST over vast stretches of the tropical Pacific, major shifts in planetary-scale atmospheric and oceanic circulation patterns, and collapse of important South American fisheries. Today, atmospheric and oceanic scientists reserve the term El Niño for these long-lasting atmosphere/ocean anomalies.

An important step in understanding El Niño came in 1924 with the discovery of the southern oscillation by the Englishman Sir Gilbert Walker (1868-1958). Monsoon failure in 1899-1900 caused terrible famines in India with the loss of a million lives. In 1904, Walker was appointed director general of observatories in India and charged with finding a way to predict the Indian monsoon. He set out on an extensive search for any possible relationship between monsoon rains and weather conditions in various parts of the world. One of his discoveries was the **southern oscillation**, a seesaw variation in air pressure across the tropical Indian and Pacific Oceans. When air pressure is low over the Indian Ocean and the western tropical Pacific, it is high east of the international dateline (180 degrees longitude) in the eastern tropical Pacific. During these conditions, monsoon rains were plentiful over India. With the opposite pressure pattern (high pressure west of the dateline and low pressure east of the dateline), monsoon rains were lighter than usual.

The broader significance of Walker's discovery of the southern oscillation was not fully recognized for more than four decades. In 1966, the Norwegian meteorologist Jacob Bjerknes, while at the University of California at Los Angeles, demonstrated a relationship between El Niño and the southern oscillation. The air pressure difference (*air pressure gradient*) across the tropical Pacific changes as air pressure to the west rises while air pressure to the east falls (and vice versa). Using extensive atmospheric/oceanic observations gathered from the tropical Pacific during the International Geophysical Year of 1957-58, Bjerknes found that an El Niño episode begins when the air pressure gradient across the tropical Pacific begins to weaken, heralding the slackening of the trade winds. Scientists refer to this link between El Niño and the southern oscillation by the acronym **ENSO**.

Not until the El Niño of 1982-83, one of the two most intense of the 20th century, did the scientific community and general public fully realized the potential worldwide impact of ENSO. Some of the effects of the 1982-83 El Niño are described in this chapter's Case-in-Point. That event spurred development of numerical models to simulate ENSO as well as deployment of a network of instrumented buoys and satellites to provide early warning of a developing El Niño. Also, the last two decades have seen increasing interest in La Niña (*the girl*), the name coined in the mid-1980s for an atmosphere/ocean interaction that is essentially the opposite of El Niño. Some scientists refer to the warm El Niño and cold La Niña as opposite extremes of the *ENSO cycle.*

Today, atmospheric scientists represent the state of the southern oscillation using an index based on the difference in sea-level air pressure at Darwin (on the north coast of Australia at 12 degrees S, 130 degrees E) versus Tahiti (an island in the central south Pacific at about 18 degrees S and 149 degrees W). When air pressure is anomalously low at Darwin, air pressure is anomalously high at Tahiti. Conversely, when air pressure is high at Darwin, it is low at Tahiti. The **southern oscillation index** is computed by subtracting the Darwin pressure from the Tahiti pressure divided by the standard deviation of that quantity (Figure 9.24). Strong positive values of the index indicate La Niña conditions whereas strong negative values of the index indicate El Niño conditions.

So important are El Niño and La Niña in year-to-year climate variability that signs of a developing El Niño or La Niña are now routinely incorporated into long-range seasonal weather outlooks worldwide (Chapter 13). Such outlooks identify areas of expected positive or negative anomalies in temperature and precipitation and guide development of regional agricultural and water management strategies. Adoption of these strategies helps lessen the impact of attendant weather extremes on water supply and food production in various parts of the world.

NEUTRAL CONDITIONS IN THE TROPICAL PACIFIC

El Niño and La Niña represent significant departures from the long-term average or *neutral* atmosphere/ocean conditions in the tropical Pacific. Understanding El Niño and La Niña first requires a look at neutral conditions, beginning with a summary of Ekman transport and upwelling.

If Earth did not rotate, frictional coupling between the wind and the ocean surface would push a thin layer of water in the same direction as the wind. This surface layer in turn would drag the layer beneath it, putting it into motion. This interaction would continue downward through successive ocean layers, like cards in a deck, each moving forward at a slower speed than the layer above. However, because Earth rotates, the

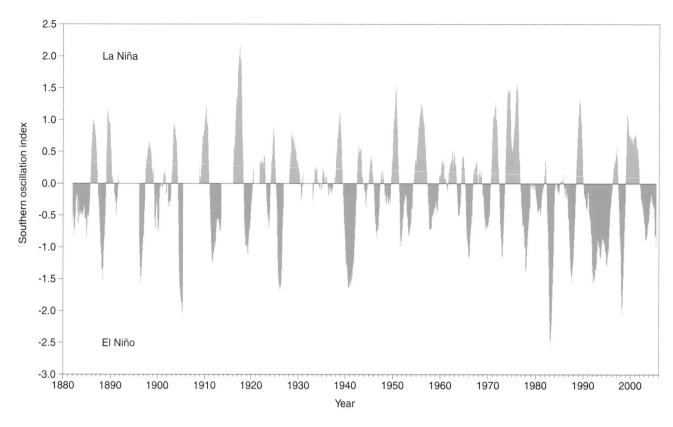

FIGURE 9.24
The variation in the southern oscillation index (computed by subtracting the sea-level air pressure at Darwin, Australia from that at Tahiti divided by the standard deviation of that quantity). Strongly positive values of the index indicate La Niña conditions whereas strongly negative values of the index indicate El Niño conditions. [NOAA, Pacific Marine Environmental Laboratory, Seattle, WA]

shallow layer of surface water set in motion by the wind is deflected to the right of the wind direction in the Northern Hemisphere and to the left of the wind direction in the Southern Hemisphere (the *Coriolis Effect*). Except at the equator, where the Coriolis Effect is zero, each layer of water put into motion by the layer above shifts direction because of Earth's rotation.

A three-dimensional graphical model uses vectors to plot the direction and speed of water layers at successive depths caused by a steady horizontal wind (Figure 9.25A). This model is known as the **Ekman spiral**, named for the Swedish physicist V. Walfrid Ekman (1874-1954) who first described it mathematically in 1905. Ekman derived his model from observations made by the Norwegian explorer Fridtjof Nansen (1861-1930). Nansen wanted to learn more about ocean currents in polar seas and in 1893 froze his 39-m (128-ft) wooden ship, the *Fram*, into Arctic pack ice about 1100 km (680 mi) south of the North Pole. His goal was to drift with the ice and cross the North Pole thereby determining how ocean currents affect the movement of pack ice. The *Fram* remained locked in

pack ice for 35 months but only came within 394 km (244 mi) of the North Pole. As the *Fram* slowly drifted with the ice, Nansen noticed that the direction of ice and ship movement was consistently 20 to 40 degrees to the right of the prevailing wind direction.

The Ekman spiral indicates that each moving layer of water is deflected to the right of the overlying layer's movement; hence the direction of water movement changes with increasing depth. In an ideal case, a steady wind blowing across an ocean of unlimited depth and extent causes surface waters to move at an angle of approximately 45 degrees to the right of the wind in the Northern Hemisphere (and about 45 degrees to the left in the Southern Hemisphere). Each successive layer moves toward the right and at a slower speed down to a depth of about 100 to 150 m (330 to 500 ft), essentially the limit of the wind's influence on horizontal water movement. In the Northern Hemisphere, the Ekman spiral predicts net water movement through a depth of about 100 to 150 m (330 to 500 ft) at 90 degrees to the right of the wind direction (Figure 9.25B). In the Southern Hemisphere, the net water

A

B

FIGURE 9.25
The Ekman spiral describes how the horizontal wind sets surface waters in motion. (A) As represented by horizontal vectors, the speed and direction of water motion change with increasing depth. (B) Viewed from above in the Northern Hemisphere, the surface layer of water moves at 45 degrees to the right of the wind direction. The net transport of water through the entire wind-driven column (i.e., the Ekman transport) is 90 degrees to the right of the wind. Because of the reversal of the Coriolis deflection in the Southern Hemisphere, Ekman transport is 90 degrees to the left of the wind south of the equator.

FIGURE 9.26
Off the northwest coast of South America, Ekman transport of surface waters is to the left of the wind direction and away from the coastline. Consequently, cold, nutrient-rich bottom waters upwell to the surface.

movement is 90 degrees to the left of the wind direction. This net water movement due to coupling between the wind and surface water is known as **Ekman transport**.

Most of the time, southerly or southwesterly winds blowing along the west coast of South America drive warm surface waters to the left (westward) via Ekman transport, away from the coast (Figure 9.26). This causes cold, nutrient-rich waters to move upward from depths of 200 to 1000 m (650 to 3300 ft), a process known as **upwelling**. Although this zone of *coastal upwelling* is narrow (typically less than 15 km or 10 mi wide), the abundance of nutrients conveyed into the sunlit surface waters spurs an explosive growth of phytoplankton populations. Those populations in turn, support a diverse

marine ecosystem and highly productive fishery. Peru's fishing industry boomed in the 1950s and 1960s and by 1970 was one of the largest in the world. At that time Peru was responsible for about 20% of the total global catch of anchovies. However, a combination of over-fishing plus the effects of the 1972-73 El Niño sent the Peruvian fishery into a tailspin from which it has not recovered.

Upwelling is also responsible for the tongue of relatively cool surface waters along the equator in the eastern tropical Pacific. Near the equator, the northeast trade winds of the Northern Hemisphere converge with the southeast trade winds of the Southern Hemisphere. The associated Ekman transport (although weak because of minimal Coriolis Effect) causes surface waters to diverge away from the equator and colder water wells up from below replacing the departing surface waters. *Equatorial upwelling* produces a strip of relatively low sea-surface temperatures along the equator from the coast of South America westward to near the international dateline.

Meanwhile, trade winds drive a pool of relatively warm surface waters westward toward Indonesia and northern Australia. The wedge of warm water increases the depth to the thermocline and raises sea level in the western tropical Pacific. (The *thermocline* is the transition zone between warm surface water and cold deep water.) The thermocline is at a depth of about 150 m (490 ft) in the western tropical Pacific and shoals to about 50 m (165 ft) deep in the eastern tropical Pacific. Water expands when heated (as well as being piled up by trans-Pacific trade winds) so that sea level is some 60 cm (2 ft) higher in the west than in the east. The contrast in sea-surface temperature between the western and eastern tropical Pacific (averaging about 8 Celsius degrees or 14.5 Fahrenheit degrees) has important implications for precipitation across the tropical Pacific. Relatively cool surface waters in the central and eastern tropical Pacific chill the overlying air and suppress convection so that rainfall is light in that region and along the adjacent western coastal plain of South America. Over the western tropical Pacific, warm surface waters heat the overlying air, strengthening convection that gives rise to heavy rainfall.

High SST in the western tropical Pacific lowers the surface air pressure whereas low SST in the eastern tropical Pacific raises the surface air pressure. Hence, during neutral conditions the east-west SST gradient reinforces the trade winds by strengthening the east-west pressure gradient. In flowing over the ocean surface, the trade winds become warmer and more humid. In the western tropical Pacific warm humid air rises, expands, and cools. Water vapor condenses into towering cumulonimbus (thunderstorm) clouds that produce heavy rainfall. Aloft this air flows eastward and sinks over the cooler waters of the eastern tropical Pacific. Sinking air is compressed and warmed so that clouds vaporize or fail to develop. This completes the large convective-type circulation known as the **Walker Circulation**, named for Sir Gilbert Walker.

WARM PHASE

With the onset of El Niño (the *warm phase*), air pressure falls over the eastern tropical Pacific and rises over the western tropical Pacific as part of the southern oscillation. The air pressure gradient across the tropical Pacific weakens and the trade winds slacken in the western and central equatorial Pacific. During a particularly intense El Niño, trade winds west of the international dateline may reverse direction and blow toward the east.

In response to these shifts in atmospheric circulation over the tropical Pacific, changes occur in surface ocean currents, SST, sea level, depth to the thermocline, and upwelling (Figure 9.27). With relaxation of the trade winds, the westward flow of the equatorial currents weakens and at times reverses direction. Hence, the thick layer of warm surface water normally in the west

drifts slowly eastward across the tropical Pacific until deflected toward the north and south by the continental landmasses, sometimes reaching as far north as the coast of western Canada and as far south as central Chile. Eastward drift of warm water is so slow that it may take several months to reach the west coasts of North and South America. In the western tropical Pacific, SST drops, sea-level falls, and the thermocline rises whereas in the eastern tropical Pacific, SST rises, sea-level climbs, and the thermocline deepens.

The impacts of these environmental changes can be severe on marine ecosystems. Arrival of warm surface waters in the eastern tropical Pacific effectively blocks upwelling along the coast of Ecuador and Peru. Deprived of nutrients, phytoplankton populations decline and the commercial fish harvest plummets. Warmer

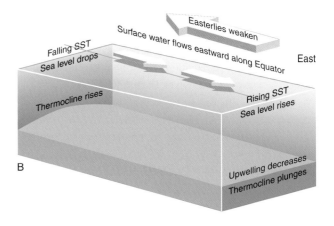

FIGURE 9.27
Schematic representation of (A) neutral (long-term average) conditions in the tropical Pacific Ocean featuring relatively strong easterlies, and (B) El Niño conditions with weaker easterlies.

surface waters can also severely stress coral reefs living in shallow tropical waters. In response to unusually high sea-surface temperatures, coral expels zooxanthallae, the symbiotic microscopic algae that supply coral with oxygen and some organic compounds produced through photosynthesis. Without zooxanthallae, coral polyps have little pigmentation and appear nearly transparent on the coral's white skeleton, a condition referred to as **coral bleaching**. Excessive bleaching can kill coral polyps, destroying the habitat for a variety of marine life. Coral bleaching also has serious economic impact on local fisheries and tourism. Extensive coral bleaching was reported during the 1997-98 El Niño.

During El Niño, lower than usual SST in the western tropical Pacific and higher than usual SST in the central and eastern tropical Pacific coupled with the change in trade wind circulation give rise to anomalous weather patterns in the tropics and subtropics. Long-term average winds blow onshore over Indonesia so that rainfall is normally abundant, but during El Niño, prevailing winds are offshore and the weather of Indonesia is dry. El Niño-related droughts may also grip India, eastern Australia, northeastern Brazil, and southern Africa. Meanwhile, warmer than usual surface waters off the west coast of South America spur convection and heavy rainfall along the normally arid coastal plain, causing flash flooding. Wetter conditions tend to occur in southern Brazil, Uruguay, and equatorial East Africa.

Apparently, El Niño also influences the intensity, frequency, and spatial distribution of tropical cyclones (e.g., hurricanes). Stronger than usual winds aloft (the subtropical jet stream) tend to inhibit the development of tropical cyclones over the Atlantic Basin (Chapter 12). Those few that do develop are usually weaker and shorter lived than usual. In the Pacific and Indian Oceans, changes in SST that accompany El Niño appear to alter the intensity and spatial distribution of tropical cyclones rather than their frequency. Because of the extensive area of warmer water over the eastern tropical Pacific, hurricanes in this region can travel farther north and west than usual.

El Niño usually brings dry weather to the Hawaiian Islands. Almost all of Hawaii's major droughts during the 20th century coincided with an El Niño event. As part of the usual atmospheric circulation changes that take place during El Niño, the North Pacific subtropical anticyclone shifts so that the associated region of descending air moves closer to the Islands. The greater than usual frequency of sinking air over Hawaii is responsible for a persistent dry weather pattern.

El Niño also has a ripple effect on the weather and climate of middle latitudes, especially in winter. A linkage between changes in atmospheric circulation occurring in widely separated regions of the globe, often thousands of kilometers apart, is known as a **teleconnection**. What causes teleconnections? Key to these linkages is the latent heat released into the atmosphere during deep convection and the buildup of thunderstorms in the tropical troposphere, one of the major controls of the planetary-scale circulation. Changes in the location of these heat sources alter wind and weather patterns worldwide. Higher than usual SST over the central and eastern tropical Pacific during El Niño heat and destabilize the troposphere. Deep convection generates towering thunderstorms that help drive atmospheric circulation, governing the course of jet streams, storm tracks, and moisture transport at higher latitudes.

A teleconnection is somewhat analogous to the effect of large boulders on a swiftly flowing stream. Boulders in the streambed induce a train of turbulent eddies that extends downstream. If the boulders are moved, the train of eddies is displaced. Thunderstorm clouds building high into the tropical troposphere deflect the upper air winds in much the same manner as boulders in a stream; that is, a shift in location of the principal area of convection eastward over the tropical Pacific during El Niño redirects the atmospheric circulation.

During typical El Niño winters, prevailing storm tracks bring abundant rainfall and cooler than usual conditions to the Gulf Coast states, from Texas to Florida (Figure 9.28). Over the northern U.S. and Canada, prevailing winds tend to blow from west to east with little meridional transport so that extremely cold air masses tend to move eastward across the Arctic and northern Canada. Persistence of this circulation pattern prevents exceptionally cold air masses from invading the northern U.S so that mild weather prevails over much of Canada, Alaska, and parts of the northern U.S. Zonal flow in the westerlies also diminishes the usual spring contrast between warm, humid air masses moving northeastward from the Gulf of Mexico and cold, dry air masses sweeping southeastward from Canada. Consequently, fewer severe thunderstorms and tornadoes break out in the Ohio and Tennessee River Valleys.

Although some weather extremes almost always accompany El Niño, no two events are exactly the same because El Niño is only one of many factors that influence inter-annual variability of climate. In southern California, for example, heavy winter rains (snows at higher elevations) have occurred during some but not all El Niño events. Record heavy rainfall in Southern

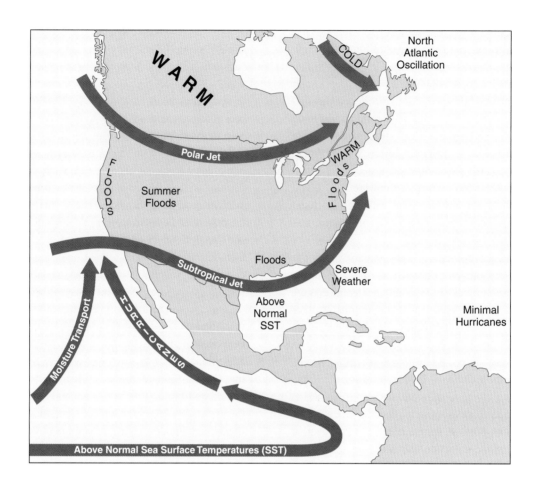

FIGURE 9.28
Principal features of the winter atmospheric circulation over North America during a typical El Niño.

California during January 1995 was linked to a shift of the jet stream (and storm track) south of its usual position over the eastern Pacific. In that case, a change in atmospheric circulation associated with El Niño was the culprit. Whereas the 1982-83 El Niño brought severe drought to eastern Australia, dry conditions in Australia during the 1997-98 El Niño were far less severe.

EL NIÑO OF 1997-98

The 1997-98 El Niño rivaled its 1982-83 predecessor as the most intense of the 20th century. Weather extremes and disease outbreaks (such as malaria and cholera, related to rainfall and standing water) worldwide claimed an estimated 22,000 lives and caused $36 billion in economic losses. This El Niño developed rapidly with the trade winds weakening and eventually reversing direction in the western tropical Pacific in early 1997. Equatorial upwelling ceased during the Northern Hemisphere summer of 1997. A pool of exceptionally warm surface waters (SST greater than 29 °C or 84 °F)

migrated eastward from the western tropical Pacific. During the Northern Hemisphere fall of 1997, SST over the eastern tropical Pacific was at least 5 Celsius degrees (9 Fahrenheit degrees) above the long-term average. Rapid warming in the eastern tropical Pacific produced new record high sea-surface temperatures each successive month from June through December 1997. By late 1997, the thermocline essentially flattened across the tropical Pacific basin, rising some 20 to 40 m (65 to 130 ft) in the west and falling more than 90 m (300 ft) in the east. Somewhat lower surface water temperatures in the west and much higher than usual surface water temperatures in the east weakened the usual east-west SST gradient. By further reducing the east-west pressure gradient, the weaker SST gradient contributed to additional slackening of the trade winds.

The 1997-98 El Niño came to an abrupt end in mid-May 1998. Trade winds strengthened rapidly, upwelling resumed along the equator and off the northwest coast of South America, and SST over the eastern tropical

Pacific plummeted in response to upwelling of very cold water. At one location along the equator (125 degrees W), the SST fell 8 Celsius degrees (14 Fahrenheit degrees) in only four weeks.

COLD PHASE

Sometimes, but not always, La Niña follows El Niño. La Niña (the *cold phase*) is a period of unusually strong trade winds and exceptionally vigorous upwelling in the eastern tropical Pacific. Like its warm counterpart, La Niña tends to persist for 12 to 18 months. During La Niña, SST anomalies (departures from the long-term average) are essentially opposite those observed during El Niño; that is, surface waters are colder than usual over the central and eastern tropical Pacific but somewhat warmer than usual over the western tropical Pacific. SST anomalies over the eastern tropical Pacific typically have a greater magnitude during El Niño than during La Niña. SST usually rise about 5 to 6 degrees Celsius (9 to 11 Fahrenheit degrees) above the long-term average during an intense El Niño but drop 2 to 3 Celsius degrees (3.6 to 5.4 Fahrenheit degrees) below the long-term average during a strong La Niña.

Accompanying La Niña are worldwide weather extremes that are often opposite those observed during El Niño. And as with El Niño, the most consistent middle latitude teleconnections appear in winter. In the tropical Pacific, lower than usual SST inhibit rainfall in the east while higher than usual SST enhance rainfall in the west, including Indonesia, Malaysia, and northern Australia during the Northern Hemisphere winter and the Philippines during the Northern Hemisphere summer. Elsewhere around the globe, the Indian monsoon rainfall (in summer) tends to be heavier than average (especially in northwest India) and wet conditions prevail over southeastern Africa and northern Brazil (during the Northern Hemisphere winter). Southern Brazil to central Argentina tend to have a dry winter. In addition, weak winds aloft during La Niña favor formation of tropical cyclones over the Atlantic Basin.

Across middle latitudes of the Northern Hemisphere, westerlies tend to be more meridional during La Niña. These winds steer cold air masses toward the southeast and warm air masses toward the northeast. Occasionally, a meridional flow pattern becomes so extreme that a blocking pattern (discussed earlier in this chapter) develops. For example, a blocking pattern in the westerlies was responsible for the severe summer drought that afflicted the central U.S. during the 1988 La Niña.

In spring, a more meridional flow pattern in the westerlies increases the likelihood of severe thunderstorms and tornadoes across the central U.S. Such a flow pattern brings together air masses that contrast in temperature and humidity, a key ingredient for severe weather development. Also in the U.S., La Niña tends to be accompanied by below average winter precipitation and mild temperatures in a band from the Southwest through the central and southern Rockies, eastward to the Gulf Coast. Winter in the Pacific Northwest tends to be cool and wet. Lower than usual winter temperatures also occur in the northern Intermountain West and north-central states.

Changes in the atmospheric circulation pattern associated with a recent La Niña were likely responsible for a persistent cut-off high that brought drought to southwestern Asia, from Iran eastward to western Pakistan. From 1998 to 2001, Afghanistan, near the center of the dry belt experienced its most severe drought in 50 years, compounding the human misery brought on by decades of political instability and civil strife. Heidi M. Cullen, a climatologist with the National Center for Atmospheric Research (NCAR) in Boulder, CO proposes that changes in the atmospheric circulation pattern were linked to exceptionally low SST in the central tropical Pacific and unusually high SST in the western tropical Pacific. These La Niña conditions brought heavy winter rains to the eastern Indian Ocean (e.g., Malaysia), a shift in the location of the subtropical jet stream, and development of a cut-off high over southwestern Asia. The cut-off high blocked the usual west to east movement of storm systems bringing an extended period of dry weather to portions of southwestern Asia. Cullen cautions, however, that not all La Niña events bring drought to the Iran-Afghanistan-Pakistan region.

PREDICTION AND MONITORING

Scientists have developed numerical models that simulate El Niño and La Niña. These models approximate oceanic processes that alter sea-surface temperatures, and the atmospheric response, including convection, clouds, and winds. Forecasters rely on two basic types of numerical models to predict the onset, evolution, and decay of El Niño (or La Niña): empirical (or statistical) models and dynamical models. An *empirical model* compares current and evolving oceanic and atmospheric conditions with comparable observational data for periods preceding El Niño (or La Niña) episodes over the prior 40 years. A match or at least some resemblance between past and present conditions is the basis for a prediction. A *dynamical model* consists of a series of mathematical equations that simulates interactions or coupling among atmosphere, ocean, and land. These so-called *coupled* models are more sophisticated than empirical models and run on supercomputers.

Two of the earliest El Niño models were developed at Scripps Institution of Oceanography in La Jolla, CA and at Columbia University's Lamont-Doherty Earth Observatory in Palisades, NY. The Scripps model is empirical whereas the Lamont-Doherty model is a coupled dynamical model. The Lamont-Doherty model successfully forecasted the 1986-87 El Niño and both models gave advance warning of the 1991-92 El Niño. But neither model successfully predicted the rapid development and intensity of the 1997-98 El Niño.

An assessment of the performance of 12 models (6 empirical and 6 dynamical) in predicting the onset, evolution, and demise of the 1997-98 El Niño was somewhat disappointing. The dynamical model operated by the Climate Prediction Center (CPC) of NOAA's National Centers for Environmental Prediction (NCEP) in Camp Springs, MD performed well in predicting the onset of the 1997-98 El Niño. But the NCEP and all other models greatly underestimated (by about 50%) the magnitude of sea surface warming in the eastern tropical Pacific and demonstrated little skill in forecasting the decay of El Niño. The NCEP model predicted gradual cooling in the eastern tropical Pacific through 1998 when in fact sea-surface temperatures plunged in May 1998.

Official forecasts of impending El Niño appeared in the spring of 1997 (after warming of the eastern tropical Pacific had already begun). Model output strongly influenced the Climate Prediction Center's winter outlook issued in November 1997 for December 1997 through February 1998. That outlook correctly predicted heavier than usual precipitation across the southern U.S. and anomalous warmth over the northern one-third of the nation. Predictions of unusually dry conditions in Indonesia, northern South America, and southern Africa were verified. Above average rainfall predicted for Peru, east Africa, and northern Argentina was also correct. But the extreme drought expected for northeast Australia did not materialize.

Reliable observational data from the tropical Pacific Ocean and atmosphere are essential for detecting a developing El Niño or La Niña and for initializing numerical models. The accuracy of dynamical models depends not only on how well their component equations simulate the coupled atmosphere/ocean/land system, but also on reliable observational data. Numerical models use those initial conditions as a starting point for predicting future states of the atmosphere and ocean as well as for verifying model predictions and results. Data are also

assimilated into model runs to correct or nudge the model as events evolve.

A major reason why dynamical models performed well in detecting the onset of the 1997-98 El Niño was the increasing amount of ocean/atmosphere observational data from the tropical Pacific. Those data were obtained by monitoring systems deployed as part of the 10-year (1985-94) international *Tropical Ocean Global Atmosphere (TOGA)* study. TOGA aimed at improving understanding, detection, and prediction of ENSO-related variability. An important product of TOGA, the *ENSO Observing System,* was fully operational by December 1994. The ENSO Observing System consists of an array of moored and drifting buoys, island and coastal tide gauges, ship-based measurements, and satellites (Figure 9.29).

One component of the ENSO Observing System is the *TAO (Tropical Atmosphere/Ocean)* array of moored buoys (small, unmanned, instrumented platforms) in the tropical Pacific Ocean (Figure 9.30). Buoys are strategically placed over an area bounded by 8 degrees N, 8 degrees S, 95 degrees W, and 137 degrees E. This instrument array, renamed TAO/TRITON in 2000, consists of approximately 70 deep-sea moorings that measure several atmospheric variables (air temperature, wind, relative humidity) as well as oceanic parameters (sea surface and subsurface temperatures at 10 depths in the upper 500 m or 1650 ft). Several newer moorings also have ocean salinity sensors, along with additional meteorological sensors. Five moorings along the equator

◆ Moored buoys   —— Satellite data relay
◄— Drifting buoys   —— Volunteer observing ships
● Tide gage stations

FIGURE 9.29
Components of the ENSO Observing System provide advance warning and monitor the development and decay of El Niño and La Niña episodes. [NOAA, Pacific Marine Environmental Laboratory, Seattle, WA]

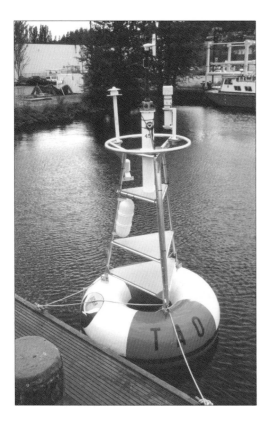

FIGURE 9.30
An instrumented TAO moored buoy photographed at NOAA's Pacific Marine Environmental Laboratory in Seattle, WA. An array of similar moored buoys gathers oceanic and atmospheric data from the tropical Pacific as part of the ENSO Observing System.

also measure ocean current velocity. Observational data are telemetered to NOAA's Pacific Marine Environmental Laboratory (PMEL) in Seattle, WA via a NOAA polar-orbiting satellite. Those data are available on the Internet in near real-time.

Remote sensing by satellite plays an important role in providing early warning of an evolving El Niño or La Niña. NOAA and NASA satellites monitor cloud cover and map sea-surface temperatures. The TOPEX/Poseidon satellite, a joint mission of NASA and the Centre National d'Etudes Spatiales in France, was launched in 1992 and provides images of ocean surface topography (Figure 9.31). Radar (microwave) altimeters onboard the satellite (orbiting at an altitude of 1340 km or 830 mi) bounce microwaves off the ocean surface to obtain precise measurements of the distance between the satellite and the sea surface. These data are combined with data from the global positioning system (GPS) satellites to produce images of surface height. Elevated topography (hills) indicates warmer than usual water whereas areas of low topography (valleys) indicate colder than usual

water. Such images can be used to calculate surface ocean currents. In December 2001, NASA and its French counterpart launched Jason 1, which is designed to replace TOPEX/Poseidon and promises more accurate ocean height measurements.

Another satellite mission that is helping scientists detect the onset and follow the evolution of El Niño and La Niña is the joint U.S.-Japanese Tropical Rainfall Measuring Mission (TRMM) launched in November 1997 (Figure 9.32). The TRMM satellite uses active radar plus passive microwave energy sensors to monitor clouds, precipitation, and radiation processes over the area between 40 degrees N and 40 degrees S. During the 1997-98 El Niño, sensors on the TRMM satellite recorded a reduction in precipitation in the western tropical Pacific and an increase in precipitation east of 150 degrees W longitude. An important feature of the satellite is its TRMM Microwave Imager (TMI), an instrument that "sees through" clouds and measures sea-surface temperatures. The TMI uses the microwave energy emitted by the sea surface to characterize its IR emission spectrum and determine its radiation temperature. Microwaves pass through clouds with little attenuation but are strongly absorbed and reflected by rainfall so that TMI can measure SST only during fair weather.

Increasingly accurate predictions of El Niño and La Niña are enabling humankind to better cope with the impacts of short-term (inter-annual) climate variability. Such forecasts allow informed strategic planning in agriculture, fisheries, and water resource management. Consider an example: Peru's economy, like that of all nations, is sensitive to climate. In Peru, El Niño is bad for fishing and often accompanied by destructive flooding. La Niña benefits fishing but may also mean drought and crop failure. Warning of a pending El Niño or La Niña prior to the start of the growing season allows agricultural interests and government officials to consult on what crops to plant to optimize production. For example, if the forecast calls for El Niño, rice is favored over cotton because rice thrives during a wet growing season whereas cotton is more drought-tolerant and is more suitable during La Niña. Also, in anticipation of heavy rains which are likely to accompany a full-blown El Niño, water resource managers can direct the gradual draw down of reservoirs to reduce potential flooding.

FREQUENCY OF EL NIÑO AND LA NIÑA

On 30 September 2003, NOAA scientists announced that they had reached a consensus among experts in the federal government and academia for a new

FIGURE 9.31
Evolution of the 1997-98 El Niño derived from changes in ocean surface height (compared to long-term averages) as measured by the TOPEX/Poseidon satellite. On the color scale, whites and reds indicate elevated areas (and warmer than normal water). In the white areas, the sea surface is 14 to 32 cm (6 to 13 in.) above normal; in the red areas it is about 10 cm (4 in.) above normal. Green indicates normal sea level whereas purple corresponds to areas that are at least 18 cm (7 in.) below normal sea level (and colder than normal water). [NASA Goddard Space Flight Center]

Tropical Rainfall Measuring Mission (TRMM)

Six – Year TRMM Climatology

TRMM Merged Precip Annual Climo   (mm/d)

0   2   4   6   8   10+

January 1998 – December 2003

FIGURE 9.32
Average rainfall in millimeters per day (mm/d) across the tropics for the six-year period January 1998 through December 2003. The region of heaviest rainfall is in the western tropical Pacific. These data were obtained from the TRMM Microwave Imager and IR sensors onboard geosynchronous satellites supplemented by conventional rain gauge measurements. [NASA, Tropical Rainfall Measuring Mission (TRMM)]

index that forms the basis for operational definitions of El Niño and La Niña. By April 2005, 26 nations had adopted the same index and definitions. Sea-surface temperatures for the index are drawn from an area of the tropical Pacific that encompasses the equatorial cold tongue, that is, the region bounded by longitude 120 degrees W and 170 degrees W, latitude 5 degrees N and 5 degrees S. El Niño is characterized by a *positive* sea-surface temperature departure from normal (based on the period 1971-2000) greater than or equal to 0.5 Celsius degree, averaged over three consecutive months. La Niña is characterized by a *negative* sea-surface temperature departure from normal (based on the period 1971-2000) greater than or equal to 0.5 Celsius degree, averaged over three consecutive months. Figure 9.33 is the record of sea-surface temperature anomalies in this area of the tropical Pacific for the period 1950-2005.

El Niño can be expected to develop about once every 3 to 7 years and to last from 12 to 18 months. Although El Niño does not always give way to La Niña, La Niña appears more likely to follow an intense El Niño rather than a weak one. This may be explained by the

fact that during an intense El Niño, the global water cycle conveys a great amount of heat out of the eastern tropical Pacific and into higher latitudes. Unusually cold water situated just below the warm surface water is poised to well up to the surface as soon as the trade winds strengthen. For example, a significant La Niña followed the intense 1997-98 El Niño.

During the second half of the 20th century, El Niño conditions prevailed 31% of the time and La Niña occurred 23% of the time. The rest of the time conditions were neutral or near-neutral. As of this writing, the most recent El Niño was a weak episode in 2004-05. Prior El Niño episodes took place in 2002-03, 1997-98, 1991-95, 1986-87, 1982-83, 1976-77, 1972-73, 1969, 1965-66, 1963, 1957-58, 1953, and 1951. During the 1980s and 1990s, La Niña was less frequent than El Niño. The most recent La Niña was in 2000-01, 1998-2000, 1995-96, 1988-89, 1973-75, 1970-71, 1964, 1955-56, 1949-1950. While all El Niño episodes share some common characteristics as described earlier in this chapter, they differ from one another in duration, intensity, and the way they develop. The same applies to La Niña.

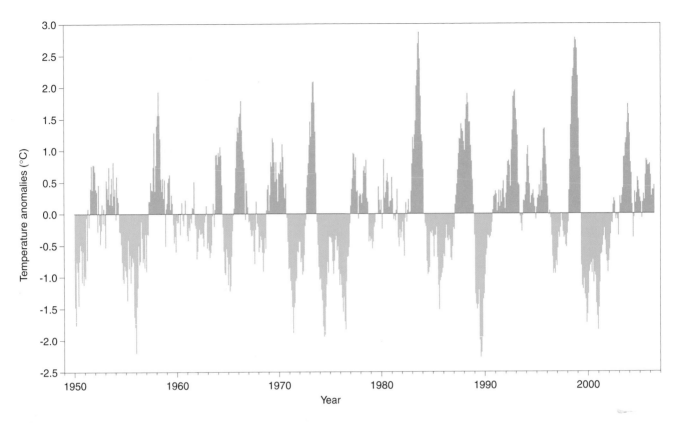

FIGURE 9.33
Sea-surface temperature anomalies (departures from long-term averages) from the region of the tropical Pacific between 5 degrees N and 5 degrees S and from 120 degrees W to 170 degrees W. El Niño is characterized by a *positive* sea-surface temperature departure from normal (based on the period 1971-2000) greater than or equal to 0.5 Celsius degree, averaged over three consecutive months. La Niña is characterized by a *negative* sea surface temperature departure from normal (based on the period 1971-2000) greater than or equal to 0.5 Celsius degree, averaged over three consecutive months. [From NOAA, Pacific Marine Environmental Laboratory, Seattle, WA]

Conclusions

We have examined the time-averaged characteristics of the planetary-scale atmospheric circulation. The main features of that circulation are the ITCZ, trade winds, subtropical highs, the westerlies, polar front, subpolar lows, polar easterlies, and polar highs. We saw that aloft (in the middle and upper troposphere), winds blow counter to the surface trades in tropical latitudes and in a west-to-east wave pattern at middle and high latitudes. Through the course of a year, these components of the planetary-scale circulation shift in tandem north and south with the sun.

In this chapter, we also focused on the linkages between the westerly winds aloft and the weather of middle latitudes. Specifically, the westerlies (1) produce horizontal divergence aloft for the development of cyclones, (2) steer storms, and (3) control air mass advection and poleward heat transport. In describing El Niño and La Niña, we emphasized the potential linkages (teleconnections) between the circulation in the tropics and higher latitudes.

Our examination of atmospheric circulation continues in the next chapter with a focus on the synoptic-scale weather systems of middle latitudes, i.e., air masses, fronts, extratropical cyclones, and anticyclones.

Basic Understandings

- The principal features of the atmosphere's planetary-scale circulation are the intertropical convergence zone (ITCZ), trade winds, subtropical anticyclones, westerlies of middle latitudes, subpolar lows, polar front, polar easterlies, and polar highs. The ITCZ, wind belts, subtropical highs, and polar front follow the sun, shifting poleward in spring and equatorward in autumn.

- Trade winds blow out of the equatorward flanks of the subtropical anticyclones, while the westerlies blow out of their poleward flanks. The east side of a subtropical anticyclone features subsiding air and dry conditions, whereas the west side is more humid and receives more rainfall.

- Aloft, in the middle and high troposphere, winds reverse direction, completing the Hadley cell circulation. At higher latitudes, upper-air winds weave from west to east as Rossby long waves, consisting of ridges (clockwise turns) and troughs (counterclockwise turns).

- Contrasts in Earth's surface temperatures in winter favor relatively high air pressure over continents and low air pressure over the ocean. In summer, this pattern reverses, with relatively low pressure prevailing over continents and high pressure over the ocean.

- In subtropical latitudes, a monsoon circulation is responsible for wet summers and dry winters. Differences in solar heating of land versus sea, topography, and seasonal shifts in the planetary-scale circulation (e.g., the ITCZ) play key roles in the monsoon circulation.

- The southwest monsoon affects the American Southwest including Arizona, New Mexico, and parts of southern Colorado, bringing a dramatic increase in rainfall to this region mainly during July and August. The southwest monsoon originates over northern Mexico during May and June and is actually the northern extension of the Mexican monsoon which is fed by moisture that originates over the Gulf of California and the Gulf of Mexico.

- The wave pattern exhibited by the upper-air westerlies varies in length, amplitude, and number. At one extreme, westerlies can be strongly zonal, that is, they blow west-to-east with little amplitude. At the other extreme, westerlies can be strongly meridional, that is, they blow west-to-east with considerable amplitude. Shifts between zonal and meridional flow patterns alter north-south air mass exchange, poleward heat transport, and cyclone development and movement.

- Cutoff cyclones and cutoff anticyclones block the usual west to east progression of weather systems and may lead to extended periods of extreme weather conditions such as drought, excessive rainfall, or periods of unusually high or low temperature.

- The polar front jet stream is a narrow corridor of high-speed winds within the westerlies; it is located near the tropopause and above the polar front. A jet streak is a region of exceptionally strong jet stream winds situated over a well-defined segment of the polar front.

- Cyclone development is most likely under the left front quadrant of a jet streak to the east of an upper-level trough. Upper-air support (horizontal divergence) is strongest in that quadrant.

- El Niño refers to anomalous atmospheric and oceanic circulation regimes associated with a lengthy period of unusually high sea-surface temperatures over a vast area of the central and eastern tropical Pacific. El Niño is accompanied by weather extremes in tropical latitudes and in other areas of the globe. La Niña is the term coined for atmosphere/ocean conditions essentially opposite El Niño.

- The southern oscillation is a seesaw variation in air pressure across the tropical Indian and Pacific Oceans. When air pressure is low over the Indian Ocean and the western tropical Pacific, it is high east of the international dateline in the eastern tropical Pacific. An El Niño episode begins when the air pressure gradient across the tropical Pacific begins to weaken, heralding the slackening of the trade winds.

- Ekman transport plays an important role in governing sea-surface temperature (SST) by affecting upwelling of ocean water. Viewed from above, the wind-driven horizontal motion of successively lower layers of ocean water forms a spiral with the current gradually turning and weakening with increasing depth. The Ekman spiral transports surface waters at an angle of about 90 degrees to the right of the wind direction in the Northern Hemisphere and to the left in the Southern Hemisphere.

- During neutral (long-term average) conditions, relatively cool surface waters in the central and eastern tropical Pacific chill the overlying air and suppress convection so that rainfall is light in that region as well as along the adjacent western coastal plain of South America. Meanwhile, over the western tropical Pacific, relatively warm surface waters heat the overlying air, strengthening convection and giving rise to heavy rainfall.

- As El Niño evolves, sea-surface temperatures rise, sea level climbs, and depth to the thermocline increases in the eastern tropical

Pacific. Meanwhile, sea-surface temperatures drop, sea level falls, and depth to the thermocline decreases in the western tropical Pacific. Conditions are drier than usual in the western tropical Pacific and wetter than normal in the central tropical Pacific.

- La Niña is a period of unusually strong trade winds, exceptionally vigorous upwelling, and lower than usual sea-surface temperatures in the eastern tropical Pacific. Weather extremes associated with La Niña are essentially opposite those that tend to occur during El Niño.

Review

1. In what sense are the subtropical anticyclones *semipermanent*?
2. Why do the world's major subtropical deserts occur on the eastern flank of subtropical anticyclones?
3. Describe the prevailing weather along the intertropical convergence zone (ITCZ).
4. How and why does the altitude of the tropopause change from equator to pole?
5. Describe the seasonal changes in the latitude of the polar front and subtropical highs.
6. Distinguish between a zonal flow pattern and a meridional flow pattern in the midlatitude westerlies. What are the implications of these two patterns for poleward heat transport?
7. How does a blocking weather pattern favor extremes in weather such as drought?
8. How does a jet streak contribute to the development of a synoptic-scale cyclone?
9. In what way is El Niño linked to the southern oscillation?
10. Why are farmers and fishermen concerned when an intense El Niño develops?

Critical Thinking

1. Speculate on how a "split-flow pattern" in the westerlies might influence the weather over North America.
2. Explain how you can determine the location of the polar front jet stream by examining the surface temperature pattern across North America.
3. Describe the relationship between the prevailing westerlies of middle latitudes and the subtropical anticyclones.
4. How does an intense El Niño influence atmospheric stability over the central and eastern tropical Pacific? How might this affect thunderstorm development?
5. How does a blocking anticyclone affect the Bowen ratio of the land surface beneath the system? What is the implication of this for the temperature of the lower atmosphere?
6. Why do extra-tropical cyclones tend to track along the margins of a broad snow-covered region?
7. What causes jet streams to accelerate in coastal areas?
8. How might indications of a developing El Niño influence long-range seasonal weather outlooks for middle latitudes?
9. Identify the characteristics of a weather pattern that would give rise to an agricultural drought over the Great Plains.
10. Explain why a trough in the 500-mb flow pattern is associated with a pool of relatively cold air.

ESSAY: Drought in Sub-Saharan Africa

Perhaps nowhere in the world has prolonged drought caused more human misery than sub-Saharan Africa, much of which is known as the Sahel. The Sahel, an Arabic term meaning "shore" or "border," is the transition zone in West Africa between the Sahara Desert to the north and the rainforest of the Guinea coast to the south. As shown on the map in Figure 1, the Sahel includes all or part of Mauritania, Senegal, Mali, Burkina Faso, Niger, and Chad. These are the poorest nations on Earth. Low average annual rainfall, considerable year-to-year variability in rainfall, and prolonged droughts has brought considerable hardship to the people of the Sahel. They are particularly vulnerable to the effects of drought because most of them depend on agriculture for their livelihood. Droughts forced them off their lands that, even in the best of times, are marginal for survival of crops and livestock. They migrated to cities in search of food and work, and many ended up in refugee camps. In the worst of times, horrible scenes of starving children, emaciated livestock, and withered crops were televised to a worldwide audience.

FIGURE 1
The Sahel of Africa.

Drought in the Sahel is the product of interactions involving the atmosphere, ocean, land, and people. The Sahel has a semiarid climate that features a rainy "high sun" season (Northern Hemisphere summer) and a dry "low sun" season (Northern Hemisphere winter). The average length of the rainy season and mean annual rainfall increases from north to south across the Sahel. At the northern edge of the Sahel (about 18 degrees N), the rainy season usually does not begin until June and may last only a month or two; mean annual rainfall typically is less than 100 mm (about 4 in.). In the extreme southern Sahel (about 10 degrees N), the rainy season is underway as early as April and persists for up to 5 or 6 months; mean annual rainfall exceeds 500 mm (about 20 in.). Shifts between the dry season and rainy season are linked to changes in prevailing winds associated with the location of the intertropical convergence zone (ITCZ). As the ITCZ follows the sun, its northward surge in spring triggers rainfall, whereas a southward shift in fall brings the rainy season to an end. During the rainy season, surface winds blow from the south and southwest, transporting humid air from over both the Atlantic and Indian Oceans. During the dry season, the Sahel is under the eastern flank of the Bermuda-Azores subtropical high and surface winds blow from the dry north and northeast.

In a summer when the ITCZ fails to move as far north as usual, or arrives late, or shifts southward early, rainfall is below average. A succession of such summers means drought. In the 20th century, the people of the Sahel endured three major long-term droughts: 1910-1914, 1940-1944, and 1970-1985. Rainfall during the 1961-1990 period was 20% to 40% lower than it was during the prior three decades, constituting the greatest 30-year anomaly in precipitation recorded anywhere in the world. Drought and famine claimed over 600,000 lives in 1972-1975 and about the same number again in 1984-1985. The reconstructed long-term climate record (based on lake-level fluctuations and historical accounts of landscape changes) indicates that droughts lasting 1 or 2 decades are the norm in the Sahel.

Some scientists argue that the principal reason for drought in the Sahel is changes in atmospheric circulation patterns (i.e., seasonal shifts of the moisture-bearing ITCZ) that are linked to anomalies in sea-surface temperature (SST). Initial studies showed that when SST is higher than normal in the eastern tropical Atlantic, south of the equator and southwest of West Africa (e.g., the Gulf of Guinea), rainfall is below the long-term average in the Sahel. In 2003 scientists at the International Research Institute for Climate Prediction at Palisades, NY announced the results of a NASA global climate model study of rainfall in the Sahel covering the period 1930 to 2000. They found that rising sea-surface temperature in the Indian Ocean was more important than changes in Atlantic SST in simulating long-term trends in Sahel rainfall. They also found that El Niño and La Niña accounted for much of the year-to-year variability in Sahel rainfall. More recently, runs of another global climate model developed at the Max Planck Institute for Meteorology in Germany found a similar dependence of decadal trends in Sahel rainfall on Indian Ocean SST.

But that is not the end of the matter. In 2005, James Hurrell of the National Center for Atmospheric Research (NCAR) and Martin Hoerling of NOAA reported on new findings regarding drought in the Sahel. In experiments in which they used 5 different numerical models to generate 80 simulations, Hurrell and Hoerling discovered that drought in southern Africa is linked to warming of the Indian Ocean. However, their model simulations indicated that moisture conditions in the Sahel depend on SST in the Atlantic Ocean rather than the Indian Ocean. Apparently, monsoon failure and drought in the Sahel were linked to late 20th century cooling of the North Atlantic. A shift to wetter conditions in the Sahel during the 1990s corresponded to the post-1990 warming of the North Atlantic.

Human activity (i.e., overgrazing, conversion of woodland to agriculture) may also contribute to persistent drought in sub-Saharan Africa by reinforcing dry conditions. Overgrazing and deforestation alter the regional radiation balance by denuding the soil's vegetative cover and degrading the quality and moisture holding capacity of soils. Soil albedo increases, evaporation decreases, convection weakens, and rainfall is less likely. What has happened in parts of the Sahel may be *desertification*, the name applied to the conversion of arable land to desert due to a combination of climate change and human land management practices. Analysis of drought in the Sahel is a good example of how the Earth system perspective provides valuable insights of the environmental factors that contribute to climate variability.

ESSAY: Defining Drought

Drought is an extended period of moisture deficit that is of particular concern to agricultural interests (Figure 1). Drought also affects the supply of water for domestic and industrial use and hydroelectric power generation. Soils dry out; crops wither and die; lakes and other reservoirs shrink; and river and stream flow slackens thereby impeding navigation. Unusually high temperatures often accompany summer drought adding to the stress on crops.

A drought usually begins gradually and without warning. In fact, it is difficult if not impossible to tell whether a spell of dry weather actually signals the onset of drought. Similarly, the end of a drought is always uncertain because one rain event, even if substantial, does not necessarily break a drought. Furthermore, whether a dry spell is a drought depends on its impact so that a distinction is made among hydrologic drought, agricultural drought, and meteorological drought.

For water resource interests, a *hydrologic drought* is a period of moisture deficit that reduces stream or river discharge and groundwater supply to levels that seriously impede water-based activities such as irrigation, barge traffic, or hydroelectric power generation. Hydrologic drought develops when the water supply is inadequate during one or successive water years. A *water year* is defined to extend from 1 October of one year through 30 September of the next year. *Agricultural drought* depends on the shorter-term supply of rainfall and soil moisture for crops during the growing season. Complicating the criterion for agricultural drought is the fact that different crops have different water requirements, and the water needs of a specific crop species change as the crop progresses through its life cycle. Inadequate moisture at a critical stage of crop growth and maturation, especially over successive growing seasons, may constitute agricultural drought. Hydrologic and agricultural droughts do not always occur at the same time.

FIGURE 1
A sample U.S. Drought Monitor map indicating the intensity of drought and the impacts. Available at http://drought.unl.edu/dm

Varying criteria have been used to define *meteorological drought*. Some meteorologists define drought as a period when the seasonal or annual precipitation falls below a certain threshold percentage (e.g., 85%) of the long-term (e.g., 30-year) average. But basing the criterion for drought on precipitation alone ignores the influence of temperature and wind on the evaporation rate. Higher temperatures and/or stronger winds increase the rate of evaporation, exacerbating the severity of drought.

One of the most popular drought indicators is incorporated in the *Palmer Drought Severity Index*. The Palmer Index uses temperature and rainfall data in a formula that gauges unusual dryness or wetness over extended intervals from months to years. The National Weather Service and the U.S. Department of Agriculture jointly compute the Palmer Index every week for each of the 344 climatic divisions across the U.S. A Palmer Index map portrays those divisions experiencing drought with negative values, while those regions receiving excess precipitation have positive index values. Index values range from greater than +4.00 for extremely wet conditions to under –4.00 for extreme drought; zero indicates long-term average moisture levels.

ESSAY: Atmosphere/Ocean Oscillations

Research on El Niño and La Niña spurred interest in other regular oscillations that involve the interaction of atmosphere and ocean and impact short-term climate variability. These include the North Atlantic Oscillation (NAO), the Arctic Oscillation (AO), and Pacific Decadal Oscillation (PDO). In general, NAO, AO, and PDO affect more restricted geographical areas and operate over longer time periods than either El Niño or La Niña.

Over the North Atlantic, the time-averaged planetary-scale atmospheric circulation features a subpolar low pressure system near Iceland (the *Icelandic low*) and a massive subtropical anticyclone centered near 30 degrees N that stretches from Bermuda to near the Azores. The *North Atlantic Oscillation (NAO)* refers to a seesaw variation in air pressure between Iceland and the Azores. When air pressure is higher than the long-term average over the Azores, it is lower than the long-term average over Iceland and vice versa. The air pressure gradient between the Bermuda-Azores subtropical anticyclone and the Icelandic low drives winds that steer storms from west to east across the North Atlantic.

The North Atlantic Oscillation influences precipitation patterns and winter temperatures over eastern North America and much of Europe and North Africa. The so-called *NAO Index* is directly proportional to the strength of the North Atlantic air pressure gradient. When the NAO Index is relatively high, stronger than usual winter winds blow across the North Atlantic moving cold air masses over eastern Canada and the U.S. so that winters tend to be colder than usual in that region. But cold air masses modify considerably as they move over the relatively mild ocean surface, warming and becoming more humid so that winters are milder and wetter than usual downstream over Europe. Meanwhile, dry winters prevail in the Mediterranean region. On the other hand, when the NAO Index is low, steering winds over the North Atlantic shift southward so that winters are colder than usual over northern Europe and wet and mild conditions prevail from the Mediterranean eastward into the Middle East. The eastern U.S. and Canada tend to experience relatively mild winters while winters in the southeast U.S. are colder than usual.

The NAO Index varies significantly from one year to the next and from decade to decade and is much less regular than the ENSO cycle. The NAO Index was generally low in the 1950s and 1960s and high from about the mid-1970s through the 1990s (with the exception of 1997-98).

Changes in winter moisture supply associated with NAO have had varied impacts in Europe and North Africa. In recent decades of relatively high NAO-Index, wetter winters have increased hydroelectric power potential in the Scandinavian nations, lengthened the growing season over northern Eurasia, but also diminished the snow cover for winter recreation. Meanwhile, a moisture deficit has been the problem in the Iberian Peninsula, the watershed of the Tigris and Euphrates Rivers, and sub-Saharan Africa.

Related to the North Atlantic Oscillation, the *Arctic Oscillation (AO)* is a seesaw variation in air pressure between the North Pole and the margins of the polar region. Associated changes in the horizontal air pressure gradient alter the speed of the band of winds aloft (the *polar vortex*) that blow counterclockwise (viewed from above) around the Arctic. Strengthening and weakening of these polar winds impact winter weather in middle latitudes and contribute to climate variability and changes in ocean circulation.

The Arctic Oscillation features a negative and positive phase. During its negative phase, the pressure gradient is weaker and the polar vortex circulation is not as strong as usual. This allows bitterly cold arctic air masses to move out of their source regions in the far north and plunge southeastward into middle latitudes with greater frequency. This brings colder than usual winter weather to most of the U.S., Northern Europe, Russia, China, and Japan. Heavy lake-effect snows are more frequent and nor'easters are more likely along the Eastern Seaboard (Chapter 10). But when the Arctic Oscillation is in its positive phase, the pressure gradient is steeper and winds encircling the Arctic are stronger. These stronger winds act as a dam to impede the southward flow of arctic air. The middle latitude westerlies also strengthen and blow more directly from west to east, flooding much of the U.S. with relatively mild air from off the Pacific Ocean (instead of frigid arctic air from Canada). Winter temperatures are milder than usual (especially east of the Rocky Mountains) and major snowstorms are less likely. Meanwhile, Alaska, Scotland, and Scandinavia are snowier than usual while California and Spain are drier.

Although during any winter the Arctic Oscillation can shift many times between its negative and positive phases, extended periods occur when either the negative or positive phase dominates the winter season. In the 1960s, the negative phase of the Arctic Oscillation prevailed. Since then, the positive phase has been more frequent, a trend that is consistent with observed climate fluctuations in middle latitudes (e.g., less frequent episodes of extreme cold and major snowstorms). Furthermore, during this recent episode of dominantly positive AO phase, winds have been delivering warmer than usual air and ocean water into the Arctic. As we will see in Chapter 15, this may at least help explain the recent shrinkage of Arctic ice cover.

The *Pacific Decadal Oscillation (PDO)* is a long-lived variation in climate over the North Pacific and North America. Sea-surface temperatures fluctuate between the north central Pacific and the west coast of North America. During a PDO *warm phase*, sea-surface temperatures are lower than usual over the broad central interior of the North Pacific and above average in a narrow strip along the coasts of Alaska, western Canada, and the Pacific Northwest. In an interesting parallel to what happens off the coast of Ecuador and Chile during El Niño, the layer of relatively warm surface waters off the Pacific Northwest Coast significantly reduces upwelling of nutrient-rich bottom water. Populations of phytoplankton and zooplankton plummet and juvenile salmon migrating to coastal areas from streams and rivers starve. On the other hand, during a PDO *cold phase*, sea-surface temperatures are higher in the North Pacific interior, lower along the coast, and are associated with the return of nutrients and salmon.

Key to the climatic impact of PDO is the strength of the subpolar *Aleutian low*, which prevails through the winter off the Alaskan coast. During a PDO *warm phase*, the Aleutian low is well developed and its strong counterclockwise winds steer mild and relatively dry air masses into the Pacific Northwest. Winters tend to be mild and dry and water supplies suffer from reduced mountain snow pack. But during a PDO *cold phase*, the Aleutian cyclone is weaker so that cold, moist air masses more frequently invade the Pacific Northwest. Winters are colder and wetter, and the mountain snow pack is thicker. PDO phases tend to last for 20 to 30 years. Cold phases persisted from 1890-1924 and again from 1947-1976 whereas warm phases prevailed from 1925-1946 and 1977 through the 1990s.

CHAPTER 10

WEATHER SYSTEMS OF MIDDLE LATITUDES

In 1966, a Jamestown, North Dakota March blizzard nearly buried utility poles. [Collection of Dr. Herbert Kroehl, NGDC. Courtesy of NGDC/NOAA].

Case in Point

Extra-tropical cyclones are major weather makers of middle and high latitudes. In the Northern Hemisphere viewed from above, surface winds blow counterclockwise and spiral inward toward the center of an extra-tropical cyclone. In addition, steering winds aloft determine the track of the storm center. Today, the complex rotational and translational motions of cyclones are verified by satellite sensors and observations by the network of weather stations.

Long before satellites and weather stations, Daniel Defoe (1660-1731), the English journalist and novelist, was the first to propose that storms generally track from west to east in middle latitudes. Defoe drew this conclusion from his study of a great storm that lashed the British Isles on 7-8 December 1703. He received reports that several days earlier a similar storm had ravaged the East Coast of North America. Defoe assumed that the storms were the same and concluded that the system had moved across the North Atlantic.

Among his many notable achievements, Benjamin Franklin (1706-1790) is credited with being the first American to discover that storms usually move in an easterly or northeasterly direction. On the evening of 21 October 1743, Franklin was at his Philadelphia home anticipating viewing a lunar eclipse at 9 p.m. However, winds picked up from the northeast and thick clouds rolled in blocking his view of the moon. Days later Franklin received via mail a Boston newspaper containing an account of the spectacular eclipse of 21 October as witnessed by its citizens, although by midnight a storm brought cloudiness and windy conditions to the city. The report that the eclipse was visible in Boston surprised Franklin because he (like most of his contemporary natural scientists) assumed that coastal storms that produced winds blowing from the northeast (a *nor'easter*) approached from a northeast direction. The fact that storm clouds obscured the eclipse in Philadelphia but not Boston (500 km or 310 mi to the northeast) until several hours later suggested to Franklin that the storm had tracked from the southwest toward the northeast. Intrigued by his discovery, Franklin checked with his correspondents living along the Eastern Seaboard and their experiences with this and prior storms. Franklin concluded that the wind direction in a storm was not an indication of the storm's direction of movement.

Driving Question:
What systems shape the weather of middle latitudes?

The ceaseless succession of synoptic-scale weather systems is largely responsible for the considerable day-to-day variability of weather in middle latitudes. In the Northern Hemisphere, middle latitudes extend from the Tropic of Cancer north to the Arctic Circle. The weather of middle latitudes is particularly dynamic because of the migration of cyclones and anticyclones that are embedded in the prevailing westerlies of the planetary-scale atmospheric circulation (Chapter 9). This latitude belt features the greatest meridional temperature contrast in the troposphere. Recall from Chapter 4 that because of imbalances between radiational heating and cooling, high latitudes experience a net heat energy deficit while the tropics have a net heat energy surplus. As a consequence, the greatest poleward sensible and latent heat transport via atmospheric and oceanic circulation occurs in middle latitudes.

In this chapter, we examine the weather conditions that accompany the major weather systems of middle latitudes: air masses, fronts, cyclones (lows), and anticyclones (highs). In addition, this chapter covers selected local and regional circulation systems. All these weather systems are interrelated as their development and movements are ultimately governed by the pattern of planetary-scale circulation.

Air Masses

An **air mass**, a huge expanse of air covering thousands of square kilometers, is relatively uniform horizontally in temperature and water vapor concentration (humidity), with both quantities typically decreasing with altitude. The properties of an air mass depend upon the type of surface over which it develops, that is, its source region. An air mass *source region* features nearly homogeneous surface characteristics over a broad area with little topographic relief, such as a great expanse of snow-covered ground or a vast stretch of ocean waters. To become uniform in temperature and humidity, an air mass must reside in its source region for several days to weeks.

Often, air mass source regions are dominated by large semi-permanent high pressure systems (e.g., the Siberian high). Subsidence of air and horizontal divergence of surface winds in an anticyclone favor uniform properties of air in the system. Light winds inhibit mixing and together with the long residence time that is typical of high pressure systems, the distinct thermal properties of the surface are transferred to the air mass. Air mass source regions are typically not found where cyclones develop or along prevailing storm tracks.

Simply put, air masses are either cold (polar, abbreviated as *P*) or warm (tropical or *T*), and either dry (continental or *c*) or humid (maritime or *m*). Air masses that form over cold snow-covered surfaces of high latitudes are relatively cold, whereas those that develop over the warm surfaces of low latitudes are relatively warm. Air masses that form over land tend to be relatively dry, whereas those that develop over the ocean are relatively humid. Based on combinations of temperature and humidity, the four basic types of air masses are: cold and dry, *continental polar* (*cP*); cold and humid, *maritime polar* (*mP*); warm and dry, *continental tropical* (*cT*); and warm and humid, *maritime tropical* (*mT*). A fifth air mass type, *arctic* (*A*) air, is dry like continental polar air but colder.

NORTH AMERICAN TYPES AND SOURCE REGIONS

All the air mass types listed above occur over North America, forming over either the landmass or surrounding ocean water in certain characteristic regions. Source regions for these air masses are plotted in Figure 10.1.

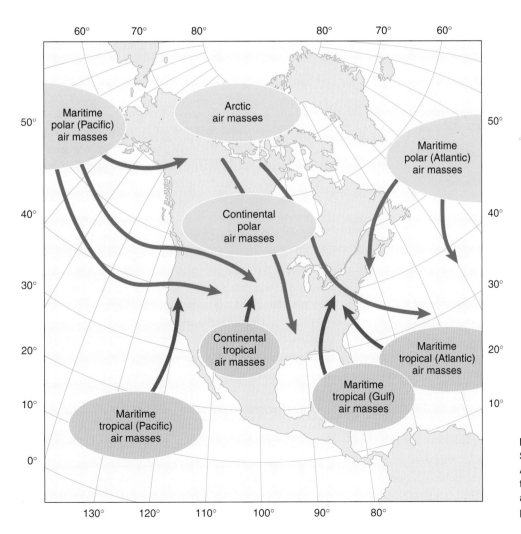

FIGURE 10.1
Source regions of North American air masses. The temperature and humidity of an air mass depend on the properties of its source region.

Continental tropical air (cT) develops over the subtropical deserts of Mexico and the southwestern United States primarily in summer and is hot and dry. **Maritime tropical air (mT)** is very warm and humid because its source regions are tropical and subtropical seas (e.g., Gulf of Mexico). This air mass retains these properties year-round and is responsible for oppressive summer heat and humidity east of the Rocky Mountains. The source regions for **maritime polar air (mP)**

TABLE 10.1
Stability, Temperature, and Humidity Characteristics of North American Air Masses

Air mass type	Source region stability		Characteristics	
	Winter	Summer	Winter	Summer
A	Stable		Bitter cold, dry	
cP	Stable	Stable	Very cold, dry	Cool, dry
cT	Unstable	Unstable	Warm, dry	Hot, dry
mP (Pacific)	Unstable	Unstable	Mild, humid	Mild, humid
mP (Atlantic)	Unstable	Stable	Cold, humid	Cool, humid
mT (Atlantic)	Unstable	Unstable	Warm, humid	Warm, humid

are the cold ocean waters of the North Pacific and North Atlantic, especially north of 40 degrees N. Along the West Coast, *mP* air brings heavy winter rains (snows in the mountains) and persistent coastal fogs in summer. Dry **continental polar air (cP)** develops over the northern interior of North America. In winter, *cP* air is typically very cold because the ground in its source region is often snow covered, daylight is short, solar radiation is weak, and nocturnal radiational cooling is extreme. In summer, when the snow-free source region warms in response to extended hours of bright sunshine, *cP* air is quite mild and pleasant.

Arctic air (A) forms over the snow- or ice-covered regions of Siberia, the Arctic Basin, Greenland, and North America, north of about 60 degrees N, in much the same way as continental polar air but in a region that receives very little solar radiation in winter, although it still radiates strongly to space in the infrared. These exceptionally cold and dry air masses are responsible for the bone-numbing winter cold waves that sweep across the Great Plains, at times penetrating as far south as the Gulf of Mexico and central Florida. For example, the so-called *Siberian Express* is the name given to an arctic air mass that forms over Siberia, crosses over the North Pole into Canada, and plunges onto the Great Plains and then south and eastward.

Air masses differ not only in temperature and humidity but also in stability. As noted in Chapter 6, stability is an important property of air because it influences vertical motion and the consequent development of clouds

and precipitation. Table 10.1 is a list of the usual stability, temperature, and humidity characteristics of North American air masses within their source regions.

MODIFICATION OF AIR MASSES

Air masses do not stay in their source regions indefinitely. As they move from place to place, their properties modify, those of some air masses changing more than others. Changes may occur in temperature, humidity, and/or stability. **Air mass modification** occurs primarily by (1) exchange of heat or moisture, or both, with the surface over which the air mass travels; (2) radiational heating or cooling; and (3) adiabatic heating or cooling associated with large-scale vertical motion.

In winter, as a *cP* air mass travels southeastward from Canada into the lower 48-states, its temperature usually modifies rapidly. Although daily minimum temperatures in the Northern Plains might dip well below −18 °C (0 °F), minimum temperatures may not drop much below the freezing point after the polar air arrives in the southern states. Rapid air mass modification occurs because, outside of its source region, polar air is usually colder than the ground over which it travels. The sun warms the snow-free ground, and the warmer ground heats the bottom of the air mass, destabilizing it and triggering convective currents that distribute heat vertically within the air mass.

A similar process of heating from below and destabilization occurs when a *cP* air mass crosses the East Coast and travels over the relatively warm waters of the western Atlantic. In addition, evaporation from the sea surface increases the water vapor concentration of the air mass. Saturation is readily achieved in the cold, humid, and relatively unstable lower levels of the air mass. Extensive areas of low clouds and fog develop. These clouds usually are organized into narrow rows, known as *cloud streets*, oriented parallel to the wind direction.

When *cP* air travels over snow-covered ground, however, modification is more limited because much of the incoming solar radiation is reflected rather than being converted to heat (via absorption). The relatively cold snow surface chills the air, increasing stability and weakening convection. Extreme nocturnal radiational cooling plays an important role in inhibiting modification of the *cP* air mass, especially when nights are long.

A tropical air mass does not modify as readily as a polar air mass because, outside of its source region, tropical air is often warmer than the ground over which it travels. The bottom of the air mass cools by contact with the ground; this cooling stabilizes the air and suppresses convective currents. Hence, cooling is restricted to the lowest portion of the air mass. By contrast, if a tropical air mass moves over a warmer surface, the air mass can become even warmer. Thus, a cold wave loses much of its punch as it pushes southward, but a summer heat wave can retain its warmth as it journeys from the Gulf of Mexico northward into southern Canada.

Air masses undergo significant changes in temperature and humidity through orographic lifting. When cool and humid *mP* air sweeps inland from off the Pacific Ocean, the air is forced up the windward slopes of coastal mountain ranges such as the Cascades and the Sierras and expands and cools adiabatically. Cooling triggers condensation or deposition (cloud development) and precipitation, primarily on the windward slopes (Chapter 6). Latent heat released during condensation (and deposition) partially offsets adiabatic cooling. Then, as the air mass descends the leeward slopes into the Great Basin, it warms adiabatically and clouds dissipate. Some evaporative cooling is associated with the dissipation of clouds, but net heating (and drying) occurs because the water vapor that was condensed and precipitated out on the windward side of the mountains is no longer available for evaporation. The same modification processes are repeated as the air mass is forced to flow up and over the Rockies. Eventually, the air mass emerges on the Great Plains considerably milder and drier than the original *mP* air mass. East of the Rockies, such an air mass is described as modified **Pacific air**.

When the westerly wave pattern aloft is dominantly zonal (Chapter 9), Pacific air floods the eastern two-thirds of the United States and southern Canada. Polar air masses stay far to the north, while tropical air masses stay to the south. Consequently, much of eastern North America experiences lengthy episodes of mild and generally dry weather.

Frontal Weather

A **front** is a narrow zone of transition between air masses that differ in density. Density differences are usually due to temperature contrasts; for this reason we use the nomenclature *cold* and *warm* fronts. However, density differences may also arise from contrasts in humidity. Although the transition zone associated with an actual front may be a hundred or more kilometers wide, traditionally a line representing a front is drawn on a weather map along the warm (less dense) edge of the transition zone. Air temperatures are nearly constant on the warm side of the front, but fall with distance from the front to a region of nearly uniform temperature in the cold air mass.

A front is also associated with a trough in the sea-level pressure pattern, a corresponding wind shift, and converging winds. Where contrasting air masses meet, the colder (denser) air forces the warmer (less dense) air to ascend. Often the ascending air cools sufficiently (via expansion) that clouds and precipitation develop. Depending on the slope of the front in the vertical plane and the motion of air relative to the front, frontal weather may be confined to a very narrow band (tens of kilometers), or it may extend over a broad region (hundreds of kilometers). In addition, the slope of the front influences the types of clouds and precipitation forming along the front. In this section, we describe the four basic types of synoptic-scale fronts: stationary, warm, cold, and occluded.

STATIONARY FRONT

A **stationary front** is just that, a front that exhibits essentially no lateral movement. For example, a stationary front develops along the Front Range of the Rocky Mountains when a shallow pool of polar air (typically about 1000 m thick) surges south and southwestward out of the Prairie Provinces of Canada. The vertical extent of the air mass is below pass level, so the shallow cold dry air mass abuts the mountain range and can push no further westward; therefore, its leading edge is marked by a stationary front paralleling the Continental Divide, the crest of the mountain range. Milder air remains in the

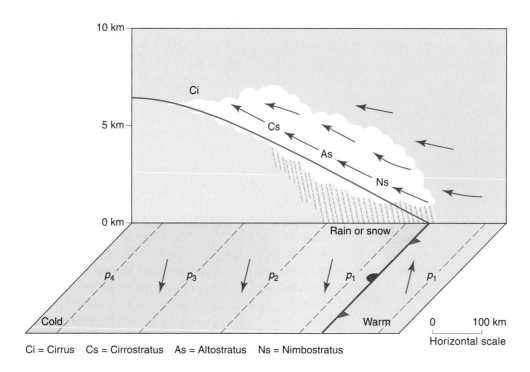

Ci = Cirrus   Cs = Cirrostratus   As = Altostratus   Ns = Nimbostratus

FIGURE 10.2
A stationary front; the vertical scale is greatly exaggerated.

Great Basin to the west of the Rockies. (On occasion, the cold air mass may be sufficiently thick that cold air pours westward through mountain passes into the Great Basin.) Similarly, a stationary front can form when any type of preexisting front becomes parallel to the upper-level flow pattern. Under the proper conditions, a stationary front can also form along a boundary in the surface temperature pattern, such as a coastline or the demarcation between a regional snow cover and bare ground.

Many features of a stationary front are common to all fronts. As shown in vertical cross section in Figure 10.2, a front slopes from Earth's surface toward colder air, or more precisely, toward denser air. A front lies in a trough in the pressure pattern on any horizontal surface intersecting the front; this is especially evident in the sea-level isobars drawn on a surface weather map. Recall that the wind blows approximately parallel to the isobars, with friction turning the wind somewhat toward lower pressure. The wind typically changes direction rather abruptly across the front. The change in wind direction and speed across a front is usually associated with convergence, which leads to upward motion, clouds, and perhaps precipitation.

A stationary front does not always have a broad region of associated clouds and precipitation as depicted in Figure 10.2. Frontal weather can vary considerably from case to case, depending on the supply of water vapor and the specifics of air motion relative to the front. In cases that do produce precipitation, the rain or snow falls mostly on the cold side of the stationary front. Warm humid air flows up and over the cooler air mass, more or less along the frontal surface. Ascending air cools by expansion, which triggers condensation and perhaps precipitation. This situation is often referred to as **overrunning** and can result in an extended period of relatively widespread cloudiness, drizzle, light rain, or light snow.

WARM FRONT

If a stationary front begins to move in such a way that the warm (less dense) air advances while the cold (more dense) air retreats, the front changes character and becomes a **warm front**. The overall characteristics of a warm front are very similar to those of the stationary front, as shown in Figure 10.3.

Differences between a warm front and a stationary front are evident in a comparison of Figures 10.3 and 10.2. The slope of the warm front (ratio of vertical rise to horizontal distance) is less near Earth's surface because surface roughness (friction) has slowed the warm front. Winds on the warm side of the front are quite similar in both instances, but air on the cold side of the warm front is retreating. Thus, the warm air advances relative to Earth's surface, rather than just gliding up and over the cold air.

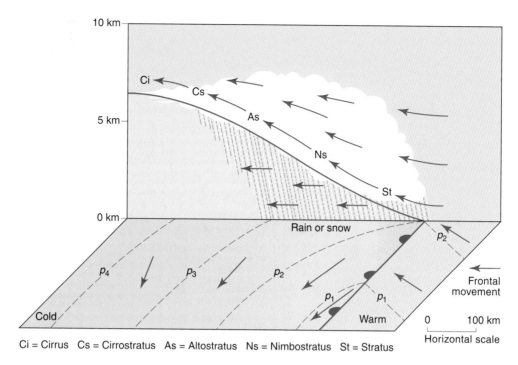

FIGURE 10.3
A warm front is the leading edge of a warm air mass that advances by overrunning denser colder and/or drier air; the vertical scale is greatly exaggerated.

As a warm front approaches some locality, clouds develop and gradually lower and thicken in the following general sequence: cirrus, cirrostratus, altostratus, nimbostratus, and stratus. This sequence of stratiform clouds reflects gentle uplift associated with overrunning in a relatively stable environment. The initial wispy cirrus clouds may appear more than 1000 km (620 mi) in advance of the surface warm front (Figure 10.4). Slowly, clouds spread laterally and form thin sheets of cirrostratus, turning the sky a bright milky white. The tiny ice crystals comprising these high clouds (bases above 7000 m or 23,000 ft) may reflect and refract sunlight to produce halos or sundogs (Chapter 14). Appearance of these optical phenomena may herald the approach of stormy weather a few days in advance.

In time, cirrostratus clouds give way to altostratus, thin clouds with bases at altitudes of 2000 to 7000 m (6500 to 23,000 ft). Soon after altostratus clouds thicken enough to block out the sun, additional lowering of the cloud deck often occurs, accompanied by light rain or snow. Steady precipitation falls from low, gray nimbostratus clouds and persists until the warm front finally passes, a period that may exceed 24 hrs. Copious amounts of rain may fall ahead of the surface warm front, and because precipitation intensity is usually only light to moderate, much of the water infiltrates the soil (as long

as the ground is unfrozen and not already saturated with water). Farmers prefer this type of rain. If the air is cold enough for the precipitation to fall in the form of snow, accumulations may be substantial.

Just ahead of the surface warm front, steady precipitation associated with nimbostratus clouds usually gives way to drizzle falling from low stratus clouds (bases below 2000 m or 6500 ft) and sometimes fog. **Frontal fog** develops when rain falling through the shallow layer

FIGURE 10.4
Thin wispy cirrus clouds may appear more than 1000 km (620 mi) in advance of a surface warm front.

of cool air at the ground evaporates and increases the water vapor concentration to saturation. After the warm front finally passes, frontal fog dissipates and skies at least partially clear because the zone of overrunning has also passed. The weather usually turns warmer and more humid (higher dewpoints).

The cloud and precipitation sequence just described for a warm front applies when the advancing warm air is stable. The sequence changes somewhat when the advecting warm air is unstable. In that situation, uplift is more vigorous and often gives rise to cumulonimbus clouds (thunderstorms) embedded within the zone of overrunning ahead of the surface warm front. Lightning, thunder, and brief periods of heavy rainfall, or perhaps snowfall, may punctuate the otherwise steady fall of light-to-moderate precipitation.

COLD FRONT

A stationary front becomes a **cold front** if it begins to move in such a way that colder (more dense) air displaces warmer (less dense) air. Over North America in winter, the temperature contrast is typically greater across a cold front than across stationary or warm fronts. In summer, however, maximum air temperatures on either side of a cold front are sometimes essentially the same. When this occurs, the density contrast between the two air masses arises from differences

in humidity rather than differences in temperature. At the same temperature and pressure, lower humidity air is denser than higher humidity air (Chapter 6). Following the passage of a cold front, both temperature and humidity typically drop. Dramatic temperature drops are less likely in summer but humidity changes can be significant.

Whereas the roughness of Earth's surface causes the slope of a warm front to decrease, it is responsible for the nose-shaped profile that characterizes a cold front as shown in Figure 10.5. The slope of a cold front is steeper (1:50 to 1:100) than the slope of a warm front (1:150 on average). Because of the steep frontal slope and the typical flow aloft across the front from the cold to the warm side, uplift is restricted to a narrow zone at or near the cold front's leading edge. Low-level air motion also differs from that in warm fronts and stationary fronts; the low-level air motion in the cold air is at least in part toward the front and forces the warm air aloft.

If the cold front advances slowly but steadily, say 30 km per hr (19 mph), the type of frontal weather depends on the stability of the warmer air. Any precipitation is likely to be showery and brief, occurring in a narrow band at or just ahead of the front, as uplift along the steep cold front is sufficiently vigorous to produce a narrow band of cumuliform clouds and convective showers. If the warm air ahead of the front is unstable, the uplift is

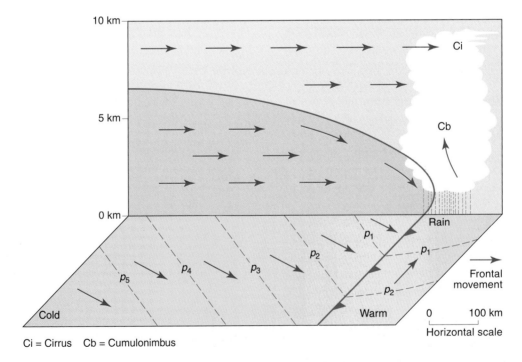

Ci = Cirrus   Cb = Cumulonimbus

FIGURE 10.5
A cold front is the leading edge of a cold and/or drier air mass that advances by displacing warmer and/or more humid air; the vertical scale is greatly exaggerated.

more vigorous, giving rise to towering cumulus congestus that build into cumulonimbus clouds with cirrus clouds blown downstream by winds at high altitudes. These thunderstorms may be accompanied by strong and gusty surface winds, hail, or other severe weather. If a well-defined cold front progresses at a relatively rapid pace, say 45 km per hr (28 mph), then a **squall line**, a band of intense thunderstorms, may develop either at the front or up to 300 km (180 mi) ahead of the front (Chapter 11). On the other hand, if the warm air is relatively stable, nimbostratus and altostratus clouds may form. Following the passage of a cold front, colder air sweeping across the warmer surface often becomes unstable, leading to gusty westerly winds along with stratocumulus clouds and intermittent light rain or snow showers (depending on the temperature).

A typical cold front trails south or southwestward from the center of an extra-tropical cyclone, as discussed later in this chapter, and progresses from west to east. In winter, cold fronts often drop southward out of Canada onto the Great Plains, even traveling as far south as the Gulf of Mexico. Southward or southwestward moving cold fronts occur east of the Appalachians in New England, but in that region, they are seen most frequently in summer and fall and are referred to as **back-door cold fronts**. These fronts often usher in welcome relief from hot weather, in the form of *cP* air from Canada or *mP* air from off the Atlantic. The Appalachians impede the westward progression of the colder air, which is then free to move farther south on the eastern side of the Appalachians along the Piedmont and coastal plains (Figure 10.6).

OCCLUDED FRONTS

Late in its life cycle, as a middle latitude cyclone moves into colder air, a front forms, known as an **occluded front**, or simply an *occlusion*. There are three types of occlusions, distinguished by the temperature contrast between the air behind the cold front and the air ahead of the warm front: cold occlusion, warm occlusion, and neutral occlusion. If air behind the advancing cold front (*cP*) is colder than the cool air (*mP*) ahead of the warm front, the cold air slides under and lifts the air in the warm sector, the cool air, and the warm front (Figure 10.7). The resulting front, known as a *cold occlusion*, has the characteristics of a cold front at the surface, but the temperature contrast between the cold and cool air masses is less than across a typical winter cold front. Weather ahead of the occlusion is similar to that in advance of a warm front, but the actual frontal passage may be marked by more showery conditions, similar to a cold front. This type of occlusion is most common over the eastern half of the North American continent, where the coldest air follows behind the front on northwest winds.

A *warm occlusion* develops when air behind the advancing cold front is not as cold as the air ahead of the warm front (Figure 10.8). This type of occlusion often occurs in the northerly portions of western coasts, such as in Europe or in the Pacific Northwest. In this case, the air behind the cold front is relatively mild (*mP*), having traversed ocean waters, whereas the air ahead of the

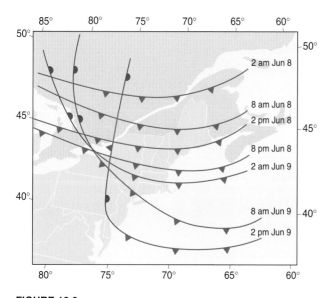

FIGURE 10.6
A back-door cold front moves across New England toward the south and southwest.

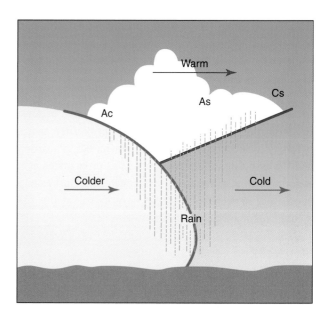

FIGURE 10.7
Schematic vertical cross-section of a cold-type occlusion with the vertical scale greatly exaggerated.

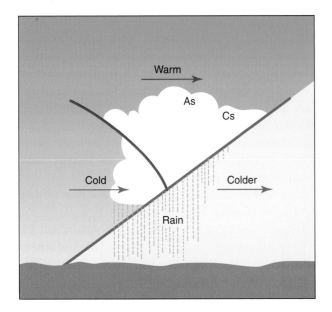

FIGURE 10.8
Schematic vertical cross-section of a warm-type occlusion with the vertical scale greatly exaggerated.

warm front is relatively cold (*cP*), having traveled over land. With this type of occlusion, the air behind the cold front slides under the warm air but rides over the colder air. Weather ahead of a warm occlusion is similar to that ahead of a warm front, with the surface front behaving as a warm front.

A *neutral occlusion* is quite common and features little temperature difference between air ahead of the warm front and air behind the cold front. Although not obvious in the surface temperature field, this type of occlusion is marked by a trough, wind-shift line, and band of cloudiness and precipitation.

Regardless of type, an occlusion can be difficult to locate from surface weather observations because the temperature contrast across the front is often small, precipitation occurs over a broad region masking the front, and the associated trough may not be as pronounced as it is for a cold or warm front. However, satellite imagery shows that an occluded front can be as sharply defined as a cold front in oceanic weather systems.

SUMMARY

At middle and high latitudes, the lower troposphere is comprised of air masses that contrast in temperature and/or humidity. Narrow transition zones, called fronts, border air masses. The motion of a front is related to the lower tropospheric motion on the cold side of the front and fronts are classified on the basis of the

movement of the cold air mass. Cold air retreats ahead of a warm front, advances behind a cold front, and moves parallel to a stationary front. Clouds and precipitation develop along fronts only when a significant density contrast exists between air masses, and the supply of water vapor is adequate. With little difference in temperature and humidity between air masses, the front may pass virtually unnoticed except for a shift in wind direction.

Properties that define a front (differences in temperature and humidity, wind shift, convergence, and pressure trough) change with time similar to the way air masses modify. If processes in the atmosphere such as a region of converging surface winds increase the density contrast between air masses, then a front forms or grows stronger; this process is called *frontogenesis*. On the other hand, if the density contrast between air masses lessens perhaps because of diverging surface winds, the front weakens; this process is known as *frontolysis*. Precipitation associated with the front also tends to increase or diminish in intensity as the front strengthens or weakens. Frontal weather occurs in combination with cyclones. We explore this relationship next.

Extra-tropical Cyclones

The **extra-tropical cyclone**, or low-pressure system (*low*), is a major weather maker of middle and high latitudes. (See summarization by Edward J. Hopkins, University of Wisconsin-Madison in Table 10.2.) Viewed from above in the Northern Hemisphere, surface winds blow counterclockwise and inward toward the center of a cyclone (Chapter 8). Surface winds converge, air rises, expands, and cools, resulting in clouds and precipitation. This section explores the life cycle and characteristics of these synoptic-scale weather systems.

LIFE CYCLE

During World War I and continuing into the 1920s, scientists at the Bergen School of Meteorology in Norway conducted ground-breaking studies of synoptic-scale weather systems. Led by Vilhelm Bjerknes (1862-1951) and including his son Jacob Bjerknes (1897-1975) and Swedish meteorologist Tor Bergeron (1891-1977), researchers investigated air masses, fronts, and cyclones. They were the first to describe the basic stages in the life cycle of an extra-tropical cyclone and for this reason this conceptual model is referred to as the **Norwegian cyclone model**. The model was derived primarily from surface weather observations; at the time researchers were unable

TABLE 10.2
Distinguishing Characteristics of a Mature Extra-tropical Cyclone

Feature	Typical value
Diameter	1500–3000 km (1000–2000 mi)
Maximum winds	55–70 km per hr (35–45 mph)
Time of occurrence	All seasons; especially winter (DJFM) in the Northern Hemisphere
Frequency	Approximately 3 per day, poleward of 30 degrees N
Lifetime	3–4 days
Energy source	Dynamic forcing (potential to kinetic energy)
Region of origin	Middle latitudes, polar front
Direction of motion	Eastward or northeastward
Lateral speed	30–65 km per hr (20–40 mph)

to monitor winds aloft routinely. Subsequent advances in atmospheric monitoring techniques—especially remote sensing by satellite—have verified the main features of the Norwegian cyclone model. Amazingly, the model remains a close approximation of our current understanding of middle latitude cyclones, even though individual cyclones may not follow the model precisely.

With adequate *upper-air support*, an extra-tropical cyclone can form and intensify. **Cyclogenesis,** the birth of a cyclone, usually takes place along the polar front directly under an area of strong horizontal divergence in the upper troposphere. As noted in Chapter 9, strong horizontal divergence aloft occurs to the east of an upper-level trough and under the left-front quadrant of a jet streak. If horizontal divergence aloft removes more mass from a column of air than is supplied by converging surface winds, the air pressure at the bottom of the column falls. Consequently, a horizontal air pressure gradient develops and a cyclonic circulation begins. A storm is born. Westerlies aloft then steer and support the cyclone as it progresses through its life cycle (Figure 10.9).

Just prior to the formation of a prototypical cyclone, the polar front is often stationary and surface winds blow parallel to the front. As the surface air pressure drops, surface winds converge and sections of the front begin to move (Figure 10.9A). West of the low center (the point of lowest sea-level air pressure) the polar front pushes toward the southeast as a *cold front*. East of the low center, the polar front advances northward as a *warm front*. The minimum pressure for the incipient low might be 1000 mb, with a single closed isobar on a

standard surface weather map, which uses a 4-mb interval between isobars. Satellite imagery shows that the narrow cloud band associated with the stationary front develops a bulge at the low center and extends along the developing warm front. The upper-level circulation pattern depicted in Figure 10.9A shows a trough to the west of the surface low, a position that is favorable for further development (*deepening*) of the system. With more horizontal divergence aloft than convergence near the surface, the surface pressure at the cyclone center continues to fall.

If the circulation pattern in the upper troposphere does not favor further development of the cyclone, the low center typically ripples along the stationary front without deepening, producing cloudiness and light precipitation along the way. Such cyclones affect only a small area and typically travel along the front at 50 to 70 km per hr (31 to 43 mph). On the other hand, if atmospheric conditions favor development of the incipient cyclone, its central pressure continues to drop, the associated horizontal pressure gradient becomes steeper, and counterclockwise winds strengthen. The upper-level trough also frequently deepens while remaining to the west of the low center, as cold air is brought into the system from the northwest.

The so-called *warm sector* of the cyclone (the area between the warm and cold fronts, occupied by warm air at the surface) becomes better defined during the early stage of storm development. At this stage in the cyclone's life cycle, fronts form a pronounced wave pattern (Figure 10.9B), hence the descriptive name *wave cyclone*. The surface cyclone may now have a central pressure of 992 mb, with perhaps three closed isobars, and typically is

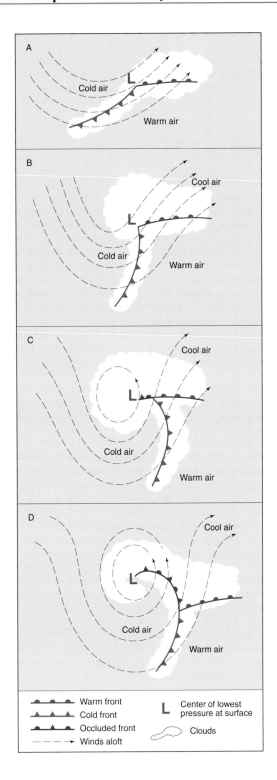

FIGURE 10.9

The life cycle of an extra-tropical cyclone (low-pressure system): (A) incipient cyclone, (B) wave cyclone, (C) beginning of occlusion, and (D) bent-back occlusion. As a wave cyclone, the system's center is located east of the upper-level trough; at occlusion, the system's center is under the upper-level trough. Air temperatures refer to conditions at Earth's surface.

FIGURE 10.10

The comma-shaped pattern of clouds on this infrared satellite image is characteristic of a well-developed extra-tropical cyclone. Note the *dry slot* to the south of the system's center over Nebraska.

moving eastward or northeastward at 40 to 55 km per hr (25 to 35 mph). A large-scale comma-shaped cloud pattern, known as a **comma cloud**, becomes apparent in satellite images at this stage, reflecting the strengthening of the system's circulation (Figure 10.10). The head of the comma extends from the low center to the northwest, with its tail trailing southward or southwestward along the cold front. Extensive stratiform cloudiness caused by overrunning appears north of the warm front.

The cold front generally moves faster than the warm front so that the angle between the two fronts gradually closes; that is, the area occupied by the surface warm sector diminishes. As the cold front closes in on the warm front, an *occluded front* begins forming near the low center, forcing the warm air aloft and causing the warm sector at the surface to occupy a smaller area away from the surface low center. Figure 10.9C represents the beginning of the occlusion stage of the cyclone's life cycle. The upper-level pattern now features a closed circulation almost above the surface cyclone. When the upper-level low center is directly over the surface low center, the system is described as *vertically stacked*. Dry air descending behind the cold front is drawn nearly into the center of the cyclone as a **dry slot** that separates the cloud band along the cold front from the comma head, now more west than northwest of the low center. The central pressure of the cyclone has dropped significantly to perhaps 985 mb in the time that elapsed between Figures 10.9B and 10.9C.

Some extra-tropical cyclones continue deepening even after formation of an occluded front. Typically, the upper-air low center is not directly over the surface low center while deepening is occurring, but it may be fairly close. These systems develop a closed, vertically stacked (or nearly so) circulation that is troposphere-deep and typically move much more slowly than previously, say 30 km per hr (20 mph), and may even stall completely. Occasionally, the track of the surface low becomes erratic, with the low sometimes moving toward the west as the system becomes "cut-off" or detached from the westerly flow in the middle to upper troposphere. The circulation tends to draw the occluded front around the low center into a configuration sometimes described as a *bent-back occlusion*. The central pressure of the low may now be 980 mb or lower, with perhaps a half dozen or more closely spaced closed isobars, and surface winds that can exceed 75 km per hr (45 mph). Such intense cyclones occur over the North Atlantic or North Pacific. Although still present, the surface warm sector is detached from the cyclone center and an occluded front forms as the warm sector is pushed aloft.

Cold, warm, and occluded fronts all come together at the point of occlusion, or **triple point**, where conditions favor formation of a new cyclone, sometimes called a *secondary cyclone*. (Note the similar appearance of the triple point with its fronts in Figure 10.9D and the incipient low with its fronts in Figure 10.9A). At this stage, the cloud pattern typically becomes a spiraling swirl with enhanced bands associated with the fronts. The spiraling cloud band may circle the center of an intense low (central pressure of 960 mb or lower) several times.

Eventually, the cyclone weakens, that is, its central pressure rises, the horizontal pressure gradient weakens, and winds diminish; this process is called **cyclolysis** or *filling*. The cyclone can weaken during any of the stages described above if its upper-air support decreases to the point that horizontal divergence aloft becomes less than horizontal convergence near the surface. Then the surface pressure at the low center rises, and the surrounding horizontal pressure gradient weakens. As the central pressure rises, the cyclone loses its identity in the sea-level pressure field and is marked only by an area of cloudy skies and drizzle. Such weakening is inevitable once the system is vertically stacked, but the filling process may not begin for many hours and may proceed slowly, allowing an intense circulation to persist for days.

The cyclone life cycle described above may occur over several days, or it may be completed in a much shorter period. If upper-air support is less favorable, the storm may spend a longer time in any one of the early stages, even weaken temporarily, and still become fully occluded. Sometimes cyclones develop with meager upper-air support (weak divergence aloft) and are poorly defined. At other times, widespread cloudiness and precipitation are linked to an upper-air or surface trough with no closed cyclonic circulation at the surface. When upper-level conditions are ideal, the entire life cycle from incipient cyclone to bent-back occlusion can occur in less than 36 hrs.

CYCLONE BOMB

Cyclones sometimes undergo explosive development. A rapidly intensifying extra-tropical cyclone, called a *bomb*, is defined as a cyclone whose central pressure drops at least 24 mb in 24 hrs. Few cyclones meet this criterion, and most of those that do satisfy it occur in winter over warm ocean surface currents such as the Kuroshio Current off the coast of Japan and the Gulf Stream off the East Coast of the United States. Because these oceanic cyclones are not closely monitored on a day-to-day basis, field experiments have investigated them using specially instrumented research aircraft. The *Genesis of Atlantic Lows Experiment (GALE)*, sponsored by a number of agencies, including the National Science Foundation (NSF), the U.S. Office of Naval Research (ONR), and the National Oceanic and Atmospheric Administration (NOAA), took place from January to March 1986; its primary goal was to observe the initial formation of oceanic cyclones in a region off the coast of North Carolina. Sponsored primarily by ONR, the *Experiment on Rapidly Intensifying Cyclones over the Atlantic (ERICA)* was conducted from December 1988 to February 1989 over the North Atlantic. The goal of ERICA was to monitor rapidly intensifying cyclones throughout their life cycle.

An extreme example of a developing cyclone was observed during ERICA on 4-5 January 1989. An incipient cyclone with a central pressure of 996 mb was first identified off Cape Hatteras, NC at approximately 7:00 p.m. (EST) on 4 January. Twenty-four hours later, the storm was located 700 km (430 mi) south of Newfoundland with a central pressure of 936 mb. The storm deepened by 60 mb in 24 hrs, 2.5 times the criterion for a cyclonic bomb!

CONVEYOR BELT MODEL

The Norwegian cyclone model provides a reasonably good description of the characteristics and life cycle of a typical extra-tropical cyclone. Improved understanding of upper-air circulation in the years since the Norwegian model was first developed led to a new three-dimensional cyclone model, combining horizontal and vertical air motions. This so-called **conveyor belt model** depicts the circulation within a mature extra-tropical cyclone in terms of three broad interacting airstreams, referred to as *conveyor belts*. Just as mechanical conveyor belts transport goods (or even people) from one location to another, atmospheric conveyor belts transport air with certain properties from one location to another and are named for the type of air they transport. The three conveyor belts are (1) warm and humid, (2) cold, and (3) dry. A schematic drawing of this model is shown in Figure 10.11.

In the conveyor belt model, a warm air stream originates in the cyclone's warm sector and follows the warm side of the cold front near the Earth's surface, south and east of the storm center. Typically, this warm and humid air stream ascends slightly as it flows northward in the cyclone's warm sector at low levels. The warm conveyor belt then ascends more rapidly as it glides northward along the sloping warm frontal surface that serves as the boundary between the warm air and the dome of cooler air to the north of the surface warm front. The ascending air expands and cools adiabatically,

water vapor condenses forming clouds, and rain or snow develops. Latent heat released during condensation adds to the buoyancy of air in the warm conveyor belt.

Recall that at this mature stage in the cyclone's life cycle, winds aloft blow more or less from the southwest, with the surface cyclone located between the upper-level trough and ridge. The warm conveyor belt thus turns from a southerly to a southwesterly or even westerly direction as it ascends over the warm front and follows the upper-level flow. This air stream therefore helps explain the broad region of stratiform cloudiness and steady precipitation north of the warm front.

While the warm conveyor belt is gliding up and over the warm frontal surface, winds in the lower troposphere in the region northeast of the surface low pressure system blow from the east or northeast and are relatively cold. This flow forms the cold conveyor belt and, at low levels, is located just to the cold (north) side of the warm front. Like the warm conveyor belt, this air stream ascends as it progresses toward the west. Warm frontal precipitation falls through the cold air stream, increasing its relative humidity to saturation so that clouds and precipitation develop in the cold conveyor belt. As the cold conveyor belt ascends, it comes under the influence of mid- and upper-level tropospheric winds and turns clockwise, following the southwesterly or westerly flow aloft. The ascending saturated cold conveyor belt produces the *comma cloud* to the northwest of the cyclone center.

The third conveyor belt is the dry air stream. Whereas air ascends at the cyclone center and along associated fronts, air descends just west of the cold front. Descending air originates aloft in the upper troposphere and lower stratosphere upstream of the upper-level trough and is very dry, especially compared to the air in the warm conveyor belt. As the dry conveyor belt descends, one branch turns southward behind the cold

FIGURE 10.11
Schematic representation of the three-dimensional circulation within an intense coastal extra-tropical cyclone showing warm, cold, and dry airstreams. [From P.J. Kocin and L.W. Uccellini, *Northeast Snowstorms*. Boston, MA: American Meteorological Society, 2004, p. 129.]

front, causing clearing skies. The other branch of the dry air stream first descends as it moves northward toward the surface low center, and then ascends as it comes under the influence of the winds aloft east of the upper-level trough. As the dry air stream moves toward the surface low center, it forms the *dry slot* that separates the head and tail of the comma cloud and is especially prominent in the later phases of the cyclone's life cycle (Figure 10.10).

CYCLONE WEATHER

As an illustration of typical extra-tropical cyclone weather, consider a winter wave cyclone that developed a well-defined warm sector as it moved into the Upper Midwest. Although the storm is still intensifying, its circulation, clouds, and precipitation already affect weather over a broad region. The typical diameter of such a cyclone is between 1000 and 2000 km (about 600 to 1200 mi). Figure 10.12 is a schematic representation of the surface winds, air temperatures, cloud shield, and precipitation pattern associated with this mature low.

Ideally, based on surface weather, a mature wave cyclone can be divided into four sectors about the low center. The lowest air temperatures occur to the northwest of the storm center, where strong and gusty northwest winds advect continental polar or arctic air southward and eastward. Because of relatively tight pressure gradients typically found on the west side of the surface low, winds are strong, making the air feel colder than the temperature might suggest (wind-chill effect). Stratiform clouds and non-convective precipitation in this northwest sector are associated with the head of the comma cloud; precipitation may be either rain or snow depending upon air temperature. The cold front is south of the low center; it is accompanied by a relatively narrow band of ascending air, cumuliform

clouds, and convective-type showers and thunderstorms. Sinking air and generally clear skies characterize much of the southwest sector of the storm system. The mildest air is in the southeast (warm) sector of the cyclone, where south and southeast winds advect maritime tropical air northward from over the Gulf of Mexico. Skies are generally partly cloudy, dewpoints are high, and scattered convective showers are possible, triggered by afternoon solar heating. To the north and northeast of the storm center is an extensive zone of overrunning as maritime tropical air surges over a wedge of cool air maintained by east and northeast winds at the surface. Skies in the northeast sector are cloudy with an extensive shield of stratiform clouds, and the non-convective precipitation is steady and substantial.

Weather conditions in the various sectors of a mature wave cyclone are consistent with our earlier description of cold and warm frontal weather. Although the flow in and around extra-tropical cyclones is mostly horizontal, uplift of air along frontal surfaces is responsible for the cloud and precipitation pattern illustrated in Figure 10.12.

PRINCIPAL CYCLONE TRACKS

The specific track taken by any extra-tropical cyclone depends on the pattern of upper-level westerlies in which the storm is embedded. The storm center tends to move in the direction of the wind blowing directly above the surface low pressure system in the mid-troposphere (i.e., at or near the 500-mb level). As a general rule, the cyclone center moves forward at about one-half the speed of the 500-mb winds. Keep in mind, however, that the upper-level circulation pattern also changes with time, and the cyclone's path shifts accordingly.

FIGURE 10.12
A mature extra-tropical cyclone centered on the border between Minnesota and Iowa, showing typical patterns of (A) surface winds, (B) surface air temperatures, and (C) areas of cloudiness and precipitation.

Principal storm tracks across the lower 48 states of the United States are plotted in Figure 10.13. All storms tend to converge toward the northeast; their ultimate destination is usually the semi-permanent Icelandic low of the North Atlantic or Western Europe. Although many storm tracks appear to originate just east of the Rocky Mountains, in reality they form over the Pacific Ocean, near the Aleutians or in the Gulf of Alaska. As a cyclone travels over the mountains, it often loses its identity temporarily but redevelops on the Great Plains just east of the Front Range of the Rockies. For more on what happens, see this chapter's first Essay, "The Case of the Missing Storm."

Cyclones that consistently follow some of the principal tracks have nicknames. The *Panhandle hook* forms to the lee of the central Rockies, moves southeastward to the Oklahoma and Texas Panhandles, before turning almost due north over the southern Plains in a hook-like path, hence the name. The *Alberta clipper* develops to the lee of the Canadian Rockies in Alberta and travels rapidly from west to east across southern Canada or the northern tier states. *Nor'easters* track toward the northeast along the East Coast. (Typical tracks of nor'easters are plotted as "Texas" and "East Gulf" in Figure 10.13.) It may be confusing to think of a storm as moving toward the northeast, while the winds in the northeast sector of the storm blow from the northeast.

Actually, nor'easters usually intensify off the North Carolina coast and then track in a northeasterly direction up the coast. In effect, two motions exist simultaneously: (1) movement of the storm center along the coast and (2) the counterclockwise circulation of winds about the storm center. The circulation of a storm is for the most part independent of the storm's path, much as the spin of a Frisbee is independent of its trajectory.

Some nor'easters intensify into powerful systems, such as the ERICA storm described earlier or the Blizzard of '88 described in the Case-in-Point of Chapter 1, bringing heavy precipitation and strong winds to the East Coast. The potential impact of a nor'easter is well illustrated by the East Coast storm of 12-15 March 1993, dubbed by the media as the "storm of the century." That storm's path enabled the system to draw into its circulation copious amounts of water vapor and dump extraordinary amounts of snow over an unusually broad area stretching from Alabama to Maine. For more on this storm, see this chapter's second Essay, "Nor'easters."

Generally, cyclones that form in the south yield more precipitation than those that develop in the north because the southerly flow in the warm sector of southern cyclones is better positioned to draw moisture-rich maritime tropical air from source regions such as the Gulf of Mexico. For this reason, Alberta cyclones typically yield only light amounts of rain or snow, whereas Colorado and Gulf-track storms often produce heavy accumulations of rain or snow. The forward speed of the cyclone also affects the total precipitation received at a particular location. For places in the path of a cyclone, a fast-moving system may yield rain or snow for only a few hours whereas a slower moving storm may precipitate for 12 hours or longer.

We have examined the linkage between extra-tropical cyclones and winds aloft. The circulation in the mid- and upper-troposphere supplies *upper-air support* (horizontal divergence) for cyclones and determines their paths. Just as the

FIGURE 10.13
Principal extra-tropical cyclone tracks across the lower 48-states of the United States.

planetary-scale circulation undergoes seasonal changes, so too do cyclones. In summer, when the mean position of the polar front and jet stream is across southern Canada, few well-organized cyclones occur in the United States, and the Alberta storm track shifts northward across Canada. In winter, however, when the mean position of the polar front and jet stream shifts southward, cyclogenesis is more frequent in the United States. Alberta-track storms are the most common because they occur year-round, whereas storms with more southerly tracks develop primarily in winter. In fact, one sign of the beginning of winter circulation patterns is the appearance of Colorado lows.

COLD SIDE/WARM SIDE

An extra-tropical cyclone has a cold side and a warm side. In Figure 10.12, the coldest air is located to the northwest of the low center (where surface winds are blowing from the northwest), while the warmest air is to the southeast of the low center (where surface winds are blowing from the south). Hence, as an extra-tropical cyclone travels eastward across the continent, the weather to the north or left (cold side) of the storm track is quite different from the weather to the south or right (warm side) of the track.

Consider, for example, the two storm tracks plotted in Figure 10.14. A winter cyclone develops over eastern Colorado. As the storm matures, it moves northeastward toward the Great Lakes region following either track A or track B, depending on the direction of the steering winds aloft. In both cases, the center of the cyclone passes within 150 km (95 mi) of Chicago. With track A, the storm moves west and then north of Chicago whereas track B takes the storm to the south and then east of the city. The storm's influence on Chicago's weather depends on its track, as summarized in Table 10.3.

If the storm follows track A, Chicago residents experience the warm side of the storm. As the storm approaches, stratiform clouds thicken and lower, with steady rain—or perhaps snow briefly at the onset—giving way to drizzle and fog after 12 to 24 hrs, signaling the arrival of the warm front. As the warm front passes over the city, skies partially clear and winds shift abruptly from east to southeast and then to the south, advecting warm and humid (*mT*) air at the surface. At this time, the warm sector is over Chicago as the low center passes to the north. Clearing is short-lived, however, as convective clouds develop and are accompanied by scattered showers and thunderstorms that herald the arrival of colder air behind the cold front. The surface cold front passes through the city and then on toward the east and northeast. Winds *veer* (turn clockwise with time), blowing initially from the southwest, then west, and finally northwest. Stratocumulus clouds follow the frontal passage and then skies again clear as the air temperature and dewpoint fall.

In contrast, if the storm takes track B, Chicago residents experience the cold side of the storm and no frontal passages. With the approach of the storm, lowering and thickening stratiform clouds accompany gusty east and northeast winds that drive steady snow or rain (depending on air temperatures) for 12 hrs

FIGURE 10.14

A winter cyclone develops over eastern Colorado and tracks northeastward toward the western Great Lakes. Track A takes the storm to the west and north of Chicago so that the city is on the warm side of the system. Track B takes the storm to the south and east of Chicago so that the city is on the cold side of the system.

TABLE 10.3
General Sequence of Weather Conditions at Chicago as Winter Cyclone Tracks West of the City (Track *A*) or East of the City (Track *B*)

	Track *A*							Track *B*		
Wind direction	E	SE	S	SW	W	NW	E	NE	N	NW
Frontal passage	-	WF	-	CF	-	-	-	-	-	-
Advection	-	Wm	Wm	Cd	Cd	Cd	-	-	Cd	Cd
Air pressure tendency	F	F	F	R	R	R	F	F	R	R
			Time $\Rightarrow$					Time $\Rightarrow$		

WF = Warm front, CF = Cold front, Wm = Warm air advection, Cd = Cold air advection
F = Pressure falling, R = Pressure rising

or longer. As the storm passes to the south of the city, winds gradually *back* (turn counterclockwise with time) to a northerly direction, precipitation tapers off to snow flurries or showers, and air temperatures drop. Finally, winds shift to northwest, the sky begins to clear, and air temperatures continue to fall in response to strong cold air advection as the low moves off to the northeast away from Chicago.

In summary, if you are located on the warm side of an extra-tropical cyclone's path, the wind direction veers with time and a cold front follows a warm front. However, if you are on the cold side of a cyclone's path, the wind direction backs with time without the passage of fronts. In winter in a northern location, substantial snowfall is much more likely on the cold side than on the warm side of a cyclone's track, with the axis of heaviest snowfall running parallel about 240 km (150 mi) to the northwest of the storm track.

WINTER STORMS

Extra-tropical cyclones develop along the polar front throughout the year. However, these storms become more intense and a greater threat to middle latitudes from late autumn, through the winter, and into early spring as the polar front shifts equatorward and the temperature contrast across the front increases. Extra-tropical cyclones are one of the most dangerous aspects of winter weather in many areas of the United States and Canada. Based upon statistics from 1986 through 2003, on average approximately 44 people are killed each year in the U.S. by winter weather. Except for the Gulf Coast and some coastal sections of southern California, few places across the country escape winter storms.

A **winter storm** is an extra-tropical cyclone that produces any combination of frozen or freezing precipitation, including snow, ice pellets (sleet) and/ or freezing rain (Chapter 7). The obvious hazard is the potentially unsafe conditions produced by heavy accumulations of snow (Figure 10.15). Ice storms form a coating of glaze on cold surfaces that makes for treacherous walking and driving conditions and can cause electrical power outages (Chapter 7). An associated hazard is the *cold wave*, which usually follows a winter storm. The strong winds of a winter storm accentuate the arrival of a cold air mass, dropping the wind-chill to potentially dangerous levels that increase the potential for frost bite and hypothermia.

The necessary ingredients for a winter storm include cold air, a moisture supply, and mechanisms that provide uplift (Figure 10.16). Cold air is needed to ensure that the precipitation falls as snow or another form of frozen precipitation. Typically, a sprawling cold high pressure system located to the north of the track of the low

FIGURE 10.15
A heavy fall of snow can seriously disrupt all forms of transportation.

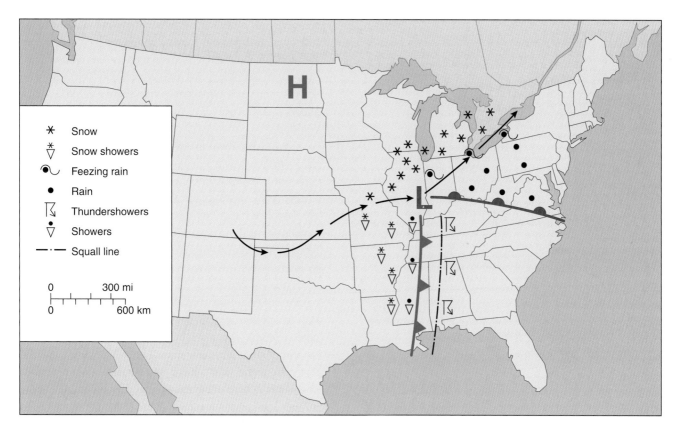

FIGURE 10.16
A schematic representation of a surface weather map showing the various forms of precipitation associated with a mature Colorado-track winter storm system.

helps bring cold air into the low. For a major snowstorm, warm and humid air needs to be brought northward into the system. Panhandle hook storms typically produce more snow across the Plains and Midwest as abundant Gulf moisture is available, whereas Alberta Clippers have little available moisture, resulting in relatively light accumulations of snow. For a winter storm moving to the northeast, the heaviest snow tends to accumulate to the west and north of the track of the low center, on the cold side of the storm.

Strong winds can also cause blowing and drifting snow, sometimes leading to blizzard conditions. During the American Civil War, the term "blizzard" referred to a heavy volley of musketry. In the spring of 1870, a writer for a newspaper in Estherville, IA was apparently the first to describe a severe snowstorm accompanied by strong winds as a blizzard. Over the following decade, use of the term became widespread. Today, the National Weather Service defines a **blizzard** as a severe storm characterized by high winds and reduced visibility due to falling or blowing snow. A blizzard requires sustained winds of 56 km per hr (35 mph) or greater and sufficient falling,

blowing or drifting snow to reduce the horizontal visibility to less than 400 m (0.25 mi). Blizzard conditions may persist long after the passage of a low pressure system as strengthening winds pick up loose snow from the ground. A *whiteout* occurs when visibility is reduced to the point that it is nearly impossible for a person to distinguish the sky from the ground—everything is white. Driving is impossible and people caught in a whiteout become disoriented and lost.

COLD- AND WARM-CORE SYSTEMS

An occluded cyclone is a cold-core system; that is, the lowest temperatures occur within the column of air above the low-pressure center. In vertical cross section, constant pressure (isobaric) surfaces dip downward toward the center of an occluded **cold-core cyclone** (concave upward) (Figure 10.17). Furthermore, the depth of the low increases with altitude implying that a cyclonic circulation prevails throughout the troposphere and is most intense at high altitudes. The thickness of an air layer defined above and below by pressure surfaces is directly proportional to the mean temperature of that

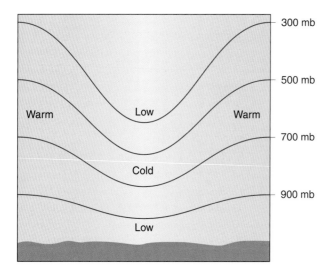

FIGURE 10.17
Vertical cross-section through an occluded cold-core extra-tropical cyclone showing isobaric (constant pressure) surfaces. The vertical scale is greatly exaggerated.

bounded air layer. The requirement that the thickness (mean temperature) be lowest at the center of the low produces the characteristic isobaric pattern. This structure is consistent with the occluded cyclone shown in Figure 10.9D.

On the other hand, the lowest air temperatures in a non-occluded wave cyclone occur northwest of the system's center and the highest temperatures are to the southeast. Figure 10.18 is a vertical cross-section through the low from northwest to southeast. Thickness (mean

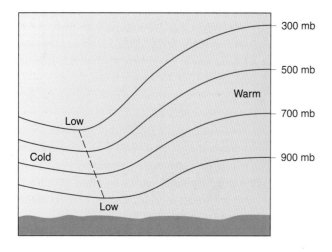

FIGURE 10.18
Vertical cross-section through a non-occluded wave cyclone from northwest (cold) to southeast (warm) showing isobaric (constant pressure) surfaces. The vertical scale is greatly exaggerated.

temperature) arguments indicate that until occlusion the low center aloft is not located above the low center near the surface, but rather is displaced to the cold side of the storm, implying that the system tilts with altitude. This structure is consistent with Figure 10.9B, which shows the upper-level trough lagging behind the surface cyclone.

A different type of low that sometimes is plotted on a surface weather map has characteristics markedly different from those of cold-core or tilted lows. Cyclones of this type are stationary, have no fronts, and generally are associated with fair weather. They form over a broad expanse of arid or semiarid land, including the interior of Mexico and the southwestern United States, in response to intense solar heating of the ground. The hot surface heats the overlying air, lowering the density of the air column over an area broad enough for a synoptic-scale low to appear on a surface weather map. This **warm-core cyclone** (or *thermal low*) is very shallow, and its circulation weakens rapidly with altitude, that is, away from the heat source (the ground). The surface counterclockwise circulation frequently reverses at some altitude, and an anticyclone overlies the thermal low in the middle and upper troposphere. While few clouds and little precipitation develop near the center of the thermal low that overlies the lower Colorado River Valley, to the east a flow of moist air on southeast winds produces afternoon showers and thunderstorms over the mountains of Arizona and New Mexico as part of the southwest monsoon (Chapter 9).

In this section, we have focused on the life cycle, tracks, and general weather conditions associated with extra-tropical cyclones. In the daily march of weather in middle latitudes, anticyclones follow cyclones.

Anticyclones

An **anticyclone** (or *high*) is, in many ways, the opposite of a cyclone (or *low*). In middle latitudes, cyclonic circulation favors the convergence (coming together) of contrasting air masses and development of fronts, clouds, and precipitation. In anticyclones, by contrast, subsiding air and diverging surface winds favor formation of a uniform air mass, no fronts, and generally fair skies (Figure 10.19). Air modifies as it moves away from a center of high pressure so that a semi-permanent anticyclone can be the source of different types of air masses. Like cyclones, anticyclones have either cold or warm cores.

FIGURE 10.19
A slow-moving anticyclone is responsible for bright sunny skies with just a few scattered clouds and light winds.

ARCTIC AND POLAR HIGHS

A **cold-core anticyclone** is actually a dome of continental polar (*cP*) or arctic (*A*) air and, depending on the specific type of air mass, is labeled either a **polar high** or an **arctic high**. Cold anticyclones are products of extreme radiational cooling over the often snow-covered continental interior of North America well north of the polar front. They are shallow systems in which the clockwise circulation weakens with altitude and frequently reverses aloft. Hence, a cold trough typically overlies a cold anticyclone.

Cold-core anticyclones are most intense (that is, they exert the highest surface pressures) in winter, when the associated air mass is coldest. The air is extremely stable in these systems, and soundings indicate a temperature inversion in the lowest kilometer or two, associated with strong subsidence and adiabatic heating above the inversion. Massive arctic or polar anticyclones with very high central pressures tend to remain stationary over their source region. The *Siberian high*, for example, is centered near Lake Baikal and from late November to early March has an average sea level pressure greater than 1030 mb. Lobes of cold air (smaller cold highs) often break away from arctic or polar highs. In North America, for example, cold air masses move out of source regions in Alaska and northwest Canada and slide southeasterly across the Prairie Provinces of southern Canada into the United States east of the Rockies. These cold anticyclones interact with the circulation of extra-tropical cyclones, helping to maintain and strengthen the temperature contrast across the cyclone's cold front. Hence, clearing skies and sharply lower temperatures usually follow winter storms.

On some occasions in winter, a particularly strong arctic high brings a surge of bitterly cold air that sweeps as far south as Florida, and rarely can even traverse the Gulf of Mexico into Central America. The resulting subfreezing temperatures can spell disaster for citrus growers. In the 1980s, for example, three exceptional cold waves invaded the Florida peninsula. For three days, beginning on Christmas Day 1983, an arctic air mass gripped Florida, dropping temperatures well below freezing through much of the state. Citrus trees covering 93,000 hectares (230,000 acres) were either killed or damaged for a total loss in excess of $1 billion. Again, on 21 January 1985, a cold wave of even greater severity than the one in 1983 further damaged surviving citrus trees. Subfreezing temperatures were reported as far south as Miami on the morning of 22 January. Losses from this double blow reduced citrus-producing acreage by almost 90% in Lake County, formerly Florida's second largest citrus-producing county. Some growers replanted, and the groves were beginning to recover when yet another deep freeze over Christmas weekend 1989 ruined much of central Florida's citrus crop.

WARM HIGHS

A **warm-core anticyclone** forms south of the polar front and consists of extensive areas of subsiding warm, dry air. Thickness arguments show that, like cold-core cyclones, warm-core anticyclones strengthen with altitude. They are massive systems with a circulation extending from Earth's surface up to the tropopause. The semipermanent subtropical anticyclones, such as the *Bermuda-Azores high*, are examples of warm-core highs. While extensions of these subtropical highs may stretch across North America, other warm-core anticyclones may develop over the interior of North America, especially in summer.

A cold high coincides with a shallow mass of cold, dense air and produces high surface air pressures compared to surrounding areas. How does a warm anticyclone produce high surface pressures? Whereas the central surface air pressure may be the same in both cold and warm anticyclones, an important difference is found in their vertical structures. The column of cold dense air in a cold-core anticyclone does not extend vertically nearly as far as the column of less dense warm air in a warm-core anticyclone. The greater mass of air over the center of a warm-core anticyclone, related to a higher tropopause, is responsible for the warm anticyclone's high surface pressure.

Cold-core anticyclones modify as they travel and may eventually become warm-core systems. As noted earlier, a cold-core anticyclone is actually a dome of relatively cold air, and as that air mass traverses land that is snow free, it is heated from below and moderates considerably, its pressure decreasing significantly. As a cold-core high drifts southeastward over the United States, air mass modification may be sufficiently great that the pressure system eventually merges with the warm-core subtropical high over the Atlantic.

ANTICYCLONE WEATHER

An anticyclone is a fair-weather system because surface winds blowing in a clockwise and outward direction (in the Northern Hemisphere) induce subsidence of air over a broad area. Because subsiding air is compressionally warmed, the relative humidity drops and clouds usually dissipate or fail to develop. Although anticyclones are fair-weather systems, they can produce extremes in weather. The lowest air temperatures of the winter are usually associated with an arctic high, whereas drought and excessive heat in summer are associated with a warm anticyclone that stalls. Sinking air also becomes more stable and a temperature inversion forms as we saw with the trade wind inversion (Chapter 9). This increased stability along with weak winds can cause an air pollution episode to develop under a slow moving or stalled anticyclone as mixing and dilution of pollutants is suppressed.

The horizontal air pressure gradient is weak over a broad region about the center of an anticyclone so that prevailing winds are light or the air is calm. At night, clear skies and light winds favor intense radiational cooling, perhaps resulting in dew, frost, or fog as air temperatures fall to the dewpoint or frost point. Away from the broad central region of an anticyclone, the horizontal air pressure gradient strengthens and so does the wind. With stronger winds, significant advection can occur. Typically, well to the east of the high center, northwest winds advect cold air southeastward, whereas to the west of the high center, southeast winds advect warm air northwestward. Air mass advection helps to increase the temperature contrast across the low pressure trough that separates highs, thereby favoring *frontogenesis*.

An understanding of the circulation in an anticyclone enables us to anticipate the sequence of weather as a high moves into and out of a middle latitude location. Consider what happens in winter as a cold anticyclone slides southeastward out of southern Canada and into the northeastern United States. The following sequence may take place over several days to a week, depending on the anticyclone's forward speed.

Ahead of the anticyclone, strong northwest winds bring a surge of cold continental polar or arctic air. Strong winds and falling temperatures produce low wind-chill temperatures. To the lee of the Great Lakes, heavy lake-effect snow showers break out (Chapter 8). Even hundreds of kilometers downwind of the lakes, instability showers bring light accumulations of snow (e.g., over the hills of West Virginia and western Pennsylvania). However, as the anticyclone drifts closer, winds slacken, skies clear, and nocturnal radiational cooling produces very low surface temperatures. Under these conditions, air temperatures dip to their lowest readings, especially where the ground is snow-covered. Then, as the anticyclone drifts away toward the southeast, winds again strengthen, but this time blowing from the south, and warm air advection begins. The first sign of warm air advection is the appearance of high, thin cirrus clouds in the western sky.

In summer, a Canadian high-pressure system causes the same advection patterns as in winter except that the temperature contrast between air masses is considerably less at that time of year. Air advected ahead of the high on northwesterly winds may be not much cooler than the air advected behind the high on southerly winds. Often, the most noticeable difference between northerly and southerly winds at middle latitudes in summer is a contrast in humidity. Air advected ahead of the high is often less humid with lower dewpoints, and therefore is more comfortable than the air advected behind the high.

At times in summer, however, an anticyclone becomes established east of the Rocky Mountains and remains in place for weeks. Such anticyclones are warm-core systems with a very deep circulation that is not readily displaced. Aloft, over the high is a warm ridge that may become cut-off from the prevailing westerly flow. With a *block* in place (Chapter 9), subsiding air associated with the anticyclone suppresses cloudiness and precipitation. Persistence of this pattern causes unusually high temperatures and eventually drought.

The pattern of air mass advection in an anticyclone also applies to an upper-level ridge. Cold air advection usually occurs ahead (to the east) of a ridge, while warm air advection occurs behind (to the west of) a ridge. The circulation in an anticyclone (or ridge) does not occur in isolation from the circulation in a cyclone (or trough). The atmosphere is a continuous fluid, with anticyclones following cyclones and cyclones following anticyclones. Northwest winds develop ahead of the high and on the back (west) side of a retreating low. Winds are caused by horizontal air pressure gradients that develop between migrating anticyclones and cyclones.

Local and Regional Circulation Systems

Air masses, fronts, cyclones, and anticyclones are synoptic-scale systems that dominate the weather of middle latitudes. Many other weather systems operating at smaller spatial and temporal scales also contribute to the variable weather of middle latitudes. In some cases, synoptic-scale systems set the boundary conditions that make smaller scale weather systems possible. We open our discussion of meso- and micro-scale systems with land and sea (or lake) breezes, chinook winds, desert winds, and mountain and valley breezes.

LAND AND SEA (OR LAKE) BREEZES

For people lucky enough to live near the ocean or a large lake, sea or lake breezes bring welcome respite from the oppressive heat of a summer afternoon. On warm days, if the synoptic-scale air pressure gradient is relatively weak, a cool wind sweeps inland from over the sea or large lake. Depending on the source, this refreshing wind is called either a **sea breeze** or a **lake breeze**. Both breezes owe their existence to differential heating of land and water.

When land and water are exposed to the same intensity of solar radiation, the land surface warms more than the water surface (Chapter 4). The relatively warm land heats the overlying air, thereby lowering air density. Compared to the land, the water is relatively cool, as is the air overlying the water. A local horizontal air pressure gradient develops between land and water, with the highest pressure over the water surface (Figure 10.20 Top). In response to this horizontal air pressure gradient, cool air sweeps inland. Aloft, continuity requires a return flow of air directed from land to water, with air rising over the relatively warm land and sinking over the relatively cool water.

Sea (or lake) breezes are shallow circulation systems, generally confined to the lowest 1000 m (3300 ft) of the troposphere. Typically, the breeze begins near the shoreline several hours after sunrise and gradually expands both inland and out over the body of water, attaining maximum strength by middle afternoon. The inland extent of the breeze varies from only a few hundred meters to tens of kilometers, depending in part on local topography.

Near sunset, the sea (or lake) breeze dies down. By late evening, however, surface winds begin to blow offshore as a **land breeze** due to a reversal in heat

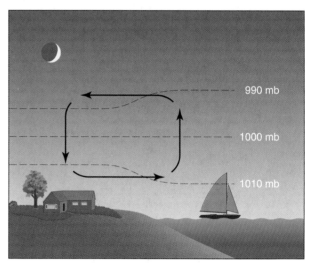

FIGURE 10.20
Vertical cross-sections showing isobaric (constant pressure) surfaces and circulation in a (Top) sea (or lake) breeze and (Bottom) land breeze. A sea (or lake) breeze blows onshore during the day whereas a land breeze blows offshore at night.

differential between land and water. At night, radiational cooling chills the land surface more than the water surface. Air over the land surface thus becomes cooler (denser) than air over the water surface. A horizontal gradient in air density gives rise to a horizontal air pressure gradient with higher pressure over the land and lower pressure over the sea (or lake). A cool offshore breeze develops, along with a return airflow aloft; air sinks over the relatively cool land and rises over the relatively warm water (Figure 10.20 Bottom). A land breeze attains maximum strength around sunrise but is generally weaker than a sea (or lake) breeze.

Earth's rotation typically does not significantly influence the direction of sea (or lake) and land breezes because the duration of these wind regimes is too brief and distances too small. In some places, however, the Coriolis Effect is responsible for a gradual shift in the direction of a sea breeze through the course of a day. Furthermore, in some localities, uplift produced along a sea-breeze front spurs the development of convective clouds and perhaps thunderstorms (Chapter 11).

CHINOOK WINDS

A **chinook wind** is a relatively warm and dry wind, which develops when air aloft is adiabatically compressed as it descends the leeward slopes of a mountain range. (The name comes from the Chinook Indians who lived along the lower Columbia River valley and coastal Washington and Oregon.) For every 1000 m of descent, the air temperature rises about 9.8 Celsius degrees (the *dry adiabatic lapse rate*). Air that flows down the slopes of high mountain ranges such as the eastern side of the Rocky Mountains in the U.S. and Canada can undergo considerable warming. As this unsaturated air warms, its relative humidity decreases. During a chinook, a band of clouds, known as the *chinook arch*, overhangs the Rocky Mountain crest marking the location where clouds that formed on the windward slopes vaporize.

Typically, a chinook develops when strong winds force a layer of stable air in the lower troposphere to ascend the windward slopes of a mountain range. When the air reaches the leeward slopes, its stability causes it to descend to its original altitude. The larger-scale circulation causes further descent of the air. For example, chinook winds may be directed down the leeward slopes of the Rocky Mountain Front Range by strong west winds associated with cyclones and anticyclones centered over the Great Plains well east of the mountains. In another case, downslope winds may be associated with the circulation produced by a large high pressure system centered over the Great Basin (in Utah) and a low pressure system tracking across the Canadian Rockies.

At the onset of a chinook, surface air temperatures often climb abruptly tens of degrees in response to the arrival of compressionally warmed air. On 6 January 1966, at Pincher Creek, Alberta, a chinook sent the temperature soaring 21 Celsius degrees (38 Fahrenheit degrees) in only 4 minutes! The sudden spring-like warmth may just as quickly give way to bitter cold as the chinook winds abate. For example, along the foot of the Rockies, a shift of synoptic-scale winds from west to north brings an abrupt end to the chinook, the return of polar or arctic air, and plunging temperatures.

According to Native American tradition, chinook means *snow eater*, referring to the catastrophic effect of the warm, dry wind on a snow cover. As noted in Chapter 6, air ascending the windward slopes of a mountain range loses much of its water vapor to condensation and deposition (cloud formation) and precipitation. As air descends the leeward slopes and is compressionally warmed, the relative humidity drops dramatically. Because the chinook is both warm and very dry, a snow cover sublimates and melts rapidly. It is not unusual for a half meter of snow to disappear in this way in only a few hours.

Chinook winds are strong and gusty and, locally, may reach destructive speeds, especially along the foothills of the Front Range of the Rocky Mountains. At Boulder, CO, in the foothills just northwest of Denver (Figure 10.21), violent downslope winds, sometimes gusting to 160 km per hr (100 mph) or higher, unroof buildings and topple power poles. On average, the community sustains about $1 million in property damage each year because of these destructive winds.

Researchers do not agree on the precise mechanism that triggers destructive chinook winds, but according to one view, strong downslope winds are linked to the disturbance of the planetary-scale westerlies as they pass over the Rockies. Recall from Chapter 7 that a prominent north-south oriented mountain range such as the Rockies deflects a westerly air flow into a *standing wave*, a stationary pattern of crests and troughs extending downwind of the mountain range that gives rise to *mountain-wave clouds*. A chinook is actually a segment of the wave that dips down the leeward slopes

FIGURE 10.21
Boulder, CO, situated in the foothills of the Rockies, experiences some particularly strong and destructive downslope winds.

of the mountain range. Apparently, in a violent chinook, very energetic turbulent eddies that are generated aloft are transported downward into the foothills so that surface winds become very strong and gusty.

Chinook-type winds are not restricted to the leeward slopes of the Rockies. A similar wind, called the *foehn* (or *föhn*) blows into the Alpine valleys of Austria, Germany, and Switzerland. The same type of warm, dry wind is drawn down the leeward slopes of the Andes in Argentina, where it is known as the *zonda*. In southern California, the **Santa Ana wind** is another chinook-type wind that typically occurs in autumn and winter. A strong high pressure system centered over the Great Basin sends northeast winds over the southwestern United States, driving air downslope from the desert plateaus of Utah and Nevada, around the Sierra Nevada, and as far west as coastal southern California (Figure 10.22). Adiabatic compression produces hot, dry winds that desiccate vegetation and contribute to outbreaks of forest and brush fires. Santa Ana winds sometimes gust to 130 to 145 km per hr (80 to 90 mph) and almost always cause some property damage. For more on the Santa Ana wind and the fire hazard in southern California, refer to this chapter's third Essay, "Santa Ana Winds and California Fire Weather."

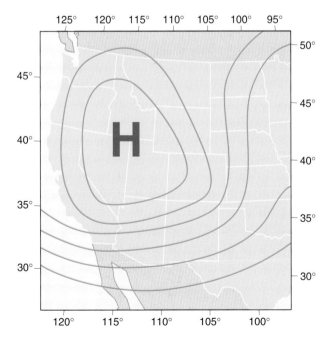

FIGURE 10.22
Schematic representation of the surface weather pattern that favors development of hot and dry Santa Ana winds over Southern California. Solid lines are isobars.

DESERT WINDS

Deserts are windy places primarily because of intense solar heating of the ground. In deserts, most of the absorbed radiation goes into sensible heating because water is scarce, vegetation is sparse, and relatively little heat is used for evapotranspiration. In some spots, the midday temperature of the ground surface can exceed 55 °C (131 °F). Such a hot surface generates a *superadiabatic lapse rate* in the lowest air layer (that is, a lapse rate greater than 9.8 Celsius degrees per 1000 m). A superadiabatic lapse rate means great instability, vigorous convection, and gusty surface winds. But with negligible water vapor, few clouds form. The strength and gustiness of the wind vary with the intensity of solar radiation so that wind speeds and gustiness usually peak in the early afternoon and during the warmest months.

A **dust devil**, a whirling mass of dust-laden air, is a common sight over flat, dry terrain. Dust devils develop on sunny days in response to local variations in surface characteristics (i.e., albedo, moisture supply, topography) that give rise to localized hot spots. Air over a hot spot is heated and forced to rise by cooler surface winds that converge toward the hot spot. Shear in the horizontal wind causes the column of rising hot air to spin about a nearly vertical axis. The source of wind shear may be nearby obstacles that disturb the horizontal wind or the overturning of air induced by extreme instability. In the process, dust is lifted off the ground and whirled about, making the system visible. Unlike a tornado, a dust devil is not linked to a cloud.

Dust devils are micro-scale systems. The most common ones are small whirls less than 1.0 m (about 3 ft) across that typically last less than a minute. On rare occasions, a dust devil exceeds 100 m (330 ft) in diameter and whirls about for 20 minutes or longer. Such intense dust devils may be visible to altitudes topping 900 m (3000 ft), but the invisible portion of the rising air column may reach 4500 m (15,000 ft).

Most dust devils are too weak to cause serious property damage. The larger ones, however, are known to produce winds in excess of 75 km per hr (45 mph) and may cause some damage. According to the National Weather Service (NWS), every year in New Mexico, several large dust devils cause substantial damage to mobile homes, travel trailers, and buildings under construction. In the spring of 1991, a powerful dust devil that fortuitously passed over anemometers at the NWS Forecast Office at Albuquerque produced a wind gust of 113 km per hr (70 mph).

Thunderstorms or migrating cyclones produce larger scale winds in deserts. Surface winds associated with these weather systems can give rise to dust storms or sandstorms, the difference between the two hinging on the size range of the loose surface sediments lifted by the wind. Dust consists of very small particles (diameters less than 0.06 mm or 0.002 in.) that can be carried by winds to great altitudes. Sand, typically covering only a small fraction of desert terrain, consists of larger particles (diameters of 0.06 to 2.0 mm or 0.002 to 0.08 in.) that are transported by the wind within about a meter of the ground. Dust storms and sandstorms can be hazardous, abruptly reducing visibility to perhaps only a few meters, contributing to vehicular accidents on highways.

The strong, gusty downdraft of a thunderstorm generates one of the most spectacular dust storms, known as a **haboob**. In a desert, rain falling from thunderstorm clouds often evaporates completely in the dry air beneath cloud base and does not reach the ground. A thunderstorm downdraft, however, exits the cloud base, striking the ground as a surge of cool, gusty air that lifts dust off the ground. The dusty mass rolls along the ground as a huge ominous black cloud that severely restricts visibility. A haboob may be more than 100 km (60 mi) wide and may reach altitudes of several thousand meters. These dust storms are most common in the northern and central Sudan especially near Khartoum. They also occur in the American southwest deserts.

MOUNTAIN AND VALLEY BREEZES

In summer, a localized circulation system may develop in wide, deep mountain valleys that face the sun (Figure 10.23). After the winter snows have melted, bare valley walls strongly absorb solar radiation and sensible heating raises the temperature of air in contact with the valley walls. Air adjacent to the valley wall becomes warmer and less dense than air at the same altitude out over the valley floor. The cooler, denser air over the valley sinks as air adjacent to the valley walls blows upslope as a **valley breeze**. The ascending valley breeze expands and cools and may trigger development of cumulus clouds near the summit.

A valley breeze is best developed between late morning and sunset. By midnight, the circulation reverses direction and persists until about sunrise. Under clear skies, nocturnal radiational cooling chills the valley walls and the air in contact with the walls also cools. Now air adjacent to the valley walls is colder and denser than the air at the same altitude above the valley floor. Air over the valley is forced to ascend as the cold, gusty **mountain breeze** blows downslope. Cold, dense air accumulates in the valley bottom where additional radiational cooling may lead to formation of fog or low stratus clouds.

Valley breeze

Mountain breeze

FIGURE 10.23
Schematic representation of the circulation in valley and mountain breezes.

Mountain and valley breezes are most common during fair weather and when synoptic-scale winds are light. Hence, these localized winds typically occur when mountainous regions are under the influence of a slow-moving anticyclone.

Conclusions

We have now examined the features of the principal weather makers of middle latitudes: air masses, fronts, cyclones, and anticyclones. We have seen how these synoptic-scale weather systems interact with one another and how they are linked to the planetary-scale circulation described in Chapter 9. Also recall from our discussion in Chapter 4 that synoptic-scale weather systems play an important role in poleward heat transport.

We also covered the characteristics of several local and regional weather systems. The domination of smaller scale weather systems by the larger scale atmospheric circulation is apparent; that is, the planetary- and synoptic-scale patterns set boundary conditions for any smaller scale circulation system. In some cases, synoptic-scale winds reinforce meso-scale winds, as when regional winds blow in the same direction as a sea or lake breeze. In other cases, synoptic-scale winds overwhelm meso-scale winds, as when northerly winds sweep along the eastern edge of the Rocky Mountains and eliminate the possibility of chinook winds. We continue our examination of weather systems in the next chapter with a look at meso-scale and micro-scale systems, including thunderstorms and tornadoes.

Basic Understandings

- Air masses are classified on the basis of temperature and humidity, characteristics that are acquired in their source region. The four basic air mass types are cold and dry, cold and humid, warm and dry, and warm and humid.

- Air masses form over land (continental) and ocean (maritime), and at high latitudes (polar) and low latitudes (tropical). Arctic air is distinguished from polar air by its bitter cold.

- Air masses modify as they travel from one place to another. The degree of modification depends on air mass stability and the nature of the surface over which the air travels, specifically whether the surface is warmer or colder than the air mass.

- A front is a narrow zone of transition between air masses that contrast in temperature or humidity. The four types of fronts are: stationary, warm, cold, and occluded. A stationary front is just that, a front that exhibits essentially no lateral movement. A stationary front becomes a cold front if it begins to move in such a way that colder (more dense) air displaces warmer (less dense) air. If a stationary front begins to move in such a way that the warm (less dense) air advances while the cold (more dense) air retreats, the front changes in character and becomes a warm front.

- An occluded front forms late in the life cycle of a wave cyclone as the system moves into colder air. The cold front sweeps around the low to overtake and merge with the warm front, forcing the warm air aloft. The three types of occluded fronts are designated cold, warm, or neutral depending on the temperature contrast between the air behind the cold front and the air ahead of the warm front.

- Weather associated with stationary or warm fronts typically consists of a broad stratiform cloud and precipitation shield that may extend hundreds of kilometers on the cold side of the surface front. Weather along or ahead of a cold front usually consists of a narrow band of cumuliform clouds and brief rain or snow showers, or thunderstorms.

- As an extra-tropical cyclone progresses through its life cycle, it is supported and steered by the upper-level circulation toward the east and northeast. An extra-tropical cyclone typically begins as a wave along the polar front and deepens as the surface air pressure continues to drop. Winds strengthen and frontal weather develops. The cyclone finally occludes as the faster-moving cold front approaches the slower-moving warm front and the upper-level trough becomes vertically stacked over the surface cyclone.

- The life cycle of an extra-tropical cyclone can vary significantly in length. A typical cyclone requires about one day in each of the stages leading up to maximum intensity. However, when conditions are favorable, a cyclone can progress from birth to peak intensity in 36 hrs or less. In some cases, the cyclone never attains occlusion, instead spending most of its life span as a weak wave cyclone rippling along a stationary front.

- The conveyor belt model describes the three-dimensional structure of a mature cyclone in terms of three air streams: warm and humid, cold, and dry.

- The track followed by a cyclone is key to the type of weather experienced at a given locality. On the cold side of the storm track, winds back with time (turn counterclockwise) and there are no frontal passages. On the warm side of the storm track, winds veer (turn clockwise) with time and a cold front follows a warm front.

- Across eastern North America, Alberta-track

cyclones are most frequent, but Colorado and coastal storm tracks are responsible for heavier precipitation, especially in winter.

- A warm-core cyclone (thermal low) is stationary, has no fronts, and is associated with hot dry weather. These relatively shallow systems develop in the American southwest desert.

- A cold-core anticyclone is a shallow system that coincides with a dome of continental polar or arctic air. Cold air advection occurs ahead of a high and warm air advection occurs behind a high.

- A warm-core anticyclone, such as a semipermanent subtropical high, extends from Earth's surface to the tropopause, and produces a broad area of subsiding warm, dry air.

- When synoptic-scale winds are weak, localized horizontal air pressure gradients can develop between land and sea (or lake). In response, winds blow onshore during the day (as a sea or lake breeze) and offshore at night (as a land breeze).

- A chinook wind consists of compressionally warmed, stable air that is forced down the leeward slopes of a mountain range by the circulation about cyclones or anticyclones.

- Intense solar heating of desert terrain produces a steep temperature lapse rate in the lowest air layer. Dust devils may develop in such unstable air. In addition, strong winds associated with thunderstorms or migrating cyclones may cause dust storms or sandstorms.

- Mountain and valley breezes develop in summer in deep, wide mountain valleys facing the sun. A valley breeze is an upslope wind that forms during the day, and a mountain breeze is a downslope wind that forms at night.

Review

1. Identify and describe the air masses that regularly invade North America.
2. How do the properties of continental polar air change between winter and summer?
3. Compare and contrast the typical cloud and precipitation pattern with a cold front versus a warm front.
4. A wave cyclone has a cold side and a warm side. Explain this statement and its significance.
5. Why does an Alberta-track cyclone typically produce less precipitation than a Colorado-track cyclone?
6. What happens when a cyclone occludes?
7. Why do most cyclones that cross the lower 48-states of the U.S. track toward the east and northeast?
8. Why is extreme nocturnal radiational cooling associated with a polar or arctic high?
9. Explain why a sea breeze will develop on some but not all summer days.
10. Why is a chinook wind both dry and warm?

Critical Thinking

1. Describe how air that originates over the Pacific Ocean modifies as it travels from west to east across the United States.
2. Why is the slope of a cold front steeper than the slope of a warm front?
3. In summer, we may experience passage of a cold front and yet the air ahead of the front has about the same temperature as the air behind the front. How can this be a "cold" front?
4. Why is air mass stability an important factor in determining the type of weather that is associated with a front?
5. Speculate on the type of weather that might develop along a sea breeze front. Justify your response.
6. A mountain valley is oriented so that at midday, one slope is in bright sunshine and the other is in shade. If synoptic-scale winds are light, describe the air circulation that develops in the valley.
7. Would you expect a monsoon circulation over any portion of North America? Support your answer.
8. Based on your understanding of how atmospheric stability influences vertical motion, explain the following observation: In spring, in the Great Lakes region, cumulus clouds develop over the land but not over the adjacent lake waters.
9. All other factors being equal, how might the depth of a lake affect the development of a lake breeze?
10. In winter, the coldest weather often occurs after an intense extra-tropical cyclone has passed through the area. Explain why.

ESSAY: The Case of the Missing Storm

A cyclone that sweeps ashore along the west coast of North America seems to disappear from the sea-level pressure pattern as it tracks inland over the mountainous West. A few days later, a low develops to the east of the Rocky Mountain Front Range, typically on the plains of Alberta or eastern Colorado. What actually happened to the storm as it crossed the mountains?

An extra-tropical cyclone tracks eastward onshore from the Pacific Ocean. Visualize the cyclone as a huge cylinder of air spinning about a vertical axis in a counterclockwise direction as viewed from above (Figure 1). The cylinder has Earth's surface as its lower boundary and the tropopause as its upper boundary. Because the tropopause remains at essentially the same altitude over the region, the column is forced to shrink in height as the cylinder moves up the windward slopes of a mountain range. The cylinder widens as it shrinks and the spin of the cylinder slows; that is, the storm's circulation weakens. As the cylinder of air then descends the leeward slopes of the mountain range, it stretches vertically and contracts horizontally, and the cyclonic spin strengthens. Weakening cyclonic circulation upslope followed by strengthening cyclonic circulation downslope account for the seeming disappearance and reappearance of the storm as it traverses mountainous terrain.

The changes in the storm's circulation are analogous to what happens to an ice skater performing a spin. The skater changes her spin rate by extending or drawing in her arms. When she extends her arms (analogous to horizontal

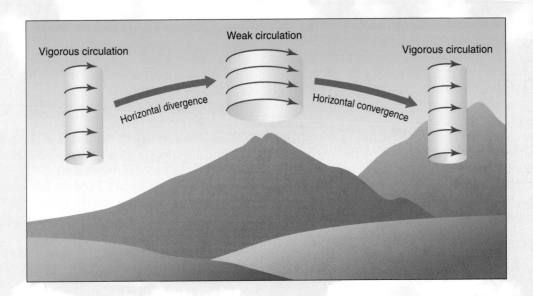

FIGURE 1
The cyclonic spin of a cylinder of air weakens as it ascends the windward slopes of a mountain range and strengthens as it descends the leeward slopes of the mountain range.

divergence and the widening of our cylinder), her spin rate slows. When the skater brings her arms close to her body (analogous to horizontal convergence and the contracting of our cylinder), she spins faster. Both the spinning skater and the cyclone passing through the mountains conserve angular momentum. Simply put, *conservation of angular momentum* means that a change in the radius of a rotating mass is balanced by a change in its rotational speed. An increase in radius (horizontal divergence) due to shrinking of the vertical column is accompanied by a reduction in rotational rate whereas a decrease in radius (horizontal convergence) due to stretching of the column is accompanied by an increase in rotational rate.

ESSAY: Nor'easters

A *nor'easter* is an intense extra-tropical cyclone that tracks along the East Coast of North America and is named for the direction from which its powerful onshore winds blow (Figure 1). They are most frequent from October through April, when seasonal contrasts in air mass characteristics (i.e., temperature and humidity) are greatest. The system moves toward the northeast and, if centered just offshore, strong onshore winds on the northern and northwestern flanks of the system (blowing from the east and northeast) can cause considerable coastal erosion, flooding, and property damage.

Warmer   Colder

FIGURE 1
Color-enhanced infrared satellite image of an intense extra-tropical cyclone (nor'easter) over the North Atlantic Ocean. [NOAA satellite photo]

Although rarely attaining the strength of even a weak hurricane, a nor'easter can pack a powerful punch because it often impacts a much greater swath of coastline than a typical East Coast hurricane. A particularly destructive aspect of either storm system is the associated storm surge. A *storm surge* is a great dome of seawater that inundates the coast; it is produced by strong onshore winds and low air pressure. The diameter of an average nor'easter is about three times that of an average hurricane. Whereas a hurricane tends to track directly from sea to land, impacting perhaps only about 100 to 150 km (60 to 90 mi) of coastline, a nor'easter often moves parallel to the coast so that its onshore winds may sweep over more than 1500 km (900 mi) of coastline. A less intense but slow-moving nor'easter can actually cause more damage than a more intense but fast-moving nor'easter. Winds in the slow-moving system blow in the same onshore direction for a longer period than is the case with the fast-moving system. Persistent onshore winds increase the likelihood of a destructive storm surge and high waves.

One of the most noteworthy nor'easters of the 20th century in terms of its widespread impact on human activities occurred on 12-15 March 1993. A major storm system tracked from the Gulf of Mexico up the Eastern Seaboard. Although the storm system's size and minimum central pressure (960 mb) were not particularly unusual, its human impact was enormous, primarily because of its track along the densely populated East Coast. This track enabled the storm system to draw into its circulation a tremendous amount of moisture from the warm ocean waters just off the coast, while the cold air inland helped the storm produce heavy snow over the highly populated areas to the north and west of its track from Alabama to Maine.

Snow fell along the Gulf Coast with 7.6 cm (3 in.) reported at Mobile, AL and up to 13 cm (5 in.) measured in the Florida Panhandle, the greatest single snowfall in the state's history. The 33 cm (13 in.) that blanketed Birmingham, AL not only set a new 24-hr snowfall record for any month, but also set records for maximum snow depth, greatest snowfall in a single storm, and maximum snowfall for a single month. Total storm snowfall was tremendous in the Appalachians including 142 cm (56 in.) at Mt. LeConte, TN and 127 cm (50 in.) at Mount Mitchell, NC. Just about every official weather station in West Virginia set a new 24-hr snowfall record with 76 cm (30 in.) reported at Beckley, WV. Further to the north, snow totaled 64 cm (25 in.) at Pittsburgh, PA, 69 cm (27 in.) at Albany, NY, and 109 cm (43 in.) at Syracuse, NY. Heavy snow was whipped by winds gusting in excess of hurricane force along the coast; Boston, MA recorded gusts to 131 km per hr (81 mph). For the first time in history, snow forced the closing of every major East Coast airport. Thousands of people were isolated in the Appalachian Mountains; more than 3 million customers were without electricity at one time; hundreds of roofs collapsed under the weight of accumulated snow; and about 200 homes on North Carolina's Outer Banks were severely damaged by winds and flooding.

In addition to property damage caused by heavy snow and high winds, a squall line associated with the storm produced 27 tornadoes in Florida, and a 3-m (10-ft) storm surge in the Gulf of Mexico flooded the Apalachicola area. All told, this nor'easter claimed about 270 lives, more than three times the combined death toll of Hurricanes Hugo and Andrew, and caused damage estimated at $7 billion (in 2002 dollars), the costliest extra-tropical cyclone in U.S. history.

In January 2006, NOAA introduced a scale that quickly categorizes the impact of major snowstorms (including nor'easters) on the Northeast. The focus on Northeast snowstorms stems from their potential disruption of transportation systems and economic effects on the rest of the nation. The *Northeast Snowfall Impact Scale (NSIS)* rates snowstorms on the basis of snowfall amount, the area affected by the snowstorm, and the population in the path of the storm. With this scale, assessment of snowstorm impact is available in days instead of weeks. Snowstorms are assigned to one of five categories: 1 (notable), 2 (significant), 3 (major), 4 (crippling), or 5 (extreme). The highest rating on the NSES results from storms producing heavy snowfall over large geographical areas encompassing major metropolitan centers. For example, the 12-15 March 1993 nor'easter rated 5 on the Northeast Snowfall Impact Scale. Development of the scale was the joint effort of Louis Uccellini, director of NOAA's National Centers for Environmental Prediction (NCEP) and Paul Kocin of *The Weather Channel*. The NSIS joins the Saffir-Simpson Hurricane Intensity Scale (Chapter 12) and the Fujita scale for tornadoes (Chapter 11) as tools for better informing the public on weather extremes.

ESSAY: Santa Ana Winds and California Fire Weather

Every autumn, *Santa Ana winds* descend the mountain slopes of interior southern California and sweep over the coastal plain to the sea. These hot dry winds, named for the Santa Ana Canyon or the Santa Ana Mountains southeast of Los Angeles, blow over a landscape parched by the long dry summer. Santa Ana winds further desiccate the vegetation, making the southern California landscape particularly vulnerable to wildfire. Also contributing to the fire danger is a shrub community known as *chaparral* that dominates the hill slopes. The tissues of these plants contain oils that readily ignite; in fact, chaparral shrubs practically explode when exposed to flame. Periodic wildfires, whipped by Santa Ana winds roar down the canyons of southern California. One of the earliest accounts of such fires was in October 1542 when Juan Rodriguez Cabrillo, whose ship lay anchored off the Los Angeles Basin, observed hot desert winds blowing and fires burning.

In southern California, winter rains usually follow the summer dry season. (Dry summers and wet winters characterize a *Mediterranean-type* climate. For example, in Los Angeles, on average, almost 95% of annual rainfall occurs from November through April.) Falling on the nutrient-rich ashes of burned vegetation, winter rains spur re-sprouting of shrubs. Furthermore, fire followed by rain also triggers germination of seeds that have been dormant in the soil. Renewal of vegetative cover helps re-stabilize hillsides denuded by wildfires. However, if heavy rains fall before vegetation has a chance to stabilize burnt-over slopes, soil and debris are washed from the bare ground and flushed into streambeds. Rainwater also percolates into the loosely consolidated upper soil layer. When this layer becomes saturated, it flows down steep hillsides as a river of mud, covering roadways and inundating homes. These mudflows are the greatest post-fire problem. Furthermore, even a single winter of below-average rainfall significantly elevates the potential for autumnal wildfires.

Native Americans adapted to this climate/fire regime of southern California by building temporary shelters that they could readily move out of harm's way. Furthermore, these people routinely set small fires (*controlled burns*) that improved the habitat for game animals and thus made hunting easier. The arrival of European settlers in southern California marked the establishment of permanent dwellings and efforts to suppress wildfires. In subsequent centuries the population of southern California grew slowly, but since the end of World War II, southern California has been one of the fastest growing regions of the nation. Hundreds of thousands of homes were constructed in the chaparral-covered foothills. A combination of urban sprawl, summer drought, fire-prone vegetation, and autumnal Santa Ana winds set the stage for highly destructive wildfires.

Such a holocaust erupted on 27 October 1993 when fifteen major fires broke out on hillsides from Ventura County south to San Diego County. Firefighters were largely unable to contain the wildfires until Santa Ana winds finally died down three days later. After several days of relatively weak winds, the regional air pressure gradient again strengthened and Santa Ana winds resumed, whipping flames through previously untouched areas of Malibu and Topanga. In the aftermath, state and federal emergency services estimated total property damage at more than $1 billion. Fires scorched more than 80,000 hectares (almost 200,000 acres) and destroyed more than 1200 structures.

About ten years later, in October 2003, southern California experienced the most devastating wildland fires in the state's history. Fourteen major fires broke out affecting Ventura, Los Angeles, San Bernardino, and San Diego counties (Figure 1). The fires claimed 24 lives, destroyed 3710 homes, and burned over 303,542 hectares (750,043 acres). Thousands of residents fled their homes and headed for evacuation centers. At the peak of the fire siege, more than 14,000 firefighters from federal, state, and local agencies battled the fires from the ground and air. Once again Santa Ana winds fanned the flames that consumed the considerable fuel (dead, dying, and diseased vegetation) that had accumulated at the wildland/urban interface.

What can be done to reduce the Santa Ana fire hazard? Nothing can be done to alter the normal sequence of summer drought, autumnal Santa Ana winds, and variable winter rains. People can change where they chose to live, however. Some people argue that zoning ordinances should be enacted and enforced that prohibit construction of houses in locales subject to natural hazards such as wildfires and mudflows. Alternatively, ordinances could require that dwellings be constructed of fireproof materials (particularly roofs and outside walls). Furthermore, chaparral vegetation could be cleared within a designated perimeter of buildings. At present, many people permit shrubby vegetation to grow up to the edge of their homes for privacy and a sense of living with nature.

If wildfire is suppressed, chaparral shrubs grow larger and denser and annually add more leaves and twigs to the ground litter layer. Because of the buildup of fuel, the chaparral, once ignited, burns even more intensely. Periodic setting of controlled burns would reduce the frequency and severity of wildfires. With such a strategy, people work with and not against the forces of nature.

Figure 1
Several massive wildfires were raging across southern California over the weekend of October 25, 2003. Whipped by the hot, dry Santa Ana winds that blow toward the coast from interior deserts, at least one fire grew 10,000 acres in just 6 hours. The Moderate Resolution Imaging Spectroradiometer (MODIS) on the Terra satellite captured this image of the fires and clouds of smoke spread over the region on October 26, 2003. [Courtesy NASA].

CHAPTER 11

THUNDERSTORMS AND TORNADOES

Approaching thunderstorm with lead gust front. [Courtesy NOAA]

Case in Point

On 3 May 1999, all the essential ingredients for an outbreak of severe weather came together in the atmosphere over Oklahoma, northern Texas, and south central Kansas. Before that day was done, more than 70 tornadoes were reported in the region. Twenty-six tornadoes struck in or near Oklahoma City. The most intense of these tornadoes (rating F5 on the Fujita tornado intensity scale) took 38 lives as it tore through Moore and Bridge Creek, southern suburbs of Oklahoma City. Two hours later, an F4 tornado claimed 6 lives at Haysville, KS.

    The rawinsonde sounding at Norman, OK early on the afternoon of 3 May indicated a shallow layer of warm, humid air near the surface with dewpoints near 21 °C (70 °F). This warm, humid layer was capped by a temperature inversion at an altitude of about 1500 m (5000 ft) with much drier air aloft. As long as the *capping inversion* was in place, convection currents could surge no higher than about 1500 m but as the hours passed the temperature and humidity contrast between the low-level and upper-level air layers grew, increasing the potential for deep convection and severe thunderstorm development. The Norman rawinsonde sounding also indicated a change in wind direction with altitude, blowing from the south at the surface to west or west-southwest aloft. This vertical *wind shear* is another key ingredient for the development of severe weather.

The afternoon arrival of a jet streak triggered the round of tornadic thunderstorms by lifting the air column and erasing the capping inversion. Convection currents surged into the upper troposphere and even into the lower stratosphere. Massive supercell thunderstorms developed explosively and spawned violent tornadoes.

Driving Question:
What conditions in the atmosphere favor development of severe convective weather systems?

Most of us are familiar with typical thunderstorm weather—the blackening sky and abrupt freshening of wind, followed by bursts of torrential rain, flashes of lightning, and rumbles of thunder. Often the system's cool breezes and rains bring welcome relief on a hot, muggy summer afternoon. For a farmer whose crops are wilting under the searing summer sun, the rains may be an economic lifesaver. Some thunderstorms become violent, however, and wreak havoc. Lightning starts fires, strong winds uproot trees and damage buildings, heavy rains cause flooding, and some thunderstorms produce destructive hail or tornadoes.

Although less than 1% of all thunderstorms spawn tornadoes, in some areas of North America, the possibility of a tornado is the principal reason why people fear thunderstorms. Tornadoes are the most intense of all weather systems. They are associated with certain severe thunderstorms and can take lives and cause considerable property damage. This chapter covers thunderstorms and tornadoes, their characteristics, life cycles, geographical and seasonal distribution, and associated hazards.

Thunderstorm Life Cycle

A **thunderstorm** is a meso-scale weather system that is accompanied by lightning and thunder, affects a relatively small area, and is short-lived. A thunderstorm is the product of vigorous convection that extends high into the troposphere, sometimes reaching the tropopause or even higher. Upward surging air currents are made visible by billowing cauliflower-shaped cumuliform clouds. A thunderstorm consists of one or more convection cells, each of which progresses through a life cycle that is divided into three stages: towering cumulus, mature, and dissipating (Figure 11.1).

TOWERING CUMULUS STAGE

If conditions in the atmosphere are favorable, cumulus clouds build both vertically and laterally (Figure 11.2). This is the initial or **towering cumulus stage** of thunderstorm formation. Over a period of perhaps 10 to 15 minutes, cumulus cloud tops surge upward to altitudes of 8000 to 10,000 m (26,000 to 33,000 ft). At the same time, neighboring cumulus clouds merge so that by the end of the cumulus stage, the storm's lateral dimension may be 10 to 15 km (6 to 9 mi).

Cumulus clouds are products of convection within the atmosphere (Chapter 4). Based on mode of origin, convection is of two types, free and forced. Intense solar heating of Earth's surface triggers *free convection*, but usually free convection is not sufficiently energetic to generate a thunderstorm. Frontal or orographic lifting or converging surface winds strengthen convection, a process known as *forced convection*. Most thunderstorms are products of forced convection.

Visualize the ascending branch of a convection current as a continuous stream of parcels of warm, unsaturated air. The rising parcels expand and initially cool at the dry adiabatic lapse rate (9.8 Celsius degrees per 1000 m) until they reach the *convective condensation level (CCL)*, where the relative humidity reaches 100%, water vapor condenses, and cumulus clouds begin forming. The more humid the air is to begin with, the less the expansional

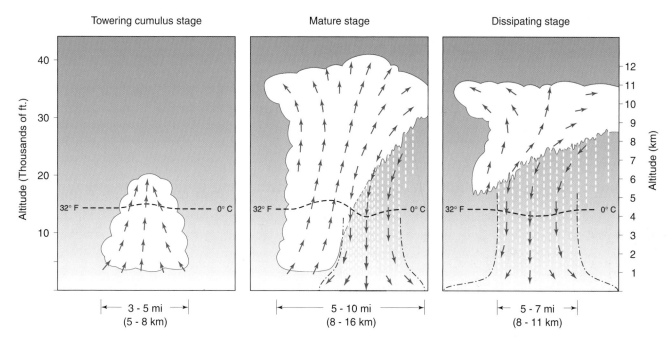

FIGURE 11.1

The life cycle of a thunderstorm cell consists of towering cumulus, mature, and dissipating stages.

cooling needed for air parcels to achieve saturation and the lower is the base of cumulus clouds. The bases of cumulus clouds usually are lower in Florida, where the relative humidity is higher, than in New Mexico, where the relative humidity is lower.

Latent heat released during condensation adds to the buoyancy of the saturated (cloudy) air parcels, and they surge upward while cooling at the moist adiabatic lapse rate (averaging 6 Celsius degrees per 1000 m). Air parcels continue ascending as long as they are warmer (less dense) than the surrounding air, that is, as long as the

ambient air is unstable (Chapter 6). Some of the saturated parcels surge through the cloud top and evaporate in the relatively dry air above the cloud, increasing the water vapor concentration of that air. Because air above the cloud is now more humid, subsequent parcels are able to ascend higher before evaporating. As this process is repeated, the cumulus cloud billows upward. A cumuliform cloud that shows significant vertical growth and resembles a huge cauliflower is known as a **cumulus congestus cloud**. If vertical growth continues, a cumulus congestus cloud builds into a **cumulonimbus cloud**, a thunderstorm cloud with characteristic anvil top, producing precipitation, lightning, and thunder.

During the cumulus stage of the thunderstorm life cycle, saturated air streams upward throughout the cell as an **updraft**. The updraft is strong enough to keep water droplets and ice crystals suspended in the upper reaches of the cloud. For this reason, precipitation does not occur during the towering cumulus stage.

MATURE STAGE

By convention, the towering cumulus stage ends and the **mature stage** begins when precipitation first reaches Earth's surface. Typically, this stage lasts about 10 to 20 minutes. The cumulative weight of water droplets and ice crystals eventually becomes so great that they can no longer be supported by the updraft. Rain, ice pellets, and snow descend through the cloud and drag the adjacent

FIGURE 11.2

Towering cumulus clouds may signal the initial stage in the development of a thunderstorm.

FIGURE 11.3
Thunderstorm cells can develop along the gust front ahead of the main thunderstorm. In this radar image, the gust front shows up as an arc-shaped band.

air downward, creating a strong **downdraft** alongside the updraft. At the same time, unsaturated air at the edge of the cloud is drawn into the cloud, a process known as *entrainment*. (Actually, entrainment continues throughout the life cycle of a thunderstorm cell.) Entrained air mixes with the cloudy (saturated) air, causing some of the water droplets and ice crystals to vaporize. The consequent evaporative cooling weakens the buoyant uplift and strengthens the downdraft.

The downdraft exits the base of the cloud and spreads out along Earth's surface, well in advance of the parent thunderstorm cell, as a mass of cool, gusty air. The downdraft is relatively cool because of evaporative cooling beneath the cloud base that offsets to some extent the compressional warming of the downdraft. At the surface, the arc-shaped leading edge of downdraft air resembles a miniature cold front and is called a **gust front**. Uplift along the advancing gust front sometimes produces additional cumuliform clouds that may evolve into secondary thunderstorm cells tens of kilometers ahead of the parent cell (Figure 11.3).

Ominous-appearing low clouds are sometimes associated with thunderstorm gust fronts. A **roll cloud** is an elongated, tube-shaped cloud that appears to rotate slowly about its horizontal axis. The roll cloud occurs behind the gust front and beneath, but detached from, the cumulonimbus cloud. How this cloud forms is not fully

understood. Although appearances might suggest otherwise, roll clouds are seldom accompanied by severe weather. This is not the case for shelf clouds. A **shelf cloud**, also called an *arcus cloud*, is a low, elongated cloud that is wedge-shaped with a flat base. This cloud appears at the edge of a gust front and beneath and attached to the cumulonimbus cloud. A shelf cloud is thought to develop as a consequence of uplift of stable warm and humid air along the gust front. Damaging surface winds may occur under a shelf cloud, and sometimes this cloud is associated with a severe thunderstorm.

A thunderstorm cell attains maximum intensity during its mature stage. Rain is heaviest (especially during the first 5 minutes or so), lightning is most frequent, and hail, strong surface winds, and even tornadoes may develop. Cloud tops can build to altitudes in excess of 18,000 m (about 60,000 ft). Strong winds at such great altitudes distort the cloud top into an anvil shape (Figure 11.4). The flat top of the anvil indicates that convection currents have reached the extremely stable air of the tropopause. Only in severe thunderstorms will convection currents overshoot this altitude, causing clouds to billow into the lower stratosphere before collapsing back into the troposphere. Temperatures within the upper portion of the cloud are so low that the anvil is composed exclusively of ice crystals, giving it a fibrous appearance.

FIGURE 11.4
When the upward billowing cumulonimbus cloud reaches the tropopause, it spreads out forming a flat anvil top.

FIGURE 11.5
In this visible satellite image, clusters of intense thunderstorm cells appear as bright white blotches over portions of Texas, Oklahoma, and Missouri. [NOAA]

SINGLE CELL	MULTICELL CLUSTER	MULTICELL LINE	SUPERCELL
Weak updraft (non-severe) or Strong updraft (severe?)	Weak updraft (non-severe) or Strong updraft (severe)	Weak updraft (non-severe) or Strong updraft (severe)	Intense updraft (Almost always severe) Mesocyclone present
Slight threat	Moderate threat	Moderate threat	High threat

FIGURE 11.6
Classification of thunderstorms and the likelihood of severe weather. [Adapted from NOAA, *Basic Spotters' Field Guide*].

Viewed from space by satellite sensors, clusters of mature thunderstorm cells appear as bright white blotches (Figure 11.5). The brightness of these clusters on visible satellite images is due to the high albedo (reflectivity) of the cloud tops. Much of the solar radiation that penetrates cumulonimbus clouds is scattered and ultimately absorbed, so that sunlight is weakened considerably when it emerges at the cloud base. For this reason, from our perspective on Earth's surface, the daytime sky darkens with the approach of a thunderstorm. White blotches on infrared satellite images are caused by the relatively cold anvil tops of cumulonimbus clouds.

DISSIPATING STAGE

As precipitation spreads throughout the thunderstorm cell, so does the downdraft, heralding the cell's demise. During the **dissipating stage**, subsiding air replaces the updraft throughout the cloud, effectively cutting off the supply of moisture provided by the updraft. Adiabatic compression warms the subsiding air, the relative humidity drops, precipitation tapers off and ends, and convective clouds gradually vaporize.

Thunderstorm Classification

Thunderstorms are **meso-scale convective systems (MCS)** and are classified based on the number, organization, and intensity of their constituent cells. Thunderstorms occur as single cells, multi-cellular clusters, and supercells (Figure 11.6).

A *single-cell thunderstorm* is usually a relatively weak weather system that appears to pop up randomly almost anywhere within a warm, humid air mass. In reality, a single-cell thunderstorm is not a random phenomenon and almost always develops along some boundary within an air mass. The boundary, for example, may be the leading edge of the rain-cooled outflow from a distant thunderstorm cell. Or it may be the edge of a bubble of cool, relatively dense air that is the remnant of another thunderstorm cell that has dissipated. At least in middle latitudes, solar-driven free convection alone usually is not sufficiently strong to generate a thunderstorm cell.

Typically, a thunderstorm cell completes its life cycle in 30 minutes or so, but sometimes lightning, thunder, and bursts of heavy rain persist for many hours. This is because most thunderstorms are multi-cellular; that is, a thunderstorm usually consists of more than one cell. Each cell may be at a different stage of its life cycle, and new cells form and old cells dissipate continually. A succession of many cells is thus responsible for a prolonged period of thunderstorm weather. Although a locality may be in the direct path of a distant, intense thunderstorm cell, the relatively brief life span of an individual cell means that severe weather may dissipate before reaching that locality. The multi-cellular nature of most thunderstorms complicates the motion of the weather system in that a thunderstorm may track at some angle to the paths of its constituent cells. For example, a thunderstorm may track from west to east, while its component cells head off toward the northeast (Figure 11.7). In terms of organization, two types of multi-cellular thunderstorms are the squall line and the meso-scale convective complex. Cells in either of these systems can produce severe weather, which is most likely to occur near the interface between the updraft and the downdraft of a mature cell.

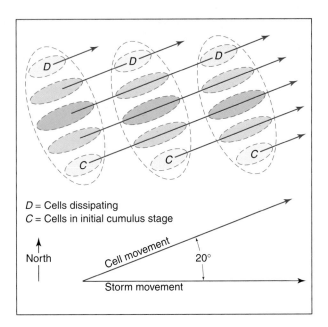

FIGURE 11.7
In this idealized situation viewed from above, the component cells of a multicellular thunderstorm travel at about 20 degrees to the eastward moving thunderstorm. As they travel toward the northeast, the individual cells progress through their life cycle.

A **squall line** is an elongated cluster of thunderstorm cells that is accompanied by a continuous gust front at the line's leading edge (Figure 11.8). A squall line is most likely to develop in the warm southeast sector of a mature extra-tropical cyclone ahead of and parallel to the cold front. (A more general name for a thunderstorm formed by uplift along cold or warm fronts is *frontal thunderstorm*.) Squall line thunderstorm cells are usually

more intense than single-cell thunderstorms because of the contribution of the synoptic-scale circulation to vertical motion. That is, the circulation within the associated low pressure system strengthens the updraft. As the squall-line gust front surges forward, warm, humid air is lifted and forced into the updraft located at the leading edge of the squall line. The heaviest rain or hail typically occurs just behind (to the west of) this updraft. Light to moderate precipitation is produced by the older cells situated behind the mature cells at the leading edge.

A **meso-scale convective complex (MCC)** is a nearly circular cluster of many interacting thunderstorm cells covering an area that may be a thousand times larger than that of a single isolated thunderstorm cell. In fact, it is not unusual for a single MCC to cover an area equal to that of the state of Iowa (Figure 11.9). MCCs are primarily warm-season (March through September) phenomena that generally develop at night and occur chiefly over the eastern two-thirds of the United States, where more than 50 may be expected in a single season.

An MCC is not associated with a front and usually develops during weak synoptic-scale flow, often near an upper-level ridge of high pressure and on the cool side of a stationary front. A low-level jet feeds warm humid air into the developing system while a low pressure system forms at mid-levels of the troposphere. Rising temperatures at low levels and radiational cooling at upper levels destabilizes the troposphere. New cells form while old cells dissipate continually within an MCC, so the life expectancy of the system is at least 6 hrs and often 12 to 24 hrs. The longevity and typically slow movement (15 to 30 km per hr, or 9 to 18 mph) of an MCC mean that

FIGURE 11.8
Radar image of a squall line stretching from Texas to Illinois. [NOAA].

FIGURE 11.9
Infrared satellite image showing meso-scale convective complexes over western Kansas and most of Arkansas. [NOAA].

rainfall is widespread and substantial. MCCs account for perhaps 80% of growing season rainfall across the Great Plains and Midwest. An MCC also has the potential of producing severe weather, including weak tornadoes, moderate-sized hail, and flash flooding.

A **supercell thunderstorm** is a relatively long-lived, large, and intense system. It consists of a single cell with an exceptionally strong updraft, in some cases estimated at 240 to 280 km per hr (150 to 175 mph). A distinguishing characteristic of a supercell is the tendency for the updraft to develop a rotational circulation that may evolve into a tornado. Because of their link to strong to violent tornadoes, supercell thunderstorms are covered in more detail later in this chapter.

Where and When

Atmospheric conditions that favor thunderstorm development vary with latitude, season, and time of day. Key to understanding the spatial and temporal variability of thunderstorms is the conditions required for their formation: (1) humid air in the low- to mid-troposphere, (2) atmospheric instability, and (3) a source of uplift.

Most thunderstorms develop within a mass of warm, humid air, that is, maritime tropical (*mT*) air, when that air mass is destabilized. Uplift is the key to destabilizing *mT* air. Usually, maritime tropical air is conditionally stable and becomes unstable (buoyant) only when lifted to the convective condensation level. Recall from Chapter 6 that *conditional stability* means that the ambient air is stable for unsaturated (clear) air parcels but unstable for saturated (cloudy) air parcels. The more humid the air, the less the ascent (expansional cooling) needed for destabilization. Most thunderstorms develop when maritime tropical air is lifted (1) along fronts, (2) up mountain slopes, or (3) via horizontal convergence of surface winds. Furthermore, cold air advection aloft and/or warm air advection at the surface enhances the potential instability of *mT* air. Either of these processes increases the air temperature lapse rate and thereby reduces ambient air stability.

Solar heating drives atmospheric convection, so it is not surprising that thunderstorms tend to be most frequent when and where solar radiation is most intense. In most places, thunderstorms are most frequent during the warmest hours of the day, but there are lots of exceptions to this rule. Meso-scale convective complexes and squall lines develop both night and day. In the Missouri River Valley and adjacent portions of the upper Mississippi River Valley, even single-cell thunderstorms are more frequent at night than during the day. One possible explanation for the nocturnal thunderstorm maximum in the upper Missouri/Mississippi Valleys is based on the role of a *low-level jet stream* of maritime tropical air that flows from off the Gulf of Mexico and northward up the Mississippi River Valley. This jet stream strengthens at night and causes warm air advection at low levels that destabilizes the air and spurs the buildup of cumuliform clouds.

Usually, thunderstorm frequency is expressed as the number of thunderstorm days per year, where a *thunderstorm day* is defined as a day when thunder is heard. This conventional method of expressing thunderstorm frequency likely underestimates the actual number of thunderstorms, particularly if more than one line of thunderstorms passes over a weather station on the same day. With this limitation in mind, thunderstorms occur with greatest frequency over the continental interiors of tropical latitudes. The steamy Amazon Basin of Brazil, the Congo Basin of equatorial Africa, and the islands of Indonesia have the highest frequency of thunderstorms in the world, experiencing at least 100 thunderstorm days per year. Because the surfaces of large bodies of water do not warm as much as land surfaces in response to the same intensity of solar radiation, thunderstorms are less frequent over adjacent bodies of water.

In the subtropics and tropics, intense solar heating may combine with converging surface winds to trigger thunderstorm development. As noted in Chapter 9, this combination characterizes the intertropical convergence zone (ITCZ), a discontinuous band of thunderstorms more or less paralleling the equator that moves north and south seasonally with the sun.

In North America, thunderstorm frequency generally increases from north to south with the highest frequency over central Florida (Figure 11.10). Some interior localities of that state average 100 thunderstorm days per year. The Florida thunderstorm maximum near Orlando is due to convergence of sea breezes that develop along both the east and west coasts of the Florida peninsula (Figure 11.11). Sea breeze convergence over the interior induces ascent of maritime tropical air and formation of cumulonimbus clouds.

Portions of the Rocky Mountain Front Range rank second to interior Florida in thunderstorm frequency over North America. On average, more than 60 thunderstorm days occur per year in a band from southeastern Wyoming southward through central Colorado and into north central New Mexico. This high thunderstorm frequency is linked to topographically related differences in heating.

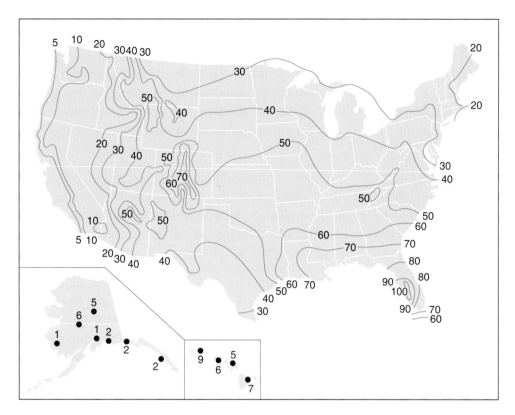

FIGURE 11.10
Average annual number of thunderstorm-days in the United States.

same altitude, but located to the east of the mountains out over the relatively flat terrain of the western Great Plains, is much cooler. As warm air rises over the mountain slopes, it is replaced by cooler air sweeping westward from over the Plains. Updrafts over the mountain slopes produce cumuliform clouds that often evolve into thunderstorm cells, particularly during the warmest hours of the day. Thunderstorm development is enhanced whenever the synoptic-scale air pressure pattern favors winds blowing from the east over the western Great Plains.

To this point, our discussion has focused on conditions conducive to thunderstorm development. Under other conditions, convection and ascent of air is inhibited and thunderstorms do not form. This is the case when air masses reside or travel over relatively cold surfaces and are thereby stabilized. For example, snow-covered ground cools and stabilizes the overlying air. Convection is suppressed, so thunderstorms are relatively rare at middle and high latitudes in winter. Nonetheless, thunderstorms can be associated with winter extra-tropical cyclones, usually developing ahead of the surface warm front as lifting over the front destabilizes the near surface air. In that case, *thundersnow* can be locally heavy.

Thunderstorms are unusual over coastal areas that are downwind from relatively cold ocean waters. For example, thunderstorms are infrequent along coastal California, where prevailing winds are onshore and a shallow layer of maritime polar air often flows inland from off the relatively cold California Current. Cool *mP* air at low levels suppresses deep convection and thunderstorm development. Thus, the average annual number of thunderstorm days is only 2 at San Francisco, 6 at Los Angeles, and 5 at San Diego.

Thunderstorms are also relatively rare in Hawaii, primarily because of the trade wind inversion (Chapter 9). At first-order weather stations such as Hilo and Honolulu,

Mountain slopes facing the sun absorb direct solar radiation and become relatively warm. The warm slopes, in turn, heat the air in immediate contact with the slopes, and that air rises. At the same time, the air at the

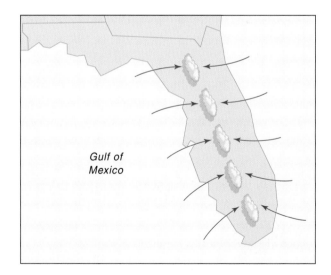

FIGURE 11.11
The relatively high frequency of thunderstorms over the interior of the Florida peninsula is linked to the convergence of sea breezes blowing inland from both the Gulf and East Coasts.

the average annual number of thunderstorm days is under 10. The trade wind inversion, at an average altitude of about 2000 m (6600 ft), restricts vertical development of towering cumulus clouds. Cumulus clouds normally do not attain the altitude needed to develop into cumulonimbus clouds.

Severe Thunderstorms

By popular convention, a **severe thunderstorm** is accompanied by locally damaging surface winds, frequent lightning, or large hail. According to the official National Weather Service (NWS) criterion, a severe thunderstorm has surface winds stronger than 50 knots (93 km per hr or 58 mph) and/or produces hailstones 0.75 in. (1.9 cm) or larger in diameter (penny-size). Such thunderstorms may also produce flash floods or tornadoes.

As a general rule, the greater the altitude of the top of a thunderstorm, the more likely it is that the system will produce severe weather. Why do some thunderstorm cells surge to great altitudes and trigger severe weather, whereas others do not? The essential factor appears to be vertical wind shear. Vertical **wind shear** is the change in horizontal wind speed or direction with increasing altitude. Weak vertical wind shear (little change in wind with altitude) favors short-lived updrafts, low cloud tops, and weak thunderstorms, whereas strong vertical wind shear favors vigorous updrafts, great vertical cloud development, and severe thunderstorms.

With weak vertical wind shear, the flow of warm humid air into the cell is relatively weak. The downdraft's outflow pushes the gust front well ahead of the system, eventually cutting off the supply of warm humid air entirely. Also, precipitation falls through and thereby weakens the updraft. With increasing vertical wind shear, however, the gust front cannot advance as far from the cell and the inflow of warm humid air is sustained for a longer period. Furthermore, most precipitation falls alongside rather than through (and against) the tilted updraft so that the updraft maintains its strength and the thunderstorm surges to great altitudes. On the other hand, if the vertical wind shear is too strong, a developing cumulonimbus cloud is torn apart.

In the United States and Canada, most severe thunderstorms break out over the Great Plains and are associated with mature extra-tropical cyclones. Severe thunderstorm cells usually form as part of a squall line within the cyclone's warm sector, ahead of and parallel to a fast-moving and well-defined cold front. The squall line appears as an ominous, twisting mass of low, dark clouds, often hundreds of kilometers long. Severe cells can produce large hail, heavy rain, and downbursts (discussed later in this chapter). Most tornadoes that do form are weak, although some squall line cells evolve into supercells that can spawn strong to violent tornadoes.

A synoptic situation that favors severe thunderstorm development is shown schematically in Figure 11.12. A mature cyclone is centered over western Kansas with a well-defined cold front trailing across the Oklahoma and Texas panhandles into West Texas and a warm front stretching southeastward from the low center. The mid-latitude (polar front) jet and a low-level (*mT*) jet, which are also plotted on the map, cross to the southeast of the cyclone center. The most intense thunderstorm cells are likely to develop near the intersection of these two jets. The *subtropical jet stream* (Chapter 9) is sometimes also present at high levels in the troposphere, blowing from west to east over the warm sector of the cyclone. In that event, intense squall lines are likely to form between the mid-latitude and subtropical jet streams.

The polar front jet stream produces strong vertical wind shear that maintains a vigorous updraft and favors great vertical development of thunderstorm cells. In addition, the jet contributes to a stratification of air that increases the potential instability of the troposphere. As described in Chapter 9, a *jet streak* induces both horizontal divergence and horizontal convergence of air in the upper troposphere. Recall that diverging horizontal winds trigger ascent of air and cyclone development under the left-front quadrant of a jet streak. Meanwhile, air converges in the right-front quadrant of a jet streak, causing weak subsidence of air over the warm sector of the cyclone. The subsiding

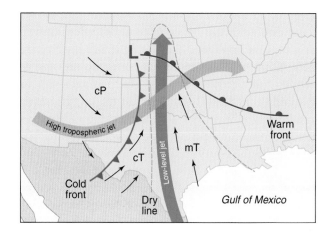

FIGURE 11.12
A synoptic weather pattern that favors development of severe thunderstorms.

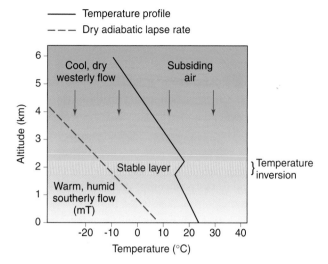

FIGURE 11.13
A temperature sounding that favors the development of severe thunderstorm cells. A capping temperature inversion separates subsiding dry air aloft from warm, humid air near the surface.

air is compressionally warmed and its relative humidity decreases. The subsiding, warming air is prevented from reaching Earth's surface by a shallow layer of maritime tropical air that surges northward as a low-level jet from over the Gulf of Mexico. The *mT* jet occurs on the western flank of the Bermuda-Azores subtropical high and is particularly strong at about 3000 m (9800 ft).

As a consequence of compressional warming, air subsiding from aloft becomes warmer than the underlying layer of maritime tropical air. A zone of transition, that is, a temperature inversion, develops between the two layers of air (Figure 11.13). An air layer characterized by a temperature inversion is extremely stable, so the two air layers do not mix and convection is confined to the surface layer of *mT* air. In this circumstance, the inversion is known as a **capping inversion**. For as long as this stratification persists, the contrast between air layers mounts; that is, subsiding air becomes drier while the underlying *mT* air becomes more humid. The potential for severe weather continues to grow; all that is needed is a trigger that causes updrafts to penetrate the capping inversion.

The necessary upward impetus may be supplied by a combination of the intense solar heating of mid-afternoon and the lifting of air caused by an approaching cold front or jet streak. Updrafts eventually break through the capping inversion, and cumulus clouds billow upward at explosive speeds that may exceed 100 km per hr (62 mph). Such updrafts can even penetrate the tropopause and surge into the lower stratosphere. A severe thunderstorm is born.

With the synoptic pattern shown in Figure 11.12, air ahead of the cold front and west of the warm, humid tongue (enclosed by a dashed line) is usually quite dry. For this reason, the western boundary of the *mT* air mass is called the **dryline**. West of the dryline and east of the cold front, hot and dry continental tropical air flows eastward and downhill from the southwest desert and Mexican Plateau. Because of the density contrast associated with differences in atmospheric water vapor content, a dryline brings about uplift in a manner similar to a cold front. A dryline can extend hundreds of kilometers from Texas northward onto the western Plains and is often the site of squall line and severe thunderstorm development. Typically, the dryline advances eastward during the day and retreats westward at night.

Sometimes, ominous pouch-like **mammatus clouds** appear at the base of the spreading anvil top of a cumulonimbus cloud (Figure 11.14). (They are also associated with a variety of other cloud types including cirrus, altocumulus, and stratocumulus.) Contrary to popular belief, mammatus clouds do not always indicate a severe thunderstorm. In fact, in the mountainous western United States, they often are associated with relatively weak convective showers. Their unusual appearance is attributed to blobs of cold, cloudy air that descend from the anvil into the unsaturated (clear) air beneath the anvil. Ice crystals at the margin of a blob sublimate, causing further cooling of the blob. This cooling offsets compressional warming of the descending air so that the blob sinks, bulging downward into the dry air. Ultimately, the size of the bulge is limited by the increasing rate of sublimation of the constituent ice crystals.

FIGURE 11.14
Pouch-like mammatus clouds occur on the underside of a thunderstorm anvil and sometimes indicate a severe storm system.

Thunderstorm Hazards

Thunderstorm hazards include lightning, downbursts, flash floods, hail, and tornadoes. Because tornadoes are an especially severe weather hazard, they are covered in a later section of this chapter.

LIGHTNING

A convective rain or snow shower is a thunderstorm if accompanied by lightning, which also produces thunder. **Lightning** is a brilliant flash of light caused by an electrical discharge within a cumulonimbus cloud or between the cloud and Earth's surface (Figure 11.15). Lightning is a weather phenomenon that can be directly hazardous to human life. Over a recent 30-year period (1971-2000), lightning annually killed an average of 73 people in the United States. According to NOAA statistics, in 2003 more people were killed by lightning than by tornadoes and hurricanes combined. Lightning's death toll may seem surprisingly high, perhaps because fatal lightning bolts are typically isolated events that seldom make headlines. A single, fatal lightning bolt is not as newsworthy as a single disastrous tornado that may take many lives. However, so many lightning strikes occur daily that fatalities and injuries add up. For tips on lightning safety, refer to this chapter's first Essay.

Lightning not only kills and injures people, it also ignites forest and brush fires. In the Rocky Mountain region, for example, lightning is the most common cause of forest fires, starting more than 9000 each year. A

FIGURE 11.15
Lightning is a brilliant flash of light associated with an electrical discharge between clouds and Earth's surface, within a cloud, or between clouds. [NOAA photograph]

person might assume that heavy rain associated with a thunderstorm would quickly quench a lightning-ignited fire. In the western basins, however, the base of a cumulonimbus cloud is usually so far above the ground (perhaps 2400 m or 8000 ft), and the air below the cloud so dry, that much if not all the rain evaporates before reaching a wildfire.

Lightning is very costly to electrical utilities, each year causing tens of millions of dollars in damage to equipment (power lines, transformers) and in service restoration expenses. A useful tool in utilities' efforts to cope with the lightning hazard is the **lightning detection network (LDN)**, a system that provides real-time information on the location and severity of lightning strokes. Each monitoring station in the network consists of direction-finding equipment that can sense electromagnetic fields associated with cloud-to-ground lightning. A computer superimposes locations of lightning strokes on a regional map. An electrical utility that subscribes to a LDN service accesses lightning data through a computer link. Such information enables the utility to mobilize repair crews more efficiently and speeds up restoration of disrupted service.

What causes lightning? The potential for an electrical discharge exists whenever a charge difference develops between two objects. A normally neutral object becomes negatively charged when it gains electrons (negatively charged subatomic particles) and positively charged when it loses electrons. That is, the object is *ionized*. When large differences in electrical charge develop within a cloud, between clouds, or between a cloud and the ground, the stage is set for lightning.

On a clear day, Earth's surface is negatively charged with respect to the upper atmosphere (ionosphere). This fair-weather charge distribution changes as a cumulonimbus cloud develops. Within the cloud, charges separate so that the upper portion and a much smaller region near the cloud base become positively charged. In between, a disk-shaped zone of negative charge forms that is a few hundred meters thick and several kilometers in diameter. At the same time, the region of negative charge in the developing cumulonimbus induces a positive charge on the ground directly under the cloud.

Air is a very good electrical insulator, so that as a thunderstorm cell forms and electrical charges separate and build, a tremendous potential soon develops for an electrical discharge. By about the time the thunderstorm cell enters its mature stage, the electrical field has strengthened to the point that the electrical resistance of air breaks down and electrons flow as a lightning discharge, thereby neutralizing the electrical charges. Lightning may forge a path between oppositely charged regions of a cloud, or between clouds or a cloud and the ground.

Why electrical charges separate within cumulonimbus clouds is not well understood, but field studies and simulations offer a promising explanation focusing on graupel and the convective circulation within cumulonimbus clouds. **Graupel** (German for *soft hail*) consists of millimeter- to centimeter-size ice pellets formed when supercooled water droplets collide and freeze on impact. Within the cloud, as graupel descend and strike smaller ice crystals in their path, opposite charges develop on the graupel and the ice crystals. For collisions that take place at temperatures below about −15 °C (5 °F), graupel particles become negatively charged while ice crystals acquire a positive charge. Vigorous updrafts separate the particles, carrying the smaller positively charged ice crystals to the upper portion of the cloud, whereas the larger negatively charged graupel concentrate mostly in the lower portion of the cloud. This mechanism can explain the positive charge of the upper portion of the cloud and the negative charge of the disk-shaped zone of the lower cloud region.

What accounts for the positive charge near the cloud base? Typically, temperatures near the cloud base are higher than −15 °C (5 °F). At those temperatures, collisions between graupel and ice crystals induce a positive charge on the graupel and a negative charge on ice crystals. Ice crystals are swept up in the updraft, leaving heavier graupel to accumulate near the cloud base, giving that region a positive charge.

Lightning discharges between a cloud and the ground pose the greatest hazard for people, although these discharges represent only about 20% of all lightning bolts, with in-cloud lightning accounting for nearly 80% of the lightning. Using high-speed photography, scientists found that a lightning flash involves a regular sequence of events. Initially, streams of electrons surge from the cloud base toward the ground in discrete steps, each about 20 to 100 m (65 to 330 ft) long. These so-called *stepped leaders* describe a faintly visible branching path and produce a narrow ionized channel. When a branch of the stepped leaders comes within about 100 m (330 ft) of the ground, it is met by a positively charged streamer ascending from the ground. A luminescent *return stroke* forms as an ascending electric current when the positive and negative electric charges recombine. The return stroke follows the path of least resistance and often emanates from tall, pointed structures such as a metal flagpole or tower. Now an ionized channel, only a few centimeters in diameter, links Earth's surface to the cloud. Electrons flow, neutralization occurs, and the channel is illuminated.

Following this initial electrical discharge, subsequent surges of electrons from the cloud, called *dart leaders*, follow the same conducting path. Each dart leader is met by a return stroke (from the ground), and the conducting path is again illuminated. Typically, a single lightning discharge consists of two to four dart leaders plus return strokes. Sometimes, a dart leader is met by a return stroke that forges a new conducting path from the ground. The result is a forked lightning bolt that strikes the ground at more than one place.

The sequence just described is the most common occurrence of cloud-to-ground lightning. In less than 10% of cases, a positively charged leader emanates from the cloud and initiates a lightning discharge. Much more rarely, positive or negative stepped leaders propagate upward from the ground and meet a return stroke surging downward from a cloud. This ground-to-cloud lightning usually is initiated from mountaintops or tall structures such as antenna towers.

Electricity flows at the astonishing rate of nearly 50,000 km (31,000 mi) per second; hence, the entire lightning sequence takes place in less than two-tenths of a second. The human eye has difficulty separating the individual flashes of light that constitute a single lightning bolt, so that we perceive a lightning flash as a flickering light. The visible lightning discharge takes on many distinctive forms (Table 11.1).

Where there is lightning, there is thunder, although sometimes we see distant lightning but can not hear the thunder. Lightning heats the air along the narrow conducting path to temperatures that may exceed 25,000 °C (45,000 °F). Such intense heating occurs so rapidly that air density cannot respond, at least initially. The rapid rise in air temperature is accompanied by a tremendous increase in air pressure locally that generates a shock wave. The shock wave propagates outward, producing sound waves that are heard as **thunder**. The first thunder we hear is generated by the nearest part of the lightning bolt. Subsequent sound waves reach us from portions of the bolt that are progressively further away; hence, the rumble of thunder. Thunderstorm cells that are more than 20 km (12 mi) away are too distant for thunder to be heard although lightning can be seen. This is called *heat lightning*, a name that is somewhat misleading because people may assume that heat causes the lightning when in fact it occurs in the same way as all other lightning.

TABLE 11.1
Types of Lightning

Ball lightning	A reddish, luminous sphere, about 30 cm in diameter, that moves rapidly along a solid surface or appears to float in air; may be accompanied by a hissing noise.
Bead lightning	Resembles a series of beads on a string; actually a normal zigzag lightning flash, segments of which are viewed end-on, giving the impression of high intensity at a series of points along the lightning channel.
Heat lightning	Light reflected by clouds from lightning in thunderstorms that are too far away for thunder to be heard.
Ribbon lightning	A lightning flash that appears to spread horizontally into a ribbon of parallel luminous streaks when a strong wind is blowing at some angle to the observer's line of sight.
Sheet lightning	Clouds illuminated by cloud-to-cloud lightning so that they appear bright white; clouds block the view of the lightning flash.
Streak lightning	Cloud-to-ground discharge that is concentrated in a single, relatively straight channel.

Light travels about a million times faster than sound so that we see lightning almost instantaneously, but we hear thunder later. The closer we are to a thunderstorm cell, the shorter is the time interval between the lightning flash and thunder. As a rule, thunder takes about 3 seconds to travel 1 km (or 5 seconds to travel 1 mi). If you must wait 9 seconds between lightning flash and thunderclap, the lightning is about 3 km (1.8 mi) away. This is the *flash-to-bang* method of determining the distance to a thunderstorm. By noting the time difference between light and thunder of successive lightning discharges, you can deduce whether the thunderstorm cell is approaching or moving away, or even predict when it is dangerously close. As a general guideline, if the time between flash and bang is 30 seconds or less, you are well advised to take precautions to avoid the lightning.

DOWNBURSTS

Severe, and sometimes not so severe, thunderstorms can produce a **downburst**, an exceptionally strong downdraft that, upon striking Earth's surface, diverges horizontally as a surge of potentially destructive winds. Downbursts occur with or without rain; if without rain, the downburst usually occurs under a curtain of *virga* (Chapter 7). The late T. Theodore Fujita (1920-1998) of The University of Chicago is credited with discovering downbursts, and he coined the term. Fujita's discovery stemmed from his airborne survey of property damage near Beckley, WV shortly after the tornado *super-outbreak*

of 3-4 April 1974. He observed storm debris spread over the countryside in a starburst pattern—distinct from the swirling pattern that is typical of tornado damage. Downbursts blow down trees, flatten crops, and wreck buildings. Based on size of affected area, Fujita classified a downburst as either a macroburst or a microburst.

A **macroburst** cuts a swath of destruction over a distance of more than 4 km (2.5 mi) with surface winds that may top 210 km per hr (130 mph). The leading edge of a macroburst may be marked by a gust front, and the system lasts up to 30 minutes. A **microburst** is smaller and shorter-lived than a macroburst. By convention, its path of destruction is 4 km (2.5 mi) or less, top surface winds may be as high as 270 km per hr (170 mph), and its life expectancy is less than 10 minutes.

Microbursts are particularly dangerous at airports, where they can play havoc with aircraft especially on takeoff or landing. Microbursts trigger *wind shear*, a change in wind speed or direction with distance, which can disturb the lift forces acting on the wings of an aircraft—perhaps causing an abrupt change in its altitude (Figure 11.16). An aircraft that flies into a microburst first encounters a strong headwind and then a strong tailwind. In a matter of seconds, the aircraft's speed relative to air can drop by more than 160 km per hr (100 mph). If this happens during takeoff or landing, the aircraft's speed may drop below the minimum required for flight. Fujita underscored the microburst hazard for aircraft when he

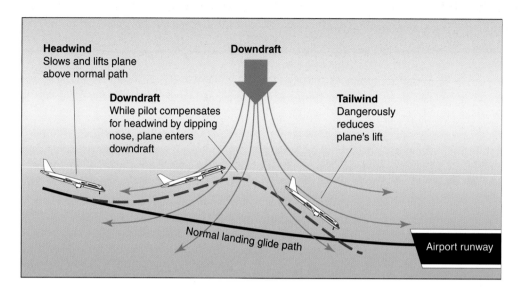

FIGURE 11.16
A microburst causes a landing aircraft to depart from its normal glide path. [Adapted from Michael Shibao, National Center for Atmospheric Research]

demonstrated that microbursts probably contributed to two commercial aircraft accidents in 1975. Apparently, in both cases, the pilots unwittingly flew their jet planes through the center of a microburst, one on takeoff and the other while attempting to land. Both planes abruptly lost altitude and crashed.

In response to the microburst hazard to aviation, the Federal Aviation Administration (FAA) required airlines to install an approved microburst detection system on their aircraft by the end of 1995. The most effective systems employ sensors that can detect wind shear using the same principle as Doppler radar (Chapter 7). The goal is to provide pilots with at least 20 to 40 seconds advance warning of microburst-induced wind shear. Such advance warning is considered sufficient for pilots to take evasive action.

A squall line or meso-scale convective complex sometimes produces a family of straight-line downburst winds that impacts a path that may be hundreds of kilometers long. At any location, the period of strongest winds typically lasts from 10 to 20 minutes or so. This severe weather system is known as a **derecho** (Spanish for *straight ahead* as contrasted with tornado, Spanish for *turning*). Gustavus Hinrichs (1836-1923), founder and director of the Iowa weather service, coined the term derecho (pronounced deh-RAY-cho) in the 1880s. The criterion for a derecho, as opposed to ordinary gusty thunderstorm winds, is sustained winds in excess of 94 km per hr (58 mph); they generally track from northwest to southeast.

On 4 July 1977, a derecho consisting of 25 individual downbursts struck several counties in northern Wisconsin, felling trees and buildings along a path that was 268 km (166 mi) long and 27 km (17 mi) wide. One person was killed, 35 were injured, and damage to buildings and timber totaled in the millions of dollars. Based on the extent of damage, surface winds may have been as high as 250 km per hr (155 mph). Twenty-two years later, on 4 July 1999, a derecho struck Minnesota's Boundary Waters Canoe Area Wilderness. In about 20 minutes, winds as high as 150 km per hr (93 mph) blew down more than 20 million trees along a path measuring 60 km (37 mi) long and 20 km (12 mi) wide. Fortunately, there were no fatalities.

FLASH FLOODS

A **flash flood** is a short-term, localized, and often unexpected rise in stream level above bankfull usually in response to torrential rain falling over a relatively small geographical area. Typically, the stream level rises and falls within 6 hrs of the rain event. Excessive rainfall may occur when successive thunderstorm cells (in a squall line or an MCC) mature over the same area. Alternatively, a stationary or slow-moving intense thunderstorm cell may produce flooding rains. A thunderstorm is stationary or slow-moving when the system is (1) embedded in weak steering winds aloft and/or (2) maintained by a persistent flow of humid air up the slopes of a mountain range.

Atmospheric conditions that favor flash floods differ somewhat from those that give rise to other types of severe weather (e.g., hail and tornadoes). Flash-flood producing thunderstorms are more common at night and form in an atmosphere with weak vertical wind shear and abundant moisture through great depths. Flash flooding is most likely in an atmosphere that is *precipitation efficient* with (1) high values of precipitable water and relative humidity, and (2) a thunderstorm cloud base having temperatures above freezing. High precipitable water and relative humidity reduces the amount of falling precipitation that vaporizes. A relatively warm cloud base favors the collision-coalescence process that leads to exceptionally heavy rainfall.

A combination of atmospheric conditions and topography contributed to the flash flood that claimed 139 lives (many of them campers) and caused $35.5 million in property damage in the Big Thompson Canyon of Colorado on 31 July 1976. Big Thompson Canyon is located in the Colorado Front Range about 80 km (50 mi) northwest of Denver along a stream that flows eastward from Rocky Mountain National Park. A persistent flow of humid air from the east up the mountain slopes triggered development of a succession of thunderstorm cells and heavy rainfall. With weak winds aloft, thunderstorm cells remained nearly stationary over essentially the same geographical area for at least 4 hrs. Rainfall in the headwaters of the Big Thompson River was estimated at 25 to 30 cm (10 to 12 in.) with perhaps 20 cm (8 in.) falling in only 2 hrs. Runoff cascaded down the steep mountain slopes and into the river that winds along the narrow canyon floor. The river rose abruptly and overflowed its banks as a flash flood. At one place along the river, the discharge (volume of water flowing per second) was more than 200 times greater than the long-term average. A wall of water almost 6 m (20 ft) high destroyed 418 houses and washed away 197 motor vehicles.

Some 21 years later, on 28 July 1997, Colorado residents were reminded of the Big Thompson Canyon disaster when a thunderstorm complex deluged nearby Fort Collins with record rainfall. Between 5:30 and 11:00 p.m. (MDT) up to 25 cm (10 in.) of rain drenched the southwest side of Fort Collins. A flash flood on Spring Creek, just downstream from where rainfall was heaviest, claimed 5 lives. Floodwaters also caused property damage (estimated at more than $200 million) over a large part of the city; especially hard-hit were buildings on the Colorado State University campus. Flood plain management measures, initiated well before the flood, particularly along Spring Creek, likely prevented greater loss of life and residential property damage. Management strategies included moving residents out of the floodway and constructing retention

basins along the floodplain that could accommodate excess water during a major rainfall event.

A combination of atmospheric conditions and topography was responsible for the extreme rainfall of 28 July 1997 (just as at Big Thompson Canyon). Fort Collins is located just east of the Rocky Mountain Front Range, about 105 km (65 mi) north of Denver. A persistent westward flow of unusually humid air over eastern Colorado toward higher terrain plus weak steering winds aloft set the stage for a succession of slow moving thunderstorm cells over the Front Range, dumping heavy rain for hours over essentially the same geographical area.

Flash flooding is especially hazardous in mountainous terrain, and motorists and campers are well advised to head for higher ground in the event of a flash flood warning (Figure 11.17). But even where the topography is relatively flat, a prolonged period of heavy rain (more than 7.6 mm, or 0.3 in., per hr) can greatly exceed the infiltration capacity of the ground. Simply put, the ground cannot absorb all the rainwater and becomes saturated. Excess water runs off to creeks, streams, rivers, or sewers or collects in other low-lying areas. If the drainage system cannot accommodate the sudden input of huge quantities of water, a flash flood is the consequence.

Because of their design and composition, urban areas are prone to flash floods during intense downpours. Concrete and asphalt make the surfaces of a city virtually impervious to water, so elaborate storm sewer systems are required to transport runoff to nearby natural drainageways. Storm sewer systems have a limited capacity for water, however, and may be unable to handle the excess runoff

FIGURE 11.17
Road sign in the Colorado Rockies warns visitors to climb to higher ground in the event of a flash flood.

produced during a torrential rainfall. Water collects in underpasses, at intersections, in dips in the roadway, and in other low-lying areas. Sometimes water levels rise so quickly in these areas that motorists are trapped in their vehicles. In many cases, motorists misjudge the depth of the water and do not realize the power of even shallow water in motion. They unwittingly drive into water that sweeps their vehicle downstream and puts their lives in extreme danger.

Severe thunderstorms are not the only culprits to trigger flash floods. Breaching of a dam or levee, or the sudden release of water during breakup of a river ice jam, can also cause an abrupt rise in water level. In any event, when in flood-prone areas, people are well advised to heed the precautions listed in Table 11.2.

HAIL

Hail is frozen precipitation in the form of balls or lumps of ice more than 5 mm (0.2 in.) in diameter, called *hailstones* (Figure 11.18). The size of hailstones is usually reported to the National Weather Service by comparison to the size of an everyday object (Table 11.3). Hailstones range in size from a pea to the size of an orange or even larger. Hail is described as *severe* if its diameter is equal to or greater than 19 mm (0.75 in.), the size of a

FIGURE 11.18
Hailstones are lumps of ice that fall from intense thunderstorm cells.

penny. *Extreme* hail has a diameter equal to or greater than 51 mm (2 in.) and accounts for less than 10% of all hail reports. In the United States, the largest hailstone on record fell at Aurora, NE on 22 June 2003. It weighed just under 455 g (1.0 lb) and measured 47.6 cm (18.75 in.) in circumference and 17.8 cm (7 in.) in diameter, about the size of a cantaloupe. Another hailstone from this same storm was large enough to punch a hole in a garage roof.

Hail almost always falls from cumulonimbus clouds that are characterized by strong updrafts, great vertical development, and an abundance of supercooled water droplets. A hailstone develops when an ice pellet is transported vertically through portions of a cumulonimbus cloud containing varying concentrations of supercooled

TABLE 11.2
Some Flash Flood Safety Tips[a]

- Avoid driving on flooded roadways or bridges. Floodwaters only 0.5 m (1.5 ft) deep can carry away most automobiles. Also, flooded roads may be undermined.
- If your vehicle stalls in high water, abandon it and seek high ground.
- On foot never attempt to cross a stream if the water level is above your knees.
- Keep children away from drainage ditches and culverts.
- Find out the elevation of your property and the flood history of your community. If there is a risk of flooding, prepare an evacuation plan.
- Exercise caution when hiking or camping in remote areas. Avoid camping in mountain valleys or near dry streambeds. Take along a battery-powered radio to monitor changing weather conditions.

[a]Based on NOAA recommendations.

TABLE 11.3
National Weather Service Hail Conversion Chart

Common objects	Diameter in cm (in.)
Penny	1.9 cm (0.75 in.)
Nickel/Mothball	2.2 cm (0.88 in.)
Quarter	2.54 cm (1.0 in.)
Half Dollar	3.2 cm (1.25 in.)
Walnut/Ping Pong Ball	3.8 cm (1.50 in.)
Golf Ball	4.4 cm (1.75 in.)
Hen Egg	5.1 cm (2.00 in.)
Tennis Ball	6.4 cm (2.50 in.)
Baseball	7.0 cm (2.75 in.)
Tea Cup	7.6 cm (3.00 in.)
Grapefruit	10.2 cm (4.00 in.)
Softball	13.7 cm (5.40 in.)

water droplets. The ice pellet may descend slowly through the entire cloud, or it may follow a more complex pattern of ascent and descent as it is caught alternately in updrafts and downdrafts. In the process, the ice pellet grows by accretion (addition) of freezing water droplets. In general, the stronger the updraft, the greater is the size of the ice pellet. For example, an updraft of about 60 km per hr (37 mph) is required to produce a hailstone 1.9 cm (0.75 in.) in diameter whereas an updraft of roughly 160 km per hr (100 mph) is needed for a 7.6 cm (3.0 in.) diameter hailstone. Eventually, when it becomes too large and heavy to be supported by updrafts, the ice pellet descends and falls out of the cloud base. If the ice does not melt completely during its journey through the above freezing air beneath the cloud, it reaches Earth's surface as a hailstone.

When an ice pellet enters a portion of the cloud containing a relatively high concentration of supercooled water droplets, water collects on the ice pellet as a liquid film, which freezes slowly to form a transparent layer, or *glaze*. When the ice pellet travels through a portion of the cloud where the concentration of supercooled water droplets is relatively low, droplets freeze immediately on contact with the ice pellet. As droplets freeze, many tiny air bubbles are trapped within the ice, producing an opaque whitish layer of granular ice, or *rime*. Hence, a hailstone is composed of alternating layers of clear (glaze) and opaque (rime) ice, which, in cross section, resembles the internal structure of an onion. Scientists have counted as many as 25 layers in a single large hailstone.

A column of hail falling from a thunderstorm cell is called a *hailshaft* and the accumulation of hail on the ground in a long, narrow strip is known as a **hailstreak** (or *hail swath*). A typical hailstreak may be 2 km (1.2 mi) wide and 10 km (6.2 mi) in length, and a single large thunderstorm may produce several hailstreaks. Based on analysis of numerous hailstorms and hailstreaks, scientists at the Illinois State Water Survey devised a model to simulate hailstreak development (Figure 11.19). Hail forms in the upper portion of a cumulonimbus cloud. After several minutes of hail formation, the updraft weakens, allowing the hail to descend within the cloud; about 4 minutes later, the first hailstones reach the ground. In the ensuing 10 minutes, as the thunderstorm continues its lateral motion, the entire volume of hail is deposited along the ground as a hailstreak.

On rare occasions, the fall of hail is so great that snowplows must be called out to clear highways. This happened in Milwaukee, WI on 4 September 1988, when a heavy fall of pea-sized hail produced drifts to 46 cm (18 in.) in some north-side neighborhoods. On 6 August 1980, at Orient, IA drifts of hail were reported to be 1.8 m (6 ft) deep. On the afternoon of 13 June 1984, hailstones as large as golf balls fell for up to 1.5 hrs in the western suburbs of Denver, CO producing an accumulation of 25 cm (10 in.), with drifts greater than a meter.

Hailstones may be large enough to smash windows and dent automobiles, but the most costly damage is to crops. In the U.S. each year, hail causes an average $1 billion in damage, primarily to crops, livestock, and roofs. Hail usually falls during the

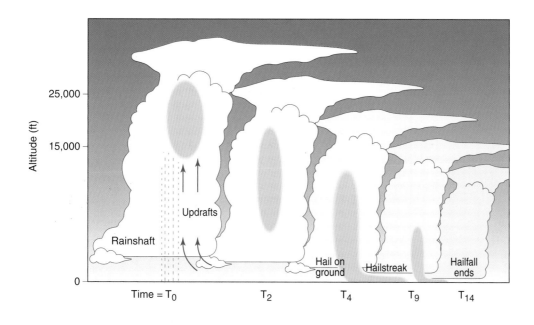

FIGURE 11.19
Model of hailstreak development. [Adapted from S.A. Changnon and J.L. Ivens, *Hail in Illinois, Public Information Brochure* 13, Illinois State Water Survey, 1987, p. 5.]

growing season and in a matter of minutes can wipe out the fruits of a farmer's year of labor. On 11 July 1990, softball-sized hailstones in Denver caused $625 million in property damage, mostly to automobiles and roofs. On 5 May 1995, the most costly hailstorm in U.S. history struck the Fort Worth, TX area. Golf ball- to baseball-size hailstones injured scores of people who were caught in the open during the storm. Total property damage was estimated at more than $2 billion. Traditionally, farmers cope with the hail hazard by purchasing insurance. Illinois farmers, for example, lead the United States in crop-hail insurance, purchasing an average annual liability coverage that tops $600 million. Refer to this chapter's second Essay for information on efforts to suppress hail formation.

According to the Storm Prediction Center (SPC) in Norman, OK, the annual number of severe hail reports in the contiguous United States increased exponentially from less than 350 in 1955 to more than 12,500 in 2002 (Figure 11.20). The upward trend likely can be attributed to greater public awareness of the hail hazard, proliferation of cell phones making it easier to file reports, improved capabilities of weather radar (especially the *WSR-88D*), and the National Weather Service's more aggressive verification of hail reports.

In the contiguous U.S., severe hail is most likely in a belt stretching northward from south-central Texas to the Valley of the Red River of the North in North Dakota and Minnesota, roughly corresponding to *tornado alley* (described later in this chapter). This locale of large hail is consistent with the region's relatively high frequency of supercell thunderstorms. Other areas of enhanced hail

activity include a band from northeastern Texas eastward to North Carolina plus northeast Colorado. The principal site of hail activity shifts seasonally from the Southeast in winter to Oklahoma by April and then to eastern Colorado and northern Minnesota by July.

Tornadoes

Of the roughly 10,000 severe thunderstorms that occur in the United States in an average year, about 10% produce tornadoes. A **tornado** is a violently rotating column of air in contact with the ground that is usually produced by a thunderstorm. The system often (but not always) is made visible by water droplets formed by condensation and/or by dust and debris that are drawn into the tornado (Figure 11.21).

Tornadoes are the most violent of all weather systems. Fortunately, most are small and short-lived and often strike sparsely populated regions. Occasionally,

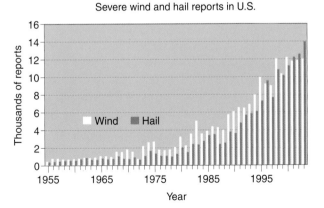

FIGURE 11.20
Annual reports of severe hail and wind occurrences in the contiguous United States have trended rapidly upward since 1955. [NOAA, NCEP, Storm Prediction Center]

FIGURE 11.21
A tornado is a small-scale weather system that has the potential of taking many lives and causing considerable property damage. [Photo by Joe Willey, Plainview, TX]

however, a major tornado outbreak causes incredible devastation, death, and injury. Over a 16-hr period on 3-4 April 1974, 148 tornadoes struck 13 states in the east central United States, the most widespread and costly outbreak of tornadoes in the nation's history. This super outbreak left 315 people dead and 6142 people injured and caused property damage in excess of $600 million. The most prolific tornado outbreak on record occurred over the Great Plains and Midwest on 29-30 May 2004. More than 180 tornadoes were reported in a 24-hr period. In early May 1999, an outbreak of particularly intense tornadoes hit portions of Oklahoma, Kansas, Texas, and Tennessee. As described in this chapter's Case-in-Point, Oklahoma City, OK was hardest hit. Fifty-five people lost their lives and property damage topped $1.1 billion.

Tornado Characteristics

Probably the most striking characteristic of a tornado is a localized lowering of cloud base into a tapered column composed of tiny water droplets. If this vortex remains aloft, it is called a **funnel cloud**, but if it extends to the ground, it is classified as a tornado. Although often funnel-shaped, in fact, tornadoes take a variety of forms, ranging from cylindrical masses of roughly uniform dimensions in cross-section to long and slender, ropelike pendants. A funnel cloud forms in response to the steep air pressure gradient that is directed from the tornado's outer edge toward its center. Humid air expands and cools as it is drawn inward toward the center of the system. Cooling of air below its dewpoint causes water vapor to condense into cloud droplets. However, if the air is exceptionally dry, a funnel cloud may not form, and the tornado may be made visible by a whirl of dust and debris that is lifted off the ground.

A funnel cloud may not reach the ground. If there is no corresponding whirl of dust or debris on the ground, the system is reported as a *funnel aloft*. The system may or may not develop into a tornado. In some cases, a whirl of dust or debris appears on the ground prior to the appearance of a funnel cloud. Furthermore, the actual tornadic circulation covers a much wider area than is suggested by the funnel cloud. Typically, the diameter of a funnel cloud is only about one-tenth the diameter of the associated tornadic circulation.

A weak tornado's path on the ground typically is less than 1.6 km (1 mi) long and 100 m (330 ft) wide, and the system has a life expectancy of only a few minutes. Wind speeds are less than 180 km per hr (110 mph). While weak tornadoes account for nearly three-quarters of all tornadoes, they account for fewer than 5% of all tornado fatalities. At the other extreme, a violent tornado can cause damage along a path more than 160 km (100 mi) long and 1.0 km (3000 ft) wide, and the lifetime of the system may be 10 minutes to more than 2 hrs. One of the broadest tornadoes on record struck Hallam, NE on 22 May 2004; its diameter was about 4 km (2.5 mi). Based on indirect measurements, wind speeds in violent tornadoes range up to 500 km per hr (300 mph).

The deadliest tornado in North American history was the Tri-State tornado of 18 March 1925. Traveling at a maximum forward speed of 118 km per hr (73 mph), the system persisted for 3.5 hrs and produced a 353-km (219-mi) path of devastation from southeastern Missouri through the southern tip of Illinois and into southwest Indiana. The tornado caused 695 fatalities and 2000 injuries, and 11,000 people were made homeless. (Actually, more than one tornado may have contributed to the Tri-State disaster.) That same day, seven other tornadoes claimed an additional 97 lives across Kentucky and Tennessee.

Most tornadoes are spawned by and travel with intense thunderstorm cells. Tornadoes and their parent cells usually track from southwest to northeast, but any direction is possible. Tornado trajectories are often erratic with many tornadoes causing a hopscotch pattern of destruction as they alternately touch down and lift off the ground. Tornadoes have been known to move in circles and even to describe figure eights. Average forward speed is around 48 km per hr (30 mph), although there are reports of tornadoes racing along at speeds approaching 120 km per hr (75 mph) (e.g., the 1925 Tri-State tornado).

An exceptionally great horizontal air pressure gradient is responsible for a tornado's vigorous circulation. The air pressure drop over a horizontal distance of only 100 m (330 ft) may equal the normal air pressure drop between sea level and an altitude of 1000 m (3300 ft), that is, a reduction of about 10%. The continually changing direction of the inward-directed pressure gradient force produces the centripetal force that maintains the rotation of the air column about a vertical axis. Most Northern Hemisphere tornadoes rotate in a counterclockwise direction (viewed from above); only about 5% rotate clockwise. While the Coriolis Effect has a negligible influence on the scale of a funnel cloud, the counterclockwise bias is inherited from the larger parent thunderstorm.

Where and When

The central United States is one of only a few places in the world where synoptic weather conditions and terrain are ideal for tornado development; interior Australia is another. Although tornadoes have been reported in all 50 states and throughout southern Canada, most occur in **tornado alley**, a north-south corridor stretching from eastern Texas and the Texas Panhandle northward through Oklahoma, Kansas, Nebraska, and into southeastern South Dakota. Central Oklahoma has the highest annual incidence of significant tornadoes (F2 or higher) per unit area, whereas local tornado frequency maxima occur from central Iowa eastward to central Indiana, and along the Gulf Coast. In terms of average annual number of tornadoes per 10,000 square miles by state, Florida is the highest with 8.4 for the period 1950-1995 (Figure 11.22).

Concentration of tornadoes over the central Plains is sometimes taken to imply that tornadoes do not occur in regions of great topographical relief. Actually, strong to violent tornadoes are largely unaffected by terrain; there are numerous examples of such tornadoes traversing rugged and even mountainous topography. On the other hand, weak tornadoes are more likely over flat than rough terrain.

Each year, the United States can anticipate between 700 and 1100 tornadoes. A new national record was set in 2004 with 1817 tornadoes reported but fatalities totaled only 35. Slightly more than half of all tornadoes develop during the warmest hours of the day (10 a.m. to 6 p.m., local time), and almost three-quarters of tornadoes in the United States occur from March to July. The months of peak tornado activity are May and June when atmospheric conditions are optimal for spurring vigorous convection and the severe thunderstorms that spawn tornadoes. As of this writing, the monthly record for greatest number of tornadoes was set in May 2003 with 559 reported; the previous monthly record was 399 in June 1992.

One factor that contributes to the spring peak in tornado frequency is the relative instability of the lower atmosphere at that time of year. During the transition from winter to summer, daylight lengthens and solar radiation incident on Earth's surface becomes more intense. Heat is transported from the relatively warm ground into the cold troposphere, but it takes time for the temperature of the entire troposphere to adjust to heating from below. The upper troposphere, in fact, usually retains its winter-like cold well into spring. The steep air temperature lapse rate (warm at low levels and cold aloft) favors deep convection and severe thunderstorm development.

Another factor that contributes to the spring tornado maximum is the greater likelihood that favorable synoptic weather conditions will occur at that time of year. Recall from earlier in this chapter that severe thunderstorms typically develop in the warm southeast sector of a strong extra-tropical cyclone. Such cyclones achieve their greatest intensity when sharp north-south temperature contrasts develop across the nation, that is, in spring when the polar front is well defined.

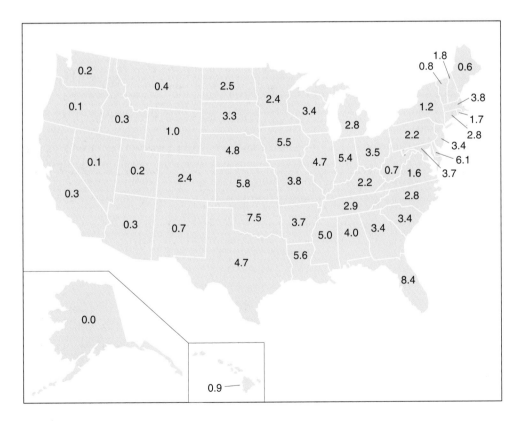

FIGURE 11.22
Average annual number of tornadoes per 10,000 square miles by state, 1950-1995. [NOAA]

From late winter through spring, tornado occurrences progress northward. In effect, the center of maximum tornado frequency follows the sun, as do the mid-latitude jet stream, the principal storm tracks, and northward incursions of maritime tropical air. By late February, maximum tornado frequency, on average, is along the central Gulf States. In April, the maximum frequency shifts to the southeast Atlantic States; in May and June, the highest tornado incidence is usually over the southern Plains, and by early summer, it moves into the northern Plains, the Prairie Provinces east of the Rockies, and the Great Lakes region. From late summer through autumn, tornado occurrence shifts southward. During spring, most tornadoes travel from southwest to northeast, steered by southwesterly winds in the middle and upper troposphere, but in summer and into fall, many tornadoes travel from northwest toward the southeast as the steering winds shift.

Your chances of experiencing a tornado are actually very slim. Less than 1% of all thunderstorms produce tornadoes, and even in the most tornado-prone regions of North America, a tornado is likely to strike a given locale only once every 250 years. There are, of course, exceptions to the rule. Tornadoes have hit Oklahoma City no fewer than 27 times since 1892. To be prepared in the event that a tornado threatens your area, study the recommendations in Table 11.4.

Tornado Hazards and the F-Scale

Tornadoes threaten people and property because of (1) extremely high winds, (2) a strong updraft, (3) subsidiary vortices, and (4) an abrupt drop in air pressure. Winds that may reach hundreds of kilometers per hour blow down trees, power poles, buildings, and other structures. Flying debris causes much of the death and injury associated with tornadoes. Broken glass, splintered lumber, and even vehicles become lethal projectiles. In violent tornadoes, the updraft near the center of the storm's funnel may top 160 km per hr (100 mph) and is sometimes strong enough to lift a railroad car off its tracks or a house off its foundation. Some tornadoes consist of two or more *subsidiary vortices* that orbit about each other or about a common center within a massive tornado. These **multi-vortex tornadoes** are usually the most destructive of all tornadoes.

TABLE 11.4
Some Tornado Safety Tips[a]

1. Seek shelter in a tornado (storm) cellar, an underground excavation, or a steel-framed or substantial reinforced concrete building.

2. Avoid auditoriums, gymnasiums, supermarkets, or other structures that have wide, free-span roofs.

3. In an office building or school, go to an interior hallway on the lowest floor or a designated shelter area. Lie flat on the floor with your head covered.

4. In a high-rise, go to the center of the building (an elevator shaft or staircase). Stay away from glass.

5. At home, go to the basement. If there is no basement, go to a small room (closet, bathroom, or interior hallway) in the center of the house on the lowest floor. Seek shelter under a mattress or a sturdy piece of furniture.

6. Stay clear of all windows and outside walls. Protect yourself from flying debris.

7. In open country, never try to outrun a tornado in a motor vehicle. Tornadoes often move too fast and their paths are too erratic to avoid even if you drive at right angles to the apparent track of the storm. Instead stop and seek shelter indoors, and if this is not possible, lie flat in a ravine, dry creek bed, or open ditch.

8. Do not seek shelter in a motor vehicle or under a highway overpass.

9. Get out of mobile homes (manufactured housing).

[a]Based on NOAA recommendations.

It was once widely believed that a tornado caused buildings to explode, presumably because the air pressure within the building could not adjust rapidly enough to the abrupt pressure drop associated with the tornado. In the event of a tornado sighting, people were advised to open windows to help equalize the internal and external air pressure. In fact, most buildings have sufficient air leaks that a potentially explosive pressure differential never develops. Hence, people are now advised to stay away from windows, closing them only if time permits. Structural damage to a building is caused either by winds slamming debris against the walls or by very strong currents of air that stream over the roof, causing it to lift. (The same lifting happens as air flows over the curved upper surface of an airplane wing.) As the roof is lifted, the walls collapse or are blown in, and the building disintegrates.

In 1971, T.T. Fujita devised a six-point intensity scale for rating tornado strength and damage to structures (Table 11.5). The **F-scale** is based on rotational wind speeds estimated from property damage and categorizes tornadoes as weak (F0, Fl), strong (F2, F3), or violent (F4, F5). An F0 tornado produces minor damage, snapping twigs and small branches and breaking some windows. F1 and F2 tornadoes can cause moderate to considerable property damage and even take lives. Fl tornadoes can down trees and shift mobile homes off their foundations, and a F2 tornado can rip roofs off frame houses, demolish mobile homes, and uproot large trees. A F3 tornado can partially destroy even well constructed buildings and lift motor vehicles off the ground. At the violent end of the F-scale, destruction is described as "devastating" to

"incredible," with the potential for many fatalities. A F4 tornado can level sturdy buildings and other structures and toss automobiles about like toys. In a F5 tornado, sturdy frame houses are lifted and transported some distance before disintegrating.

Fortunately, F5 tornadoes are rare. Of the 800 or so tornadoes that strike the United States in an average year, perhaps only one will be rated F5. Since 1950 in the contiguous U.S., only 50 tornadoes rated F5. When one does occur, however, the impact can be catastrophic. In about 1 minute, a F5 tornado leveled the village of Barneveld, WI on 8 June 1984; 100 homes were totally destroyed and nine lives were lost. The Xenia, OH tornado, which was part of the super outbreak of 3-4 April 1974, rated F5 over a portion of its 51-km (32-mi) path and claimed 34 lives.

In 1997, the American Meteorological Society reported that, in a typical year, 86% of all tornadoes are weak, 13% are strong, and only about 1% are violent. The few violent systems are responsible for the majority of all fatalities, however. Between 1961 and 1990, the average annual number of fatalities from tornadoes was 82, with 42% reported in April and 17% in May. In an average year, tornadoes injure about 1500 people.

As a tornado travels along the ground and progresses through its life cycle, its rating on the F-scale can fluctuate as the system's intensity changes. The Wichita-Andover, KS tornado of 26 April 1991 is an example. As shown in Figure 11.23, the tornado first touched down near Clearwater, KS about 5:57 p.m. (CDT) and then tracked northeastward to just north of El Dorado, KS where it dissipated about 7:10 p.m. The tornado rated F3 or F4 along most of its 77-km (48-mi) path. However, the rating rose to F5 as the tornado demolished all 241 mobile homes at the Golden Spur Mobile Home Park in Andover, KS. This tornado was responsible for 17 deaths.

The Tornado-Thunderstorm Connection

Most strong to violent tornadoes are spawned by a highly organized convective system known as a *supercell thunderstorm* (or just *supercell*). Supercells are very energetic with updraft speeds sometimes in excess of 240 km per hr (150 mph); they can last for several hours and produce more than one tornado. Schematic views of a tornadic supercell are shown from the side in Figure 11.24 and from above in Figure 11.25.

TABLE 11.5
The Fujita Tornado Intensity Scale

F-Scale	Category	Estimated wind speed	
		km/hr	mi/hr
0	Weak	65-118	40-73
1		119-181	74-112
2	Strong	182-253	113-157
3		254-332	158-206
4	Violent	333-419	207-260
5		420-513	261-318

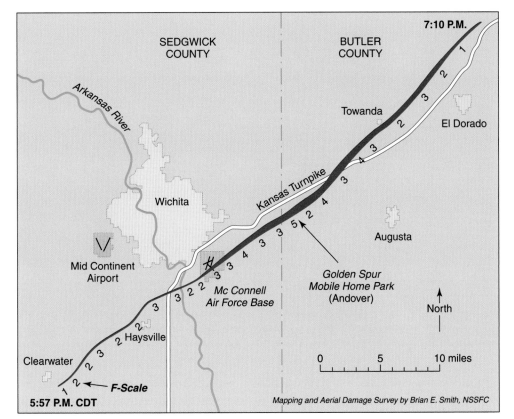

FIGURE 11.23
Path of the Wichita-Andover, Kansas tornado of 26 April 1991. Numbers along the path indicate rating on the Fujita tornado intensity scale which is based on property damage. [NOAA]

FIGURE 11.24
Schematic view of a tornadic supercell thunderstorm. [Adapted from NOAA, *Advanced Spotter's Field Guide*]

FIGURE 11.25
Plan view of a tornadic super-cell thunderstorm. [Adapted from NOAA, *Basic Spotters' Field Guide*]

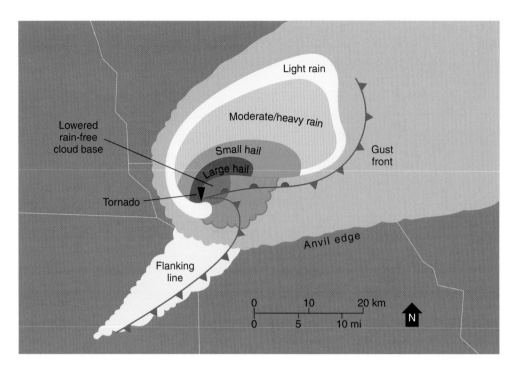

Tornado development in a supercell begins with an interaction between the updraft and the larger-scale horizontal wind. In a tornadic supercell, the horizontal wind exhibits strong vertical shear in both speed and direction. That is, the wind strengthens and veers (turns clockwise) with altitude, from south or southeast at the surface to southwest or west aloft. This shear in wind speed causes the air to rotate about a horizontal axis in a rolling motion. When this rotation interacts with the updraft, the tube of rotating air is tilted from a horizontal to nearly vertical orientation. The shear in the horizontal wind direction also adds to this rotation of air about a vertical axis. Consequently, the updraft spins in a counterclockwise direction (viewed from above), forming a **mesocyclone**, 3 to 10 km (2 to 6 mi) across. Initially, the mesocyclone develops in the middle troposphere and stretches vertically, but in only about 10% of all cases does a mesocyclone evolve into a tornado.

A **wall cloud** (or *inflow cloud*), a roughly circular lowered portion of the rain-free base of a thunderstorm, often accompanies a mesocyclone (Figure 11.26). A wall cloud is typically about 3 km (2 mi) in diameter and forms in the region of strongest updraft, usually to the rear (south or southwest) of the main shaft of precipitation. The updraft draws humid, rain-cooled air into the system, and as that air ascends, expands and cools, water vapor begins to condense at an altitude that is lower than cloud base. Hence, the base of the thunderstorm descends as a wall cloud. As foreboding as they may appear, most wall

clouds do not produce tornadoes. Tornadic wall clouds typically are relatively long-lived, preceding the tornado by perhaps 10 to 20 minutes. Rotation of the wall cloud is obvious and persistent, becoming violent just prior to appearance of the tornado. Also, surface winds blowing in toward a tornadic wall cloud are strong (in the range of 40 to 55 km per hr, or 25 to 35 mph).

A mesocyclone circulation is most intense at an altitude of about 6100 m (20,000 ft), and from there it builds both upward and downward. Meanwhile, the updraft strengthens as more air converges toward the base of the supercell. The updraft sometimes becomes so strong that it overshoots the top of the thunderstorm and

FIGURE 11.26
A thunderstorm wall cloud may accompany a mesocyclone but most do not produce a tornado..

produces a dome-like cloud bulge on top of the spreading anvil cloud. In a tornadic supercell, the mesocyclone narrows and builds downward toward the ground. Relatively low air pressure in the mesocyclone causes water vapor to condense so that a funnel cloud forms. As the spinning column of air narrows, its circulation strengthens, sometimes to extremely high speeds. (This increase in wind speed is analogous to what happens when an ice skater performs a spin: As the skater pulls her arms closer to her body, her spin rate increases.) A tornado typically appears near the updraft and toward the rear of a supercell. Hence, in some instances, a shaft of heavy rain falling between the tornado and an observer makes visual detection of an approaching tornado difficult.

At about the same time that the tornadic circulation begins to descend towards Earth's surface, a downdraft develops near the rear edge of the supercell. The downdraft strikes the Earth's surface within minutes of the tornado touchdown and begins to wrap around the tornado and mesocyclone. Eventually, the downdraft completely surrounds the tornado and mesocyclone and cuts off the inflow of warm, humid air. Consequently, the tornado weakens. As the tornado dissipates, its funnel shrinks, tilts and develops a ropelike appearance.

Although supercells typically produce the most devastating tornadoes, potentially destructive tornadoes can develop in multi-cellular clusters. Squall-line tornadoes are most common in cells located just north of a break in the line or in the southernmost (*anchor*) cell. Perhaps 90% of all North American tornadoes are spawned by thunderstorms that are associated with mature extra-tropical cyclones. Most other tornadoes are products of convective instability triggered by hurricanes. In fact, many hurricanes that make landfall along the southeastern United States coast are accompanied by tornadoes. Tornadoes often develop on the northeast flank of an Atlantic hurricane, after the system has turned toward the north and northeast (Chapter 12).

In some cases relatively weak tornadoes develop without any pre-existing mid-level mesocyclone. Instead, the initial rotation develops in the atmospheric boundary layer. For example, very weak tornadoes can spin off a thunderstorm gust front. Recall that a *gust front* is the leading edge of a downdraft after it strikes the ground and begins spreading out ahead of a thunderstorm cell. These short-lived tornadoes are sometimes called *gustnadoes*. Another example of a non-supercell tornado that begins as swirling winds at the Earth's surface is a *landspout*. An updraft builds and pulls the swirling air upward. Vertical stretching causes the horizontal rotation to strengthen as

the updraft eventually reaches cloud base. The landspout is made visible by ground debris that is pulled into the circulation.

Monitoring Tornadic Thunderstorms

Scientific understanding of tornadoes and their genesis is somewhat tentative because direct monitoring of tornadoes generally is not feasible; traditional weather instruments are not durable enough to withstand tornadic winds. Between 1981 and 1983, storm chasers from the University of Oklahoma tried to deploy a 180-kg (400-lb) tornado-resistant instrument package in the path of tornadoes without much success. Today, storm chasers rely primarily on photography, balloon-borne instruments that monitor atmospheric conditions surrounding severe storms, and portable Doppler radar that can resolve the circulation within supercells (Figure 11.27).

In communities where severe weather is a major concern, volunteer *storm spotters*, trained by National Weather Service personnel, monitor atmospheric conditions for signs of severe thunderstorms. Spotters provide a valuable service that complements weather radar, satellites, and networks of weather instruments and lightning detectors. But even trained storm spotters must be cautious of phenomena that may resemble tornadoes or funnel clouds. For more on this topic, refer to this chapter's third Essay, "Tornado Look-Alikes."

As noted in Chapter 7, weather radar is an indispensable tool in monitoring severe weather systems. Operating in the reflectivity mode, weather radar cannot detect a tornado directly, but in some cases when the

FIGURE 11.27
Truck-mounted portable Doppler weather radar unit (*Doppler On Wheels*).

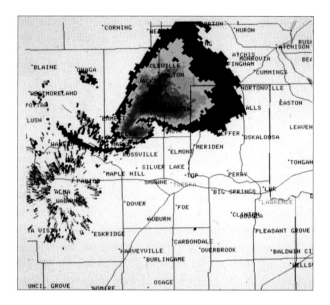

FIGURE 11.28
Weather radar image showing a hook echo which may indicate air circulation in a developing tornado. [NOAA, National Weather Service]

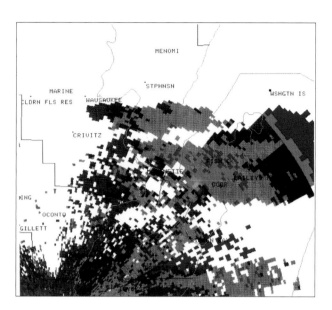

FIGURE 11.29
A tornado vortex signature (TVS) is visible near the center of this Doppler weather radar image. [NOAA, National Weather Service]

parent mesocyclone is present, a hook-shaped echo appears on the radar screen on the southeast side of a severe thunderstorm cell (Figure 11.28). A **hook echo** is produced by rainfall as it is drawn around the mesocyclone within a severe thunderstorm.

Weather radar operating in the velocity (Doppler) mode monitors the circulation within a weather system rather than just the intensity, location, and general displacement of an area of precipitation. Doppler radar sees inside severe thunderstorms and detects mesocyclones, developing tornadoes, gust fronts, and strong wind shear associated with microbursts. Mesocyclone signatures are sometimes identified up to 30 minutes prior to formation of a tornado and at distances up to 230 km (140 mi) from the storm system. Doppler radar can monitor a tornado as it evolves from a mesocyclone and before it descends to Earth's surface. A tornadic circulation within several tens of kilometers of the radar may show up on the radar image as a *tornado vortex signature (TVS)*, a small region of rapidly changing wind direction within a mesocyclone (Figure 11.29). Doppler radar provides the public with more advance warning of severe weather than was possible with reflectivity-only radars. Advance warning of up to 10 minutes or more (compared to less than 5 minutes with the conventional radars in use in the late 1980s) is feasible and has saved many lives.

Although the advent of Doppler weather radar has greatly improved the ability of meteorologists to forecast tornadoes, storm spotters and visual surveillance

of thunderstorms are still needed for several reasons: (1) Not all tornadoes are associated with mesocyclones and these tornadoes are particularly difficult to forecast. (2) Most mesocyclone signatures and some tornado vortex signatures are not associated with tornadoes. (3) Many tornado-bearing thunderstorms do not produce distinctive radar signatures and some storms give false signatures. (4) The resolution of radar imagery is not fine enough to detect some severe weather phenomena.

According to scientists at NOAA's Storm Prediction Center, the annual number of tornado reports has trended upward, doubling since the mid-1950s (Figure 11.30). (On the other hand, the number of tornadoes rated

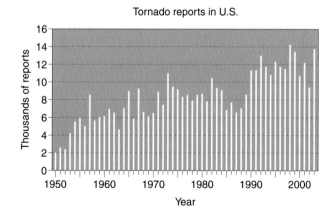

FIGURE 11.30
Annual number of reports of tornadoes in the United States for the period 1950-2003. [NOAA, NCEP, Storm Prediction Center]

F2 or higher declined from about 200 per year in the mid-1950s to about 100 per year today.) Is the upward trend in tornado reports the consequence of a major shift in atmospheric conditions—perhaps climate change? Probably not. More likely, the reason for the upward trend is a combination of non-meteorological factors. Today, more people live in rural areas and observe storms meaning that storm damage that would have gone unseen in the past is now reported. Furthermore, people today tend to have greater weather awareness and access to better and more convenient communications systems (e.g., cell phones) to report sightings of tornadoes. The spread of storm spotter networks and the advent of Doppler radar are also major contributing factors.

Conclusions

Thunderstorms are the products of convection currents that surge to great altitudes within the troposphere. As such, thunderstorms channel excess heat at Earth's surface into the atmosphere via a combination of sensible and latent heating. Thunderstorms are thus most frequent in the warmest regions of Earth, especially over the continental interiors of tropical latitudes. Most thunderstorms consist of more than one cell, each of which completes its life cycle (i.e., towering cumulus, mature, dissipating stages) in under an hour. A thunderstorm cell reaches its maximum intensity during its mature stage when it produces lightning, heavy rain, and strong gusty surface winds.

Although less than 1% of all thunderstorms produce tornadoes, in some areas of North America, the possibility of a tornado is the principal reason why people are fearful of thunderstorms. A tornado is a short-lived, small-scale weather system that is usually spawned by a severe thunderstorm. Tornado development requires a special combination of atmospheric conditions and terrain, so tornadoes are most frequent in spring over the central United States. Hazards of tornadoes are extremely high winds, a powerful updraft, subsidiary vortices, and an abrupt drop in air pressure. The intensity of a tornado is rated on the F-scale from F0 (weak) to F5 (violent) based on wind speed estimated from property damage. The most intense tornadoes develop in the strong updraft of supercell thunderstorms.

We continue our discussion of weather systems in the next chapter with a focus on tropical cyclones (e.g., tropical storms and hurricanes).

Basic Understandings

- A thunderstorm is a mesoscale weather system produced by strong convection currents that surge to great altitudes in the troposphere. The life cycle of a thunderstorm cell consists of a three-stage sequence: towering cumulus, mature, and dissipating.

- During the towering cumulus stage, cumulus clouds build vertically and laterally, updrafts characterize the entire system, and there is no precipitation. The mature stage begins when precipitation reaches Earth's surface. At that stage, updrafts occur alongside downdrafts and the system attains peak intensity. During the dissipating stage, subsiding air spreads through the entire cell and clouds vaporize.

- A thunderstorm usually consists of more than one cell, each of which may be at a different stage in its life cycle. A cluster of thunderstorm cells may track in a different direction than the individual constituent cells.

- Most thunderstorms develop in a maritime tropical air mass as a consequence of uplift (1) along fronts, (2) on mountain slopes, (3) via convergence of surface winds, or (4) through intense solar heating of Earth's surface.

- Thunderstorms develop along boundaries within a maritime tropical air mass, as a squall line along or ahead of a cold front, or in a meso-scale convective complex (MCC). MCCs account for a substantial portion of growing season rainfall over the Great Plains and Midwest.

- Worldwide, thunderstorms are most common over the continental interiors of tropical latitudes. In North America, thunderstorm days are most frequent in central Florida where converging sea breezes induce uplift of maritime tropical air, while thunderstorms are also frequent on the eastern slopes of the central and southern Rockies, associated with heating of the mountain slopes and orographic lifting. Convection is inhibited and thunderstorms are unlikely to develop in air masses that reside or travel over relatively cold surfaces and are thereby stabilized.

- Severe thunderstorm cells typically form along a squall line ahead of a fast-moving, well-defined cold front associated with a mature extra-tropical cyclone. The polar front jet stream causes dry air to subside over a surface layer of maritime tropical air. This produces a layering of air that sets the stage for explosive convection and development of severe thunderstorms.

- Lightning is a brilliant flash of light produced by an electrical discharge within a cloud, between clouds, or between clouds and the ground. Cloud-to-ground lightning consists of a very rapid sequence of events involving stepped leaders, return strokes, and dart leaders.

- The reason for electrical charge separation within a cumulonimbus cloud is not well understood, but collisions between graupel and ice crystals, plus updrafts and downdrafts within the cloud likely play important roles.

- Some thunderstorm cells produce downbursts, which are intense downdrafts that spread out (diverge) at Earth's surface as potentially destructive winds. Based on size, a downburst is classified as either a macroburst or microburst. A squall line or meso-scale convective complex sometimes produces a family of straight-line downburst winds, known as a derecho.

- A flash flood is a short-term, localized, and often unexpected rise in stream level causing the stream to flow over its banks. Flash flooding is a special hazard in mountainous terrain, where steep slopes channel excess runoff into narrow stream and river valleys, and in urban areas, where impervious surfaces cause excess runoff to collect in low-lying areas.

- Hail develops in intense thunderstorm cells characterized by strong updrafts, great vertical development, and an abundant supply of supercooled water droplets.

- A tornado is a small mass of air that whirls rapidly about a nearly vertical axis and is usually made visible by condensed water vapor (funnel cloud), and dust and debris drawn into the system.

- An exceptionally steep horizontal air pressure gradient between the tornado center and outer edge is the force ultimately responsible for the violence of a tornado.

- Most tornadoes occur in spring within a corridor stretching from Texas northward to southeastern South Dakota, from central Iowa eastward to central Indiana, and along the Gulf Coast states.

- Synoptic weather conditions that favor the outbreak of tornadoes progress northward (with the sun), from the Gulf Coast in early spring to southern Canada by early summer.

- When a tornado strikes, very high winds, a strong updraft, subsidiary vortices, and an abrupt air pressure drop are responsible for considerable property damage. Based on rotational wind speed estimated from damage to structures, tornadoes are classified as weak, strong, or violent on the F-scale. Most tornadoes are weak (F0 or F1), but most fatalities are caused by rare violent tornadoes (F4 or F5).

- Most intense tornadoes develop out of a mesocyclone that forms in the strong updraft of a supercell thunderstorm. A rotating mesocyclone circulation is generated by an interaction between a thunderstorm updraft and strong vertical shear in the horizontal wind.

- Doppler radar monitors the circulation within a severe thunderstorm and can provide advance warning of tornado development.

Review

1. Identify and describe the characteristics of each of the three stages in the life cycle of thunderstorm cell.
2. What is a *gust front*? Explain how a gust front can spur development of secondary thunderstorms.
3. Describe why so many thunderstorms form over the interior of the Florida peninsula.
4. In what sector of a mature extra-tropical cyclone are strong thunderstorms most likely to form? Justify your answer.
5. What is a *microburst* and why might it pose a hazard for aircraft that are taking off or landing?
6. Why is flash flooding a particular hazard in mountainous terrain and in urban areas?
7. List the characteristics of hail-producing thunderstorms.
8. Where is *tornado alley*?
9. What is the basis for the *F-scale* of tornado intensity?
10. Compare and contrast a tornado with a dust devil.

Critical Thinking

1. Compare and contrast a sea breeze front with a gust front.
2. What causes the anvil shape of a thunderstorm top?
3. Thunderstorms may track at an angle to the paths of their constituent cells. What is the significance of this behavior for thunderstorm forecasting?
4. Explain the diurnal and seasonal variations in thunderstorm occurrence. Also explain why thunderstorms are rare along the coast of southern California and over snow-covered terrain.
5. How and why does a tilted updraft affect the likelihood of hail formation?
6. How is the diameter of hailstones an indicator of the intensity of its parent thunderstorm cell?
7. Does the centripetal force operate in a tornado? Explain your response.
8. Comment on whether reflectivity-only radar can be used to determine the precise altitude of a thunderstorm top.
9. Compare and contrast a tornado and a downburst. How do the patterns of property damage differ?
10. A cloud bulge appears on the anvil top of a thunderstorm. Why might this feature suggest a severe thunderstorm?

ESSAY: Lightning Safety

The odds of being struck and killed by lightning are actually very slim, about 1 in 600,000. By comparison, the odds of being struck and killed by an auto are more than 50 times greater. Although the danger of lightning cannot be ignored, some simple precautions will minimize the risk of injury during a thunderstorm. No place is absolutely safe, but the risk can be significantly reduced in even the most lightning-prone area of the nation (south and central Florida, where an estimated 10 lightning bolts strike every square kilometer of land annually).

Even as a thunderstorm approaches, some people believe that they are safe as long as it is not raining. They continue doing what they have been doing, even if it is an inherently dangerous activity during a thunderstorm (e.g., getting in that one last hole of golf or inning of baseball). Unfortunately, lightning can strike well outside the area of rainfall. In fact, lightning has been reported as far as 16 km (10 mi) beyond the main shaft of thunderstorm precipitation. And in arid or semi-arid regions, thunderstorm precipitation may completely vaporize in the dry air below cloud base. Such thunderstorms still produce lightning.

When a thunderstorm threatens, use the *flash-to-bang* method to determine the distance to the thunderstorm and whether it is approaching you (described elsewhere in this chapter). If the time between flash and bang is 30 seconds or less, the wisest strategy is to seek shelter in a house or other building, avoiding contact with conductors of electricity that provide pathways for lightning. These include pipes (do not shower), stoves (do not cook), and wires (do not use the computer or land-line telephone). Electrical appliances pose no hazard if grounded, but why tempt fate by assuming they are properly wired? Also, it is a good idea to wait 30 minutes following the last thunderclap before resuming outdoor activities as thunderstorms can still develop behind the main line of thunderstorms.

Some confusion surrounds the safety of motor vehicles during a lightning storm. Contrary to popular belief, the rubber tires of a motor vehicle provide occupants with little or no protection from lightning. When lightning strikes a motor vehicle, the electrical current is conducted over the metal surface of the vehicle, through the steel frame to the tires, and then to the ground. Without direct contact with the metal frame, passengers usually escape injury. All things considered, a person is much safer inside a motor vehicle (not a convertible, the open back of a pickup truck, or a golf cart) than outdoors during a thunderstorm.

What about the lightning threat to aircraft? Pilots steer clear of thunderstorm cells not only because of lightning but also because of the associated strong wind shear and the possibility of hail. All large aircraft (and many small ones) carry so-called static discharge wicks on various trailing edges of the craft that are designed to bleed electrical charges back into the atmosphere. This prevents a build-up of electrical charge and lessens the chance of a lightning discharge between clouds and aircraft.

If caught out in the open and a building or an auto is not accessible when a thunderstorm approaches, find shelter under a cliff, in a cave, or in a low area, such as a ravine, a valley, or even a roadside ditch (not subject to flooding). A group of people in the open should spread out, staying several meters apart. Avoid (1) tall, isolated structures, such as trees, telephone poles, and flagpoles, (2) metallic objects, such as wire fencing, rails, wire clotheslines, bicycles, and golf clubs, (3) high areas, such as the tops of mountains, hills, and roofs, and (4) bodies of water such as swimming pools and lakes. Stay off riding lawn mowers and farm tractors (unless equipped with a metal cab). While isolated trees in open spaces are hazardous, a thick grove of small trees surrounded by taller trees may offer safe haven.

If outdoors and your hair stands on end or your skin tingles, lightning may be about to strike nearby. Immediately crouch down with only the balls of your feet touching the ground, placing your hands on your knees, and bend forward. In this way, you present the smallest possible target for a return stroke. Do not lie flat on the ground because if lightning does strike, the electrical charge running along the ground can pass through you. Such a charge traveling through your body between your head and feet while you lie on the ground will deliver much more electrical energy to you than if the charge runs along the ground between your feet as you crouch. Furthermore, unless they are wet, shoes will reduce the charge conducted to your body should a current move along the ground.

Contrary to popular belief, lightning can strike the same structure more than once (as long as the structure was not destroyed). The top of the Empire State Building in New York City typically is struck more than 20 times a year, and on one occasion was hit 15 times in only 15 minutes.

Two of every three people *struck* by lightning recover fully. Most survivors are jolted by a nearby lightning bolt and are not hit directly. Such near misses, however, can produce severe burns because of the intense heat generated by lightning. If an electrical current from a lightning strike passes through the body, however, it can disrupt a special system in the heart that generates rhythmical electrical impulses that control the regular contractions of the heart muscle. If the disruption is severe, heart muscles are unable to work together and cardiac output declines. Blood flow can slow to the point that body tissues are damaged by an inadequate supply of oxygen and nutrients, a condition known as *circulatory shock*. However, the body possesses a number of mechanisms that attempt to return cardiac output to normal.

Emergency medical personnel should be summoned immediately for a lightning-strike victim. Meanwhile, cardiopulmonary resuscitation (CPR) or mouth-to-mouth resuscitation may revive the victim. Covering the victim with a blanket or additional clothing will reduce heat loss from the body. It is a myth that victims of lightning strikes carry an electrical charge; they should be attended to without delay. Treatment can aid bodily processes that counteract shock. Hence, if circulatory shock is not severe, the victim usually recovers.

With severe electrical disruption of the heart, circulatory shock can reach a critical stage whereby shock breeds more shock. That is, reduced cardiac output causes the circulatory system (including the heart) to deteriorate, which in turn, causes a further reduction in blood flow. This condition, known as *progressive shock*, can trigger a vicious cycle of cardiovascular deterioration. Without immediate medical intervention, progressive shock can rapidly reach a critical stage where the person cannot be saved.

ESSAY: Hail Suppression[1]

Humankind's efforts to suppress hail have deep historical roots. In 14th century Europe, church bells were rung and cannons fired in the belief that the attendant noise would ward off hail. A period of particularly intense hail suppression activity took place in the grape-growing regions of Austria, France, and Italy during the late 19th century. M. Albert Stiger, a wine grower and burgomaster of Windisch-Feistritz, Austria, designed and built a funnel shaped hail suppression cannon. Stiger believed that the smoke particles in the cannon fire would inhibit hailstone development. Amazingly, in experimental firings in 1896-97 at Windisch-Feistritz, Stiger reported no hail, although severe hail damage occurred in neighboring areas.

Word of Stiger's apparent success spread throughout the vineyard regions of Europe, and hail cannons soon became commonplace (Figure 1). There were so many cannons that accidental shooting of people became a serious problem in some localities. After Stiger's much heralded success was not duplicated elsewhere, interest in hail cannons rapidly waned, and by 1905 this early attempt at weather modification ended.

FIGURE 1
An unusually large hail suppression cannon used in Casale, Italy in the late 19th century. [Morgan, G.M., 1973. "A general description of the hail problem in the Po Valley of northern Italy," *J. Appl. Meteorol.,* 12:338-353.]

1 Much of this discussion is based on S.A. Changnon, Jr., and J.L. Ivens, "History Repeated: The Forgotten Hail Cannons of Europe," *Bulletin of the American Meteorological Society* 62(1981):368-375.

The modern era of hail suppression experimentation began after World War II. Although founded on a much better, albeit incomplete, understanding of cloud physics, the new techniques shared some similarities with earlier efforts. For example, until the practice was outlawed in the early 1970s, farmers in Italy routinely fired explosive rockets into threatening clouds in an attempt to shatter developing hailstones. In the former Soviet Union, scientists fired silver iodide (AgI) crystals, a cloud-seeding agent, into cumulonimbus clouds. They hypothesized that AgI crystals would stimulate the formation of large numbers of small ice pellets (graupel), which would melt long before reaching the ground, instead of the normal development of small numbers of larger ice pellets that reach the ground as hailstones.

U.S. agricultural losses to hail total hundreds of millions of dollars every year. It is not surprising then that U.S. scientists set out to test the Soviet hypothesis of hail suppression and to learn more about hail-producing thunderstorms. To these ends, the *National Hail Research Experiment* was launched over northeastern Colorado in 1972. Although much was learned about hailstorms, three years of seeding potential hail-producing thunderstorms failed to confirm the Soviet hypothesis. Some scientists, however, questioned the experimental design and whether it was a viable test of the Soviet technique. In an interesting parallel with events in 19th century Europe, declining public confidence in the effectiveness of modern hail-suppression efforts brought an end to federal funding of hail suppression research in 1979.

ESSAY: Tornado Look-A-Likes

Experienced sky watchers are well aware that a number of atmospheric phenomena resemble funnel clouds or tornadoes. These include waterspouts, virga, scud clouds, and dust devils. Even distant smoke plumes are sometimes mistaken for tornadoes.

A *waterspout* is a tornado-like system that occurs over the ocean or over a large inland lake (Figure 1). It is so named because it consists of a whirling mass of water that appears to stream out of the base of its parent cloud, which can be either cumulus congestus or cumulonimbus. A waterspout is usually considerably less energetic, smaller, and shorter-lived than a tornado. The rare intense waterspout may well be a tornado that formed over land and then traveled out over a body of water, while on occasion a waterspout becomes a tornado upon moving ashore. In any event, boaters should steer clear of waterspouts.

Virga or scud clouds are sometimes mistaken for a tornado or funnel cloud because their occurrence might coincidently exhibit a cylindrical or funnel-shaped profile. *Virga* is a curtain of rain or snow that vaporizes prior to reaching the ground (Chapter 7). *Scud clouds* (also called *fractus clouds*) are low, ragged stratiform or cumuliform cloud elements that are not attached to a thunderstorm cloud. Virga and scud clouds lack organized rotation about a vertical or near-vertical axis, clearly distinguishing them from tornadoes or funnel clouds. In deserts, or wherever the soil dries out, intense solar heating often gives rise to a swirling mass of dust, known as a *dust devil* (Chapter 10). A dust devil resembles a tornado, but forms near the ground, is not attached to any clouds, and causes little if any property damage.

Figure 1
Multiple waterspouts off the Bahamas Islands. [NOAA, Historic NWS Collection, photo by Dr. Joseph Golden, NOAA.]

CHAPTER 12

TROPICAL WEATHER SYSTEMS

Hurricane Emily, July 2005. [Courtesy NOAA]

Case in Point

On Sunday evening, 28 August 2005, the effects of the approaching Hurricane Katrina were beginning to be felt along the north central Gulf Coast as the storm's outer rain bands swept ashore. Within 24 hours, Katrina's ferocious winds, storm surge, and torrential rains would devastate the Gulf Coast of Louisiana and Mississippi, obliterating coastal communities and devastating New Orleans. According to the National Weather Service, Katrina was the third most intense hurricane (minimum central air pressure of 920 mb) (after the "Labor Day" hurricane of 1935 and Hurricane Camille in 1969) to make landfall on the United States since reliable records began in 1851. Katrina claimed at least 1300 lives and, in terms of economic loss, Katrina ranks as the most destructive hurricane to strike the United States.

Katrina began in the southeastern Bahamas on 23 August 2005 as the twelfth tropical depression of the season; the next day the system strengthened to a tropical storm and was assigned its name. Katrina intensified as it slowly moved northwestward and then westward through the Bahamas. On Thursday, 25 August, Katrina made landfall at 6:30 a.m., EDT, between Hallandale Beach and North Miami Beach in south Florida as a category 1 hurricane on the Saffir-Simpson Hurricane Intensity Scale, producing maximum sustained winds of 130 km per hr (80 mph) and heavy rain (more than 12.5 cm or 5 in. in southeast Florida). Katrina lost some strength during the seven hours it took to pass southwestward over the southern tip of the Florida peninsula. Tracking almost due west and fueled by the warm waters of the Gulf of Mexico, the storm quickly intensified and gradually turned toward the northwest and then north. By the afternoon of 26 August, Katrina was a major hurricane. As a precaution, public officials issued mandatory evacuation orders for the people of New Orleans, LA, Gulfport, MS, and sections of Mobile, AL. Earlier, personnel on platforms and oil rigs in the Gulf were evacuated.

By the morning of Sunday, 28 August, Katrina was a category 5 hurricane with maximum sustained surface winds of 282 km per hr (175 mph) and a minimum central pressure of 902 mb, the fourth lowest

on record for an Atlantic hurricane. Katrina weakened to a strong category 3 prior to making landfall at 7:10 a.m. on Monday, 29 August in southern Plaquemines Parish just south of the town of Buras, LA at the mouth of the Mississippi River (Figure 12.1). Maximum sustained winds were 202 km per hr (125 mph) to the east of the storm center with hurricane force winds extending 195 km (120 mi) from its center, driving a 6 to 9 m (20 to 30 ft) storm surge that reached well inland along the Louisiana and Mississippi Gulf coast and as far east as Mobile, AL, flooding parts of the city. Several hours later, after passing over Breton Sound and Lake Borgne, the eye of

FIGURE 12.1
Satellite image of Katrina making landfall as a category 3 hurricane on the Louisiana coast on 29 August 2005. Katrina would be the most destructive hurricane in U.S. history. [NOAA]

the storm made another landfall at the mouth of the Pearl River on the Louisiana-Mississippi border. By then, Katrina had weakened somewhat but was still a category 3. At 11 p.m., EDT, the north/northeast moving system was centered near Columbus, MS. Now downgraded to a tropical storm, maximum sustained winds diminished to 97 km per hr (60 mph) with a central pressure estimated at 973 mb. Along much of Katrina's path, total rainfall exceeded 20 to 25 cm (8 to 10 in.).

Topography made New Orleans particularly vulnerable to Hurricane Katrina. The city occupies a bowl between the Mississippi River and Lake Pontchartrain. Much of the bowl, home to more than 1 million residents and businesses, is up to 1.8 m (6 ft) below sea level. The people of New Orleans depend on earthen levees and concrete floodwalls to keep the water out and pumps to remove flood waters. However, according to the U.S. Army Corps of Engineers, the levees were designed to withstand a hurricane no stronger than a category 3. A combination of strong winds, storm surge, and heavy rainfall caused numerous breaches in the levee system, the pumps failed, and up to 80% of New Orleans was flooded to depths that in many places reached 6 m (20 ft).

Although warned in advance of the approaching potentially catastrophic storm, thousands of people either were unable or chose not to evacuate New Orleans. As weather conditions deteriorated and floodwaters began to rise, many people fled to the Louisiana Superdome, the city's shelter of last resort. On Monday, 29 August, winds gusting to more than 160 km per hr (100 mph) ripped off part of the roof of the Superdome and knocked out electricity. There about 30,000 people spent many days in overcrowded, deplorable conditions without adequate food, water, sanitary facilities, or air conditioning. Other residents of New Orleans fled the rapidly rising waters, climbing to the upper floors, attics or roofs of their homes where they awaited rescue by boat or helicopter. The damage to New Orleans was so extensive that recovery is likely to take years.

Making matters worse, less than a month after Katrina had expended its wrath on Louisiana, Mississippi, and Alabama, another potentially catastrophic hurricane again threatened the U.S. Gulf Coast. Moving on a westward course from the Caribbean, on 20 September 2005, Hurricane Rita skirted the Florida Keys and northern Cuba accompanied by heavy rain and strong winds. As it moved out over the warm waters of the Gulf of Mexico, Rita rapidly intensified to a category 5. Maximum sustained winds reached 282 km per hr (175 mph) and its minimum central pressure fell to 897 mb, distinguishing Rita as the third most intense Atlantic hurricane (in terms of air pressure) since records began in the mid 19th century.

Rita made landfall as a category 3 hurricane at 3:30 a.m., EDT, on Saturday, 24 September on the extreme southwest coast of Louisiana near Sabine Pass, TX. Sustained winds up to 195 km per hr (120 mph), torrential rains, and storm surge caused considerable structural damage, flooding, and power outages. Rita drifted northward at 19 km per hr (12 mph) and by 11 a.m., EDT, was centered near Jasper, TX and had weakened to a category 1. Although New Orleans was spared a direct hit by Rita, the heavy rains and storm surge associated with the approaching storm caused new breaks in the recently repaired levee system. Flood waters up to 1.5 m (5 ft) deep spread over parts of the city.

Driving Question:
What conditions are required for the development of tropical cyclones?

This chapter focuses on tropical weather systems, primarily tropical cyclones. **Tropical cyclones** are synoptic-scale low-pressure systems that originate over the tropical ocean and include tropical depressions, tropical storms, hurricanes, and typhoons. At maturity, a tropical cyclone is one of the most intense and potentially most destructive storms on Earth. We describe the characteristics, geographical and seasonal distribution, life cycle, and hazards of tropical cyclones. We also consider in separate sections, trends in hurricane frequency, the hurricane threat to the southeastern United States, efforts to forecast hurricanes based on atmospheric conditions around the globe, and unsuccessful experiments to modify hurricanes. We set the stage by summarizing some of the basic characteristics of weather in the tropics.

Weather in the Tropics

The tropics, the belt between the Tropics of Cancer and Capricorn (from 23.5 degrees N to 23.5 degrees S), exhibits very little seasonal variation in temperature. Temperatures are uniformly high in response to year-round high noontime solar altitude and nearly uniform day length (Chapter 3). In fact, in much of the tropics, the diurnal (day to night) temperature variation is greater than the range in monthly mean temperatures through the course of a year.

In the tropics, broad expanses of air are uniformly warm and humid so that fronts and frontal weather are not present. Intense solar radiation heats Earth's surface driving deep convection and isolated afternoon thunderstorms that produce brief bursts of heavy rain. For reasons presented in Chapters 4 and 11, thunderstorms are more frequent over continents and large islands than the adjacent ocean. Sometimes thunderstorm cells are aligned as narrow bands known as *tropical non-squall clusters*. On other occasions, a band of more intense cells forms, similar to a squall line of middle latitudes. In these so-called *tropical squall clusters*, winds can be strong and gusty and rainfall may persist for several hours and can be very heavy especially at the onset. The ITCZ (intertropical convergence zone) stimulates thunderstorm activity and its north-south seasonal shifts are responsible for seasonal variations in precipitation in portions of the tropics (Chapter 9). The ITCZ follows the sun, moving northward in the Northern Hemisphere spring and southward in the Northern Hemisphere autumn. The rainy season is summer (high sun) and the dry season is winter (low sun).

Little variation in the thermal and moisture properties of tropical air means that there is little horizontal variation in surface air pressure. Hence, isobaric analysis is of little value in routine weather analysis and forecasting in the tropics. Instead, meteorologists rely upon streamline analysis. A **streamline** is a line drawn on a map that is everywhere parallel to the wind direction and portrays graphically the horizontal flow of air. Streamline analysis can be used to identify regions of divergence and convergence such as associated with an easterly wave. As described later in this chapter, an *easterly wave* is an important weather-maker in the tropics and sometimes is the precursor of a tropical cyclone.

Lengthy episodes of tranquil warm weather are typical of the tropics, but occasionally tropical cyclones develop that bring torrential rains and strong winds. The most feared and potentially most destructive of these tropical cyclones is the hurricane.

Hurricane Characteristics

Hurricane is likely derived from *Haracan*, the name of the storm god of the Taino people who inhabited Caribbean islands at the time of Spanish exploration of the New World. A **hurricane** is an intense cyclone that originates over tropical ocean waters, usually in late summer or early fall (when tropical waters are warmest), and has a maximum sustained wind speed of 119 km per hr (74 mph) or higher. By convention in the United States, *sustained wind speed* is a one-minute average measured at the standard anemometer height of 10 m (33 ft).

A convenient way to describe a hurricane is to contrast it with the extra-tropical cyclone examined in Chapter 10. A hurricane develops in a uniform mass of very warm and humid air, so the system has no associated fronts or frontal weather (Figure 12.2). Air pressure is distributed symmetrically about the system's low-pressure center so that isobars plotted on a surface weather map form a pattern of closely spaced nearly concentric circles. Typically, the central pressure at sea level is considerably lower and the horizontal air pressure gradient much greater in a hurricane than in an extra-tropical cyclone. Reconnaissance aircraft extrapolated a surface air pressure of 882 mb (26.05 in.) at the center of Hurricane Wilma while the storm was over the northwest Caribbean Sea early on 19 October 2005. If accurate, this is the lowest sea-level air pressure on record in the Western Hemisphere. A hurricane is usually a much smaller system, averaging a third the diameter of a typical extra-tropical cyclone. Rarely do hurricane-force winds extend much more than 120 km (75 mi) beyond the system's center. Structurally, a mature hurricane is a warm-core low that weakens rapidly with altitude, especially above 3000 m (9800 ft). In the upper troposphere, at altitudes above about 12,000 m (40,000 ft), the circulation usually becomes anticyclonic (clockwise when viewed from above in the Northern Hemisphere). Recall that an extra-tropical cyclone is a cold-core system whose circulation strengthens with altitude.

At the center of a hurricane is an area of almost cloudless skies, subsiding air, and light winds (less than 25 km per hr or 16 mph), called the **eye** of the storm (visible in Figure 12.1). The eye generally ranges from 10 to 65 km (6 to 40 mi) across, shrinking in diameter as the hurricane intensifies and winds strengthen. At a hurricane's typical rate of forward motion, the eye may take up to an hour to pass over a given locality. People are sometimes lulled into thinking the storm has ended when skies clear and winds abruptly slacken following a hurricane's initial blow. They

FIGURE 12.2
Schematic diagram of the internal structure of a hurricane. Note that the vertical dimension is greatly exaggerated. [From NOAA, Hurricane. Washington, DC: Superintendent of Documents, 1977]

may be experiencing passage of the hurricane's eye; heavy rains and ferocious winds will soon resume but blow from the opposite direction.

Bordering the eye of a mature hurricane is the **eye wall**, a ring of thunderstorm (cumulonimbus) clouds that produce heavy rains and very strong winds (Figure 12.3). The most dangerous and potentially most destructive part of a hurricane is the portion of the eye wall on the side of the advancing system where the wind blows in the same direction as the storm's forward motion. On that side, hurricane winds combine with the storm's forward motion producing the system's strongest surface winds. In the Northern Hemisphere, this dangerous semicircle of high winds (and high ocean waves) occurs on the right side of the hurricane when facing in the direction of the system's forward movement. Cloud bands, producing heavy convective showers and hurricane-force winds, spiral inward toward the eye wall. Meanwhile, at high altitudes cirrus or cirrostratus clouds spiral outward from the system.

Intense, long-lived hurricanes often undergo an *eye wall replacement cycle*. Over a period of a day or so, the main eye wall collapses and the storm weakens. Then an outer eye wall contracts and takes the place of the original eye wall. The hurricane then intensifies.

Whereas hurricanes differ substantially from extra-tropical cyclones, they share some characteristics with intense storms that sometimes develop over the ocean at high latitudes. For more on these systems, refer to this chapter's first Essay, "Polar Lows with Hurricane Characteristics."

Where and When

Conditions required for a tropical cyclone to form are: relatively high sea-surface temperatures (SST), adequate Coriolis Effect, and weak vertical wind shear. In addition, relatively humid air in the mid-troposphere (near 4900 m or 16,000 ft) favors tropical cyclone development. To a

FIGURE 12.3
The eye wall of Hurricane Katrina taken on 28 August 2005, as seen from a NOAA P-3 hurricane hunter aircraft while the storm was over the Gulf of Mexico. [NOAA]

large extent, these requirements dictate where and when tropical cyclones form.

Tropical cyclones require a sea-surface temperature of at least 26.5 °C (80 °F) through an ocean depth of about 45 m (150 ft) or more. Such exceptionally warm ocean water sustains the system's circulation by the latent heat released when water vapor, evaporated from the ocean surface, is conveyed upward and condenses within the storm system. Recall from Chapter 6 that temperature largely governs the rate of evaporation of water, so the higher the sea-surface temperature, the greater is the supply of latent heat for the storm system. Furthermore, the spray from breaking ocean waves readily evaporates adding to the supply of water vapor that condenses and releases latent heat in the developing tropical cyclone.

A tropical cyclone that moves over colder water or makes landfall, however, loses its warm-water energy source and weakens. The strong winds of a tropical cyclone can bring about a drop in sea-surface temperatures. Cyclonic winds induce *Ekman transport* and divergence of surface waters under the storm system, bringing cold water to the surface (Chapter 9). Until the normal thermal structure of the ocean is restored, lower than usual SST can inhibit development of subsequent tropical cyclones over the same region of the ocean. In addition, atmospheric scientists discovered that changes in SST associated with warm- and cold-core ocean rings influence tropical cyclone development. A **ring** is a large turbulent eddy that forms when a meander in a current forms a loop that pinches off, separating from the main ocean surface current. Ocean water to the north of the Gulf Stream is relatively cold with temperatures averaging less than 10 °C (50 °F). Rings that form on the north side of the Gulf Stream have entrained relatively warm water from the Sargasso Sea whereas rings that form on the south side of the Gulf Stream have entrained relatively cold water. In the Northern Hemisphere, *warm-core rings* rotate in a clockwise direction, have diameters to 200 km (125 mi), and consist of a pool of warm water that may reach a depth of 1500 m (4900 ft). *Cold-core rings* rotate in a counterclockwise direction, are larger (diameters to 300 km or 185 mi) and their associated pool of cold water may reach the ocean floor (to a depth of more than 4000 m or 13,000 ft). Tropical cyclones may intensify over warm-core rings but weaken over cold-core rings.

The second requirement for tropical cyclone development is a significant Coriolis Effect; that is, the influence of Earth's rotation must be sufficiently strong to initiate a cyclonic circulation. As noted in Chapter 8, the Coriolis Effect weakens toward lower latitudes and is

zero at the equator. With very rare exceptions, tropical cyclones do not form within 5 degrees of the equator (a distance of about 480 km or 300 mi). One exception to this rule was Typhoon Vamei which formed near Singapore on 27 December 2001. Vamei was centered near 1.5 degrees N and its circulation extended into both hemispheres producing maximum sustained surface winds of 140 km per hr (87 mph).

The first two conditions that favor tropical cyclone formation (i.e., high SST and sufficient Coriolis Effect) occur only over certain portions of the ocean. The main ocean breeding grounds for tropical cyclones along with average storm trajectories are plotted in Figure 12.4. Most hurricanes form in the 8- to 20-degree latitude belts. Major hurricane breeding grounds are: (1) the tropical North Atlantic west of Africa (including the Caribbean Sea and Gulf of Mexico), (2) the North Pacific Ocean west of Mexico, (3) the western tropical North Pacific and China Sea, where a hurricane is called a *typhoon* (from the Cantonese, *tai-fung*, meaning great wind), (4) the South Indian Ocean east of Madagascar, (5) the North Indian Ocean (including the Arabian Sea and the Bay of Bengal), and (6) the South Pacific Ocean from the east coast of Australia eastward to about 140 degrees W. In the Indian Ocean and near Australia, hurricanes are simply called *cyclones*.

The requirement of high sea-surface temperature makes the occurrence of tropical cyclones seasonal (Figure 12.5). Changes in sea-surface temperature lag the regular seasonal variations in incoming solar radiation. Sea-surface temperatures reach a seasonal maximum roughly 6 to 8 weeks after the date of most intense solar radiation. Most Atlantic hurricanes develop when surface waters are warmest, that is, in late summer and early autumn; the official hurricane season runs from 1 June to 30 November, with the peak hurricane threat for the U.S. coastline between mid-August and late October.

The third requirement for tropical cyclone development is weak vertical wind shear (less than about 37 km per hr or 23 mph) between the surface and upper troposphere. Weak vertical wind shear allows a cluster of cumulonimbus clouds to organize over tropical seas, the first step in the evolution of a hurricane. By contrast, vigorous vertical wind shear implies strong west to east winds in the middle and upper troposphere that shear off the tops of westward tracking thunderstorms, preventing the systems from building vertically and organizing. During El Niño, winds are unusually strong at altitudes near 12,000 m (40,000 ft) over the Atlantic hurricane breeding ground. Hence, Atlantic hurricanes usually are

FIGURE 12.4
Tropical cyclone breeding grounds are located only over certain regions of the world ocean. Arrows indicate average hurricane trajectories.

FIGURE 12.5
The frequency of Atlantic basin hurricanes and tropical storms by date (number of storms per 100 years). The date of peak frequency occurs about 2.5 months following the summer solstice. [NOAA]

infrequent during El Niño. For example, the Atlantic hurricane season of 1997 occurred during an intense El Niño and produced 3 hurricanes, only one of which made landfall on the U.S. coast.

Strong *wind shear* is the principal reason hurricanes rarely form off the east or west coasts of South America (although Caribbean hurricanes occasionally impact the north coast of Venezuela). Furthermore, the intertropical convergence zone (ITCZ) usually is absent over the Southern Hemisphere ocean and without the ITCZ, there is no source of synoptic-scale vorticity (spin) or convergence needed for tropical cyclone development. Nonetheless, on 28 March 2004, a rare hurricane that formed in the South Atlantic Ocean made landfall as a category 1 system on the coast of Brazil about 800 km (500 mi) south of Rio de Janeiro. Hurricane Catarina, as it was later called, claimed at least two lives, destroyed 500 homes, and left 1500 people homeless.

A worldwide average of about 88 named tropical cyclones develops each year and approximately one-half reach hurricane strength. The western Pacific Ocean, with its vast expanse of warm surface waters, is the most active area for tropical cyclones, with roughly 24 systems each season (1945-2004), of which about 16 intensify into typhoons. Some of these typhoons can become very intense. A typhoon with maximum sustained winds of 240 km per hr (150 mph) or greater is called a *supertyphoon*. Typically, four supertyphoons develop in the western Pacific annually.

Only hurricanes spawned over the tropical Atlantic, Caribbean Sea, and Gulf of Mexico pose a serious threat to coastal North America. Based on the period 1931 to 2004, a seasonal average 10.2 named tropical storms form over these waters. Of these systems, on average about 6 intensify into hurricanes and of these 2.4 become major hurricanes. On average, two hurricanes strike the U.S. coast each year. The 2005 Atlantic hurricane season set a new record with 27 named tropical cyclones; the previous record was 21 set in 1933. In 2005, 14 Atlantic tropical cyclones became hurricanes (a new record) and 4 major hurricanes struck the U.S. (also a record). The 1995 Atlantic hurricane season was the third most active in recorded history with 19 tropical storms, 11 of which attained hurricane strength. However, the annual number of hurricanes may have little bearing on the number of landfalling hurricanes and their impact. Whereas only 4 hurricanes occurred during the 1992 Atlantic season, one of them, Hurricane Andrew, was the second most costly in terms of property damage in U.S. history, amounting to $34.3 billion (in year 2000 dollars).

Hurricanes have hit every Atlantic and Gulf Coast State from Texas to Maine. Florida is the most hurricane-prone of all the states, with 64 hurricanes crossing its coastline between 1900 and 2004. In the same period, Texas was second with 38, while North Carolina had 29 and Louisiana 27 hurricanes.

The primary breeding ground for hurricanes in the Atlantic shifts east and west with the seasons. Early in the hurricane season (May and June), hurricanes form mostly over the Gulf of Mexico and the western Caribbean. By July, the main area of hurricane development begins to shift eastward across the tropical North Atlantic. By mid-September, most hurricanes develop in a belt stretching from the Lesser Antilles (in the eastern Caribbean Sea) eastward to south of the Cape Verde Islands (off Africa's West Coast). After mid-September, hurricanes again originate mostly over the Gulf of Mexico and the western Caribbean.

The Pacific Ocean off Mexico and Central America ranks second to the western North Pacific in average annual number of tropical cyclones (15.2 per year between 1966 and 2004); the majority of these (8.4) develop into hurricanes. And yet, the Pacific Coast of North America is rarely a target of hurricanes. Prevailing winds (northeast trades) are directed offshore and usually steer tropical cyclones that form west of Central America away from the coast. Also, the southward flowing cold California Current plus upwelling just off the southern California (and Baja California) coast produce sea-surface temperatures that normally are too low to sustain hurricanes that travel toward the northeast. However, during unusual atmospheric/oceanic circulation regimes, hurricanes have struck coastal Southern California and even traveled over the Desert Southwest. For example, on 9-10 September 1976, Hurricane Kathleen crossed Baja California and tracked near Yuma, AZ, bringing torrential rains and floods to the Imperial and Lower Colorado River Valleys. Another example was Hurricane Nora in September 1997. Nora made landfall on 25 September near Punta Eugenia on the Baja California coast with maximum sustained winds of 137 km per hr (85 mph). The system weakened to a tropical storm and crossed into the United States near the California/Arizona border. Rainfall up to 7.5 cm (3 in.) was common in the Desert Southwest and some mountain locations in Arizona reported almost 30 cm (12 in.). For comparison, Yuma, AZ normally receives 7.64 cm (3.01 in.) of precipitation annually.

The Hawaiian Islands are sometimes threatened by tropical cyclones that develop over the central tropical Pacific or track westward into that region from the Pacific hurricane breeding grounds west of Mexico. Fortunately, in an average year, only 3 to 4 tropical cyclones affect the central Pacific and since 1957 only 4 hurricanes have impacted the Islands. However, the most recent one, Iniki in September 1992, devastated the island of Kauai. Iniki tracked directly over the island with estimated maximum sustained winds of 185 km per hr (115 mph) with gusts to 258 km per hr (160 mph). A storm surge of 1.5 m (5 ft) topped by wind-driven waves caused extensive flooding. Seven people lost their lives. Total property damage was estimated at $2.3 billion (in year 2000 dollars), making this the most costly natural disaster in the history of the State of Hawaii.

Life Cycle of a Hurricane

The first sign that a hurricane may be in the making is the appearance of an organized cluster of cumulonimbus clouds over tropical seas. This region of convective activity is labeled a **tropical disturbance** if a center of low pressure is detected at the surface. Chances are that the tropical disturbance was triggered by the ITCZ, a trough in the westerlies that intruded into the tropics from middle latitudes, a West African disturbance line (similar to a squall line), or a wave (or ripple) in the easterly trade winds (an *easterly wave*).

The majority of tropical cyclones that threaten North America develop out of convective cloud clusters associated with easterly waves traveling westward off the West African coast. In fact, easterly waves are precursors of perhaps 65% of all named tropical cyclones in the Atlantic basin. An **easterly wave** is a ripple in the tropical easterlies (trade winds) featuring a weak trough of low pressure (Figure 12.6). The system likely owes its origin to the disturbance of the prevailing easterlies by the Ethiopian Highlands of East Africa. They are most common from August through October. An easterly wave propagates from east to west across the tropical Atlantic generally more slowly than the flow in which it is embedded. Some waves pass over Central America and into the eastern Pacific where they can trigger tropical cyclone development.

Over the ocean, to the west of the trough line within an easterly wave is an area of horizontal divergence in the lower troposphere, a shallow moist layer, and fair weather. To the east of the trough line is an area of intense lower-tropospheric convergence, a deep moist layer, and heavy rain showers. Convergence on the east side of an easterly wave helps to organize convective activity into a developing tropical cyclone. Storm systems originating in

this way over the Atlantic are referred to as *Cape Verde-type hurricanes.*

Only a small percentage of convective cloud clusters in the tropical Atlantic actually evolve into full-blown hurricanes for the following reasons: (1) Subsidence of air on the eastern flank of the Bermuda-Azores anticyclone and the associated *trade-wind inversion* inhibit deep convection (Chapter 9). (2) Vertical wind shear (change of horizontal wind with altitude) over the tropical Atlantic is usually too great for hurricane formation; strong horizontal winds aloft disrupt deep convection. (3) The middle troposphere is usually too dry; low vapor pressure at these levels inhibits intensification of the system.

Atmospheric conditions that inhibit tropical cyclone development over the North Atlantic appear to be associated with the **Sahara air layer (SAL)**. SAL is an elevated mass of dry dusty stable air originating over the Sahara Desert of North Africa. In 2004, J.P. Dunion of the University of Miami and C.S. Velden of the University of Wisconsin-Madison reported on a special satellite-based technique they used to track SAL's movement westward from North Africa across the tropical North Atlantic, over the Caribbean, and into the Gulf of Mexico. This technique enabled them to observe interactions between the SAL, easterly waves, and tropical cyclones.

Over its desert source region, the Sahara air layer is well mixed up to an altitude of almost 5500 m (18,000 ft)—near the 500-mb level. However, as SAL advances westward over the ocean, it is underlain by a layer of cool, humid air (the *marine layer*) with a depth of about 900

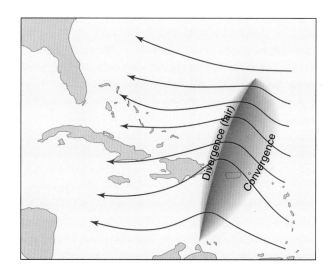

FIGURE 12.6
Schematic drawing of an easterly wave moving westward across the western tropical Atlantic. An easterly wave may play an important role in triggering the development of a tropical cyclone.

to 1800 m (2900 to 5900 ft). An elevated temperature inversion separating the warm SAL above from the cool marine layer below reinforces the pre-existing trade wind inversion. In the SAL's interior, this inversion coupled with strong vertical shear in the prevailing easterly winds suppresses the deep convection required for tropical cyclone development. Furthermore, as a tropical storm nears the Sahara air layer, its circulation draws in dry stable air producing downdrafts. Hence, when SAL engulfs a tropical cyclone (or an easterly wave), convection diminishes and the system weakens even though sea surface temperatures are above the threshold for tropical cyclone formation. On the other hand, a tropical cyclone that has weakened as a result of an encounter with SAL may quickly regain strength after the system moves beyond the influence of the SAL.

SAL is most frequent from late spring through early fall, overlapping much of the Atlantic hurricane season. SAL typically covers an area of the Atlantic that is somewhat larger than the 48 contiguous United States and maintains its Saharan characteristics as it travels many thousands of kilometers westward over the Atlantic. Suppression of convection by SAL may explain why tropical cyclones are less common in the North Atlantic than in the eastern North Pacific.

If atmospheric/oceanic conditions favor hurricane development and if those conditions persist, the surface air pressure falls and a cyclonic circulation develops. Water vapor condenses within the storm, releasing latent heat of vaporization, and the heated air rises. Expansional cooling of the rising air triggers more condensation, release of even more latent heat, and a further increase in buoyancy. Rising temperatures in the core of the storm, coupled with anticyclonic outflow of air aloft, cause a sharp drop in surface air pressure, which in turn, induces more rapid convergence of humid air at the surface. The consequent uplift surrounding the developing *eye* leads to additional condensation and release of latent heat.

Through these processes, a tropical disturbance intensifies and its winds strengthen. When maximum sustained wind speeds reach 37 km per hr (23 mph) or higher, the developing system is called a **tropical depression**. When maximum sustained wind speeds reach at least 63 km per hr (39 mph), the system is classified as a **tropical storm** and assigned a name, such as Alberto or Beryl. For more on naming hurricanes, refer to this chapter's second Essay. Once maximum sustained winds reach 119 km per hr (74 mph) or higher, the storm is officially designated a hurricane. As a hurricane weakens and decays, the system is downgraded by reversing this classification scheme.

Hurricanes that form over the Atlantic near the Cape Verde Islands usually drift slowly westward with the trade winds (along the southern flank of the Bermuda-Azores subtropical high) across the tropical North Atlantic and into the Caribbean. At this stage in the storm's trajectory, it is not unusual for the system to travel at a mere 10 to 20 km per hr (6 to 12 mph) and take a week to cross the Atlantic. Once over the western Atlantic, however, the storm usually picks up speed and begins curving northward along the western flank of the Bermuda-Azores high, and then northeastward as the system is caught in the westerlies of middle latitudes. Precisely where this curvature takes place determines whether the hurricane enters the Gulf of Mexico (perhaps then tracking up the lower Mississippi River Valley or over the Southeastern States), moves up the Eastern Seaboard, or curves northward into the Atlantic.

Upon reaching about 30 degrees N, an Atlantic hurricane may begin to acquire extra-tropical characteristics as colder air circulates into the system and fronts develop. From then on, the storm resembles a cold-core extra-tropical cyclone and completes its life cycle usually over the North Atlantic. Many hurricanes, however, depart significantly from the track just described. Some of the hurricane tracks plotted in

FIGURE 12.7
Tropical cyclone trajectories are often erratic, as shown by these samples. As indicated by the shaded area, however, Atlantic tropical cyclones initially drift westward and curve toward the north and northeast when they reach the western Atlantic. [From NOAA, Hurricane. Washington, DC: Superintendent of Documents, 1977]

Figure 12.7, for example, are very erratic. A hurricane can describe a complete circle or reverse direction. Since the middle of the 20th century, seven named tropical cyclones moved westward from the Atlantic to the Pacific, while two storms moved eastward from the Pacific to the Atlantic. In November 1999, Hurricane Lenny (only the fifth Atlantic basin storm in November on record to achieve category 3 or 4 status) tracked toward the east and northeast across the Caribbean Sea—opposite the direction of motion of most Atlantic basin hurricanes. According to the Tropical Prediction Center/National Hurricane Center, this unusual track caused unprecedented wave and storm surge damage to westward facing harbors on Caribbean islands. During the 20th century only three other hurricanes tracked mostly east or northeastward through the Caribbean.

Some hurricanes, fueled by warm Gulf Stream waters, maintain tropical characteristics far north along the Atlantic Coast. The eye of Hurricane Hazel, for example, was still discernible when the system passed over Toronto, ON in October 1954, after making landfall about 1100 km (700 mi) to the south near Cape Fear, NC. The remnants of Hazel moved northward into Ontario and became one of the most memorable storms in Canadian history. Winds gusted to 120 km pr hr (75 mph) and up to 18.3 cm (7.2 in.) of rain fell. Eighty people died mostly from flooding in the Toronto area.

New England, situated more than 25 degrees of latitude north of the usual Atlantic hurricane breeding grounds, has been the target of many full-blown hurricanes. The most deadly of these was the unnamed hurricane of 21 September 1938 (category 3) that raced through New England and into Canada at an estimated 80 km per hr (50 mph). A storm surge ravaged the New England coast, with a 4-m (16-ft) wall of water sweeping into downtown Providence, RI. Winds gusting over 200 km per hr (125 mph) severely damaged forests, and torrential rains caused flash flooding of rivers and streams. Fatalities were estimated at 600 and property damage totaled $400 million ($4.7 billion in year 2000 dollars). A more recent New England hurricane was Bob (category 2) in August 1991. Hurricane Bob moved swiftly up the East Coast from its origin over the northern Bahamas. The storm center passed just east of Cape Hatteras, NC and then remained offshore until striking Rhode Island's south coast. The eye then passed just east of Boston, MA and Portland, ME. Top wind speed was 185 km per hr (115 mph), the death toll was 18, and property damage totaled $2.0 billion (in year 2000 dollars).

Hurricane Hazards

Hazards of hurricanes are (1) heavy rains and inland flooding, (2) strong winds, (3) tornadoes, and (4) storm surge. According to research conducted by scientists at the Tropical Prediction Center/National Hurricane Center, in the 30-year period from 1970 to 1999, freshwater floods were responsible for almost 60% of the 600 U.S. deaths attributed to tropical cyclones or their remnants. One hundred thirty-eight people drowned either in or while attempting to abandon their motor vehicles. In those three decades, far more people (351) died from inland flooding than from coastal storm surge flooding (only 6 deaths). For example, of the 56 people who perished during Hurricane Floyd (1999), 50 drowned due to inland flooding. On the other hand, the majority of the more than 1300 fatalities associated with Hurricane Katrina in August 2005 were caused by the storm surge. The storm surge remains as the most serious potential impact of a landfalling hurricane and is the primary reason why people are evacuated from low-lying coastal areas.

INLAND FLOODING

Hurricanes and tropical storms produce very heavy rainfall with amounts typically in the range of 13 to 25 cm (5 to 10 in.). Even if the system tracks well inland, heavy rains often persist and may trigger costly flooding (Figure 12.8).

In June 1972, rains from the remnants of Hurricane Agnes accounted for much of the storm's $8.4 billion (in year 2000 dollars) in property damage. Agnes

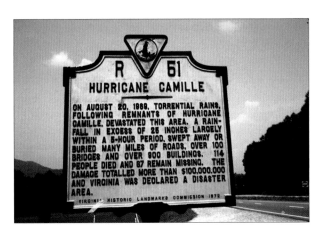

FIGURE 12.8
This roadside marker in central Virginia commemorates the fatalities and property damage caused by the torrential rains associated with the remnants of Hurricane Camille in August 1969.

FIGURE 12.9
The track of Hurricane Agnes in June 1972. This relatively weak system brought flooding rains from Virginia north to New England.

tracked up the Eastern Seaboard from southwest of the Florida Keys to North Carolina and then northward into Pennsylvania (Figure 12.9). The storm brought beneficial rains to the Southeast, which had been experiencing a dry spell, but heavy rains in the mid-Atlantic region were anything but beneficial. During the week prior to Agnes' arrival, frontal showers and thunderstorms produced soaking rains from Virginia to New England. Rainfall averaged 3 to 8 cm (1 to 3 in.) and locally topped 15 cm (6 in.). Agnes' torrential rains falling on already saturated soils produced runoff that triggered many record-breaking river crests and devastating floods.

Heaviest rains from Agnes fell in a band about 350 km (215 mi) wide from western North Carolina northeastward into central New York State. In this hilly terrain, rainfall totals were quite variable but generally ranged from 20 to 30 cm (8 to 12 in.) during the period 18-25 June. Some localities reported total rainfall in excess of 46 cm (18 in.) with more than 25 cm (10 in.) falling in only 24 hours. Flooding was particularly severe in central Pennsylvania where rising waters forced more than 250,000 people from their homes. The Susquehanna River crested at 4 to 5.5 m (13 to 18 ft) above flood stage. Of the 122 fatalities attributed to Agnes, 50 were in Pennsylvania, and flood damage in that state accounted for almost two-thirds of total storm damage.

The impact of Agnes pales in comparison to the devastation caused by Hurricane Mitch in 1998. Mitch was the deadliest hurricane to strike the Western Hemisphere since the "Great Hurricane of 1780," estimated to have killed up to 22,000 people on the Caribbean islands of Martinique, St. Eustatius, and Barbados. The final death toll from Mitch likely will never be known, but the official loss of life was listed at 11,000 with thousands more missing. More than 3 million people were made homeless or had their lives and livelihoods severely affected and the estimated total property damage was at least $5 billion.

Mitch began as a weak tropical depression on 22 October 1998. By 2100 UTC on 26 October, the system's sea-level central pressure had dropped to 905 mb with sustained winds of 290 km per hr (180 mph) and gusts well over 320 km per hr (200 mph), placing the storm in the category of most powerful hurricanes (category 5). Mitch remained at this high level of intensity for 33 consecutive hours. After threatening Jamaica, Mitch tracked westward and by 2100 UTC on 27 October, was centered about 95 km (60 mi) north of Trujilo on the north coast of Honduras. Over the next two days, Mitch slowly drifted southward and finally made landfall, devastating offshore islands and coastal areas of Honduras. Mitch then drifted westward through the mountainous interior of Honduras, finally reaching the border with Guatemala on 31 October. Although winds slowly abated, orographically induced rainfall was torrential, falling at the rate of 30 to 60 cm (12 to 24 in.) per day in many mountainous regions and totaling in some places as much as 190 cm (75 in.) for the duration of the storm. Flooding and mudflows swept away entire villages and their inhabitants, virtually destroyed the infrastructure of Honduras, and devastated parts of Nicaragua, Guatemala, Belize, and El Salvador.

Alberto and Allison are other examples of how devastating rains can be produced by the remnants of a tropical cyclone. The first tropical storm of the 1994 season, Alberto never achieved hurricane status, yet its rains took a terrible toll in a band from southeastern Alabama to central Georgia. Alberto developed in the western Caribbean Sea and strengthened to a tropical storm on 1 July. After drifting slowly west/northwestward, Alberto turned northward, and on the morning of 3 July, came ashore near Fort Walton Beach, FL with peak sustained wind speeds near 97 km per hr (60 mph). The storm then weakened rapidly as it drifted across southeastern Alabama and into central Georgia.

Alberto likely would have received little notoriety except that its moisture-rich remnants slowly meandered over central Georgia and eastern Alabama for three days.

Many area weather stations reported 3-day (3-5 July) rainfall totals in excess of 25 cm (10 in.). Americus, GA set an all-time state record for 24-hr rainfall with 53.6 cm (21.1 in.). This record stood until 20 July 1997 when 82.6 cm (32.52 in.) fell at Dauphin Island Sea Lab, GA. Alberto's torrential rains caused rivers to rise to record high crests, and flooding was extensive. The Ocmulgee River at Macon, GA broke its old record by 1.7 m (5.5 ft) when it crested at more than 5.2 m (17 ft) above flood stage. Most of the storm's 32 fatalities were victims of floodwaters. Property damage was estimated at $1 billion.

With maximum sustained winds of 97 km per hr (60 mph), Allison was a minimal tropical storm before moving ashore at the eastern end of Galveston Island, TX on 5 June 2001 with sustained winds of 80 km per hr (50 mph). Yet this weak system produced near-record rainfall and massive flooding from eastern Texas across the Gulf States and along the mid-Atlantic coast. Allison ranks as the most deadly and costly tropical storm ever to strike the U.S. mainland.

Because of weak steering winds aloft, Allison followed an erratic path from 4 through 9 June, describing a meandering counterclockwise loop over eastern Texas, weakening to a tropical depression on the 7th, and twice soaking the Houston metropolitan area (Figure 12.10). During the period 4-9 June, rainfall totals in the Houston

area included 94 cm (36.99 in.) at Port of Houston and 90.1 cm (35.67 in.) at Greens Bayou. The system's remnant circulation then drifted southward into the northwestern Gulf of Mexico where it intensified into a *subtropical cyclone* (a weather system having characteristics of both tropical and extra-tropical cyclones). On the 11th, Allison moved inland over Louisiana where torrential rains totaled 75.8 cm (29.86 in.) at Thibodaux and 70 cm (27.55 in.) at Salt Point. The system slowly drifted over southeastern Mississippi and then moved northeastward to eastern North Carolina where it again stalled on 14 June. Tallahassee, FL recorded a 24-hr record rainfall of 25.7 cm (10.13 in.) from the 11th to the 12th. On 17 June, Allison tracked toward the northeast off the mid-Atlantic coast and eventually dissipated on the 19th over the North Atlantic southeast of Nova Scotia. All told, Allison took the lives of 41 people (including 23 in Texas and 8 in Florida) and caused at least $5 billion in property damage.

WIND

From 1970 to 1999, about 12% of tropical cyclone fatalities were wind-related. Winds pushing on the outside walls of buildings exert a pressure that increases dramatically as winds strengthen. *Wind pressure*, the force per unit area caused by air in motion, increases with the square of the wind speed. Hence, doubling the wind speed increases the wind pressure on an external wall by a factor of four ($2^2 = 4$). Furthermore, debris transported by the wind and hurled against structures exacerbates the damage potential of strong winds.

Meteorologists have assumed that strong gusts are responsible for the most serious hurricane wind-related property damage. After detailed analysis of the aftermath of Hurricane Andrew, however, T.T. Fujita argued that small but powerful whirlwinds embedded in the hurricane circulation were responsible for the most severe property damage. Whirlwinds combined with the larger-scale hurricane circulation to produce winds estimated at 320 km per hr (200 mph). Based on mode of origin, Fujita described these whirlwinds as *spin-up vortices*. Apparently, small eddies spin off the eye wall and are stretched vertically by powerful convection currents. Stretching accelerates the eddy circulation.

Hurricane winds diminish rapidly once the system makes landfall, so that most wind damage is confined to within about 200 km (125 mi) of the coastline. In fact, the database of hurricane tracks maintained by the Tropical Prediction Center/National Hurricane Center shows no hurricane centered more than about 325 km (200 mi) inland in the United States. Two factors account for the abrupt

FIGURE 12.10
Radar-determined cumulative rainfall over southeast Texas (Houston and Galveston near center) produced by the remnants of tropical storm Allison for the period ending on 10 June 2001.

drop in wind speed once a hurricane makes landfall. A hurricane over land is no longer in contact with its energy source, warm ocean water. In addition, the frictional resistance offered by the rougher land surface compared to the sea surface slows the wind and shifts the wind direction toward the low-pressure center of the system (Chapter 8). This wind shift causes the storm to begin to fill; that is, its central pressure rises, the horizontal air pressure gradient weakens, and winds slacken.

Although winds weaken once a hurricane makes landfall, the system may produce tornadoes (Chapter 11). As a hurricane moves over land its surface winds weaken rapidly while winds aloft remain strong. The wind shear that is created between horizontal winds at the surface and aloft contributes to tornado development. Usually only a few tornadoes occur with a hurricane, but in 1967, Hurricane Beulah reportedly spawned as many as 115 tornadoes across southern Texas. About the same number of tornadoes accompanied Hurricane Ivan as it tracked northward along the Eastern Seaboard in 2004. Tornadoes are most likely after the hurricane enters the westerly steering current and curves toward the north and northeast; they form mostly to the northeast of the storm center, often outside the region of hurricane-force winds.

FIGURE 12.11

Onshore winds and low air pressure associated with a hurricane cause a dome of water to move shoreward, causing considerable coastal erosion and flooding. Adding to the destructive potential of a storm surge are wind-driven waves and floating debris.

STORM SURGE

A **storm surge** is a dome of ocean water, perhaps 80 to 160 km (50 to 100 mi) wide that sweeps over the coastline near the hurricane's landfall (Figure 12.11). A storm surge is caused by strong winds and low barometric pressure and is most likely on the side of the approaching hurricane where winds are onshore. Wind-driven waves with heights of at least 1.5 to 10 m (5 to 33 ft) top the dome of sea water and armed with floating debris are responsible for much of the structural damage attributed to

a storm surge. A storm surge can demolish marinas, piers, cottages, and other shoreline structures, erode beaches, and wash out coastal roads and railway beds. In extreme cases, entire communities are washed away.

Prior to 1970, storm surges were responsible for the majority of hurricane-related fatalities. In fact, in October 1972, the American Meteorological Society adopted a policy statement that attributed 90% of all hurricane-related fatalities near the U.S. coast to the combination of storm surge and accompanying high waves. Subsequently, a better-informed population, early storm warnings, and evacuation of people from vulnerable coastal areas spurred a sharp decline in storm surge related deaths. As pointed out earlier in this chapter, during the 30-year period from 1970 to 1999, the majority of hurricane-related deaths in the United States were from drowning in freshwater floods while only 6 deaths were due to storm surges. Then there was Katrina in 2005 and the death and destruction caused by its storm surge. With the recent upsurge in the frequency of major hurricanes (discussed later in this chapter), coastal residents are advised to remain vigilant should a hurricane threaten, for history recounts many catastrophic storm surges.

A storm surge accounted for much of the considerable loss of life in a hurricane that struck the southeast United States on 27 August 1893, one of six hurricanes to strike the U.S. mainland that year (a record number that was equaled in 1916 and 1985). The unnamed hurricane came ashore at night just north of Savannah, GA with little warning. U.S. Weather Bureau meteorologists predicted that the hurricane, first detected at Nassau in the Bahamas the previous day, would make landfall somewhere along the East Coast south of New York. The actual track placed the system's dangerous semicircle, the band of strongest onshore winds, over the Sea Islands of Beaufort County, SC. Most of the inhabitants of the Sea Islands were freed slaves, their children and grandchildren. They were primarily farmers who raised a highly valued variety of cotton. No telegraph lines connected the islands to the mainland so there was no warning of the hurricane's approach. With no means of evacuation, residents were completely at the mercy of 175 to 210 km per hr (110 to 130 mph) winds and a 3.7 to 4.6 m (12 to 15 ft) storm surge that swept over the islands. Some 20,000 to 30,000 people were left homeless, their crops were destroyed, and the death toll was estimated at 2000 (and possibly as high as 2500). The Sea Islands disaster came at a time of national recession and prior to the time of organized federal or state natural disaster assistance. Intervention by the Red Cross was all that saved the survivors from almost certain famine.

In the most deadly natural disaster in U.S. history, more than 8000 people perished, mostly by drowning, when a hurricane storm surge of over 4.6 m (15 ft) devastated Galveston, TX on 8 September 1900. Ocean waters flooded the entire city located on a barrier island, where the highest elevation in the city was only 2.7 m (8 ft). Some 3600 homes were destroyed; a dam of wreckage that built up some six blocks inland from the beach probably spared the business district total destruction. To protect the city from future storm surges, the U.S. Army Corps of Engineers elevated the city an average of some 3 m (10 ft) and erected a massive concrete seawall along much of the city's Gulf shore.

Hurricane Camille, an exceptionally intense system with winds to 300 km per hr (186 mph), produced a maximum storm surge of 7.3 m (24.3 ft) at Pass Christian, MS on 17 August 1969. The total death toll from the storm was 256, about half from coastal flooding. The surge destroyed or badly damaged more than 18,000 homes and 700 businesses. Scientists had a difficult

time in determining the maximum storm surge produced by Hurricane Katrina in August 2005 because the storm destroyed many of the local tide gauges, but it appears likely that Katrina's storm surge was higher than that of Camille. In 1970, one of the most disastrous storm surges ever flooded the Bay of Bengal coast of East Pakistan (now Bangladesh). A storm surge of nearly 7 m (23 ft) spread over the vast low-lying coastal plain of the Ganges Delta, claiming an estimated 300,000 lives mostly by drowning because there was no high ground for people to seek refuge.

Strong onshore winds plus relatively low air pressure are responsible for a hurricane storm surge. Relatively low air pressure in a hurricane causes sea level to rise (about 0.5 m for every 50 mb drop in pressure or about 1 ft for every 1 in. of mercury drop in pressure). The height of a storm surge is the difference between the observed rise in local sea level and the regular astronomical tide. In general, a storm surge of 1 to 2 m (3 to 6.5 ft) can be expected with a weak hurricane, whereas the storm surge accompanying a violent hurricane may top 5 m (16.4 ft). According to NOAA researchers, storm surge height depends on many factors including the intensity and speed of the hurricane, direction of hurricane motion relative to the shoreline, slope of the seafloor along the shore, configuration of the shoreline, and the height of the astronomical tide. The greatest potential for a highly destructive storm surge occurs with strong onshore winds, along a shallow sloping shoreline, during high tide, and in densely populated areas lacking coastal buffers such as barrier islands, coral reefs, marshes, or swamps. Typically, the rise in sea level in a storm surge lasts for 4 to 8 hours but it may take days for floodwaters to recede.

A special numerical model developed in 1979 by NOAA accurately predicts the location and height of a storm surge. Weather forecasters report considerable success with the **SLOSH (Sea, Lake, and Overland Surges from Hurricanes)** model. Using output from SLOSH and consulting local topographic maps, forecasters can identify areas most likely to be inundated by floodwaters when a hurricane threatens. Hypothetical hurricanes are simulated using various combinations of storm intensity, forward speed, and expected location of landfall to predict the maximum high water levels for various SLOSH basins along the coast. Public safety officials use this information to develop evacuation plans. SLOSH model coverage includes the entire East and Gulf Coasts, as well as parts of Hawaii, Guam, Puerto Rico, and the Virgin Islands.

FIGURE 12.12
Radar reflectivity image of the spiral rain bands associated with Andrew as it came ashore as a category 5 hurricane south of Miami Beach, FL on 24 August 1992. [NOAA]

Trends in Hurricane Frequency

In recent years, the frequency of intense hurricanes has increased. In 2005, researchers at the Georgia Institute of Technology and the National Center for Atmospheric Research (NCAR) reported that the number of category 4 and 5 hurricanes worldwide nearly doubled over the 35-year period, 1970-2004 (Figure 12.13). This upward trend occurred even though the overall number of hurricanes worldwide has declined since the 1990s. In the 1970s, the number of category 4 and 5 hurricanes globally averaged about 10 per year; but since 1990, that number has increased to about 18 per year. Much of the increased frequency of intense hurricanes occurred in the North Pacific, Southwest Pacific, and Indian Ocean with a slightly smaller increase in the North Atlantic.

The only region of the globe where tropical cyclone activity has increased recently is the North Atlantic (Figure 12.14). According to NOAA, since 1995 the average annual number of named tropical cyclones (tropical storms and hurricanes) is 13 compared to 8.6 during the previous 25-year period 1970-1994. Since 1995, the Atlantic averages 7.7 hurricanes per season, 3.6 of which are major hurricanes. In the 25 years prior to 1995, the seasonal average for hurricanes was 5, with 1.5 rated major.

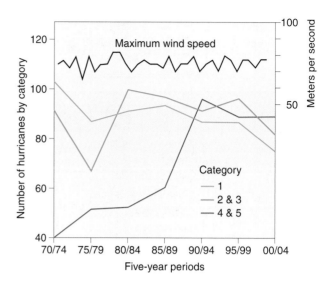

FIGURE 12.13
Recent upward trend in the number of intense (category 4 and 5) hurricanes. [Modified after Peter Webster, Georgia Institute of Technology.]

Why the recent increase in Atlantic hurricanes? Several factors contribute. Sea surface temperatures (SST) have been higher in the tropical Atlantic. An amplified ridge, favorable for tropical cyclones, has been in place over the central and eastern North Atlantic. Vertical wind shear has weakened in the deep tropics over the central North Atlantic. In addition, the African easterly jet stream has been more favorable for tropical cyclone development.

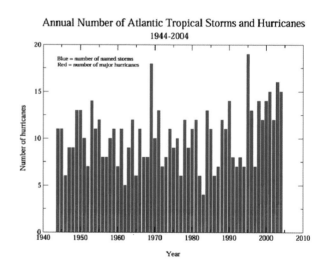

FIGURE 12.14
Annual number of Atlantic tropical storms and hurricanes, 1944-2004. [NOAA]

TABLE 12.2
Most Intense U.S. Hurricanes at Landfall (based on lowest central pressure), 1900-2005[a]

Rank	Hurricane	Year	Category	Pressure (mb)
1	Florida Keys	1935	5	892
2	Camille (MS, LA, VA)	1969	5	909
3	Katrina (LA, MS, AL)	2005	3	920
4	Andrew (FL, LA)	1992	5	922
5	FL Keys, south TX	1919	4	927
6	FL (Lake Okeechobee)	1928	4	929
7	Donna (FL, eastern US)	1960	4	930
8	TX (Galveston)	1900	4	931
8	LA (Grand Isle)	1909	4	931
8	LA (New Orleans)	1915	4	931
8	Carla (Texas)	1961	4	931

[a]From NOAA, Tropical Prediction Center/National Hurricane Center

1988. The wave followed a steady west-northwest track and seven days later strengthened to a hurricane while south of Puerto Rico. Gilbert then passed over the length of Jamaica on the 12th, intensified over the northwest Caribbean with the minimum central pressure falling to a then record low 888 mb, and on 14 September made landfall as a category 5 hurricane near Cozumel on Mexico's Yucatan Peninsula. At landfall, maximum sustained winds were estimated at 275 km per hr (171 mph). Gilbert then tracked northwestward over the Gulf of Mexico and made its final landfall (as category 3) on the coast of Mexico about 200 km (125 mi) south of the Texas border. Gilbert brought much death and destruction to both Mexico and Jamaica. The death toll was 202 in Mexico and 45 in Jamaica, and combined property damage in the two countries topped $4 billion.

TABLE 12.3
The Ten Deadliest U.S. Hurricanes, 1900-2005[a]

Rank	Hurricane	Year	Category	Deaths
1	Unnamed, Galveston, TX	1900	4	8000[+]
2	Unnamed, Lake Okeechobee, FL	1928	4	1836
3	Katrina, LA, MS and AL	2005	3	>1300
4	Unnamed, Florida Keys/south TX	1919	4	600[&]
5	"New England"	1938	3[*]	600
6	"Labor Day," Florida Keys	1935	5	408
7	Audrey, SW LA and N TX	1957	4	390
8	Unnamed, NE United States	1944	3[*]	390[#]
9	Unnamed, Grand Isle, LA	1909	4	350
10	Unnamed, New Orleans, LA	1915	4	275

[a]From NOAA, Tropical Prediction Center/National Hurricane Center
+ May actually have been as high as 10,000 to 12,000.
& Over 500 lost on ships at sea; 600-900 estimated deaths.
[*]Moving at more than 48 km per hr (30 mph).
Some 344 of these lost on ships at sea.

FIGURE 12.12
Radar reflectivity image of the spiral rain bands associated with Andrew as it came ashore as a category 5 hurricane south of Miami Beach, FL on 24 August 1992. [NOAA]

Trends in Hurricane Frequency

In recent years, the frequency of intense hurricanes has increased. In 2005, researchers at the Georgia Institute of Technology and the National Center for Atmospheric Research (NCAR) reported that the number of category 4 and 5 hurricanes worldwide nearly doubled over the 35-year period, 1970-2004 (Figure 12.13). This upward trend occurred even though the overall number of hurricanes worldwide has declined since the 1990s. In the 1970s, the number of category 4 and 5 hurricanes globally averaged about 10 per year; but since 1990, that number has increased to about 18 per year. Much of the increased frequency of intense hurricanes occurred in the North Pacific, Southwest Pacific, and Indian Ocean with a slightly smaller increase in the North Atlantic.

The only region of the globe where tropical cyclone activity has increased recently is the North Atlantic (Figure 12.14). According to NOAA, since 1995 the average annual number of named tropical cyclones (tropical storms and hurricanes) is 13 compared to 8.6 during the previous 25-year period 1970-1994. Since 1995, the Atlantic averages 7.7 hurricanes per season, 3.6 of which are major hurricanes. In the 25 years prior to 1995, the seasonal average for hurricanes was 5, with 1.5 rated major.

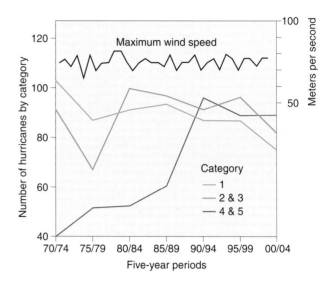

FIGURE 12.13
Recent upward trend in the number of intense (category 4 and 5) hurricanes. [Modified after Peter Webster, Georgia Institute of Technology.]

Why the recent increase in Atlantic hurricanes? Several factors contribute. Sea surface temperatures (SST) have been higher in the tropical Atlantic. An amplified ridge, favorable for tropical cyclones, has been in place over the central and eastern North Atlantic. Vertical wind shear has weakened in the deep tropics over the central North Atlantic. In addition, the African easterly jet stream has been more favorable for tropical cyclone development.

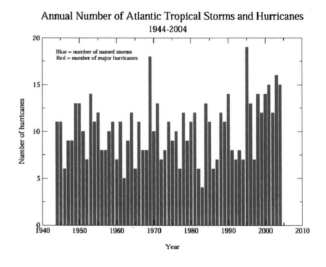

FIGURE 12.14
Annual number of Atlantic tropical storms and hurricanes, 1944-2004. [NOAA]

A storm surge accounted for much of the considerable loss of life in a hurricane that struck the southeast United States on 27 August 1893, one of six hurricanes to strike the U.S. mainland that year (a record number that was equaled in 1916 and 1985). The unnamed hurricane came ashore at night just north of Savannah, GA with little warning. U.S. Weather Bureau meteorologists predicted that the hurricane, first detected at Nassau in the Bahamas the previous day, would make landfall somewhere along the East Coast south of New York. The actual track placed the system's dangerous semicircle, the band of strongest onshore winds, over the Sea Islands of Beaufort County, SC. Most of the inhabitants of the Sea Islands were freed slaves, their children and grandchildren. They were primarily farmers who raised a highly valued variety of cotton. No telegraph lines connected the islands to the mainland so there was no warning of the hurricane's approach. With no means of evacuation, residents were completely at the mercy of 175 to 210 km per hr (110 to 130 mph) winds and a 3.7 to 4.6 m (12 to 15 ft) storm surge that swept over the islands. Some 20,000 to 30,000 people were left homeless, their crops were destroyed, and the death toll was estimated at 2000 (and possibly as high as 2500). The Sea Islands disaster came at a time of national recession and prior to the time of organized federal or state natural disaster assistance. Intervention by the Red Cross was all that saved the survivors from almost certain famine.

In the most deadly natural disaster in U.S. history, more than 8000 people perished, mostly by drowning, when a hurricane storm surge of over 4.6 m (15 ft) devastated Galveston, TX on 8 September 1900. Ocean waters flooded the entire city located on a barrier island, where the highest elevation in the city was only 2.7 m (8 ft). Some 3600 homes were destroyed; a dam of wreckage that built up some six blocks inland from the beach probably spared the business district total destruction. To protect the city from future storm surges, the U.S. Army Corps of Engineers elevated the city an average of some 3 m (10 ft) and erected a massive concrete seawall along much of the city's Gulf shore.

Hurricane Camille, an exceptionally intense system with winds to 300 km per hr (186 mph), produced a maximum storm surge of 7.3 m (24.3 ft) at Pass Christian, MS on 17 August 1969. The total death toll from the storm was 256, about half from coastal flooding. The surge destroyed or badly damaged more than 18,000 homes and 700 businesses. Scientists had a difficult time in determining the maximum storm surge produced by Hurricane Katrina in August 2005 because the storm destroyed many of the local tide gauges, but it appears likely that Katrina's storm surge was higher than that of Camille. In 1970, one of the most disastrous storm surges ever flooded the Bay of Bengal coast of East Pakistan (now Bangladesh). A storm surge of nearly 7 m (23 ft) spread over the vast low-lying coastal plain of the Ganges Delta, claiming an estimated 300,000 lives mostly by drowning because there was no high ground for people to seek refuge.

Strong onshore winds plus relatively low air pressure are responsible for a hurricane storm surge. Relatively low air pressure in a hurricane causes sea level to rise (about 0.5 m for every 50 mb drop in pressure or about 1 ft for every 1 in. of mercury drop in pressure). The height of a storm surge is the difference between the observed rise in local sea level and the regular astronomical tide. In general, a storm surge of 1 to 2 m (3 to 6.5 ft) can be expected with a weak hurricane, whereas the storm surge accompanying a violent hurricane may top 5 m (16.4 ft). According to NOAA researchers, storm surge height depends on many factors including the intensity and speed of the hurricane, direction of hurricane motion relative to the shoreline, slope of the seafloor along the shore, configuration of the shoreline, and the height of the astronomical tide. The greatest potential for a highly destructive storm surge occurs with strong onshore winds, along a shallow sloping shoreline, during high tide, and in densely populated areas lacking coastal buffers such as barrier islands, coral reefs, marshes, or swamps. Typically, the rise in sea level in a storm surge lasts for 4 to 8 hours but it may take days for floodwaters to recede.

A special numerical model developed in 1979 by NOAA accurately predicts the location and height of a storm surge. Weather forecasters report considerable success with the **SLOSH (Sea, Lake, and Overland Surges from Hurricanes)** model. Using output from SLOSH and consulting local topographic maps, forecasters can identify areas most likely to be inundated by floodwaters when a hurricane threatens. Hypothetical hurricanes are simulated using various combinations of storm intensity, forward speed, and expected location of landfall to predict the maximum high water levels for various SLOSH basins along the coast. Public safety officials use this information to develop evacuation plans. SLOSH model coverage includes the entire East and Gulf Coasts, as well as parts of Hawaii, Guam, Puerto Rico, and the Virgin Islands.

TABLE 12.1
Saffir-Simpson Hurricane Intensity Scale

Category	Central pressure mb (in.)	Wind speed km/hr (mi/hr)	Storm surge m (ft)	Damage potential
1	≥ 980 (≥ 28.94)	119-154 (74-95)	1-2 (4-5)	Minimal
2	965-979 (28.50-28.91)	155-178 (96-110)	2-3 (6-8)	Moderate
3	945-964 (27.91-28.47)	179-210 (111-130)	3-4 (9-12)	Extensive
4	920-944 (27.17-27.88)	211-250 (131-155)	4-6 (13-18)	Extreme
5	< 920 (< 27.17)	> 250 (> 155)	> 6 (> 18)	Catastrophic

SAFFIR-SIMPSON INTENSITY SCALE

Like tornadoes, hurricanes have a rating system, known as the **Saffir-Simpson Hurricane Intensity Scale** after its designers, H.S. Saffir, a consulting engineer, and R.H. Simpson, former director of the National Hurricane Center. Developed in the early 1970s and first included in hurricane advisories in 1975, the scale rates hurricanes from 1 to 5 corresponding to increasing intensity (Table 12.1). The scale provides an estimate of potential coastal flooding and property damage from a hurricane landfall. Wind speed is the primary determining factor for a hurricane's rating on the Saffir-Simpson Scale as storm surge heights are highly dependent on underwater topography and other factors in the region of landfall. Each intensity category specifies (1) a range of central air pressure, (2) a range of maximum sustained wind speed, (3) storm surge potential, and (4) the potential for property damage.

Property damage potential rises rapidly with ranking on the Saffir-Simpson Scale. Destruction from a category 4 or 5 hurricane is 100 to 300 times greater than that caused by a category 1 hurricane. A category 1 (weak) hurricane generally causes no real damage to buildings but may affect unanchored mobile homes, shrubbery, and trees and cause minor damage to piers. With a category 2 (moderate) hurricane, we can expect some damage to roofing materials, doors, and windows of buildings. Damage to trees, mobile homes, and piers can be considerable and small craft in unprotected anchorages may break free of their moorings. A category 3 (strong) hurricane can destroy mobile homes, cause some structural damage to small residences and utility buildings, and blow down large trees. Flooding is likely along the coast and some evacuation may be necessary. With a category 4 (very strong) hurricane, the roof structure of small residences may fail. Beaches experience major erosion and considerable damage is done to structures near the shore. Major coastal flooding requires massive evacuation of residential areas. In a category 5 (devastating) hurricane, we can expect loss of roofs from many homes and industrial buildings. In some instances, buildings experience complete failure. Major coastal flooding is likely requiring massive evacuation of residential areas.

Of the 176 hurricanes that struck the U.S. Atlantic or Gulf coasts between 1901 and 2004, 65 (about 37%) were classified as major; that is, they rated 3 or higher on the Saffir-Simpson scale. The 25 major hurricanes that made landfall along the Gulf or Atlantic coast between 1949 and 1990 accounted for three-quarters of all property damage from all landfalling tropical storms and hurricanes during the same period. Tables 12.2 and 12.3 list the most intense, and the 10 deadliest hurricanes, respectively, to strike the United States since 1900.

The last Atlantic basin hurricane to make landfall as a category 5 was Andrew (Figure 12.12). In the three hours it took Hurricane Andrew to cross extreme southern Florida on the morning of 24 August 1992, its peak sustained winds of 266 km per hr (165 mph), with much stronger gusts, contributed to the deaths of 15 people and left 180,000 homeless. With property damage estimated at $34.3 billion (in 2000 dollars), Andrew at the time was the costliest hurricane in U.S. history. To make matters worse, Andrew continued to track west and northwestward across the Gulf of Mexico and, two days later, struck the Louisiana coast where it claimed four more lives and caused an additional $400 million in property damage.

The next prior Atlantic hurricanes to make landfall as a category 5 storm were Gilbert in September 1988 and Camille in August 1969. Gilbert originated as a tropical wave off the West African coast on 3 September

Multi-decadal changes in North Atlantic SST appear to be related to alternating weakening and strengthening of the ocean conveyor-belt system. North Atlantic SST rise and fall over a 60-70 year quasi-periodic cycle known as the *Atlantic Multidecadal Oscillation (AMO)*. Recall from Chapter 4 that the ocean conveyor-belt system transports heat energy through the ocean basins and is linked to surface ocean currents such as the Gulf Stream. When the conveyor slows, SST fall, and tropical cyclones are less frequent. Relatively cool AMO years and reduced tropical cyclone activity prevailed in the Atlantic from 1903 to 1925 and again from 1971 to 1994. When the conveyor strengthens, SST rise, and tropical cyclones are more frequent. Relatively warm AMO years and increased tropical cyclone activity prevailed in the Atlantic from 1926 to 1970, and we are currently in a warm phase that began in 1994.

Hurricane Threat to the Southeast United States

From 1981 through 2000, only 10 major hurricanes (category 3 or higher) made landfall on the U.S. mainland, which was similar to the 1971 through 1990 interval when only 9 major hurricanes reached the U.S., but down from 14 during 1951-1970 and 18 in 1931-1950. Between 10 August 1980 and 17 August 1983, no hurricanes struck the United States. The infrequency of major hurricanes during the 1970s and 1980s lulled many coastal residents of the southeast United States into a false sense of security and encouraged development and population growth in areas that could be devastated by a major hurricane. In spite of Hugo in 1989 and Andrew in 1992, population growth continued unabated. Development of the U.S. coastal zone is now proceeding at a pace that is 2 to 3 times the national average. More and more resort hotels, high-rise condominiums, and expensive homes are being constructed perilously close to the shoreline and even among coastal sand dunes (Figure 12.15).

In 2005, the National Oceanic and Atmospheric Administration (NOAA) reported that the coast is now home to about 53% of all Americans. Some 153 million people currently reside in coastal counties—some 33 million more than in 1980—and the population is expected to swell by 12 million in the next decade. By convention, a county is described as coastal if it is on a coast (i.e., Atlantic, Gulf, Pacific, Great Lakes) or at least 15% of the county's land area is in a coastal watershed. The 673 coastal counties represent 17% of the nation's land area and have three times the nation's average population density.

FIGURE 12.15
The relative infrequency of hurricanes and tropical storms in the 1970s and 1980s lulled some residents of coastal areas into a false sense of security and inspired construction of cottages, condominiums, and hotels within meters of high-tide level. [Courtesy of Joseph Schlueter]

About 45 million permanent residents inhabit hurricane-prone portions of the nation's coastline. Population growth is most rapid from Texas through the Carolinas with Florida leading the nation in both population growth and hurricane potential. The population of Florida's coastal counties increased 75% between 1980 and 2003. Until the recent upturn in hurricane frequency, most Atlantic and Gulf Coast residents never experienced the full impact of a major hurricane. Some of them may have weathered with relative ease a weak hurricane or the fringes of a strong system. But such an experience may lull them into complacency so that they are less likely to prepare adequately should a major hurricane threaten. Compounding the problem of the growth of the resident population in the Southeast is the arrival of holiday, weekend, and seasonal visitors at seaside resorts. During vacation periods, the population of some of these locales swells ten- to one-hundred fold. Many of these resorts are located in low-lying coastal areas or on exposed beaches that are subject to rapid inundation by a storm surge.

Public safety officials are concerned by the post-1995 trend toward a greater number of tropical cyclones in the Atlantic basin. The Atlantic hurricane seasons of 2004 and 2005 were particularly active with considerable loss of life and property damage caused by landfalling hurricanes. During the 2004 Atlantic hurricane season, 15 named tropical cyclones formed; 9 intensified into hurricanes and of these, 6 became major hurricanes. Eight tropical cyclones formed during August—a new

FIGURE 12.16
Tracks of three of the four hurricanes that struck Florida in 2004. [Tropical Prediction Center/National Hurricane Center]

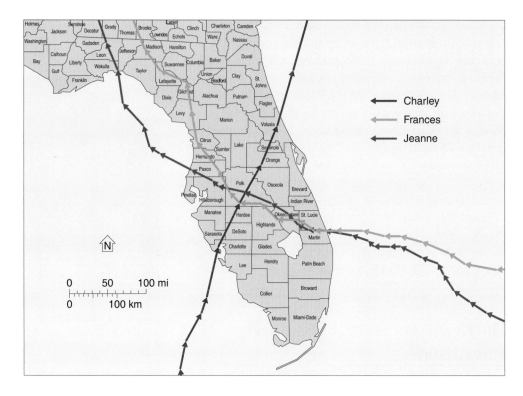

record for the month. Four hurricanes (Charley, Frances, Ivan, and Jeanne) struck Florida (Figure 12.16). The total death toll across the western Atlantic, Caribbean, and Gulf of Mexico was more than 3100, the second greatest number of tropical cyclone fatalities in 30 years. While many of the deaths occurred in Haiti due to flooding from Hurricane Jeanne, the direct death toll in the U.S. was 60 and property damage (from 5 landfalling hurricanes) hit a record $44 billion. As noted earlier, these losses were greatly exceeded in 2005.

BARRIER ISLANDS

The hurricane danger is particularly acute for people living on or visiting the nearly 300 barrier islands that fringe portions of the Atlantic and Gulf coasts, from Maine to Texas. A **barrier island** is an elongated, narrow accumulation of sand oriented parallel to the coast and separated from the mainland by a lagoon, estuary, or bay. Barrier islands vary in length from a few hundred meters to more than 100 km (62 mi). Padre Island is the longest of the nation's barrier islands extending more than 180 km (112 mi) along the lower Texas Gulf Coast.

A barrier island is a continually changing system. Sea waves breaking on the shores of a barrier island dissipate their energy by shifting sands and modifying the shape of the island. A barrier island gradually migrates toward the mainland as sediments settle in the land-side

lagoon while waves erode the ocean side of the island. A barrier island faces the open ocean and absorbs the brunt of powerful storm-driven sea waves and storm surges thereby providing some protection for coastal beaches, estuaries, wetlands, and shoreline structures. In some cases, a storm surge will breach a barrier island, forming a new tidal inlet (Figure 12.17).

Many barrier islands have been developed, especially for cottages and resorts, and the sand is now temporarily stabilized under a layer of asphalt or concrete. Some coastal cities, including Atlantic City, NJ, Miami Beach, FL, and Virginia Beach, VA are built entirely on barrier islands. Such exposed locations are particularly vulnerable to the ravages of high winds and storm surge associated with tropical cyclones. On developed barrier islands, much of the energy of storm waves would be expended in demolishing buildings and roads instead of shifting sands. Conflict is inevitable between rigid structures such as roads and buildings and the inherently dynamic (changeable) platforms (i.e., barrier islands) upon which they are built.

EVACUATION

Evacuation of people from barrier islands, as well as other low-lying coastal areas, is the traditional strategy in the event of a major storm threat (Figure 12.18). The effectiveness of coastal evacuation plans was tested in the

FIGURE 12.17
Aerial photographs of a section of a barrier island at Pine Beach, FL before and after the island was severed by a breach caused by Hurricane Ivan in mid-September 2004. [U.S. Geological Survey]

FIGURE 12.18
In hurricane-prone areas, evacuation routes are marked by special road signs. In some hurricane-prone coastal communities, public safety officials are rethinking the traditional evacuation strategy that clogs highways with too many escaping motor vehicles. Instead, they are considering "vertical" evacuation, that is, evacuation to the upper floors of sturdy public buildings.

late summer of 1985 when Hurricane Elena (category 3) menaced the Gulf of Mexico coast (Figure 12.19). For four days, Elena followed an erratic path over the Gulf of Mexico, first heading toward southern Louisiana, then the Florida panhandle, and later central Florida before reversing direction and finally coming ashore near Biloxi, MS on 2 September. Nearly a million people from Sarasota, FL to New Orleans, LA were forced to leave coastal communities and flee to inland shelters. Some returned home only to evacuate again as Elena changed course. Although property damage was considerable ($2 billion in year 2000 dollars) because of extensive flooding and winds that exceeded 160 km per hr (100 mph), only 4

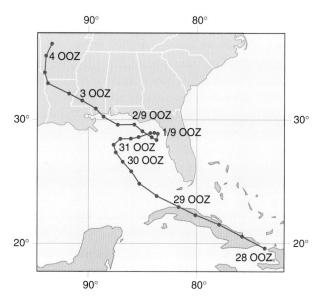

FIGURE 12.19
The erratic track of Hurricane Elena from 28 August through 4 September 1985. The hurricane's position is reported every 6 hours.

fatalities were attributed to Elena and none in the area of hurricane landfall. Timely evacuation of residents of low-lying coastal areas also saved many lives when category 4 Hugo (September 1989) and category 5 Andrew (August 1992) threatened.

The potential downside of evacuation was illustrated in September 1999 when Floyd, an unusually massive hurricane, threatened much of the Eastern Seaboard. In the greatest evacuation in U.S history, more than 2 million residents of the coastal area from South Florida to South Carolina took to the roads and fled inland. In many areas the result was gridlock—too many vehicles on too few highways. As it turned out, Floyd spared most of the evacuated area and made landfall near Cape Fear, NC on 16 September 1999 as a category 2 system. The gradually weakening storm crossed eastern North Carolina and Virginia and then tracked northeastward along the New Jersey coast and became an extra-tropical cyclone over New England. Torrential rainfall, totaling as much as 38 to 50 cm (15 to 20 in.) over portions of eastern North Carolina and Virginia caused extensive inland flooding, 56 deaths, and property damage of at least $6 billion. Floyd's track along the East Coast required the posting of hurricane warnings from South Florida to Massachusetts.

Successful evacuation of coastal communities hinges on sufficient advance warning of a hurricane's approach, but as noted earlier in this chapter, hurricanes are notorious for sudden changes in direction, forward speed, and intensity. (In retrospect, about 75% of all coastal storm evacuations prove to be unnecessary.) A hurricane's erratic behavior is especially troublesome for people living in isolated localities (e.g., a barrier island linked to the mainland by a single bridge) and congested cities where highway systems have not kept pace with population growth. In such places the time required for evacuation may be lengthy. The *Federal Emergency Management Agency (FEMA)* estimates evacuation times during the peak tourist season as 50-60 hrs for New Orleans, LA and Fort Myers, FL, 40-49 hrs for Ocean City, MD, 30-39 hrs for the Florida Keys and Cape May County, NJ, and 20-29 hrs for Long Island, NY, Atlantic City, NJ, the Outer Banks of North Carolina, and Galveston, TX.

As coastal communities continue to grow, the time required for evacuation of their population lengthens. Evacuation must begin earlier when a tropical cyclone is farther away and greater uncertainty surrounds its likely track. Such uncertainty necessitates a broader zone of evacuation that translates into greater economic losses associated with evacuation (e.g., closed businesses). As a general rule, the cost of evacuation amounts to about $1 million per mile of coastline. Cognizant of the problem of lengthy evacuation times, some coastal communities are considering the option of *vertical evacuation*, moving people to shelters on the upper floors of well-constructed public buildings. Vertical evacuation may be a viable alternative to sending people fleeing on congested roads and highways for large urban areas where evacuation options are limited.

Other strategies adopted or advocated by public safety and other government officials to minimize the loss of life and property to hurricanes are (1) stringent building codes, (2) preservation of mangrove swamps, and (3) elimination of federal floodplain insurance. Building codes may call for new homes to be more wind resistant by requiring bolts that anchor the floor to the foundation and steel brackets that attach the roof to the walls. In addition, in many areas, all new buildings must be elevated above the once-in-a-century flood level. Some buildings are constructed so that the lower floor gives way to flood waters, thus reducing damage to main structural supports (Figure 12.20). Unfortunately, many structures were built prior to these tough codes, and stringent building codes are not always enforced.

Mangrove swamps along tropical coastlines are the final line of natural defense against hurricanes and other ocean storms. Their extensive root systems anchor soil and vegetation and dissipate the energy of a storm surge. In too many cases, however, shoreline development has destroyed these swamps, often because the vegetation obstructed the ocean view for residents

FIGURE 12.20
This home, located on North Carolina's Outer Banks, is designed so that the first floor will give way to storm-surge floodwaters. The second and third floor living area of the home is supported by wooden beams driven deeply into the sand.

of seaside dwellings. Preservation of mangrove swamps and other natural buffers, such as coastal sand dunes, has received renewed emphasis in hurricane-prone areas.

A controversial strategy is to eliminate federal flood insurance for flood-prone coastal areas as has been done already on undeveloped portions of barrier islands. Some people argue that by providing policies at low cost, federal flood insurance programs actually encourage development in flood-prone areas. Furthermore, this insurance enables homeowners to rebuild structures destroyed by flooding in the same hazardous location.

Long-Range Forecasting of Atlantic Hurricanes

Since the early 1980s, Professor William M. Gray and his colleagues at Colorado State University's Tropical Meteorology Project have issued long-range forecasts of Atlantic basin hurricane activity for the upcoming hurricane season. Forecasts specify the number of expected tropical cyclones, hurricanes, and intense hurricanes. The forecast also includes the probability that at least one major (category 3 or higher) hurricane will make landfall on the U.S. coast from Texas to Maine, the U.S. East Coast including Peninsula Florida, the Gulf Coast from the Florida Panhandle westward to Brownsville, TX, and the Caribbean. The initial extended range forecast is issued in early December, 6 months in advance of the start of the official hurricane season. Subsequent updated hurricane forecasts are made public early in the months of April, June, August, September, and October.

The basis of Gray's original hurricane forecasting technique was his discovery of an apparent linkage between the frequency of major hurricanes in the tropical Atlantic and rainfall in West Africa. Gray also factored into his forecasting scheme the stratospheric *quasi-biennial oscillation (QBO)* that also appears related to Atlantic basin hurricane activity. The QBO is a reversal of the winds in the lower portion of the tropical stratosphere (from west to east and then reverse) over a period that averages about 26 months.

Gray's forecasting scheme gave reasonably skillful results (predicted values nearer to observed values than to the long-term average) until the 1995-2001 seasons when for some unexplained reason, the forecasting scheme ceased to be skillful. Gray and his colleagues discontinued the original technique and developed a new one based on statistical relationships and historical analogs. The new December forecasting method does not utilize West

African rainfall and diminishes the role of the QBO. It depends primarily on empirical relationships between Atlantic Basin hurricane activity and a combination of atmospheric factors in various parts of the world derived from a 52-year record. In addition to the QBO, five prediction factors are used that encompass measures of the September to November North Atlantic and Pacific surface pressure and height of the 500-mb surface. In addition, forecasters comb the historical database for appropriate analogs, that is, global atmosphere/ocean conditions that are similar to the current October to November conditions for the initial forecast. Analogs may provide indications as to what the following hurricane season may bring. The new hurricane forecasting scheme was implemented in December 2002 for the subsequent hurricane season and so far has exhibited significantly better skill than Gray's original long-range forecasting method.

Hurricane Modification

Spurred by six destructive hurricanes that lashed the U.S. East Coast during the mid-1950s, atmospheric scientists stepped up efforts to learn more about hurricanes and to devise hurricane modification techniques. To these ends, the U.S. government funded *Project STORMFURY* beginning in 1961. Until the project's termination in 1983, staff scientists advanced our understanding of the formation, structure, and dynamics of tropical cyclones; improved hurricane forecasting; and upgraded hurricane reconnaissance methods. The original goal of hurricane modification, however, was never realized.

The working hypothesis of Project STORMFURY was that seeding hurricanes with silver iodide (AgI) crystals would reduce wind strength. The argument went as follows: Seeding the band of convective clouds just beyond the *eye wall* would trigger additional latent heat release (as supercooled water droplets converted to ice crystals) and enhance convection. This artificially invigorated convection would then dominate convection in the eye wall, and a new eye wall would form at a greater distance from the storm center. Thereby, the band of strongest winds would be displaced farther out from the eye center and the hurricane's circulation would weaken (just as a skater's spin rate slows when she extends her arms).

The 1960s and 1970s presented few opportunities for hurricane seeding experiments primarily because few hurricanes met the selection criteria. Systems selected for seeding had to be mature, relatively intense, expected to remain far from land for at least 24 hrs following seeding, and have a well-developed eye wall. Some success was reported, however, in reducing winds (between 10% and 30%) in four hurricanes that were seeded. Later, these apparent successes were dismissed when new data called into question the original Project STORMFURY hypothesis. For one, it was discovered that convective clouds in hurricanes contain too little supercooled water for seeding to be effective. For another, monitoring of unmodified hurricanes found that changes in eye-wall diameter occur as part of the system's natural evolution. It is likely, then, that STORMFURY's apparent success at hurricane modification was by chance rather than by seeding.

Conclusions

Hurricanes are intense, long-lived, tropical cyclones that develop over tropical ocean waters but can track into middle latitudes. The requirements of relatively high sea-surface temperature, significant Coriolis Effect, and weak vertical wind shear restrict hurricane formation to certain regions of the globe. In the Atlantic basin, these systems initially drift westward in the trade winds and then turn north and northeastward as they are caught up in the prevailing westerlies of middle latitudes. Torrential rains, inland flooding, strong winds, and storm surge associated with a hurricane can take many lives and cause considerable property damage. Based on intensity and potential for storm surge and property damage, a hurricane is assigned a rating from 1 to 5 on the Saffir-Simpson Scale.

With this chapter, we have completed our description of the genesis, life cycle, and characteristics of the major atmospheric circulation systems that affect the weather of middle latitudes. In the next chapter, we examine the techniques and challenges of weather forecasting.

Basic Understandings

- Weather in the tropics exhibits very little seasonal temperature variation because of year-round high noontime solar altitude and nearly uniform day length. Rainfall is primarily the result of convective activity driven by intense solar heating. Principal weather systems that bring rainfall to the tropics are the ITCZ, easterly waves, and tropical cyclones.
- A hurricane is a violent tropical cyclone with a maximum sustained wind speed of 119 km per hr (74 mph) or higher that originates over tropical ocean waters, usually in late summer or early fall. The warm-core low pressure system develops in a warm and humid air mass, has no fronts, and on average is about one-third the diameter of an extra-tropical cyclone.
- At the center of a hurricane is an area of almost cloudless skies, subsiding air, and light winds, called the eye of the storm. The most dangerous and potentially most destructive part of a hurricane is the portion of the eye wall on the side of the advancing system where the wind blows in the same direction as the storm's forward motion.
- For a tropical cyclone to develop, sea-surface temperatures must be 26.5 °C (80 °F) or higher through a depth of about 45 m (150 ft), the Coriolis Effect must be sufficient (latitude of more than 5 degrees north or south of the equator) to initiate a cyclonic circulation, and the vertical wind shear must be relatively weak. The first two requirements mean that tropical cyclone development is limited to certain regions of the tropical ocean. Weak winds aloft allow a cluster of cumulonimbus clouds to organize over tropical seas, the first stage in the evolution of a hurricane.
- The annual number of hurricanes may have little bearing on the number of hurricanes that make landfall and their impact.
- Most major hurricanes that make landfall in North America originate as convective cloud clusters associated with easterly waves. An easterly wave is a westward-propagating ripple in the trade winds featuring a weak trough of low pressure and areas of diverging and converging winds.
- Atmospheric conditions that inhibit tropical cyclone development over the Atlantic appear to be associated with the Sahara air layer, an elevated mass of dry dusty stable air that originates over the Sahara Desert and moves westward over the ocean.
- With favorable atmospheric and sea-surface conditions, some convective cloud clusters evolve into a tropical disturbance that can intensify into a tropical depression, tropical storm, and finally a hurricane.
- The track of a hurricane can be erratic although in the Atlantic there tends to be a westward drift at low latitudes and a more rapid northeastward movement at middle latitudes, following the circulation of the

Bermuda-Azores subtropical high. Some Atlantic hurricanes, fueled by warm Gulf Stream waters, maintain tropical characteristics far north along the Eastern Seaboard.

- Hazards of hurricanes include heavy rains, inland flooding, strong winds, tornadoes, and storm surge. The storm surge is the most serious potential impact of a landfalling hurricane and is the principal reason why people are evacuated from low-lying coastal regions.

- Once a hurricane makes landfall, it quickly loses its warm-water energy source and experiences the frictional resistance offered by the greater surface roughness of land versus water. Its circulation weakens rapidly; hence, most wind damage is confined to within about 200 km (125 mi) of the coastline. Torrential rains often continue well inland, however, and can cause severe flooding.

- Although winds weaken once a hurricane makes landfall, the system may produce tornadoes. Tornadoes form mostly to the northeast of the storm center and often outside the region of hurricane-force winds.

- A storm surge is a dome of ocean water topped by high waves that is driven onshore by storm winds.

The greatest potential for coastal flooding and erosion occurs along a shallow sloping shoreline when a storm surge coincides with high tide.

- Based on intensity and potential for flooding and property damage, a hurricane is rated from 1 (weak) to 5 (very intense) on the Saffir-Simpson Hurricane Intensity Scale.

- In recent years, the frequency of intense hurricanes (categories 4 and 5) has increased. Also, since 1995, the number of tropical cyclones in the Atlantic is greater likely because of higher sea-surface temperatures, weaker vertical wind shear, and more favorable atmospheric circulation patterns.

- Rapid population growth in the coastal zone coupled with the lull in intense hurricane activity during the 1970s and 1980s has heightened the hurricane hazard in the southeastern United States. The hurricane danger is particularly acute for people living on or visiting the barrier islands that fringe portions of the Atlantic and Gulf coast.

- Attempts to modify hurricanes through cloud seeding have been unsuccessful. However, from such efforts has come a greater understanding of the dynamics of hurricanes.

Review

1. Compare and contrast the properties of a tropical cyclone with those of an extra-tropical cyclone.
2. Why are fronts not associated with hurricanes?
3. Describe the weather within the eye of a hurricane.
4. Identify the conditions necessary for development of a tropical cyclone.
5. Why is it unusual for a hurricane to strike southern California?
6. How is it possible for a full-blown hurricane to strike New England?
7. What is potentially the most destructive impact of hurricanes on low-lying coastal areas?
8. What is the greatest hazard posed by a tropical cyclone that tracks well inland?
9. Describe the changes that take place in a hurricane as the system tracks from the sea to land.
10. Why are barrier islands particularly vulnerable to a hurricane storm surge?

Critical Thinking

1. Why is sea-surface temperature a critical factor in the development of tropical cyclones?
2. Suppose that efforts to modify hurricanes are successful. Speculate on what this might mean for poleward heat transport.
3. Speculate on why property damage due to landfalling hurricanes in the U.S. is on the upswing.
4. In view of the requirements for hurricane development, why are hurricanes rare on either coast of South America?
5. Describe the relationship between the circulation of the Bermuda-Azores anticyclone and the usual path taken by *Cape Verde-type* hurricanes.
6. Why are fronts essentially absent in the tropics?
7. Explain the advantages of streamline analysis over isobaric analysis in the tropics.
8. Why is extensive inland flooding often associated with a tropical cyclone?
9. What happens when a tropical cyclone develops extra-tropical characteristics?
10. How does topography affect the impact of a landfalling tropical cyclone?

ESSAY: Polar Lows with Hurricane Characteristics

Some intense storms that form over the ocean off the coasts of Alaska and Norway have characteristics in common with hurricanes and tropical storms. For this reason, these polar lows are sometimes called *Arctic hurricanes*.

Polar lows are similar to tropical hurricanes in several respects. Both are relatively small-scale cyclones that are highly symmetric and feature a relatively warm core. Most clouds are convective with a ring of cumulonimbus clouds surrounding a clear calm eye, and strongest winds are associated with those cumulonimbus clouds. Both systems are triggered by other pre-existing atmospheric disturbances and both derive their energy from the ocean surface.

Arctic hurricanes differ from tropical hurricanes in the following ways: Arctic hurricanes are shallower systems that develop in cold air north of the polar front and evolve to full maturity in only 12 to 24 hrs. On the other hand, tropical hurricanes form in warm, humid air and may require 3 to 7 days to attain full strength. In addition, Arctic hurricanes travel nearly twice as fast as tropical hurricanes. Sustained wind speeds are somewhat higher in a tropical hurricane than in an Arctic hurricane. Maximum sustained wind speeds are about 110 km per hr (68 mph) in an Arctic hurricane and, by convention, must be 119 km per hr (74 mph) or higher in a tropical hurricane.

In a tropical hurricane, the flux of heat from the sea-surface to the atmosphere is the principal source of energy that sustains the system. Most of this energy flux consists of latent heating (that is, evaporation of water at the sea-surface and subsequent condensation and release of latent heat within the storm system). Much less important is sensible heating (that is, conduction and convection of heat from the sea-surface to the atmosphere). Although the total heat flux from sea to air is roughly the same for both Arctic and tropical hurricanes, sensible heating plays a proportionally greater role in Arctic hurricanes.

As noted elsewhere in this chapter, a tropical hurricane is triggered by the ITCZ, a trough in the westerlies, or an easterly wave. The trigger for an Arctic hurricane may be a polar trough or jet streak. Development is most likely along a front that marks the transition zone between modified and unmodified arctic air. Arctic air is modified (becoming milder and more humid) by virtue of its trajectory over ocean water.

ESSAY: Naming Hurricanes

When sustained winds in a tropical depression reach 63 km per hr (39 mph), the intensifying system is designated a *tropical storm* and assigned a name. This practice is intended to improve communication between forecasters and the general public especially because tropical storms or hurricanes are relatively long-lived weather systems and more than one may occur in the same ocean basin at the same time.

Originally, hurricanes were identified by their latitude and longitude and later by letters of the alphabet. Late in the 19th century, an Australian forecaster Clement Wragge (1852-1922) was apparently the first to apply women's names to tropical cyclones; he also named them for politicians he disliked. During World War II, U.S. Army Air Corps and Navy meteorologists informally applied women's names to tropical cyclones. From 1950 to 1952, tropical cyclones in the North Atlantic were labeled using the phonetic alphabet (e.g., Able, Baker, etc.). In 1953, U.S. Weather Bureau meteorologists began using an alphabetical sequence of female names for tropical storms and hurricanes in the Atlantic basin. Women's names were first used for tropical cyclones near Hawaii in 1959 and for the rest of the northeast Pacific basin the next year. Starting in 1978, the list consisted of alternating male and female names in alphabetical order, in English, Spanish, and French. The same practice began in the Atlantic basin in 1979 (Table 1). Six lists of names are repeated every 6 years. In the event that more than 21 named tropical cyclones occur in a single season, the National Hurricane Center uses the Greek alphabet, beginning with Alpha. This happened during the 2005 Atlantic hurricane season.

TABLE 1
Hurricane Names in the Atlantic Basin

2006	2007	2008	2009	2010
Alberto	Andrea	Arthur	Ana	Alex
Beryl	Barry	Bertha	Bill	Bonnie
Chris	Chantal	Cristobal	Claudette	Colin
Debby	Dean	Dolly	Danny	Danielle
Ernesto	Erin	Edouard	Erika	Earl
Florence	Felix	Fay	Fred	Fiona
Gordon	Gabrielle	Gustav	Grace	Gaston
Helene	Humberto	Hanna	Henri	Hermine
Isaac	Ingrid	Ike	Ida	Igor
Joyce	Jerry	Josephine	Joaquin	Julia
Kirk	Karen	Kyle	Kate	Karl
Leslie	Lorenzo	Laura	Larry	Lisa
Michael	Melissa	Marco	Mindy	Matthew
Nadine	Noel	Nana	Nicholas	Nicole
Oscar	Olga	Omar	Odette	Otto
Patty	Pablo	Paloma	Peter	Paula
Rafael	Rebekah	Rene	Rose	Richard
Sandy	Sebastien	Sally	Sam	Shary
Tony	Tanya	Teddy	Teresa	Tomas
Valerie	Van	Vicky	Victor	Virginie
William	Wendy	Wilfred	Wanda	Walter

Source: NOAA, Tropical Prediction Center/National Hurricane Center

The names of very destructive hurricanes have been removed from the list. The following is a list of retired names for the Atlantic Ocean, Caribbean Sea, and Gulf of Mexico since 1965: Betsy, 1965; Inez, 1966; Beulah, 1967; Edna, 1968; Camille, 1969; Celia, 1970; Agnes, 1972; Carmen and Fifi, 1974; Eloise, 1975; Anita, 1977; David and Frederic, 1979; Allen, 1980; Alicia, 1983; Elena and Gloria, 1985; Gilbert and Joan, 1988; Hugo, 1989; Diana and Klaus, 1990; Bob, 1991; Andrew, 1992; Luis, Marilyn, Opal and Roxanne, 1995; Cesar, Fran, and Hortense, 1996; Georges, Mitch, 1998; Floyd and Lenny, 1999; Keith, 2000; Allison, Iris, and Michelle, 2001; Isidore and Lili, 2002; Fabian, Isabel, and Juan, 2003; Charley, Frances, Ivan, and Jeanne, 2004.

In the northwest Pacific Basin, women's names were used for tropical cyclones from 1945 to 1979. Then, alternating male and female names were used until 1 January 2000. On that date, the World Meteorological Organization's Typhoon Committee adopted a unique list of Asian names, most of which are not personal names but rather the names of flowers, animals, birds, and trees. Furthermore, the list of names is organized by the contributing nation (in alphabetical order). The Tokyo Typhoon Centre of the Japanese Meteorological Agency is responsible for assigning names from this list to developing tropical storms.

Separate lists of names are maintained for the southwest Indian Ocean (west of 90 degrees E), western Australia (90 degrees to 125 degrees E), northern Australia (125 degrees to 137 degrees E), and eastern Australia (137 degrees to 160 degrees E). Lists of names are also available for the regions near Fiji and Papua New Guinea. Tropical cyclones in the north Indian Ocean are not assigned names.

CHAPTER 13

WEATHER ANALYSIS AND FORECASTING

National Weather Service Weather Watches and warnings for 2 December, 2005, on the NWS Interactive Weather Information Network. [Courtesy NOAA]

Case in Point

In the late 19th century John P. Finley of the U.S. Army Signal Corps pioneered tornado forecasting. Finley enlisted the aid of volunteer observers in the Midwest to help him document the occurrence and tracks of tornadoes. By mid-1884, about 950 "tornado reporters" were gathering observational data. Finley also consulted records of tornado sightings by weather networks operated by the U.S. Army Medical Department, the Smithsonian Institution, the Army Corps of Engineers, and the Army Signal Corps. Finley's criteria for a tornado was a funnel cloud observed by a credible witness or indications of a violently rotating wind based on the pattern of property damage. From his analysis of these data plus his personal observations in tornado-prone areas of the country, Finley developed a list of rules for forecasting tornadoes and began issuing the first tornado predictions on an experimental basis on 10 March 1884.

Finley's experiment in tornado forecasting lasted only two years and his forecasts were not issued to the public. In 1886, the Army Signal Corps banned the use of the word "tornado" in weather forecasts, although a special warning could be included if violent storms were possible. This action stemmed from the fear that a tornado forecast would cause the general public to panic, resulting in more harm than the storm system itself. Six decades would pass before "tornado" was included in an official U.S. Weather Bureau forecast.

In the late 1940s and early 1950s, U.S. Air Force Air Weather Service meteorologists Major Ernest J. Fawbush and Captain Robert C. Miller developed a method for forecasting tornadoes but issued those forecasts primarily for military installations. Fawbush and Miller's interest in tornado forecasting stemmed from their experience with a tornado that struck Tinker Air Force Base in Oklahoma City, OK on 20 March 1948, injuring 8 people and causing more than $10 million in damage to aircraft. The tornado struck without warning while Miller was on duty. In response the commanding general of the Oklahoma City Air Materiel Area almost immediately directed Tinker's meteorologists to study the possibility of tornado forecasting. After analyzing atmospheric conditions preceding the 20 March tornado as well as other tornadoes and finding similarities, Fawbush and Miller developed a list of six atmospheric

conditions that together precede a tornado outbreak. On 25 March, only five days after the earlier tornado, those same atmospheric conditions came together again in the vicinity of Oklahoma City prompting Fawbush and Miller to issue their first tornado forecast. Base personnel enacted a newly drawn-up tornado safety plan (e.g., moving aircraft to hangers, diverting approaching aircraft, and seeking shelter). In fact, a tornado developed along a squall line and followed a track similar to the earlier tornado through Tinker Air Force Base. This time, no one was injured although damage to planes amounted to about $6 million.

The Fawbush-Miller tornado forecasting method proved so successful that it was extended to other areas near military bases. In spite of this success, the U.S. Weather Bureau remained reluctant to issue tornado forecasts. Francis W. Reichelderfer (1895-1983), chief of the U.S. Weather Bureau (USWB) from 1938 until 1963, believed that tornado forecasting was not sufficiently precise for distribution to the general public. However, on 6 May 1949, Fawbush and Miller correctly forecast a tornado that struck Amarillo, TX, killing 7 and injuring 82. Shortly afterward, Reichelderfer authorized USWB forecasters to include the possibility of severe or destructive local storms if warranted in forecasts for public distribution. Eventually, the U.S. Weather Bureau followed the lead of the Air Weather Service, forming the Severe Local Storm Warning Center (now the Storm Prediction Center in Norman, OK). The ban on the use of the word "tornado" in weather forecasts for civilians was finally abolished on 17 March 1952, when meteorologists at the new center issued the first tornado watch.

Driving Question:
What is the process involved in making a scientific forecast of the weather?

Most people readily recall occasions when an erroneous weather forecast upset their plans. It may have been an unexpected thundershower that brought an abrupt end to a softball game, or a raging blizzard that appeared instead of the anticipated clearing skies, or the promised spring-like weekend that turned out to be anything but spring-like. People seem to remember missed weather forecasts all too clearly and overlook the fact that most forecasts are on target.

Weather forecasts, especially for the next day or so, are quite accurate and forecasters achieve some skill with forecasts out to 7 days. Nonetheless, most people readily recall occasions when the weather pulled unpleasant, and in some cases, hazardous surprises on them. In many situations, these surprises were not from the lack of a weather forecast, watch, or warning. The fact is changes in weather or the potential for change, including the more dramatic and hazardous changes, are routinely predicted to a high degree of accuracy. Unfortunately, forecasts might not reach as far into the future as we would like or need. The quality of weather forecasts, especially short-term forecasts, is such that it has become more important than ever to know the latest forecast. Simply stated, people who know what the weather is and what it is likely to be, benefit in many ways.

Of course, not all weather events are predicted nor are they currently predicted with the accuracy one would like beyond a few days. Our present understanding of the workings of the atmosphere and our ability to monitor it are neither perfect nor complete. Also, weather forecasts are not always prepared to the detail we might desire for our particular situation. Weather prediction will never be perfect because forecasters will always be working with incomplete information on the initial state of the atmosphere and some scientific questions are yet to be answered. However, when viewed with the objectivity of statistical analysis, short-range weather forecasting is surprisingly accurate. The U.S. **National Weather Service (NWS)**, an agency of the **National Oceanic and Atmospheric Administration (NOAA)**, issues 24-hr weather forecasts that are correct nearly 85% of the time. The popular notion that weather forecasting is not very accurate stems from the simple fact that a missed forecast is more memorable because of the inconvenience a person might experience.

How are weather forecasts made? What are the limits of forecast accuracy? On the basis of what you learn in this course, how can you make your own weather forecasts? These are the principal questions addressed in this chapter.

International Cooperation

The atmosphere is a continuous fluid that envelops the globe, so that weather observation, analysis, and forecasting require international cooperation. The American naval officer Matthew Fontaine Maury (1806-1873) was an early leader in international efforts to coordinate meteorology at sea. Maury helped convene the first International Meteorological Conference held in Brussels in August 1853. At a subsequent meeting in Vienna in September 1873, an agreement was drafted to form the *International Meteorological Organization (IMO)*. The IMO was founded in 1878 by representatives of the newly formed weather services of a dozen sea-faring nations, including the United States. In 1951, the IMO became the **World Meteorological Organization**

(WMO), an agency of the United Nations. Today, the WMO, headquartered in Geneva, Switzerland, coordinates the efforts of 189 nations and territories in a standardized global weather-monitoring program known as *World Weather Watch (WWW)*. WWW combines standardized observing systems, communications facilities, and data analysis/forecasting centers operated by member nations and territories to make available meteorological information internationally.

At standard observation times, the state of the atmosphere is monitored worldwide. This *Global Observing System* consists of 5 geostationary and 4 polar-orbiting satellites along with almost 10,000 land stations—about 4000 of which contribute data to regional synoptic weather networks. Additional observational data are gathered by more than 7000 ships at sea, reconnaissance and commercial aircraft (*Aircraft Communications Addressing and Reporting System*), weather radar, almost 1000 radiosonde stations, and 300 moored and drifting buoys equipped with automated weather stations. The *Global Data-Processing System (GDPS)* makes available meteorological analyses and various forecast products to WMO member nations via the *Global Telecommunications System (GTS)*. Observational data are transmitted to the three World Meteorological Centers (located near Washington, DC, Moscow, Russia, and Melbourne, Australia), where maps and charts representing the current state of the atmosphere are prepared. From human and computer analysis of this information, weather forecasts are prepared. Maps, charts, and forecasts are then sent to regional and national meteorological centers where weather information and forecasts are generated and interpreted for each center's area of responsibility and distributed to local weather service forecast offices and then to the public.

Timely and accurate weather forecasts for the United States are the responsibility of the **National Centers for Environmental Prediction (NCEP)**, part of NOAA's National Weather Service. Originally established as the former National Meteorological Center in 1958, NCEP is headquartered in Camp Springs, MD, just outside Washington, DC. NCEP's goal is to "protect life and property, as well as mitigate economic loss, by providing accurate forecasts and forecast guidance products to weather service field offices." NCEP meteorologists produce short-term national forecasts as well as longer-term weather and climate outlooks. At present, meteorologists issue weather forecasts out to 7 days and climate predictions for two weeks to a year or so. Nine centers comprise NCEP: Central Operations,

Environmental Modeling Center, Hydrometeorological Prediction Center, Ocean Prediction Center, Climate Prediction Center (all located in Camp Springs, MD), Aviation Weather Center (Kansas City, MO), Storm Prediction Center (Norman, OK), Tropical Prediction Center (Miami, FL), and the Space Environment Center (Boulder, CO). We have more on NCEP later in this chapter.

Weather forecasting entails (1) acquisition of present weather data, (2) graphical depiction of the state of the atmosphere by plotting those data on maps and charts, (3) analysis of data and maps, (4) prediction of the future state of the atmosphere, and (5) dissemination of weather information and forecasts to the public.

Acquisition of Weather Data

Since invention of the first weather instruments in the 17th century, weather observation has undergone considerable refinement (Chapter 2). Denser monitoring networks, more sophisticated calibrated instruments and communications systems, and better trained weather observers have produced an increasingly detailed, reliable, and representative record of weather and climate.

SURFACE WEATHER OBSERVATIONS

Over 2000 stations across the United States routinely monitor surface weather. As of this writing, nearly 70% of them are automatic weather stations. These stations may be operated by any of the following: (1) National Weather Service personnel, (2) the staff of other government agencies, including the *Federal Aviation Administration (FAA)*, or (3) private citizens or businesses in cooperation with the NWS. At sea and on the Great Lakes, more than 2000 ships also voluntarily gather weather data.

The NWS also maintains networks of automated weather stations in locations where manned observations are not feasible. These include, for example, more than 110 automated weather stations operated by the **National Data Buoy Center (NDBC)**. Some NDBC stations are attached to moored buoys in offshore locations (including the Great Lakes), and others are at lighthouses, fishing piers, and offshore oil platforms. NDBC stations provide data on storm intensity and track and are considered an essential part of the hurricane warning system. Satellites relay data from the buoy network to users.

Weather stations gather data for (1) preparation of weather maps and forecasts, (2) exchange with other nations, and (3) use by aviation. Stations report cloud height and sky cover, wind speed and direction, visibility, precipitation type and amount, air temperature, dewpoint, and air pressure. Also, airport weather stations report altimeter settings for guidance to aviation.

Weather observations must be taken at the same time everywhere so as to accurately represent the state of the atmosphere. To this end, weather observers adhere to **Coordinated Universal Time (UTC)** (or *Universel Temps Coordinné*), previously known as *Greenwich Mean Time (GMT)*, the time along the prime meridian, 0 degree longitude. (The prime meridian passes through the Old Royal Observatory, Greenwich, England.) For reference, at 0600 UTC, it is midnight Central Standard Time (CST) in Chicago, IL and 10 p.m. Pacific Standard Time (PST) in San Francisco, CA. For more on time keeping, see the first Essay in Chapter 1.

During the 1990s, weather-observing facilities of the National Weather Service underwent extensive restructuring and modernization with the goal of upgrading the quality and reliability of weather observation and forecasting. NWS Weather Forecast Offices were consolidated at 122 sites across the United States, each with a designated area of forecast and warning responsibility (Figure 13.1). The National Weather Service replaced old weather radars with Doppler radars at 113 sites nationwide. The FAA and the U.S. Department of Defense (DOD) operate another 39 Doppler units. As noted in Chapters 7 and 11, Doppler radar offers significant (possibly life saving) advantages over the old weather radar in providing more advance warning of the development and approach of severe weather systems.

FIGURE 13.1
Exterior view of a National Weather Service Weather Forecast Office.

FIGURE 13.2
Sensors of the NWS Automated Surface Observing System.

FIGURE 13.3
A meteorologist checks the calibration of a rain gauge at a NWS cooperative weather station. These stations provide data that are useful for hydrologic, agricultural, and climatic purposes.

Automated weather stations replaced the old manual system of hourly observations. A joint effort of the NWS, FAA, and DOD, the **Automated Surface Observing System (ASOS)** consists of modern sensors, computers, and fully automated communications ports (Figure 13.2). As of this writing, a network of 862 ASOS units operates continuously (updating observations every minute, 24-hrs a day), feeding observational data to NWS Forecast Offices and local airport control towers. Using FAA ground-to-air radio, ASOS transmits computer-generated voice observations directly to aircraft flying near airports. ASOS reports a variety of weather elements: temperature (ambient, dewpoint), pressure (sea-level, altimeter setting), wind (direction, speed), precipitation accumulation, visibility (to at least 16 km or 10 mi), obstructions to vision (e.g., fog, haze), present weather, and sky condition (cloud height and amount of cloud cover) up to 3660 m (12,000 ft). In addition, ASOS detects significant changes in weather (e.g., wind

shift, rapid pressure changes, beginning and ending times for precipitation). Similar to ASOS is the *Automated Weather Observation System (AWOS)*, located at many small airports. As of this writing, 429 AWOS units are operating in the U.S.

Besides the numerous land-based weather stations that provide information of potential use for weather forecasting and aviation, another 11,700 cooperative weather stations are scattered across the United States (Figure 13.3). These stations are cooperative in that people volunteer their time and labor to monitor instruments and the NWS provides instruments and data management. The principal function of the **NWS Cooperative Observer Network** is to record daily precipitation and temperatures for hydrologic, agricultural, and climatic purposes. Observers report 24-hr precipitation totals and maximum/minimum temperatures based on observations made daily by 8 a.m., local time; some observers also report river levels. Traditionally, observers telephoned reports to the local NWS Weather Forecast Office but a new program that automates cooperative stations enables the observer to enter data into a microcomputer that formats and transmits data to computer workstations in the NWS Advanced Weather Interactive Processing System (AWIPS) (described later).

UPPER-AIR WEATHER OBSERVATIONS

As noted in Chapter 2, meteorologists still rely primarily on radiosondes to monitor conditions in the troposphere and lower stratosphere (Figure 13.4). A **radiosonde** is a radio-equipped instrument package carried aloft by a balloon that transmits to a ground station temperature, pressure, and humidity profiles (soundings) to a maximum altitude of about 30,000 m (100,000 ft). In addition, winds at various levels in the atmosphere are computed by tracking the balloon's drift using a radio direction-finding antenna (a *rawinsonde* observation). Worldwide, readings are taken twice each day, at 0000 UTC and 1200 UTC.

As of this writing, the National Weather Service is implementing the *Radiosonde Replacement System (RRS)* to upgrade the current generation of radiosondes. The RRS consists of a global positioning system (GPS) tracking antenna, GPS radiosondes that operate at a radio frequency of 1680 MHz, plus a NT-based computer workstation. The new system will provide more detailed and accurate upper-air data. Readings will be available at 1-second intervals, corresponding to altitude levels about 5 m (16 ft) apart.

The U.S. operates almost 90 radiosonde observation (RAOB) stations, a quarter of which use special high-altitude balloons that obtain data from altitudes above 30,000 m (100,000 ft). About 70 RAOB stations are located in the continental U.S., 14 in Alaska, 2 in Hawaii, and one each in Guam and Puerto Rico (Figure 13.5). Occasionally, meteorological rockets reach much higher altitudes (up to 100 km or 62 mi) but data from these probes are primarily for research purposes. In some urban areas, low-level soundings (up to 3000 m or 9800 ft) monitor atmospheric conditions to assess air pollution potential. Satellites, weather radar, aircraft, wind profilers, and *dropwindsondes* (similar to a radiosonde but dropped from an aircraft) also supply upper-air weather data. Satellite-derived observational data currently account for 84% of all data assimilated by NCEP numerical models.

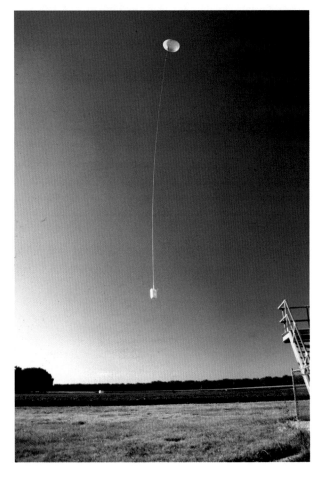

FIGURE 13.4
A radiosonde instrument package carried aloft by a balloon measures vertical profiles of temperature, pressure, and humidity to a maximum altitude of about 30,000 m (100,000 ft).

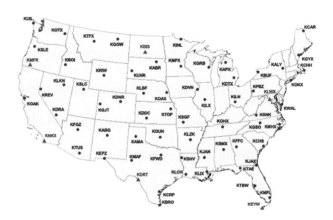

FIGURE 13.5
Map showing locations of rawinsonde stations in the coterminous US. Those sites in red are part of the international Global Climate Observing System. [NOAA]

Weather Data Assimilation, Depiction and Analysis

Weather data collected from surface and upper-air stations in the network are assembled at national weather centers where these data are subjected to quality control prior to being displayed on maps for weather analysis or used in numerical weather prediction models. Accurate observational data must be obtained rapidly from as many locations as possible. Computers at the *Hydrometeorological Prediction Center (HPC)*, one of the National Centers for Environmental Prediction (NCEP), use special symbols for plotting weather observations on synoptic and hemispheric maps. The weather reported by each observation station is depicted on a map by following a conventional **station model**. The station model in Figure 13.6 shows symbols for surface weather conditions. By international agreement, the same station model and symbols are used throughout the world, thereby overcoming language barriers and permitting easy interpretation of weather data by meteorologists anywhere.

Weather systems are three-dimensional so that both surface and upper-air weather maps are needed to represent the state of the atmosphere. A very different approach is used for the two types of maps, however. Surface weather data are plotted on a constant-altitude surface (usually sea-level), whereas upper-air weather data are plotted on constant-pressure (isobaric) surfaces.

SURFACE WEATHER MAPS

It is standard practice for meteorologists to adjust surface air pressure readings to sea level (Chapter 5), thereby eliminating the influence of station elevation on air pressure readings. This procedure enables meteorologists to compare surface air pressure readings at weather stations that are located at different elevations above sea level. The adjusted air pressure readings are plotted on surface weather maps. Meteorologists (or their computers) draw **isobars**, lines of equal air pressure, at 4-mb intervals, a procedure that requires interpolation between stations. An isobaric analysis reveals the location of such features as anticyclones (*highs*) and cyclones (*lows*), troughs and ridges, as well as horizontal air pressure gradients (Figure 13.7).

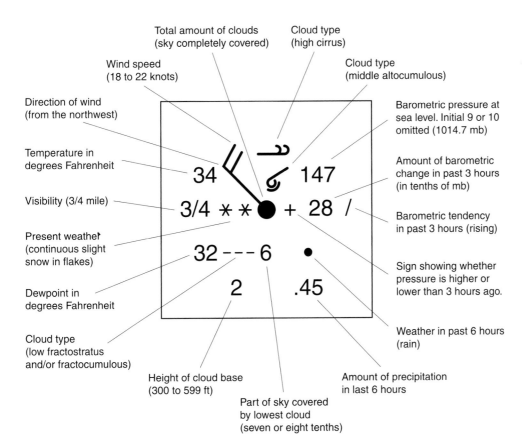

FIGURE 13.6
Surface weather station model.

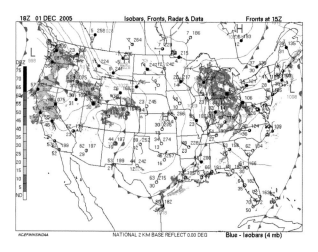

FIGURE 13.7

Sample isobaric analysis on a surface weather map. Isobars, lines of constant air pressure, are drawn at 4-mb intervals. [NOAA].

FIGURE 13.8

Sample 500-mb analysis. Solid blue lines are contours of height drawn at intervals of 60 m; red dashed lines are isotherms drawn at 5 Celsius degree intervals. [NOAA]

On surface weather maps, a cyclone center, where air pressure is lowest locally, is indicated by the symbol *L* or *Low*. Closely spaced isobars surrounding the storm center indicate a relatively steep horizontal air pressure gradient and strong surface winds. Fronts originate at the storm center and isobars bend as they cross fronts. This bending of isobars is consistent with the fact that fronts often are found in troughs. Because we can infer surface wind direction from the isobar pattern, bending of isobars at fronts indicates that the wind changes direction as we cross a front. As noted in Chapter 10, a wind shift is one of the characteristics associated with a frontal passage. A relatively weak horizontal air pressure gradient (widely spaced isobars) and weak winds or calm air generally occur over a broad area about the center of an anticyclone (mapped as *H* or *High*).

Surface synoptic weather maps are drawn every 3 hrs for North America and at 6-hr intervals for the Northern Hemisphere. Special maps and charts are also constructed that summarize a variety of surface weather elements including, for example, maximum and minimum temperatures for a 24-hr period, precipitation amounts for 6 and 24 hrs, and observed snow cover. An animated national composite radar reflectivity loop is also updated every 30 minutes or less.

UPPER-AIR WEATHER MAPS

Upper-air weather data acquired mostly by radiosondes are plotted on constant-pressure surfaces following a modified station model. Applying basic laws of atmospheric physics, meteorologists compute the altitudes corresponding to these pressure values. For example,

meteorologists determine the altitude of the 500-mb surface, that is, the altitude where the air pressure is about one-half its average sea-level value. By plotting altitudes of the 500-mb level as monitored simultaneously by all radiosonde stations across North America, meteorologists construct a map representing the topography of the 500-mb surface (Figure 13.8). The 500-mb map is particularly useful for weather forecasting because the atmospheric circulation at that level closely approximates the upper-level steering winds and the trough and ridge patterns responsible for the development and displacement of surface weather systems such as extra-tropical cyclones.

Meteorologists (or their computers) draw height contour lines where the 500-mb level is at the same altitude, interpolating between weather stations. By convention, height contours are labeled in meters above sea level and the contour interval (difference between successive contours) is 60 m. Dashed lines, also plotted on the map, are *isotherms*, lines of equal temperature, labeled in degrees Celsius. Arrows and barbs represent wind direction and speed at the 500-mb level.

The altitude of a pressure surface (such as the 500-mb level) varies from one place to another, primarily because of differences in mean temperature of the air below that pressure surface. Air pressure drops with altitude more rapidly in cold air than in warm air. Raising the temperature of air reduces its density so that greater altitudes are required for warm air to exhibit the same drop in pressure as cold air. This means, for example, that the 500-mb level is at a lower altitude where the air below is relatively cold, but at a higher altitude where the air below is relatively warm. Hence, height contours plotted on an isobaric surface (e.g., the 500-mb chart) always show a gradual slope downward from the warm tropics to the colder polar latitudes.

Upper-air observations indicate that horizontal winds generally parallel the height contour lines at the 500-mb level. Where contours are closely spaced (a relatively steep height gradient), winds are strong, and where contours are far apart (a relatively weak height gradient), winds are light. Why are winds associated with a gradient in the height of a pressure surface? A height gradient develops in response to a horizontal gradient in air temperature, and with a horizontal air temperature gradient, there are also horizontal gradients in air density and air pressure. As discussed in Chapter 8, a horizontal air pressure gradient generates wind. The 500-mb surface is so far above the *atmospheric boundary layer* that the planetary- and synoptic-scale winds are essentially *geostrophic* where contours are straight, and *gradient* where contours are curved. Large-scale winds blowing at the 500-mb level are the product of interactions among a horizontal height gradient, the Coriolis Effect, and the centripetal force.

On upper-air weather maps, contours exhibit both cyclonic (counterclockwise) and anticyclonic (clockwise) curvature. These are the *troughs* and *ridges*, respectively, in the prevailing westerlies described in Chapter 9. Contours sometimes define a series of nearly concentric circles, perhaps indicating a cutoff or blocking circulation pattern. At the center of a ridge, the air column is relatively warm and contour heights are high, so we label the ridge with an *H*. An upper-air ridge often is linked to a warm-core anticyclone at the surface. In contrast, near the center of a trough, the air column is relatively cold and contour heights are low, so the trough is labeled with an *L*. An upper-air trough may be linked to a cold-core extra-tropical cyclone at the surface. Warm-core cyclones (thermal lows) and cold-core anticyclones (polar and arctic highs) are too shallow to appear on 500-mb maps. Interestingly, a ridge may be found on upper-air charts above a warm-core cyclone such as a thermal low (Chapter 10) or hurricane (Chapter 12). Similarly, a trough may occur above a shallow cold-core high.

Winds blowing across regional isotherms produce cold or warm air advection (Chapter 4). **Cold air advection** takes place where winds blow from colder localities toward warmer localities. **Warm air advection** occurs where winds blow in the opposite direction. Warm air advection causes the 500-mb surface to rise, whereas cold air advection lowers the 500-mb surface.

Cold air advection between the surface and 500-mb thus deepens troughs and weakens ridges, whereas warm air advection strengthens ridges and weakens troughs. When cold air advects into troughs at the same time that warm air advects into ridges, the circulation becomes more meridional. On the other hand, if warm air advects into troughs while cold air advects into ridges, the circulation becomes more zonal. As described in Chapter 9, shifts in the upper-air circulation pattern between meridional flow and zonal flow have important implications for north/south air mass exchange and the development and track of extra-tropical cyclones.

NCEP's Hydrometeorological Prediction Center issues 500-mb maps twice each day based on upper-air observations at 0000 UTC and 1200 UTC. One set of maps covers North America and another covers the Northern Hemisphere. Although we have focused our discussion of upper-air weather maps on the 500-mb level, similar analyses are routinely constructed twice daily for the 850-, 700-, 300-, 250-, 200-, and 100-mb levels. The 300-, 250-, and 200-mb charts are useful in locating the polar front jet stream. Lines, called *isotachs*, are drawn on these charts connecting points having the same wind speed and they highlight the regions of strongest upper tropospheric winds, which represent the location of the jet stream. The altitude of the jet stream depends on the mean temperature of the underlying air column and is lower in winter than in summer. Hence, for jet stream analysis, meteorologists rely upon the 300-mb chart during the coldest time of year and the 200-mb chart during the warmest time of year. The display of the position of the jet stream on these upper tropospheric charts helps meteorologists locate regions of divergence and convergence that provide upper-air support for the development of surface weather systems.

The deluge of real-time weather information (e.g., weather maps, satellite images, soundings, composite radar maps) has spurred development of computerized data management systems. An example is **McIDAS (Man-computer Interactive Data Access System)**, developed by scientists at the Space Science and Engineering Center at the University of Wisconsin-Madison. McIDAS ingests weather data and integrates and organizes those data into guidance products for potential users. Products include two- and three-dimensional composite images. Users access McIDAS on a computer terminal, select some satellite image or other data display, and may choose, for example, to overlay different fields of data.

McIDAS inspired the new computer workstations that have been operating at NWS Weather Forecast

FIGURE 13.9
AWIPS (Advanced Weather Interactive Processing System) workstation at a National Weather Service Forecast Office. AWIPS enables meteorologists to overlay and interpret a variety of graphical meteorological data.

Offices since 2000. This **Advanced Weather Interactive Processing System (AWIPS)** receives and organizes ASOS data plus analysis and guidance products from the National Centers for Environmental Prediction and enables the meteorologist to display, process, and overlay images, graphics, and other data (Figure 13.9).

Weather Prediction

Meteorologists at the Hydrometeorological Prediction Center analyze satellite images and weather observations plotted on surface and upper-air weather maps and computer model output. From these analyses, they prepare general short- to medium-range weather forecasts for the United States. They issue short-term 12-, 24-, 36-, and 48-hr forecasts plus medium-range 3- to 7-day extended outlooks each day, and weather outlooks up to 10 days three times weekly. Based upon the guidance provided by these forecasts plus the output of regional numerical models, NWS Weather Forecast Offices prepare detailed short-term forecasts for their region of responsibility. In addition, the *Climate Prediction Center* generates monthly (30-day), seasonal (90-day), and multi-seasonal outlooks.

Weather forecasting is an extremely challenging endeavor, primarily because it involves many variables and a vast quantity of weather data. For these reasons, computerized numerical models of the atmosphere have been developed to assist forecasters.

NUMERICAL WEATHER FORECASTING

The fundamentals of scientific weather forecasting were proposed in the early 20th century, first in 1904 by the Norwegian scientist Vilhelm Bjerknes (1862-1951), who provided the first schematic outline for numerical weather prediction and later by English physicist Lewis F. Richardson (1881-1953) who envisioned a large amphitheatre of clerks who would use desk calculators to compute a forecast. However, the absence of sufficiently rapid computing capabilities made these early ideas unfeasible. In the early 1950s, John von Neumann (1903-57) and Jule Charney (1917-81) pioneered the use of electronic computers for weather forecasting at the Institute for Advanced Study at Princeton University. A primitive computer, less powerful than today's personal computer, successfully forecast the horizontal air pressure pattern at 5000 m (16,400 ft) altitude over North America 24 hrs in advance. By 1955, computers were routinely generating weather forecasts from surface and upper-air weather observations.

An electronic computer is programmed with a numerical model of the atmosphere, that is, a model consisting of computational versions of the mathematical equations that relate winds, temperature, pressure, and water vapor concentration. Beginning with present (real-time) weather data, numerical models predict the values of various atmospheric properties on a uniform grid of points on pressure surfaces for some time in the future—say a few minutes from now. With these predicted conditions as a new starting point, another forecast is then computed for the subsequent few minutes. The computer repeats this procedure again and again until weather maps are generated for the next 12, 24, 36, and 48 hrs (or longer). In this iterative process, more than a trillion computations are performed each second on a vast array of observational data; hence the need for a high-speed electronic computer (supercomputer) that can accommodate huge quantities of data. (In fact, meteorology pioneered the application of supercomputers.) As of this writing, NCEP's latest high performance supercomputer (IBM SP at the Bowie Computer Center, Bowie, MD) ingests daily over 123 million global observations, performs 1.495 trillion calculations per sec, and produces 100 gigabytes of information that is the basis of 174,314 guidance products issued daily by NCEP.

Some computerized numerical models of the atmosphere are designed to operate over different spatial scales depending on the forecast range. For medium-range forecasts (up to 10 days), observational data are fed into the computer from all over the globe, because within that forecast range a weather system may travel thousands of kilometers. On the other hand, for short-range forecasts (up to 3 days), the model utilizes data drawn from a more restricted region of the globe. Compared to a global model, a regional model offers the advantage of greater resolution of data over a smaller area of interest. Thus, tomorrow's forecast of weather across the nation is based upon data obtained from all over the North American continent and surrounding ocean, but the run of forecasts for the next week requires data from around the globe.

NCEP computers are programmed with several different numerical models of the Earth-atmosphere system that differ in spatial scale, resolution, and forecast period. The *North American Mesoscale Model (NAM)* divides the troposphere into 60 vertical levels with 12 km (7.4 mi) between data points. NAM generates forecasts every 6 hours out to 84 hrs (3.5 days). Another basic regional forecast model is the *Nested Grid Model (NGM)* which has 16 vertical levels with data points at intervals of 80 km (50 mi); that numerical model issues forecasts twice daily, at 0000 UTC and 1200 UTC. Since its introduction in 1984, the NGM has proved its value especially in predicting East Coast winter storms. The *Eta model*, a more recent NCEP numerical model, provides greater resolution than the NGM; it consists of 60 levels with 10 km (6 mi) between data points. The Eta model is run four times per day. The *Rapid Update Cycle (RUC)* model features 50 levels with a horizontal resolution of 20 km (12 mi). RUC provides short-range (3 to 12 hrs) numerical weather guidance for general forecasting, as well as for aviation and severe weather forecasting (at a frequency of every 1 to 3 hrs per day). The *Global Forecast System (GFS)* consists of two 64-level models operating at different resolutions and forecast periods. The T382 model has a horizontal data interval of about 35 km (22 mi) and forecasts out to 180 hrs (7.5 days). The T190 model has a horizontal resolution of about 70 km (43 mi) and generates forecasts to 384 hrs (16 days) four times per day.

Meteorologists routinely employ two techniques to optimize the skill of weather forecasting based on numerical models: (1) **ensemble forecasting** and (2) **model comparison**. In the first, a numerical model generates several forecasts, each based on slightly different sets of initial conditions. If the forecasts are consistent, then the forecast is considered reliable. In the second technique, a comparison is made among forecasts made by several different models (i.e., NCEP models and models operated by other national weather services). If they all agree, then the forecast is issued with a relatively high level of confidence. Using either technique, if forecasts are inconsistent, any one forecast is considered unreliable.

Not all weather forecasts are the primary responsibility of NCEP's Hydrometeorological Prediction Center. Special forecast centers are responsible for predicting tropical cyclones (hurricanes and tropical storms), severe weather, river flow and flooding, and weather for mariners, and providing guidance information for domestic and international aviation. Also scientists at the Space Environment Center at Boulder, CO predict the "weather" of Earth's near-space environment for satellite and space shuttle operations.

FORECASTING TROPICAL CYCLONES

In 1873, the U.S. Army Signal Corps (then in charge of the nation's system of weather observation and forecasting) began gathering weather reports from Havana and Santiago, Cuba, to help detect tropical cyclones in the Caribbean. A hurricane was plotted for the first time on a surface weather map on 28 September 1874 (centered offshore near Savannah, GA). In 1890, with the transfer of weather observation and forecasting responsibilities from military to civilian hands (the U.S. Weather Bureau in the Department of Agriculture), primary emphasis was on observing and forecasting weather over the continent with little attention paid to tropical cyclones. Although six land-falling hurricanes claimed more than 4000 U.S. lives in 1893, the primary impetus for expanding the number of weather stations in the Caribbean was the Spanish-American War of 1898 and President William McKinley's (1843-1901) fear of what a hurricane near Cuba could do to the U.S. fleet. A U.S. Weather Bureau office was even established in Havana.

In subsequent decades, technological advances in communications and remote sensing greatly benefited the monitoring and understanding of tropical cyclones. Invention of the radio made possible ship-to-shore reports on the state of the atmosphere and seas near tropical cyclones; the first such report was filed in August 1909. By the late 1930s, the upper-air was regularly monitored providing insights on the relationship between tropical cyclones and steering winds aloft. Beginning in the late 1950s, weather radar at coastal stations observed rain bands and other features of an approaching hurricane. Since the 1960s, sensors onboard weather satellites have proved valuable in tracking and monitoring changes in tropical cyclones as they progress through their life cycle. The importance of satellites in data gathering is underscored by the fact that there is only one upper-air station for 10 million square km (4 million square mi) of the tropical and subtropical Atlantic. Furthermore, in recent decades, coastal and offshore buoys provide information on sea-surface conditions.

Specially instrumented reconnaissance aircraft complement satellite, radar, and buoy surveillance of tropical cyclones when they threaten any land in the Atlantic, Caribbean, Gulf of Mexico, Hawaii, or California. Reconnaissance flights into tropical cyclones began during World War II and originally involved aircraft from both the U.S. Navy and Army Air Forces (later the U.S. Air Force). Today, the 53rd Weather Reconnaissance Squadron, a U.S. Air Force reserve unit, conducts most hurricane reconnaissance from Keesler Air Force Base in Biloxi, MS. In addition, NOAA supports special aircraft designed for hurricane research and reconnaissance. Based at MacDill Air Force Base in Tampa, FL, these flights gather data for input into computer models at the Hydrometeorological Prediction Center with products sent on to the National Hurricane Center.

Reconnaissance aircraft fly directly through and over the storm to determine the location of the eye, measure wind speeds, and since 1997 obtain soundings by deploying global positioning system (GPS) dropwindsondes. A *dropwindsonde* (similar to a radiosonde except that the instrument package is dropped from an aircraft) provides data from flight-level (usually about 3000 m or 10,000 ft) down to Earth's surface. Based on several hundred GPS dropwindsonde soundings, meteorologists determined that surface wind speeds in the hurricane eyewall average about 90% of what they are at flight-level. Today, National Hurricane Center meteorologists typically use a factor of 90% to estimate a hurricane's maximum surface winds from flight-level measurements. Also, by extrapolating from air pressure readings at flight-level, meteorologists estimate the sea-level air pressure at the storm center.

During the 1940s, responsibility for forecasting Atlantic hurricanes was split among U.S. Weather Bureau offices in New Orleans, Miami, Washington, DC, Boston, and San Juan. In 1967, the U.S. Weather Bureau office in Miami was officially designated as the **National Hurricane Center (NHC)**. In 1984, the NHC was separated from the Miami NWS Weather Forecast Office. Today, responsibility for forecasting tropical cyclones that could impact the U.S. is divided between the National Hurricane Center on the campus of Florida International University in Miami, FL (Figure 13.10) and the Central Pacific Hurricane Center in Honolulu, HI. The NHC is responsible for issuing statements covering tropical storms and hurricanes in the North Atlantic basin (including the Gulf of Mexico and the Caribbean Sea) and the eastern Pacific basin (to 140 degrees W). When a tropical cyclone develops in the central Pacific (west to the international dateline), the Honolulu NWS

Forecast Office activates the Central Pacific Hurricane Center that is responsible for issuing tropical cyclone watches, warnings, and advisories.

The NHC is a branch of the *Tropical Prediction Center (TPC)*. Through a WMO agreement, the TPC has responsibility for producing and coordinating analysis and forecasting of tropical cyclones for 24 nations in the Americas, Caribbean, and for the waters of the North Atlantic, Caribbean Sea, Gulf of Mexico, and the eastern North Pacific. The *Tropical Analysis and Forecast Branch* of the TPC provides year-round marine weather analysis and forecasts for the tropical and subtropical waters of the eastern North and South Pacific and the North Atlantic basin.

At the NHC, meteorologists watch for development of tropical cyclones over the Atlantic basin (including the Caribbean and Gulf of Mexico) primarily from 1 June through 30 November, plus the eastern Pacific from 15 May through 30 November. The Center operates the SLOSH model for prediction of storm surges, prepares and distributes hurricane watches and warnings for the public, conducts research on hurricane forecasting techniques, and sponsors public awareness programs. Local NWS Weather Forecast Offices transmit information from the NHC as advisories, warnings, or special weather statements to people in their areas of responsibility. The goal is to provide at least 12 hrs of daylight warning for coastal residents so that they can prepare for a hurricane and evacuate if necessary.

The principal challenge for NHC forecasters is predicting the track and intensity of a hurricane. Such forecasts are issued every 6 hrs and, until 2001, covered periods up to 72 hrs in the future. In 2001, the track forecast period was extended to 96 hrs (4 days) and 120 hrs (5 days). The basis for hurricane track forecasts is a blend of climatology

FIGURE 13.10
Exterior view of the Tropical Prediction Center/National Hurricane Center in Miami, FL.

(records of tracks of similar hurricanes in the past), special numerical models, and the experience of the forecaster (Figure 13.11). How skillful are these track forecasts? Figure 13.12 shows trends in the error of Atlantic hurricane track forecasts (in nautical miles) for forecast periods of 72 hrs, 48 hrs, and 24 hrs in advance from 1990 to 2004, and for 120 hrs and 96 hrs from 2001 to 2004. Trend lines indicate that hurricane track errors were cut in half in 15 years. Further reduction in track error likely will come with better numerical models and higher quality observational data that are fed into the models. Research directed at improving track forecast models focuses primarily on better simulations of the oceanic energy source, interactions of tropical cyclones with the surrounding atmosphere, and the storm system's internal dynamics.

While track forecasts have improved, numerical models have not done well in predicting changes in the intensity of tropical cyclones—especially rapidly intensifying systems. With rapid intensification, a category 1 or 2 hurricane can become a category 4 or 5 system in less than 24 hours. As shown in Figure 13.13, intensity forecast error increases as the forecast period lengthens.

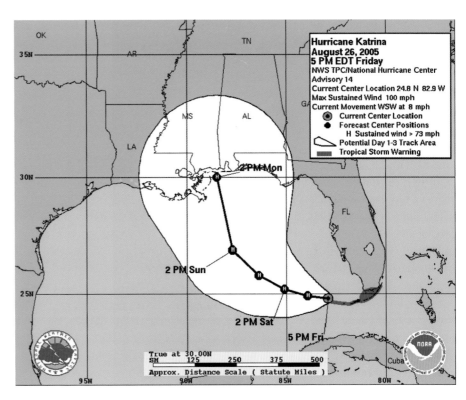

FIGURE 13.11
Track forecast for Hurricane Katrina issued at 5 p.m. EDT on 26 August 2005. The white area (the "cone of uncertainty") encompasses possible variations in the track based on output of many numerical models. [NOAA, National Hurricane Center]

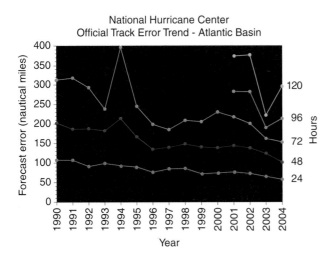

FIGURE 13.12
Atlantic hurricane track forecast error (in nautical miles) for forecast periods of 72, 48, and 24 hours (1990-2004) and for forecast periods of 120 and 96 hours (2001-2004). [NOAA]

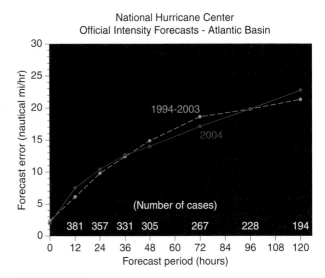

FIGURE 13.13
With lengthening forecast period, the Atlantic hurricane basin intensity forecast error (in nautical miles per hour) increases. [NOAA]

If the hurricane track forecast is on target, the SLOSH model can accurately predict the location and height of the storm surge (a dome of water pushed ashore by storm winds) along coastal areas (Chapter 12). By consulting local topographic maps, public safety officials use SLOSH predictions to identify areas likely to be inundated by floodwaters and order evacuation of residents accordingly.

Since the 1983 hurricane season, the NHC has included a probability forecast as part of its advisory statements. Probability is defined as the percent chance that the

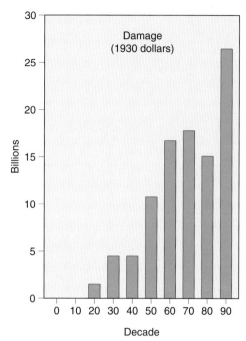

FIGURE 13.14
During the 20th century, tropical cyclone fatalities in the United States trended downward, whereas property damage trended upward. [NOAA]

center of a hurricane or tropical storm will pass within 105 km (65 mi) of any one of 46 designated Gulf and East Coast communities from Brownsville, TX to Eastport, ME. The first probability forecast is usually issued 72 hrs in advance of the storm's anticipated landfall. At that time, by convention, the probability of a hurricane landfall is set no higher than 10% for any community. Probabilities increase to 13% to 18% at 48 hrs, 20% to 25% at 36 hrs, 35% to 50% at 24 hrs, and 60% to 80% at 12 hrs, prior to the storm's expected landfall.

A *hurricane watch* is issued for a coastal area when sustained winds of 119 km (74 mi) per hr or higher are possible within the next 36 hrs; a *hurricane warning* means that hurricane conditions are expected in 24 hrs or less. (Watches and warnings are also issued for tropical storms.) The uncertainty in hurricane track forecasts and the considerable threat posed by a hurricane requires forecasters to over-warn the public. That is, hurricane watches and warnings are issued for a stretch of coastline that is much longer than the diameter of the approaching hurricane. Over-warning is costly for people who prepare for a hurricane that never shows up. Millions of dollars are spent on preparations, such as boarding up windows and closing businesses, and additional millions of dollars are lost due to disruption of commerce and industry. And the cost of evacuation can be considerable.

Nonetheless, these costs are outweighed by the benefits of being prepared just in case. The lull in Atlantic hurricane activity during the 1970s and 1980s coupled with more skillful hurricane forecasting and more effective public response programs was responsible for a dramatic decline in hurricane related fatalities during the 20th century (Figure 13.14). This all changed in August 2005 when Hurricane Katrina claimed more than 1300 lives along the Louisiana and Mississippi Gulf Coast. Also, during the 20th century, the dollar cost of property damage skyrocketed, presumably because of greater coastal development.

FORECASTING FOR AVIATION

As of 1 October 1995, the National Severe Storms Forecast Center (NSSFC) in Kansas City, MO became the *Aviation Weather Center (AWC)* and the *Storm Prediction Center (SPC)*. The AWC remains in Kansas City where it shares facilities with the National Weather Service Training Center (Figure 13.15). The SPC moved to Norman, OK in 1997 and is co-located with the *National Severe Storms Laboratory (NSSL)*, a center for severe weather research.

Meteorologists at the Aviation Weather Center issue warnings, forecasts, and analysis of weather conditions for aviation interests. These functions support the Federal Aviation Administration (FAA) Air Traffic

FIGURE 13.15
The National Weather Service Training Center co-located with the Aviation Weather Center at Kansas City, MO. [Photo by R.S. Weinbeck]

Control responsibility to safely and efficiently manage the nation's airspace. According to NOAA's National Weather Service, weather is a factor in more than one-quarter to one-half of all aviation accidents each year. In addition, weather-related aviation delays result in an estimated economic loss of $1 billion per year. AWC meteorologists issue forecasts for weather conditions that may impact domestic and international airspace during the subsequent 24 hours, analyze weather hazards for aircraft in flight, and generate warnings that are made available to the aviation community immediately. Forecasts complement airport terminal and enroute forecasts provided by local NWS Weather Forecast Offices. In addition to the public safety aspect, efficient use of aviation forecasts has proven economically beneficial to airlines through fuel savings.

FORECASTING SEVERE STORMS

Meteorologists at the Storm Prediction Center (SPC) monitor atmospheric conditions for potential development of severe local storms, including severe thunderstorms and tornadoes over the contiguous U.S. The SPC also monitors heavy rain, blizzards and fire weather and issues guidance products for these hazards. Products are used by NWS Weather Forecast Offices, emergency managers, broadcast meteorologists, aviation interests, and other groups.

Several times daily, the SPC issues *convective outlooks* identifying areas around the nation expected to experience both severe and non-severe thunderstorms over the following 1 to 3 days. Outlooks specify areas of severe thunderstorm risk (slight, moderate, or high) depending on the coverage and intensity of thunderstorms expected in a region. With the passage of time as the threat of severe weather becomes better defined, SPC meteorologists issue a *mesoscale discussion*, which describes the evolving severe weather threat (including non-thunderstorm hazards such as heavy snow). If severe thunderstorm development is imminent or likely to occur in the next several hours, the SPC issues watches for severe thunderstorms or tornadoes as appropriate. Watches alert the public to the threat for severe weather and activate storm spotter networks. Watches essentially fine-tune forecast areas identified in the convective outlook. A typical watch encompasses about 65,000 square km (25,000 square mi) and is valid for 4 to 6 hrs. Beginning in 2005, watches apply to geographic areas defined by counties. Warnings are issued by the local NWS Weather Forecast Office.

Statistics on verification of severe weather watches issued by the Storm Prediction Center

---

The AWC provides a number of products and services. These include the following:

Area Forecasts—weather conditions for six geographical areas issued three times daily.
SIGMET Advisories—issued for severe turbulence, severe icing, intense sand or dust storms or volcanic dust clouds. These advisories are provided to pilots, dispatchers, and air traffic controllers, apply to all aircraft flying at or below 45,000 ft, and are valid for up to four hours.
AIRMET Advisories—issued for less severe weather hazards.
Collaborative Convective Forecast Product—issued every two hours and provides two-, four-, and six-hour forecasts of convective activity.
Convective SIGMETs—inflight advisories for thunderstorms that are especially hazardous for aviation; issued for three geographical areas each hour.
Low Level Significant Weather Charts—depict areas of low cloud ceilings and visibilities, turbulence, and freezing levels; cover the 48 contiguous states and southern Canada and extend from the surface to 24,000 ft.

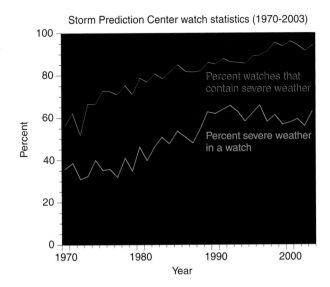

Storm Prediction Center watch statistics (1970-2003)

Percent watches that contain severe weather

Percent severe weather in a watch

FIGURE 13.16
Upward trend in the skill of severe weather watches issued over the period 1970-2003. [NOAA, Storm Prediction Center]

demonstrate significant improvement from 1970 through 2003. As shown in Figure 13.16, the percent of watches that actually contained severe weather trended upward as did the percent of cases of severe weather in a watch area.

RIVER AND FLOOD FORECASTING

The U.S. Army Signal Corps began the first river and flood forecast service in 1872. A disastrous flood on the Kansas River in 1903 prompted Congress to make the river and flood forecast service a special division of the U.S. Weather Bureau (now the National Weather Service). By 1913, the service had expanded to 483 river gauging stations (many operated by the U.S. Geological Survey). In 1946, the Weather Bureau established the nation's first *River Forecast Centers (RFCs)* at Cincinnati, OH and Kansas City, MO. Currently, 13 RFCs serve the nation with the primary goal of minimizing the loss of life and property damage caused by floods by providing the public with timely river and flood forecasts (Figure 13.17).

At RFCs, staff hydrologists and hydro-meteorologists develop river, reservoir, and flood forecasts using special numerical models that simulate the response of river and stream flow to rainfall and snowmelt. The objective is to predict the volume of water that runs off the land surface into a river or stream, the discharge at specific locations along major rivers or small streams near urban areas, and variations in river discharge and stage (height of the river) as the water volume moves downstream. In late winter and early spring, RFC staff prepares spring snowmelt outlooks

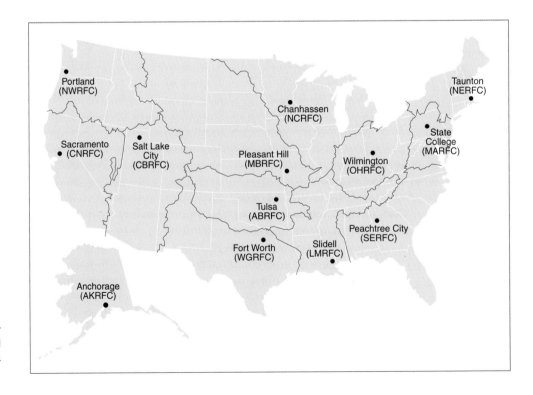

FIGURE 13.17
Locations of the River Forecast Centers (RFCs) and their regions of responsibility. [NOAA]

to identify the potential for spring flooding, assuming a normal rate of snowmelt. Specialized services include low flow forecasts during dry periods, ice advisories for navigable rivers in winter, and reservoir inflow forecasts. Forecasts are forwarded to personnel at local NWS Weather Forecast Offices who in turn issue forecasts and outlooks for water resource managers, emergency management officials, and the public. Flood forecasts specify the expected height of the flood crest, the date and time when the river is expected to flood, and the date and time when the river is likely to return to its banks.

MARINE FORECASTING

Meteorologists and oceanographers at NCEP's *Ocean Prediction Center* in Camp Springs, MD issue forecasts, warnings, and other guidance information for a diverse user community including mariners, fisheries, and recreational boaters. The goal is to "ensure the safety of life and property at sea, manage marine natural resources and protect the environment." Operations benefit marine safety, navigation, fisheries, and the health of coastal ecosystems. Analysis and forecasting cover such conditions as wind, waves, fog, and ice accretion. In addition, the Ocean Prediction Center works with the National Weather Service Forecast Offices, the Federal Emergency Management Agency, and the U.S. Coast Guard Search and Rescue in responding to emergency situations. For more on marine weather analysis and forecasting, refer to this chapter's first Essay.

FORECAST SKILL

Just how accurate are today's computer-guided weather forecasts? This question can be answered by comparing the skill of modern weather forecasting with that of predictions based on *persistence* (forecasting no change in present weather) or *climatology* (forecasts derived from past weather records). On this basis, weather forecasting skill declines rapidly for periods longer than 48 hrs and is minimal beyond 10 days.

Several factors contribute to the drop in forecasting skill. Computerized forecasts are only as accurate as the input (observational) data and predictive equations (numerical models) allow them to be. Errors are introduced by (1) missing or inaccurate observational data, (2) failure of weather stations to detect all meso-scale and micro-scale circulation systems, and (3) imprecise equations in numerical models that include assumptions and first approximations. Unfortunately, the adverse effects of errors in initial conditions grow cumulatively as the forecast period lengthens. In today's numerical models of the atmosphere, the impact of even small errors doubles about every 2 to 2.5 days over the forecast period. When computerized numerical models are run out to 10 days, some elements of daily forecasts are useful for some localities to about 6 or 7 days. Beyond that, chaos, the term for sensitivity to initial conditions, sets in. For more on chaos and the limits to weather forecasting, see this chapter's second Essay.

The accuracy of numerical weather forecasting, particularly in the 1- to 5-day range, has shown slow but steady improvement over the past few decades, and prospects for continued progress are good. This optimistic outlook stems from: (1) a better understanding of atmospheric processes that makes possible the development of more realistic numerical models of the Earth-atmosphere system, (2) larger and faster computers, (3) more reliable and sophisticated observational tools, including Doppler radar and remote sensing by satellite, and (4) denser weather observational networks worldwide.

Although computerized numerical models have revolutionized weather forecasting, computers are never likely to replace human weather forecasters (Figure 13.18). The products of computerized numerical models function as guidance materials for the forecaster. He or she must understand the basic atmospheric processes, and the characteristic errors and biases of the various numerical models and weather-observing systems. As much as numerical weather prediction has advanced in recent years, the best forecasters still rely heavily on personal experience and intuition, tempered by their knowledge of how the Earth-atmosphere system works. A good forecaster does not start with the model output in preparing a forecast, but rather he or she begins with

FIGURE 13.18
A computer is not likely to replace a meteorologist.

previous and current observations, forming a view of what the atmosphere has been doing and ideas on what is likely to happen in the future. Furthermore, special local or regional conditions may call for significant modification of a computer-generated weather forecast. Forecasters must analyze and interpret computerized predictions and adapt those forecasts as necessary to regional and local circumstances. Consider an example.

Suppose that an intense early winter extra-tropical cyclone tracks northeastward through the Midwest, across central Illinois, and into eastern Lower Michigan, as shown in Figure 13.19. Muskegon, MI is on the cold, snowy side of the storm's path, so residents experience snow and strong northeast winds. After the storm passes, the wind shifts to the north and then northwest, and cold air advection begins. A computerized numerical model might predict clearing skies for Muskegon, but local conditions dictate a different result. Strong winds from the northwest advect cold, dry air across the relatively warm waters of Lake Michigan, giving rise to localized *lake-effect snows* on the lake's downwind eastern shore (Chapter 8). Because of this local effect, northwest winds may bring more snow to Muskegon after the storm has passed than northeast winds did when the storm was nearby.

FIGURE 13.19
An early winter cyclone tracks northeastward through the Midwest, causing heavy snowfall at Muskegon, MI.

LONG-RANGE FORECASTING

Meteorologists at NCEP's *Climate Prediction Center* in Camp Springs, MD prepare 30-day (monthly), 90-day (seasonal), and multi-seasonal generalized climate outlooks that map areas where the probability of total precipitation and temperature is expected to depart from normal, that is, long-term averages (Figure 13.20). Outlooks are issued from two weeks to 13 months in advance for the contiguous U.S., Hawaii, and other Pacific islands.

A promising area of research in long-range weather forecasting relies on identification of teleconnections. A **teleconnection** is a linkage between changes in atmospheric circulation occurring in widely separated regions of the globe, often many thousands of kilometers apart. For example, Jerome Namias (1910-97) and his colleagues at the Scripps Institution of Oceanography argued that a coupling between ocean and atmosphere triggered the 1988 Midwestern drought. Anomalously cold surface water in the central and eastern tropical Pacific (associated with La Niña) plus unusually warm surface water to the north (near Hawaii) interacted with the atmospheric circulation to produce a long-wave pattern that was more meridional than usual. As described in Chapter 9, this circulation pattern featured a warm anticyclone that persisted over the central contiguous United States through much of the spring and summer of 1988. Severe drought was the consequence.

Identification of teleconnections associated with El Niño and La Niña is the primary basis for extension of long-range forecasting to multi-seasons. As described in detail in Chapter 9, meteorologists report success in predicting the onset of El Niño a year or so in advance and have identified linkages between El Niño and weather anomalies in middle latitudes—especially during winter.

Successfully forecasting the prevailing circulation pattern at the 700-mb level is the first step in predicting the probability of monthly temperature and precipitation departures from normal. The present circulation pattern is extrapolated into the future, although an effort is also made, based on historical data, to identify features of the present pattern that are most likely to persist. The prevailing westerly flow at the 700-mb level permits identification of areas of strong warm and cold air advection as well as the principal storm tracks. Predictions of surface temperature and precipitation anomalies are derived from this analysis.

A somewhat different approach is taken for 90-day outlooks (issued once each month near mid-month). Forecasters rely more on long-term trends and recurring

FIGURE 13.20

Sample monthly and seasonal outlook maps of the probability of total precipitation and temperature departing from normals, i.e., long-averages. *A* indicates a probability of higher than normal values whereas *B* indicates a probability of lower than normal values. [NCEP's Climate Prediction Center] events, attempting to isolate persistent circulation features from prior months and seasons. A suite of 20 NCEP *Global Climate Model (GCM)* runs yield a mean prediction. Model runs depend heavily on tropical Pacific sea-surface temperatures specified by a coupled ocean-atmosphere model. The model-generated outlook accounts for the influence of not only El Niño and La Niña, but also low frequency fluctuations such as the North Atlantic Oscillation (Chapter 9).

In January 1995, meteorologists at the Climate Prediction Center began issuing 15-month (multi-seasonal) outlooks for regions of expected positive and negative anomalies in temperature and precipitation. Each month 13 forecasts are issued, each one covering a 3-month period. The first forecast covers the three months beginning two weeks from the date of the forecast's release. Each subsequent 3-month forecast overlaps the previous one by two months.

SINGLE-STATION FORECASTING

Even without access to an official NWS forecast, short-term weather prediction based on weather observations at one location, known as **single-station forecasting**, may be derived from the principles of weather behavior examined in this course. Because such forecasts are based on rules applied at only one location, they tend to be generalized and tentative, with complications often cropping up as local conditions are modified by changes elsewhere. Table 13.1 is a sample list of rules of thumb applicable to middle latitudes. You may wish to add to this list. Other approaches base forecasts on fair-weather bias, persistence, or climatology.

Analysis of records of past weather events may aid single-station weather forecasting. Such records reveal a **fair-weather bias**. That is, fair-weather days outnumber stormy days almost everywhere. In fact, if we boldly predict that all days will be fair, we probably will be correct more than half the time. The only merit of such an exercise is to establish a baseline for evaluating the skill of more sophisticated weather forecasting techniques. That is, we would expect traditional forecasting methods to score higher than forecasting methods based solely on fair-weather bias.

Another characteristic behavior of weather is **persistence**, that is, the tendency for the same weather episode to persist for some period of time. For example, if the weather has been cold and stormy for several days, the weather may well continue that way for many more days. Weather records show, however, that at middle latitudes one weather type typically gives way to another weather type

TABLE 13.1
Some Rules of Thumb for Single-Station Weather Forecasting

- At night, air temperatures are lower if the sky is clear than if the sky is cloud-covered.
- Clear skies, light winds, and snow-covered ground favor extreme nocturnal radiational cooling and very low air temperatures by sunrise.
- Steadily falling air pressure often signals the approach of stormy weather whereas rising air pressure suggests that continued fair weather or improving weather is in the offing.
- Appearance of cirrus, cirrostratus, and altostratus clouds, in that order, indicates overrunning ahead of a warm front and the likelihood of precipitation.
- A counterclockwise wind shift from northeast to north to northwest (called *backing*) is usually accompanied by clearing skies and cold air advection.
- A clockwise wind shift from east to southeast to south (called *veering*) is often accompanied by clearing skies and warm air advection.
- A wind shift from northwest to west to southwest is usually accompanied by warm air advection and increasing clouds.
- If radiation fog lifts by late morning, a fair afternoon is likely.
- With west to northwest winds, a steady or rising barometer, and scattered cumulus clouds, fair weather is likely to persist.
- Towering cumulus clouds by mid-morning forewarn of afternoon thunderstorms.

very abruptly, usually in a day or less. Weather forecasts based on persistence alone are therefore prone to error.

A third approach is based on **climatology**; that is, we prepare a weather forecast for a particular day based on the type of weather that occurred on the same day in years past. Suppose, for example, that the climate record of your area indicates that it has rained on 9 August only 12 times in the past 100 years. Accordingly, you predict the probability of rain next 9 August to be only 12%, and you confidently plan a picnic for that day. The problem with the climatology approach is that, statistics aside, there is no guarantee that it will not rain next 9 August.

PRIVATE SECTOR FORECASTING

Our discussion thus far has focused mainly on the role of the federal government in weather forecasting. In addition, many private sector meteorologists analyze weather maps and other guidance materials supplied by the National Centers for Environmental Prediction. Many television and radio stations and some newspapers employ their own meteorologists or contract with private forecast services. Some private meteorologists tailor their forecasts to the specific needs of their commercial, agricultural, or industrial clients. For example, a private weather forecaster retained by an appliance store chain might alert store executives to a pending heat wave so that stores might be stocked with an adequate supply of fans and air conditioners. Another private forecaster might advise an electric power utility of expected summer temperatures so the energy supplier can better anticipate customer demand for air conditioning. A private forecaster might provide frost and freeze warning service for orchards or cranberry bogs. In this way, private sector forecasters supplement the efforts of government weather forecasters.

Communication and Dissemination

Weather maps, charts, and forecasts issued by the National Centers for Environmental Prediction are transmitted to local NWS Weather Forecast Offices to guide staff meteorologists in preparing specific forecasts for their areas of responsibility. Weather information is then distributed to public safety officials and the general public via a variety of communications systems.

The National Weather Service issues outlooks, watches, warnings, and advisories when hazardous weather threatens. An *outlook* is provided for people who require considerable advance notice so that they might adequately prepare for a specific weather event. For example, the outlook for flooding from spring snowmelt in the Upper Midwest may be issued many weeks in advance.

When hazardous weather is occurring or appears possible or probable, the National Weather Service issues event-specific watches, warnings, and advisories. These statements cover severe local storms, winter storms, floods, hurricanes, and non-precipitation hazards. A **weather watch**, such as a severe thunderstorm watch or winter storm watch, is indicated when hazardous weather is possible based on current or anticipated atmospheric conditions. The actual occurrence or timing of hazardous weather can be uncertain. People in the designated area need not interrupt their normal activities except to remain alert for threatening weather and to keep the television or radio on for further information. A **weather warning** (e.g., tornado warning, heavy snow warning) is issued when hazardous weather is taking place somewhere in the region or is imminent. People are advised to take all necessary safety precautions. *Advisories* refer to anticipated weather hazards that are less serious than those covered by a warning. Examples include a winter weather advisory, heavy surf advisory, or heat advisory.

The local NWS Weather Forecast Office issues a *tornado warning* only after detection of a thunderstorm that is known or likely to include a tornado. Indication of a tornadic circulation is based on Doppler radar and/or reports of funnel clouds or cloud-base rotation by specially trained storm spotters. A warning covers a much smaller area than a watch, usually all or part of a single county, and specifies the location of the tornado, its anticipated path, and the time when the tornado is expected in the warning area. Tornado warnings usually are valid for 30 to 60 minutes.

Winter storm warnings may specify heavy snow, blizzard conditions, or an ice storm. Usually, a *heavy snow warning* is issued if snowfall is expected to total at least 10 to 15 cm (4 to 6 in.) in less than 12 hrs, or at least 15 to 20 cm (6 to 8 in.) in less than 24 hrs; exact thresholds depend upon the locale. A *blizzard warning* means that falling or blowing snow is expected to be accompanied by sustained winds (or frequent gusts) of 56 km (35 mi) per hr or higher, reducing visibility to less than 400 m (1300 ft). Conditions are expected to persist for at least 3 hrs. A *severe blizzard* produces winds stronger than about 73 km (45 mi) per hr, visibility near zero because of blowing snow, air temperature below −12 °C (10 °F), and dangerously low wind-chills. An *ice storm warning* indicates that potentially dangerous accumulations of freezing rain or sleet are expected on the ground and other exposed surfaces.

To alert the public to the flash flood hazard, personnel at the local NWS Weather Forecast Offices issue watches, warnings, and advisories. A *flash flood watch* indicates that flash flooding is possible within or close to the designated watch area based on current or anticipated weather conditions. Residents of the watch area are advised to prepare to take action in the event that a flash flood warning is issued or flooding is observed. A *flash flood warning* is issued when a dangerously rapid rise in river level is imminent in the warning area or is currently occurring due to heavy rain (or dam failure). The public is advised to take appropriate action immediately. An urban and small stream flood advisory alerts the public to potential flooding that may cause inconvenience but is not life threatening for those living in the affected area. These advisories are issued when heavy rain is anticipated, which could flood streets and other low-lying urban areas, or if small streams are expected to reach bank full.

Because weather is changeable, weather observations and guidance information such as weather maps, forecasts, watches, and warnings must be communicated as rapidly as possible both nationally and internationally. For this reason, the World Meteorological Organization and weather services of its member nations maintain elaborate communications networks consisting of a variety of systems. Weather information is relayed by satellite, radio, Internet, and facsimile systems (which reproduce maps, charts, and satellite images). Modernization of U.S. National Weather Service facilities is making the weather communications network more efficient and reliable. Earlier in this chapter, we described the Automated Surface Observing System (ASOS) and the Advanced Weather Interactive Processing System (AWIPS).

The public receives regular weather reports and forecasts via commercial and public radio, the NOAA weather radio, commercial television, cable-TV (*The Weather Channel* and others), the Internet, and newspapers (Chapter 1). In many cities, weather information is also available via recorded telephone announcement systems.

Conclusions

Weather forecasting is a complex and challenging science that depends on the efficient interplay of weather observation, data analysis by meteorologists and computers, and rapid communication systems. Meteorologists have achieved a very respectable level of skill for short-range weather forecasting. Further improvement is expected with denser surface and upper-air observational networks, more precise numerical models of the atmosphere, larger and faster computers, and more sophisticated techniques of remote sensing by satellite. If these advances are to be realized, however, continued international cooperation is essential, for the atmosphere is a continuous fluid that knows no political boundaries.

Basic Understandings

- The fluid nature of the atmosphere means that international cooperation is required in gathering and interpreting surface and upper-air weather data. To this end, the World Meteorological Organization (WMO) coordinates an international effort of weather observation, analysis, and forecasting.

- Timely and accurate weather forecasts for the United States are the responsibility of the National Centers for Environmental Prediction (NCEP), part of NOAA's National Weather Service. NCEP's goal is to "protect life and property, as well as mitigate economic loss, by providing accurate forecasts and forecast guidance products to weather service field offices." Nine centers comprise NCEP, each responsible for forecasting specific weather or other environmental phenomena.

- Weather forecasting entails acquisition of present weather data, graphical depiction of the state of the atmosphere on weather maps and charts, computer-aided analysis of data and maps, prediction of the future state of the atmosphere, and dissemination of weather information and predictions to the public.

- Surface weather is monitored at land stations and by automated weather stations and ships at sea. Rawinsondes (profiling temperature, pressure, humidity, and wind), radar, aircraft, and satellites monitor the atmosphere above the Earth's surface. Modernization of the National Weather Service during the 1990s upgraded NWS Weather Forecast Offices, and installed the Automated Surface Observing System (ASOS) and Doppler radar.

- Using standard station models, surface weather observations are plotted on constant altitude (sea-level) maps whereas upper-air weather observations are plotted on maps of constant pressure (isobaric) surfaces (e.g., 500-mb map). The altitude of a specific pressure surface varies from one place to another primarily because of differences in mean temperature of the air below that pressure surface. For example, the 500-mb surface is at a lower altitude where the air below is relatively cold, but at a higher altitude where the air below is relatively warm.

- The NWS Advanced Weather Interactive Processing System (AWIPS) consists of computer workstations that ingest and organize ASOS, satellite, and radar data plus analysis and guidance products from the National Centers for Environmental Prediction. AWIPS enables meteorologists to display, process, and overlay images, graphics, and other data.

- With numerical weather forecasting, an electronic computer is programmed with a mathematical model of the Earth-atmosphere system that relates winds, temperature, pressure, and humidity. Current weather observational data are used to initialize the model and the model then predicts a future state of the atmosphere. With the predicted conditions serving as a new starting point, another forecast is computed for a subsequent period of time. Repeated iterations yield weather forecasts for the next 12, 24, 36, and 48 hrs or beyond.

- Special forecast centers are responsible for predicting tropical cyclones (hurricanes and tropical storms), severe weather (e.g., tornadoes), weather for domestic and international aviation, river flow and flooding, and weather for mariners.

- Although the skill of short- and medium-range weather forecasting has improved steadily in recent decades, forecasting skill declines rapidly for periods longer than 48 hrs and is minimal for periods beyond 10 days. Errors are introduced by missing or inaccurate observational data, failure of weather stations to detect all micro-scale and meso-scale weather systems, and equations in numerical models that include imprecise assumptions and first approximations. These errors in initial state grow with the forecast period.

- NCEP's Climate Prediction Center prepares 30-day, 90-day, and multi-seasonal generalized climate outlooks that identify the probability of departures from normal (long-term average) of temperature and total precipitation. Teleconnections, linkages between changes in atmospheric circulation occurring in widely separated regions of the globe, are particularly useful in long-range weather forecasting. Examples are winter weather anomalies at middle latitudes during El Niño or La Niña episodes.

- Single-station weather forecasting is based upon principles of meteorology, fair-weather bias, climatology, or persistence of weather episodes.

Review

1. Why does weather forecasting require international cooperation?
2. Describe the principal steps involved in the preparation of weather forecasts.
3. What meteorological data do airport weather stations report specifically for aviation interests?
4. If it is midnight Eastern Standard Time (EST), what is the time in UTC?
5. Distinguish between surface weather maps and upper-air weather maps.
6. What is the basic mission of the Storm Prediction Center (SPC)?
7. Distinguish between *weather watches* and *weather warnings*.
8. What is the role of computerized numerical models in weather forecasting?
9. Why does weather forecast skill decline as the forecast period lengthens?
10. Explain why computer models are never likely to replace human weather forecasters.

Critical Thinking

1. List the sources of weather data over the ocean.
2. Explain why warm air advection causes the 500-mb surface to rise and why cold air advection causes the 500-mb surface to lower.
3. Explain why cold-core anticyclones and warm-core cyclones do not appear on 500-mb maps.
4. Why are winds associated with contour gradients on upper-air weather maps?
5. On average in middle latitudes in summer, a 500-mb ridge develops over the continents and a 500-mb trough occurs over the ocean. In winter, it is the reverse: A 500-mb trough develops over the continents and a 500-mb ridge occurs over the ocean. Please explain.
6. The density of weather observation stations is much greater over continents then over the ocean. Speculate on how this difference might influence a scientist's ability to represent accurately the state of the atmosphere.
7. Why are special forecast centers (e.g., Storm Prediction Center) needed?
8. Identify some of the factors that RFC hydrometeorologists must consider in forecasting floods.
9. Identify some possible local effects that must be taken into account in forecasting the weather for a coastal location.
10. What property of the atmosphere favors teleconnections?

ESSAY: Marine Weather Statements

Weather systems moving across the ocean can produce life-threatening conditions not only for mariners at sea but also for residents of coastal communities. Hence, NOAA's National Weather Service (NWS) has a facility that monitors the weather, prepares weather forecasts, and issues warnings for marine and coastal interests. The NWS area of responsibility includes coastal and open waters of the Atlantic and Pacific Oceans, the Gulf of Mexico, and the Great Lakes. Data used in preparation of these forecasts are obtained from a variety of sources, including ships, buoys, and satellites.

Coastal or near shore forecasts are intended for those mariners staying in coastal waters that are roughly within about 37 km (20 nautical mi) of the Atlantic coast and within 110 km (60 nautical mi) of the Pacific coast. Offshore forecasts are for those mariners operating farther from the coast, typically a day or more from safe harbor, or from about 37 to 463 km (20 to 250 nautical mi) offshore of the Atlantic coast and 110 to 463 km (60 to 250 nautical mi) offshore of the Pacific coast. High seas forecasts are mainly geared for large ocean-going vessels operating more than 463 km (250 nautical mi) out to sea. In addition to forecasts, various marine-related advisories, watches and warnings are issued to the public. These pertain to a variety of severe weather types as well as unusual water, wave, and current conditions that could affect life and property.

The Ocean Prediction Center (OPC), formerly known as the Marine Prediction Center (MPC), is the component of the National Centers for Environmental Prediction (NCEP) that issues marine forecasts (out to 5 days) for coastal and offshore waters as well as the high seas of the western North Atlantic (west of 35 degrees W) and much of the North Pacific poleward of 30 degrees N to 66 degrees N. This NCEP center, located in Camp Springs, MD, also issues marine warnings for conditions not involving tropical weather systems, which is the responsibility of the Tropical Prediction Center/National Hurricane Center (discussed elsewhere in this chapter).

The following watches, warnings, and advisories can be issued by the National Weather Service for several types of coastal events:

Coastal flood watch -- Issued to alert coastal residents of the possibility of the inundation of land areas along the coast within the next 12 to 36 hrs.

Coastal flood warning -- Issued to warn residents of coastal areas that land areas along the coast will be inundated by sea water above the typical tide action.

Heavy surf advisory -- Issued to inform the public that high ocean surf might pose a threat to life or property. The criteria for such advisories depend upon the locale, but typically these include minimum wave heights of 2.4 to 3.7 m (8 to 12 ft) with periods on the order of 10 seconds. The heavy surf is typically produced by large ocean swells associated with a distant storm system over the ocean, supplemented at times by astronomical high tides.

Tsunami watch/warning -- Issued by the National Weather Service to either alert residents in coastal regions along the Pacific Ocean that an impending tsunami (seismic sea wave) may cause damage to low lying regions. The type of bulletin is based on the magnitude and the location of the source underwater geological event.

Small-craft advisory -- Issued to advise mariners of sustained (exceeding two hours) weather and/or sea conditions, either present or forecast, potentially hazardous to small boats. These conditions generally include winds of 18-33 knots (21-38 mph) and/or dangerous wave conditions. Small-craft advisories may be issued also for hazardous sea conditions or lower wind speeds that may affect small craft operations. Advisories can be issued up to 12 hrs prior to the onset of adverse conditions. The small-craft advisory signals for this condition consist of one triangular red pennant by day, and a red lantern over a white lantern by night.

Small-craft warning -- Issued as a warning for marine interests of impending winds up to 28 knots (32 mph); used mostly in coastal or inland waters.

Gale warning -- A storm warning for marine interests of impending winds associated with an extra-tropical cyclone with speeds ranging from 34 to 47 knots (39 to 54 mph) within a 24-hr period. The storm warning signals for this condition are two triangular red pennants by day, and a white lantern over a red lantern by night.

Storm (also known as whole-gale) warning -- A warning for marine interests of impending winds associated with an extra-tropical cyclone that are greater than 48 knots (55 mph). The storm-warning signals for this condition are one square red flag with black center by day, and two red lanterns by night.

Special marine warning -- A warning issued for marine interests of potentially hazardous over-water events of relatively short duration, usually up to 2 hrs. Typically, these warnings are issued for strong to severe thunderstorms that may include strong winds, frequent lightning, heavy rain or waterspouts.

Marine weather information, including forecasts and warnings, are transmitted to mariners and other interested parties by a variety of methods. The U.S. Coast Guard transmits weather maps to ships at sea by HF Radiofax and forecasts by either voice (HF, VHF or MF radio) or text transmission (NAVTEX). Coastal and near shore forecasts (typically within about 40 km (25 mi) of shore) can be obtained from the NOAA Weather Radio network of stations (Chapter 1). Graphics and text are also available on the Internet through the National Weather Service.

ESSAY: Chaos and the Limits to Forecasting

Can the fluttering of a butterfly's wings in Brazil eventually spawn a tornado in Texas? This question, originally attributed to Edward N. Lorenz, an atmospheric scientist at the Massachusetts Institute of Technology, provides the key to understanding the limits to weather forecasting and why modern science can fly a person to the moon but cannot accurately predict the weather more than 10 days from now. In the early 1960s, Lorenz coined the term *butterfly effect* in reference to the fact that future states of certain systems (e.g., the Earth-atmosphere system) are highly sensitive to initial conditions. Even the slightest differences in initial conditions can rapidly magnify with time making long-range forecasting of weather events untenable.

A system consists of a number of components that function and interact in an orderly manner. The human respiratory and digestive systems are familiar examples. A *dynamical system* is one whose evolution from an initial state can be described by one or more mathematical equations. The Earth-atmosphere is a dynamical system and, as noted elsewhere in this chapter, meteorologists have built computerized numerical models that attempt to predict its future behavior.

As the forecast period lengthens beyond a few days or so, however, weather forecasts derived from numerical models quickly go awry. The problem is not so much the accuracy of the component equations as it is the imprecise description of the initial state of the system. That description is based on weather observations from a network of widely spaced stations utilizing instruments whose measurements are not always reliable or representative. The system is so sensitive that even slight changes in initial conditions can give rise to totally different forecasts. Hence, meteorologists cannot accurately forecast the weather more than 10 days from now. On the other hand, scientists know much more precisely the initial conditions and governing physical laws that enabled them to send a manned rocket to the moon.

Researchers with NOAA's National Weather Service have experimented with two techniques to detect the butterfly effect: (1) *ensemble forecasting* and (2) *model comparison*. In the first, a numerical model generates several forecasts, each based on slightly different sets of initial conditions. If the forecasts are consistent, then the forecast is considered reliable. In the second technique, forecasts generated by many different models for the same period are compared. If they all agree, then the forecast is issued with relatively high confidence. If, however, through either technique, forecasts are inconsistent, then any one forecast is considered unreliable.

According to *chaos theory*, internal instabilities cause complex behavior in a system. Because its initial conditions are imperfectly known, the Earth-atmosphere is a chaotic dynamical system. The term chaotic should not be construed as implying random behavior, however. Certain physical laws govern the system so that there are boundaries within which chaos takes place; that is, the chaos has a certain underlying order or structure. For example, in the Northern Hemisphere, winds about a cyclone will always blow in a counterclockwise direction regardless of the storm's track.

A dynamical system whose initial conditions are known with precision may be drawn toward some stable state known as an *attractor*. Hence, an attractor imposes predictability. In a chaotic dynamical system, on the other hand, there is some range of possible future states that is encompassed by so-called *strange attractors*. Strange attractors contain the system's preferred behaviors and hence, if identified, can be used to predict the future state of the system.

Not surprisingly, some scientists are searching for strange attractors, that is, the structure in complex climate data. Others are searching for multiple attractors. The latter effort is inspired by the fact that the atmosphere shifts between a finite number of circulation patterns. This may imply that the system follows one attractor for a period of time and then shifts to another.

The dimensions of a strange attractor indicate the complexity of a system. In effect, the number of dimensions provides modelers with an estimate of the number of variables needed to describe the behavior of the system. From studies to date, the Earth-atmosphere system appears to have a relatively high dimensional strange attractor. Chaos theory thus raises the question as to whether there are internal constraints on the ultimate predictability of weather. It also prompts the question as to whether the recent global warming trend might be merely an expression of the natural variability of the Earth-atmosphere system.

CHAPTER 14

LIGHT AND SOUND IN THE ATMOSPHERE

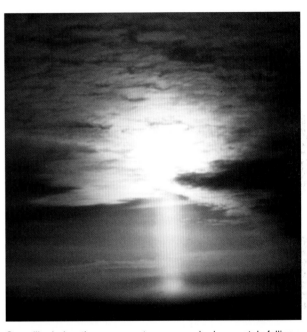

Sun pillar below the sun - most cases require ice crystals falling from a cloud. [Courtesy Historic NWS Collection, NOAA]

Case in Point

Fata Morgana is an example where meteorology provides a scientific explanation for myth and legend. Fata Morgana is an optical phenomenon in which images of distant objects such as houses and bluffs are distorted vertically to resemble castles or walls with spires. According to tradition, the mirage was named after Morgan le Fay reputed to be the half-sister of King Arthur. Legend has it that she was a fairy enchantress who could change her shape, a skill she may have learned from Merlin the Magician. Morgan le Fay lived in a submerged castle which she could elevate to above the sea surface. Sailors who were drawn to the castle thinking it was a safe harbor were lured to their deaths on rocky beaches.

 The Fata Morgana phenomenon is a *mirage*, an optical illusion caused by refraction (bending) of light rays as they travel through the atmosphere. It occurs where alternating layers of cold and warm air occur near the ground or over a water surface. Fata Morgana is most commonly observed on the horizon after sunrise following a clear calm night of extreme radiational cooling and the development of low-level temperature inversions. It is a complex mirage with multiple distortions of images in which several images of an object are superimposed. While one image may be upright, others can be inverted and as air layers move up and down, the images undergo rapid changes.

 In addition to occurrences in coastal areas, Fata Morgana is relatively common in high mountain valleys in winter (e.g., Colorado's San Luis Valley) and over the frozen Arctic Ocean.

Driving Question:
What is responsible for the various optical phenomenon observed in the atmosphere and how does sound propagate through the atmosphere?

A mirage such as Fata Morgana is one of many types of optical phenomena that occur in the atmosphere and involve visible light. Others include the blue of the daytime sky, halos, rainbows, and twilight. These are subjects of the science of *atmospheric optics*. This chapter focuses on the cause and the meteorological significance of various atmospheric optical phenomena. We then examine the role of the atmosphere in the propagation of sound plus sounds of meteorological origin.

Atmospheric Optics

As the sun's rays travel through the atmosphere, they are scattered, reflected or refracted by cloud droplets or ice crystals, or by raindrops. The consequence is a variety of optical phenomena, including halos, rainbows, coronae, and glories. In these cases, refraction (bending of light) occurs when solar radiation travels from one transparent medium into another (i.e., from air into water or ice). Solar rays are also refracted as they pass through the atmosphere because of variations in the density of air. This type of refraction gives rise to mirages. In addition, scattering of sunlight by particles within the atmosphere is responsible for the blue of the daytime sky, the white of clouds, a red horizon at sunset, and twilight. In observing various atmospheric optical phenomena, extreme caution should be exercised so as not to look directly at the sun except when it is near the horizon because the intense solar rays can cause irreparable damage to your eyes.

VISIBLE LIGHT AND COLOR PERCEPTION

Sunlight, which is visible light, represents only a small portion of the electromagnetic spectrum. Recall from Chapter 3 the relationship between color and wavelength in the visible portion of the electromagnetic spectrum. The visible portion of the spectrum bounds the region of maximum intensity of light emitted from the sun, an object with a radiating temperature of approximately 6000 K. In fact, visible light that is received from the sun represents approximately 45% of the total solar irradiance (rate of energy incident on a unit surface area). In 1666, Sir Issac Newton (1643-1727) passed sunlight through a glass prism and onto a screen. He discovered that the prism separated white light into a spectrum of colors. Thus, he determined that white sunlight is polychromatic, that is, composed of several individual primary colors.

The human eye is light sensitive, capable of detecting electromagnetic radiation having wavelengths between 0.38 and 0.76 micrometers (the normal photopic range), with the greatest sensitivity at approximately 0.55 micrometers. Light activates rods and cones in the retina of the eye. Rods, which are concentrated in the peripheral portions of the retina, respond to radiation of all visible wavelengths. Therefore, rods distinguish between light and dark and are responsible for scotopic vision. Cones, which are concentrated in the central portion of the retina, respond to radiation at specific wavelengths in the visible range. Therefore, cones distinguish colors and are responsible for photopic vision.

Color is a sensation produced through the excitation of the cones in the retina by radiation at discrete wavelengths within the visible region of the electromagnetic spectrum. The normal human eye (no color blindness) perceives color. The primary colors of the spectrum are monochromatic, extending over very limited specific wavelength regions of the visible spectrum. White light contains light of all colors striking and stimulating the cone detectors in the eye with nearly uniform intensity. Black light contains no light in the visible portion of the electromagnetic spectrum and hence, does not stimulate any of the detectors of the retina.

We see some objects because their temperature is relatively high so that they emit visible radiation. For these objects, such as the sun or a glowing piece of hot metal, the perceived color contains visible electromagnetic radiation with wavelength bands surrounding the wavelength of maximum emission from the object, as described by Wien's displacement law (Chapter 3). The temperature of most objects on Earth, such as humans, vegetation, and soil, is such that they do not emit visible radiation. Their perceived color is that of the visible wavelength bands reflected by the object; light of all other visible wavelengths is absorbed by the object. For example, something green, such as a plant leaf, reflects only radiation in the green portion of the visible electromagnetic spectrum, while the radiation from all other visible wavelengths that falls upon the leaf is absorbed by the leaf. Moonlight is reflected sunlight and under most atmospheric conditions appears white.

RED SUN, WHITE CLOUDS, AND BLUE SKY

Scattering of sunlight is responsible for the blue color of the daytime sky (Figure 14.1). **Scattering** occurs when tiny particles in the atmosphere interact with light waves and send those light waves in different directions. If the radius of the scattering particles is much smaller than the wavelength of the scattered light, then the amount of scattering varies with wavelength. This happens, for example, when visible light is scattered by the gas molecules (mostly nitrogen and oxygen) composing air. In a now classic experiment performed in 1881, the English physicist and mathematician Lord Rayleigh (1842-1919) demonstrated that this type of scattering is inversely proportional to the fourth power of the wavelength. Hence, violet light, at the short-wavelength end of the visible spectrum, is scattered much more efficiently than red light, at the long-wavelength end of the visible spectrum. This optical effect is known as **Rayleigh scattering**.

As sunlight travels through the atmosphere, component colors are selectively scattered out of the solar beam: violet is scattered more than blue, blue

FIGURE 14.1
Scattering of sunlight by air molecules is responsible for the blue of the daytime sky. Scattering of sunlight by the tiny ice crystals and water droplets composing clouds is responsible for the white of clouds.

FIGURE 14.2
The setting sun turns the horizon red on a clear evening.

more than green, green more than yellow, and so forth. Dependence of scattering on wavelength predicts that scattered sunlight should be mostly violet. But the daytime sky appears blue rather than violet. One reason is the greater sensitivity of the human eye to blue light rather than violet light, so that the sky appears bluer than it really is. (The cones in the eye register the dominantly violet/blue/green illumination as blue.) Another factor contributing to the blue of the daytime sky is dilution of violet light by all the other scattered colors; although the other colors are scattered less than violet, they tend to wash violet into blue.

We can now understand why the setting sun turns the horizon red on a clear evening (Figure 14.2). When the sun is on the horizon, the path of the solar beam through the atmosphere is about 40 times longer than when the sun is directly overhead. Consequently, at sunset (or sunrise), the interaction (e.g., scattering) between incoming solar radiation and the atmosphere's component gas molecules is considerable. Arriving at sea level, the horizontal solar beam has about 23% of its initial red light but only 0.000006% of its initial violet light. Just before sunrise or just after sunset (during twilight), the clear sky horizon turns red. On the moon, which has a highly rarefied atmosphere, Apollo astronauts found that the sun appears as a white disk in a black sky and stars are visible even in bright sunshine. Since scattering of sunlight is inconsequential in the lunar atmosphere, the lack of diffuse sunlight means that dark shadows are cast by lunar boulders (Figure 14.3).

The result is different when the particles doing the scattering are much larger than the wavelength of light. In such instances, scattering is not wavelength dependent; that is, visible radiation is scattered more or less equally

FIGURE 14.3
In this scene of the surface of the moon, the sky appears black and the boulder casts black shadows. [NASA]

at all wavelengths. The particles composing clouds (i.e., water droplets and/or ice crystals) are sufficiently large to scatter sunlight in this way. For this reason, sunlit clouds when seen from above or the side have the same color as the sun, that is, they are white during the day and red or pink at sunrise and sunset.

Particles that are about the same size as the wavelength of light are responsible for **Mie scattering**, named for the German physicist Gustav Mie (1868-1957). In 1908, Mie demonstrated that particles having diameters slightly less than 1 micrometer scatter the most light for their size (scatter most efficiently). Aerosols (solid and liquid particles suspended in the atmosphere) between about 1 and 2 micrometers in diameter scatter red light more efficiently than violet light. Sulfurous aerosols injected into the stratosphere by violent volcanic eruptions are in this size range and are responsible for the enhanced red and orange sunsets that may persist for more than a year following such an eruption. For example, vivid sunsets were reported worldwide following the eruption of Krakatoa in 1883 and Mount Pinatubo in 1991. Most non-volcanic aerosols have diameters of 0.02 to 0.5 micrometer and scatter sunlight with equal efficiency at all wavelengths. Hence, an abundance of these aerosols turn the sky a hazy white. In this chapter's Essay, we describe the reason for the blue haze that often overhangs heavily forested areas.

HALO

A **halo** is a whitish (sometimes slightly colored) ring of light surrounding the sun or the moon (Figure 14.4). It forms when the tiny ice crystals that compose high, thin clouds such as cirrus or cirrostratus refract the sun's rays. **Refraction** is the bending of light as it passes from one transparent medium (such as air) into another transparent medium (such as ice or water). The light rays bend because the speed of light is greater in air than

FIGURE 14.4
This halo about the sun is caused by refraction of sunlight by tiny ice crystals composing high thin clouds. [Photo by E.J. Hopkins.]

A

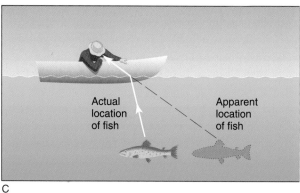

B

C

FIGURE 14.5
Light rays may be refracted (bent) as they travel from one transparent medium into another as in (A) where a light ray is refracted as it travels from air to water. The speed of light is less in water than in air, so the light ray is bent toward a line drawn perpendicular to the water surface, and angle *r* is less than angle *i*. (B) Light rays that enter the water at a 90 degree angle are not refracted. (C) Refracted light can be deceptive. The fish appears to be farther away from the boat than it really is because of refraction and because human perception assumes that light always travels in a straight line.

in ice or water. Refraction occurs whenever light rays strike the interface between two different transparent media at an angle other than 90 degrees (Figure 14.5). Rays of light striking water or ice surfaces at 90 degrees are not refracted.

An analogy helps explain refraction. Suppose you are driving your auto along a highway and suddenly encounter a patch of ice along the right side of the road. The right wheels travel over the ice, while the left wheels remain on dry pavement. You apply the brakes. Because of frictional differences between the tires and the road, the left side of the car slows while the right side of the car slips on the ice; hence, the auto swerves to the left. The swerving of the auto is analogous to a light ray bending toward the medium in which light travels more slowly.

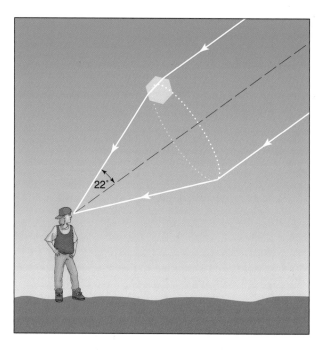

FIGURE 14.6
A ray of sunlight is refracted as it passes through a hexagonal ice crystal from one side (top side in the drawing) to another side (bottom side in the drawing). The angle between the two sides of the ice crystal is 60 degrees. This type of refraction produces a 22-degree halo centered on the sun or moon.

Ice crystals composing clouds occur as hexagonal (six-sided) plates, columns, or dendrites (stars). Most halos are formed when light is refracted upon entering and exiting either plates or columns. A light ray entering an ice crystal through one rectangular side and exiting through another rectangular side is refracted by at least 22 degrees (Figure 14.6). If ice crystals are relatively small and randomly oriented, most rays are refracted at 22 degrees so that light is focused in a luminous circle having a radius of about 22 degrees. Suppose, for example, that you see a halo around the moon. Visualize two lines: one joining you with the moon's center, and the other line joining you with any point on the halo. The angle between the two imaginary lines is 22 degrees. For reference, the halo's radius appears to be the same as the width of this book when held at arm's length.

A less commonly seen halo has a radius of about 46 degrees about the sun (or moon). In this case, columnar ice crystals with diameters in the range of 15 to 25 micrometers refract the light. Light rays travel through an ice crystal from one rectangular side to the top or from side to base rather than from side to side (Figure 14.7).

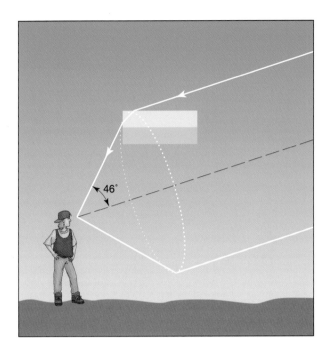

FIGURE 14.7
In a less common situation than shown in Figure 14.6, a ray of sunlight is refracted from side to top or base, or vice versa, as it passes through a columnar ice crystal. The angle between the side and top or base is 90 degrees. This type of refraction produces a 46-degree halo centered on the sun or moon.

The Zuni tribe of New Mexico has a weather proverb that interprets a halo to be a harbinger of stormy weather: "When the sun is in his house, it will rain soon." The phrase "in his house" refers to the sun surrounded by a halo. Cirrus and cirrostratus clouds may signal the beginning of overrunning as warm humid air is lifted by the circulation associated with an approaching low pressure system (cyclone). However, the appearance of a halo around the sun (or moon) is no guarantee that precipitation will follow. Cirrus or cirrostratus clouds may spread as much as 1000 km (620 mi) ahead of the storm center, and the storm could change direction or even weaken and die out prior to reaching your location.

Sometimes light is concentrated on either side of the sun as two brilliant spots, known as **sundogs** (because they appear to follow the sun around the sky), also called *parhelia* (from the Greek, meaning "beside the sun") (Figure 14.8). Cirrus clouds composed of relatively large plate-like ice crystals are responsible for sundogs. Because of air resistance, the top and bottom surfaces of these crystals remain nearly horizontal as they fall through the atmosphere. The rectangular sides of the ice crystals are vertically oriented so that light is refracted either to the right

or left so that sundogs always appear at the same altitude as the sun. Side-to-side refraction concentrates light in two spots about 22 degrees on either side of the sun. In some cases, sundogs are part of a 22-degree halo.

An ice crystal acts like a glass prism and disperses sunlight into its component colors. The more energetic short-wavelength end of the visible spectrum (violet light) is refracted the most, so that the violet portion of a sundog is farthest from the sun. The less energetic long-wavelength end of the visible spectrum (red) is refracted the least, so the red portion of a sundog is closest to the sun. Because of the optics involved, halos and sundogs are brightest at low solar altitudes and when ice clouds are relatively thin.

Because ice crystals refract sunlight, you may wonder why halos are only weakly colored at best. In fact, ice crystals disperse light into its component colors, but because the size and shape of ice crystals vary more than the size and shape of raindrops, the colors produced by an assemblage of ice crystals tend to overlap one another rather than form discrete bands. In halos, colors therefore wash out, although occasionally a reddish tinge is visible on the inside of a halo (as in Figure 14.4).

A bright light shaft sometimes appears as a vertical extension above the setting or rising sun. This shaft, called a *sun pillar*, may have a length from 5 to 20 degrees above the sun, generally tapering to a point. These pillars are usually not colored, except when the sun is at or below the horizon, when they become reddish. Sun pillars are produced by reflection of sunlight off the bottom basal faces of horizontally oriented ice crystals; generally, large sized plates and prism crystals (capped columns) are involved.

FIGURE 14.8
Bright colored spots appearing on either side of the sun and at the same elevation, called parhelia or sundogs, are caused by refraction of sunlight by plate-like ice crystals falling through the atmosphere.

FIGURE 14.9
A rainbow is a nearly circular arc of color caused by refraction and internal reflection of sunlight by falling raindrops. Refraction disperses visible light into its component colors.

RAINBOW

A **rainbow** is a circular arc of concentric colored bands, caused by a combination of refraction and reflection of sunlight (or rarely of moonlight) by raindrops (Figure 14.9). In the early 1600s, René Descartes (1596-1650) conducted experiments that explained the optics of the rainbow. Sunlight striking a shaft of falling raindrops is refracted twice and internally reflected by each drop of rain. As shown in Figure 14.10, a solar ray is refracted as it enters a raindrop; then the ray is reflected by the inside back of the drop before being refracted again as it exits the drop. Each person sees his or her own rainbow.

Because of reflection, a rainbow appears to an observer who has his or her back to the sun and is facing a distant rain shower (Figure 14.11). A rainbow never forms when the sky is completely cloud covered; the sun must be shining. Because of geometric considerations, the sun can be no higher than 42 degrees above the local horizon in order for someone on the ground to see a rainbow. If the solar altitude is greater than 42 degrees, then the returning solar rays are not directed towards Earth's surface. Hence, a rainbow is more likely during a morning or evening shower than a shower at noon. You can create your own rainbow at any time on a sunny day by directing the spray from a garden hose so that you look down and observe the spray with the sun at your back. At middle latitudes, weather systems usually progress from west to east so that appearance of a rainbow to the east in the early evening usually signals improving weather. Rain showers are moving away toward the east and clearing skies are approaching from the west, where the sun is setting. Conversely, a morning rainbow to the west signals approaching rain.

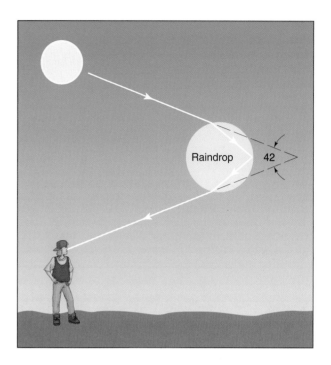

FIGURE 14.10
With a primary rainbow, a solar ray is refracted upon entering a raindrop, reflected internally, and refracted again upon exiting the raindrop.

Similar to a glass prism, raindrop refraction disperses sunlight into its component colors forming the concentric bands of color of a *primary rainbow*. From outer to innermost band, the colors are red, orange, yellow, green, blue, and violet. In many cases, a much dimmer, *secondary rainbow* appears about 8 degrees above the primary rainbow (visible in Figure 14.9). Double reflection within raindrops produces the secondary rainbow with the order of colors reverse that of the primary rainbow (Figure 14.12).

CORONA

At times, a series of alternating light and dark concentric rings appear to surround the moon or, less often, the sun when one looks at these light sources through a thin cloud veil. This optical phenomenon is known as a **corona** (not to be confused with the region of hot rarefied and ionized gases that surrounds the sun). Typically, a corona is only a few degrees in radius and is far smaller than a halo. It is caused by diffraction of light around similarly sized water droplets that compose a thin, translucent veil of altocumulus, altocumulus lenticularis, or stratocumulus clouds. Often only one ring is actually observed. Smaller sized cloud droplets usually produce the best corona.

FIGURE 14.11
A rainbow appears to an observer who has his or her back to the sun and faces a distant rain shower.

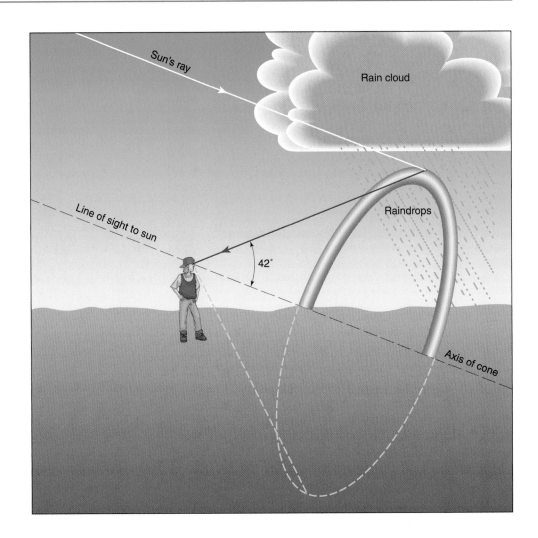

FIGURE 14.12
Refraction of solar rays by raindrops plus double reflection within raindrops produces a dimmer secondary rainbow just above the primary rainbow. A secondary rainbow is visible in Figure 14.9.

FIGURE 14.13
Iridescent clouds exhibit brilliant spots or borders of colors, usually red and green. [Photo by E.J. Hopkins.]

FIGURE 14.14
A glory appears centered on the shadow of an aircraft on a deck of clouds below. [Photo by E.J. Hopkins.]

Diffraction is the slight bending of a light wave as it moves along the boundary of an object such as a water droplet, with production of an interference pattern as light waves bend behind the obstruction. Where the crests of one light wave coincide with the crests of another wave, interference is constructive and a larger wave results, with a bright band due to greater illumination. On the other hand, where the crests of one wave coincide with the troughs of another wave, the interference is destructive, and the waves cancel each other leading to a dark band. Where light waves interfere constructively, we see a ring of bright light, and where they interfere destructively, we perceive darkness. If cloud droplets are uniform in size, a corona will be colored with blue-violet on the inside and red on the outside of each ring. Dependency of diffraction on wavelength is responsible for this separation of color: the longer wavelength red light is diffracted more than the shorter wavelength blue-violet light.

Diffraction also is involved in **iridescent clouds**. These are thin clouds with nearly uniformly sized cloud droplets (usually altocumulus, cirrostratus, or cirrocumulus) having bright spots, bands, or borders of delicate colors, usually red and green (Figure 14.13). Iridescent clouds typically appear up to about 30 degrees from the sun.

GLORY

Prior to the age of aircraft travel, about the only way a person could view a glory was from the top of a lofty mountain peak. To see a glory, an observer must be in bright sunshine above a warm cloud or fog layer, and the sun must be situated so as to cast the observer's shadow

on the clouds below. The observer then sees a **glory** as concentric rings of color centered about the shadow of his or her head. Although less distinct, the colors of a glory are the same as in a primary rainbow, with the innermost band being violet and the outermost band being red. Today, aircraft pilots and observant passengers often see a glory around the shadow of their aircraft on a cloud deck below (Figure 14.14).

A glory depends on much the same optics as a primary rainbow with two important differences, that is, the size of the reflecting and refracting particles, and the direction of reflected and refracted light. Whereas rainbows occur when sunlight strikes a mass of falling raindrops, glories are the consequence of sunlight interacting with a mass of much smaller suspended water droplets of uniform size (radii less than about 25 micrometers) that compose a cloud. In both cases, the sun's rays undergo refraction upon entering the droplet, followed by a single internal reflection, and refraction upon exiting the droplet. In a glory, sunlight is refracted and reflected directly back toward the sun due to the small droplet size. A small spherical cloud droplet diffracts light rays ever so slightly toward the droplet, so that light rays incident on a cloud droplet parallel those returning from the cloud droplet (Figure 14.15). The diffraction patterns produce bands that may be slightly colored.

The special optics of a glory explains why it appears about the shadow of the observer who is situated in the direct path of both the incident solar rays and the returning (refracted and reflected) solar rays. This also explains an observation that must have fascinated ancient mountain mystics. Suppose that you and a friend are

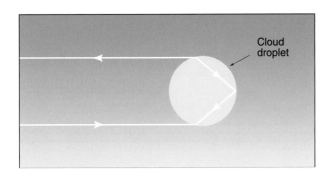

FIGURE 14.15
In the special optics that produce a glory, both the incident and returning solar rays are diffracted slightly toward the surface of the cloud droplet. Consequently, the incident and returning rays follow parallel paths.

standing side by side high on a mountain slope at a site favorable for viewing a glory (cloud deck or fog bank below and the sun behind your shoulder). On the cloud deck below, you see your own shadow next to that of your friend, but a glory appears about your head and not about your friend's head. Lest you presume that you have been singled out, note that your friend has the opposite observation, for your friend sees a glory only about his or her head. The fact is that each observer is in a position to view only one glory.

MIRAGE

Appearances can be deceiving, especially in the case of mirages. A **mirage** is an optical phenomenon in which an image of some distant object appears to be displaced from its normal view. Distant buildings or hills can appear higher or lower than they really are. A nonexistent pool of water may suddenly appear on the highway ahead, or a sailboat viewed from shore may appear upside down. Mirages are caused by the refraction of light rays within the lower atmosphere.

Light travels at different speeds through different transparent substances. Light changes speed, for example, as it travels from air into an ice crystal. For reasons discussed earlier in this chapter, a light ray is refracted at the interface between two different transparent media. The speed of light also varies within a single medium if the density of that medium is not uniform. Hence, light rays bend as they pass through a substance of varying density, such as the atmosphere.

If the density of the atmosphere were the same throughout, then light rays would always travel along straight paths at constant speed, and no refraction would occur. As described in Chapter 5, however, air density

varies with changes in temperature and pressure. Because our concern here is with optical phenomena that occur within the lower troposphere and involve relatively short viewing distances, we need not be concerned with the influence of horizontal air pressure gradients on air density. For the same reason, we also ignore the effects of horizontal temperature gradients on air density. But we cannot ignore the effect of vertical temperature profiles on the change of air density with altitude.

As a rule, light rays traveling through the atmosphere are refracted such that denser air is on the inside (concave side) of the bend, and less dense air is on the outside (convex side) of the bend. Air density almost always decreases with altitude so that light reflected from a distant object follows a downward curved path to the observer. Because human perception is based on the assumption that light travels in a straight path, to the observer the object appears to be higher than it really is.

If the air temperature decreases with altitude at less than the usual rate, or if there is a *temperature inversion* (an increase of temperature with altitude), air density decreases with altitude at a faster rate than normal. Hence, light rays reflected from a distant object bend more sharply than usual before reaching the viewer and objects appear higher that normal. This is called a *superior mirage*. On the other hand, if the lowest air layer features a greater than usual temperature lapse rate, rays are refracted less than normal and objects appear lower than we usually see them. This is called an *inferior mirage*.

These are a few examples of the many possible types of mirages. As the vertical air temperature profile becomes more complex, so too do the types of mirages that can appear. Recall our discussion of Fata Morgana in this chapter's Case-in-Point. Fata Morgana involves the simultaneous occurrence of superior and inferior mirages. The familiar oasis mirage in a desert is an inverted image of the sky seen below the horizon. The bluish colored mirage is caused by the light from the sky that arrives at the observer's eye by a curved ray, not the reflection of the skylight from a non-existent water surface. All mirages are displacements or distortions of something real.

SUNRISE-SUNSET AND TWINKLING STARS

Because the atmosphere refracts sunlight, the image of the setting or rising sun that we see is slightly higher in the sky than it would be without an atmosphere. One implication of this involves the length of daylight on the equinox. As noted in Chapter 3, on the equinox, day and night are assumed to be of equal length (12 hrs) everywhere (except right at the poles).

Actually, days are slightly longer than nights on the equinox. At Washington, DC, for example, day length on the autumnal equinox of 22 September 2005 was 12 hrs and 7 minutes. The *length of daylight* is defined as the period between sunrise and sunset, and sunrise and sunset occur when the upper edge of the solar disk is just visible on the unobstructed level horizon. Because the sun appears higher than it actually is at both sunrise and sunset, there is slightly more than 12 hrs between sunrise and sunset on the equinox.

The shape of the sun or moon near the horizon appears distorted from the usual circular disk, especially when strong atmospheric stratification is present. Rays from the lower rim of the disk are lifted more than the rays from the upper rim, thereby flattening the perceived solar or lunar disk. However, atmospheric refraction is not responsible for the larger apparent size of the sun or moon near the horizon than at higher altitude angles. This enlargement effect is an optical illusion, caused by how we judge the apparent size based upon the presence of reference landmarks near the horizon.

As light from stars and other celestial bodies passes through the atmosphere, fluctuations in air density (mostly due to temperature differences) cause rapid changes in brightness. This explains the apparent twinkling of stars at night. Light rays reaching the observer from a star may be momentarily turned away from the observer's line of sight by turbulent air motions, causing an abrupt change in the apparent luminosity of the star. This phenomenon, known as **scintillation**, is especially noticeable on cold, clear nights, when rapid, small-scale fluctuations in air density alter the path of starlight through the atmosphere. The planets, with larger diameters, have a more constant luminosity because their light is not as affected by scintillation.

TWILIGHT

Scattering of sunlight is also responsible for **twilight**, the period following sunset or before sunrise when the sky is illuminated. In this discussion, assume that the sky is not cloud covered. Multiple scattering of sunlight by constituents of the upper atmosphere illuminates the sky. Because of geometrical considerations involved with the path of the apparent sun with respect to the local horizon, the length of twilight varies with latitude and time of year. The annual range increases with latitude so that in polar regions, for example, the length of twilight ranges from 24-hrs to none at all. The tropics, on the other hand, have relatively short twilight duration. At middle latitudes, twilight length is longer

near the solstices, but shorter at the equinoxes. Twilight is divided into three sequential stages based on the level of illumination: civil twilight, nautical twilight, and astronomical twilight.

Illumination during *civil twilight* is just adequate for outdoor activities without the need for artificial lighting. It covers the period between sunrise/sunset and when the center of the sun's disk is 6 degrees below the horizon. On a clear day, a faint purple glow may develop over a large region of the western sky during the latter portion of civil twilight in the evening. During *nautical twilight*, light is sufficient to distinguish the outlines of distant objects on the ground. While the ocean horizon is visible at the beginning of nautical twilight during the evening, it is not at the end when the center of the sun's disk has sunk to 12 degrees below the horizon. *Astronomical twilight* occurs when the center of the sun's disk is between 12 and 18 degrees below the horizon. Sixth magnitude stars are visible directly overhead.

At the beginning of evening twilight, observant sky watchers may see crepuscular rays or the green flash. **Crepuscular rays** appear as beams of sunlight radiating from the sun. They consist of alternating light and dark bands (solar rays and shadows) that diverge in a fanlike pattern from the vicinity of the solar disk near twilight (Figure 14.16). The rays are visible because of scattering. Actually, solar rays are parallel and only appear to diverge because of the perspective of the observer. Crepuscular rays can also occur anytime during the day as the sun's rays pass through holes in clouds or between clouds in a hazy sky.

FIGURE 14.16
Crepuscular rays consist of alternating light and dark bands that appear to diverge fanlike from the sun's position during twilight.

The **green flash** is a thin green rim that appears briefly at the upper edge of the sun at sunrise or sunset and is best seen on a distant horizon when the atmosphere is very clear. The green flash is primarily the consequence of atmospheric refraction and scattering of light from a low sun. Refraction is most pronounced when the sun is on the horizon and, as noted earlier, blue/violet light at the short wavelength end of the visible spectrum is refracted (bent) more than red light at the long wavelength end. This explains the red rim at the bottom of the low sun and should produce a blue/violet rim at the top of the solar disc. However, Rayleigh scattering removes most of the blue/violet light leaving behind a sliver of green.

The sliver of green produced by atmospheric refraction alone is too small to be seen by the naked eye. With an ideal temperature profile (e.g., superadiabatic lapse rate near the surface), the atmosphere acts like a lens to magnify the green rim to visible proportions. The green flash is actually a mirage that appears as an island of green light floating above the setting or rising sun. At middle latitudes, the sun rises and sets so quickly that the green flash lasts only about 1 second (hence the "flash" designation). But at polar latitudes, the sun rises and sets more slowly and the green flash can lasts upward of 30 minutes.

Atmospheric Acoustics

Vibrations of an object generate sound waves that propagate outward in all directions. The sensation of hearing is the stimulation of auditory nerves in the ear by vibrations, that is, sound waves. Sound waves enter the ear and cause the eardrum and inner ear to vibrate. In response, auditory nerves send impulses to the brain. Unlike electromagnetic waves that can travel through a vacuum, sound waves require a transmitting medium such as air or water. Without this medium, all would be silent. Our focus in this section is sound transmission in the atmosphere and sounds produced by atmospheric phenomena.

SOUND WAVES

A **sound wave** is a compressional wave, consisting of alternate compressions and rarefactions of air. Transmission of sound energy is via alternating increases and decreases in air pressure produced by waves that radiate outward from a source, much like the waves generated by a stone tossed into a quiet pool of water. *Wave frequency* is the number of oscillations

per second, measured in hertz (Hz). With increasing frequency, the sound increases in pitch. The audible range for most humans is between 20 and 20,000 Hz. Also, the attenuation of sound waves is directly proportional to the square of the frequency. Hence, low frequency sound waves can propagate greater distances than high frequency sound waves. In fact, audible sound waves can travel thousands of kilometers through the atmosphere. The 1883 violent eruption of Krakatoa, a volcano in the Sunda Strait between Java and Sumatra in Indonesia, was heard as far away as Rodriguez Island, 4653 km (2885 mi) across the Indian Ocean.

The intensity (loudness) of sound depends on the pressure exerted by sound waves and is measured in *decibels (dB)*. Decibel levels corresponding to the sound of a variety of devices and activities are listed in Table 14.1. Any sound over 85 dB is potentially harmful for humans, and over 120 dB is painful.

Wind and air temperature affect the speed of sound waves traveling through the atmosphere. The speed of a sound wave is the sum of the speed of sound through the medium (air) plus the motion of the medium (wind). Hence, sounds are heard better downwind of the source than upwind. In addition, atmospheric turbulence (that tends to increase with increasing wind speed) helps to dissipate the energy of sound waves. Sound waves propagate by collisions of gas molecules and the average kinetic-molecular activity of gases increases with rising temperature. Hence, sound

TABLE 14.1
Sound Decibel (dB) Levels[a]

Soft whisper, quiet library	30
Rustling leaves	40
Rainfall, refrigerator	50
Normal conversation, air conditioner	60
City or freeway traffic, sewing machine	70
Hair dryer, alarm clock	80
Power lawn mower, motorcycle	90
Garbage truck, snowmobile	100
Shouting in one's ear, dance club, race car	110
Jet plane taking off, car stereo on full volume, band practice	120
Live rock music, jack hammer	130
Firecracker, nearby gunshot blast, jet engine	140

[a]Source: U.S. Congress Select Committee on Children, Youth, and Families

waves travel faster in warm air than cold air. At sea-level air pressure and an air temperature of 0 °C (32 °F), the speed of sound is 332 m (1088 ft) per second. Raising the air temperature to 20 °C (68 °F) increases the speed of sound to 343 m (1125 ft) per second.

Dependence of the speed of sound on wind and temperature is the operating principle of the *sonic anemometer*, an instrument that emits sound waves to measure wind speed (Figure 8.3). Sound waves are transmitted in opposite directions across known paths. The speed of propagation of those sound waves equals the vector sum of the speed of sound in air (at the measured temperature) plus the wind speed. Hence, the wind speed can be calculated by comparing the actual speed of sound to the speed based on temperature alone. The sonic anemometer is scheduled to replace the cup anemometer as the standard wind speed sensor in NOAA's National Weather Service observing systems (e.g., ASOS).

A change in air temperature with distance (*temperature gradient*) alters the speed of sound causing bending or refraction of sound waves. Like light waves, sound waves are refracted away from regions where they travel fastest. Only in air layers that are isothermal (uniform temperature) do sound waves propagate in straight lines. When the air temperature decreases with altitude (the usual condition in the troposphere), sound waves follow a path that is concave upward; that is, sound is deflected upward (away from the warmer air at the surface). When the air temperature increases with altitude (a *temperature inversion*), the path of sound waves curves downward; that is, sound is deflected downward toward the colder air at the surface. This explains why in winter human voices can sometimes be heard over horizontal distances of several kilometers within a mass of arctic air. In an arctic air mass, over a broad area winds are light or the air is calm (no turbulent dissipation) and the coldest air is at the surface. Sound waves originating near the ground follow a path convex to the sky as they are refracted by the warmer air aloft back to the ground some distance away. On the other hand, elevated observers can hear sounds traveling up from the ground better than those hearing sounds traveling downward.

Refraction of sound waves explains the formation of an **acoustic shadow**, an area where sound is not heard even though the area is close to the source of sound. For example, news reports from American Civil War battlefields described situations when the sounds of cannon fire were not heard at positions near the battle whereas more distant observers could readily hear the sounds of battle. Charles D. Ross of Longwood College,

VA estimates that acoustic shadows and blockage of sound waves by hills affected the outcome of 10 Civil War battles. For example, at Gettysburg, PA, a Confederate commander could not hear an artillery barrage that was meant to signal his troops to attack Union forces. Those forces then defeated another Confederate force.

Sound waves produced by multiple sources can also undergo interference patterns. Constructive interference causes louder sounds whereas destructive interference results in quiet zones.

THUNDER

Where there's lightning, there's thunder, although sometimes we see distant lightning but do not hear the thunder. **Thunder** is the sharp clap or rumbling sound heard following a lightning discharge (Chapter 11). Lightning heats the air along the narrow conducting path to temperatures that may top 25,000 °C (45,000 °F). The rapid rise in air temperature is accompanied by a tremendous increase in air pressure locally that generates a shock wave. The shock wave propagates outward, producing sound waves that are heard as thunder. The initial thunder clap we hear is generated by the nearest part of the lightning bolt. Subsequent sound waves reach us from portions of the bolt that are progressively further away; hence, the rumble of thunder.

Thunderstorm cells that are more than 20 km (12 mi) away are too distant for thunder to be audible although lightning is observed. This is called *heat lightning*. Thunder (sound waves) is refracted upward away from the surface layer of warm air that is usually associated with a thunderstorm (cumulonimbus) cloud. Light waves are also refracted but much less than sound waves so that lightning is seen but thunder is not heard.

In the atmosphere, light travels about a million times faster than sound so that we see lightning almost instantaneously, but we hear thunder later. The closer we are to a thunderstorm cell, the shorter is the time interval between the lightning flash and thunder. As a rule, thunder takes about 3 seconds to travel 1 km (or 5 seconds to travel 1 mi). If you must wait 9 seconds between lightning flash and thunderclap, the lightning is about 3 km (1.8 mi) away. This is the *flash-to-bang* method of determining the distance to a thunderstorm. By noting the time difference between light and thunder of successive lightning discharges, you can deduce whether the thunderstorm is approaching or moving away, or even predict when it is dangerously close. As a general guideline, if the time between flash and bang is 30 seconds or less, you are well advised to take precautions to avoid the lightning.

SONIC BOOM

A **sonic boom** can be loud enough to break windows. They are caused by aircraft traveling at speeds that exceed the speed of sound, known as *Mach 1*. Mach is named for the Austrian physicist Ernst Mach (1838-1916) who studied sound. An aircraft moving at Mach 2 is traveling at twice the speed of sound.

Noise from an aircraft moving at subsonic speeds propagates in all directions faster than the forward speed of the aircraft. When a plane accelerates past the "sound barrier" to supersonic speeds, the plane moves faster than the leading edge of the pressure wave generated by the aircraft. A narrow conical zone of compressed air is produced in the form of a shock wave through which the pressure changes greatly over a short distance. The shock wave propagates at the same speed as the aircraft. Listeners in the area affected by the sudden increase in pressure will hear a sonic boom, similar to a thunderclap, but the pilot does not hear it.

AEOLIAN SOUNDS

Winds blowing over obstacles such as roofs, telephone or power transmission wires produce humming, singing or whistling sounds called **aeolian sound**. Turbulent eddies that form immediately downwind of the obstacle are responsible for the sounds. Thinner wires produce smaller eddies and a higher pitch than thicker wires. During the cold of winter, wires contract and become taut. The increased tension is transmitted to the utility poles that act as sounding boards (similar to a piano sounding board) and the volume of humming, singing or whistling increases. Also, the pitch increases with higher wind speeds.

Other sounds of meteorological origin include the rattle of ice pellets (sleet), sizzle of snow, clatter of hail, patter of rain, and the rustle of leaves. Many people describe the sound of a nearby tornado as similar to the roar of a passing freight train.

Conclusions

We have seen that interactions of sunlight (or moonlight) with clouds or rainfall produce a variety of optical phenomena including halos, rainbows, coronae, and glories. These interactions involve reflection, refraction, and/or diffraction. In these cases, refraction takes place as light rays pass from one transparent medium into another (e.g., air to water or air to ice). In addition, because of variations in density within the atmosphere, light rays are refracted and give rise to mirages and the green flash.

Scattering of sunlight by air molecules is wavelength-dependent and responsible for the blue of the daytime sky whereas scattering of sunlight by cloud particles (droplets and ice crystals) is uniform across wavelengths and accounts for the white of clouds.

We have also seen that sound propagation through the atmosphere is influenced by wind and temperature. Sound waves can be refracted by the atmosphere and travel great distances. Furthermore, atmospheric phenomena produce a variety of sounds.

Basic Understandings

- Rayleigh scattering of sunlight by the molecules composing air accounts for the blue of the daytime sky. If the radius of the scattering particles is much smaller than the wavelength of the scattered light, then the amount of scattering is inversely proportional to the fourth power of the wavelength of the light being scattered. The human eye's greater sensitivity to blue light than violet light plus the dilution of violet light by the other scattered colors also play a role in the blue of the sky.

- Scattering is not wavelength dependent when light is scattered by particles having a radius that is much greater than the wavelength of the radiation being scattered. This is the case for clouds and explains why clouds appear white during the day and pink or red near sunset or sunrise. Mie scattering applies to particles that have diameters about the same as the wavelength of visible light. Scattering of visible light is most efficient for particles having a diameter of 1 micrometer.

- A halo is a whitish (or slightly colorized) ring of light surrounding the sun or moon, formed when the ice crystals in high thin clouds refract the sun's rays. Refraction is the bending of light as it passes from one transparent medium into another. Cirrus clouds composed of relatively large plate-like ice crystals are responsible for sundogs, brilliant spots of light located on either side of the sun.

- A rainbow is a circular arc of concentric colored bands, caused by a combination of refraction and internal reflection of sunlight by raindrops. In many cases a much dimmer secondary rainbow appears about 8 degrees above the primary rainbow. Double reflection within raindrops produces a secondary rainbow with the order of colors reverse that of the primary rainbow.

- A corona consists of alternating light and dark rings that surround the moon (or less often the sun) caused by diffraction of light around water droplets that compose a thin, translucent veil of altocumulus or stratocumulus clouds. Diffraction is the slight bending of a light wave as it moves along the boundary of an object such as a water droplet, producing an interference pattern.

- A glory consists of concentric rings of color that appear around a shadow and is caused by interactions between sunlight and a uniform mass of water droplets composing a warm cloud. The optics of a glory differ from that of a rainbow in that spherical cloud droplets diffract light rays ever so slightly toward the droplet, so that light rays incident on a cloud droplet parallel those returning from the cloud droplet.

- A mirage is an optical phenomenon in which an image of some distant object appears to be displaced from its normal view. It is caused by refraction of light as it travels through the atmosphere. Changes in air density that accompany variations in the vertical temperature profile are responsible for the refraction of light.

- As light from stars and other celestial bodies passes through the atmosphere, fluctuations in air density (mostly due to temperature differences) cause rapid changes in brightness. This explains the apparent twinkling of stars at night.

- Twilight is a period after sunset or before sunrise when the sky is illuminated and is a product of scattering of sunlight by components of the upper atmosphere. Based on decreasing level of illumination, twilight is designated civil, nautical, and astronomical.

- Possible phenomena near twilight include crepuscular rays and the green flash. Crepuscular rays consist of alternating light and dark bands (solar rays and shadows) that appear to diverge in a fanlike pattern from the sun's position at about twilight. The green flash is a thin green rim that appears briefly at the upper edge of the sun at sunrise or sunset and is primarily

the consequence of atmospheric refraction and scattering of light from a low sun.

- A sound wave is a compressional wave, consisting of alternate compressions and rarefactions of air. Transmission of sound energy is via alternating increases and decreases in pressure produced by waves that radiate outward from a source.

- Wind and air temperature affect the speed of sound waves traveling through the atmosphere. The speed of a sound wave is the sum of the speed of sound through the medium (air) plus the motion of the medium (wind). Hence, sound is heard more clearly downwind of the source than upwind. Sound waves propagate by collisions of gas molecules and the average kinetic-molecular activity of gases increases with rising temperature. Hence, sound waves travel faster in warm air than cold air.

- A change in air temperature with distance alters the speed of sound causing refraction of sound waves. Sound waves are refracted away from regions where they travel fastest. When the air temperature decreases with altitude (the usual condition in the troposphere), sound waves follow a path that is concave upward; that is, sound is deflected upward (away from the warmer air at the surface). When the air temperature increases with altitude (a temperature inversion), the path of sound waves curves downward; that is, sound is deflected downward toward the colder air at the surface.

- Thunder is the sharp clap or rumbling sound emitted during a lightning discharge. Lightning heats the air along the narrow conducting path to temperatures that may top 25,000 °C (45,000 °F). The rapid rise in air temperature is accompanied by a tremendous increase in air pressure locally that generates a shock wave that propagates outward, producing sound waves that are heard as thunder.

- Winds blowing over obstacles such as roofs, telephone or power transmission wires produce humming, singing or whistling sounds called aeolian sound. Turbulent eddies that form immediately downwind of the obstacle are responsible for these sounds.

Questions for Review

1. Why do raindrops and ice crystals refract light rays?
2. What type of cloud produces a halo around the sun or moon?
3. What causes the colors of a primary rainbow?
4. Distinguish between a primary and a secondary rainbow.
5. What does the appearance of an evening rainbow suggest about the weather later at night? Justify your response.
6. Compare and contrast the optics of a rainbow with those of a glory.
7. Explain why you can view only your own glory.
8. Explain the blue of the daytime sky.
9. Why do aerosols turn the daytime sky a hazy white?
10. Distinguish between sound waves and electromagnetic waves.

Critical Thinking Questions

1. Distinguish among reflection, refraction, and diffraction in the atmosphere.
2. Explain why a halo around the moon can be a harbinger of stormy weather.
3. What is the relationship between parhelia and a halo around the sun?
4. Identify the various optical effects that are responsible for a green flash.
5. What causes red sunsets?
6. What causes clouds to exhibit various colors?
7. Explain why the daytime sky appears blue rather than violet.
8. Explain the time lag between a lightning flash and thunder.
9. Describe an atmospheric condition that favors formation of an acoustic shadow.
10. Identify the various factors that influence sound propagation in the atmosphere.

ESSAY: Blue Haze

Many heavily forested areas are often shrouded in a blue haze. In fact, blue haze is such a usual feature of some regions that its presence is reflected in their names. The Blue Ridge Mountains of Virginia, the Blue Mountains of Australia, and the Blue Hills outside Boston are examples. Also, the Cherokee Indians' name for the Great Smokey Mountains of Tennessee was the "Place of Blue Smoke." Studies suggest that blue haze plays a major role in the generation of tropospheric ozone, an important component of photochemical smog that plagues the air quality of many metropolitan areas. These findings have raised questions concerning the composition and production of blue haze as well as the most appropriate strategy to reduce tropospheric ozone (O_3).

Scientists have established that blue haze is a complex and variable mixture of gaseous hydrocarbons (volatile organic compounds) emitted by vegetation. One major class of these volatile hydrocarbons is essential oils, compounds that are responsible for the characteristic aroma of certain plant foliage. Familiar examples of plants that produce essential oils include peppermint, sage basil, and pine and eucalyptus trees. Essential oils serve to protect plants from herbivores because these compounds have toxic properties.

Air quality research indicates that isoprene is often the most common hydrocarbon component of blue haze. Isoprene is a breakdown product of a compound in the synthetic pathway that leads to the production of essential oils. Many, but not all, plants emit isoprene, and isoprene emissions are strongly influenced by leaf temperature. Over short periods of time, isoprene emissions from leaves of the most temperature-sensitive species can increase tenfold with a rise in air temperature of 10 Celsius degrees (18 Fahrenheit degrees). Hence, the highest levels of atmospheric isoprene occur on hot summer days when winds are light. Furthermore, isoprene readily reacts with nitrogen oxides in the presence of sunlight to form ozone.

The role of blue haze in the generation of ozone prompts the question as to what fraction of all atmospheric hydrocarbons are biogenic (natural origin) and what fraction can be attributed to anthropogenic sources (e.g., motor vehicles, power plants, and industry). What fraction of emissions is of local or distant origin? The answers to these questions are important because federal law mandates that individual states reduce tropospheric ozone levels. Ozone abatement efforts thus far have focused primarily on reduction of anthropogenic sources, but if biogenic sources comprise a major component of atmospheric hydrocarbons, ozone abatement strategies would need to be reevaluated.

Monitoring of hydrocarbon levels has brought some surprises. In heavily wooded Atlanta, GA, for example, a study found that 83% of all hydrocarbon emissions were biogenic with isoprene accounting for most of the natural volatile organic compounds. This and similar findings from other urban areas indicate that biogenic emissions of hydrocarbons can override efforts to reduce anthropogenic sources. Furthermore, short of cutting down millions of trees, nothing can be done to reduce biogenic hydrocarbons.

In addition to hydrocarbons, the other main ingredient in the generation of tropospheric ozone is nitrogen oxides, most of which have anthropogenic (industrial, transportation) sources. Given the relatively high levels of biogenic hydrocarbons and the inability to control their emissions, many air quality specialists are arguing for a shift in ozone-abatement strategies from a reduction of anthropogenic hydrocarbons to a reduction of anthropogenic nitrogen oxides.

CHAPTER 15

CLIMATE AND CLIMATE CHANGE

Erratics, huge boulders displaced from their natural geologic location by glaciers, are often found many kilometers from any other bedrock of their type. [Photo by John T. Andrews, INSTAAR and Department of Geological Sciences, University of Colorado, Boulder; courtesy of NOAA/NCDC/Paleoclimatology Program]

Case in Point

The summer of 1816 is famous for its anomalous cold weather. In fact, 1816 is sometimes described as "the year without a summer." Unseasonable snowfall and freezes damaged many crops in the then mostly agrarian northeastern United States and adjacent portions of Canada. More than 90% of the corn crop, the prime food staple, was lost. Some superficial accounts of events of that summer give the impression that unusual cold persisted throughout the summer and affected the entire civilized world. Such was not the case.

In the Northeast, the summer of 1816 was punctuated by several episodes of unseasonably cold weather. Killing frosts struck northern and interior southern New England, as well as Quebec, in early June and July and again in late August. The June cold snap was accompanied by moderate to heavy snowfalls in some highlands. No sooner had farmers replanted their frozen crops than a killing freeze would strike again. The miserably short and disastrous growing season came to an end with a general hard freeze on 27 September.

These brief but unusually cold episodes interrupted longer spells of seasonably warm weather. June and July mean temperatures were 1.6 to 3.3 Celsius degrees (3 to 6 Fahrenheit degrees) below average. Individually, these monthly anomalies fall within the expected range of climatic variability. Some previous and subsequent Junes, Julys, and Augusts have been as cold as the summer months of 1816, if not colder. What is most notable about the summer of 1816 is the persistence of a strong negative temperature anomaly through all three summer months. Nevertheless, that summer in the Northeast as a whole fell within the range of expected climatic variability.

What about the weather elsewhere during the summer of 1816? We know that it was probably not the same everywhere as in the Northeast, for climatic anomalies typically are geographically non-uniform in both magnitude and sign. Unfortunately, little weather information is available from the central and western United States and Canada because few settlements existed there at the time. France, Germany, and Great Britain experienced an unusually cold summer, but this is not surprising. The westerly long-wave pattern responsible for advecting unseasonably cold air into the Northeast would also favor Western Europe with the same anomalous weather. The two localities are typically one wavelength apart. In contrast, available data indicate that east-central and eastern Europe experienced a warmer than usual summer.

The purpose of this discussion is not to diminish the climatic significance of the summer of 1816 or the hardships that people suffered then. It is, rather, to show that weather extremes typically fall within an expected range of climatic variability. We have more to say about the possible cause of the cold of the summer of 1816 later in this chapter.

Driving Question:
How and why does climate change?

This chapter covers some of the basics of Earth's climate system, controls of climate, global patterns of climate, and climate change. We examine the instrument-based and reconstructed climate record with the objective of learning more about how climate changes through time. These lessons of the climate past are useful in establishing a perspective on the present climate and how climate might change in the future. Two of the most obvious lessons of the climate past are: (1) climate changes over a broad range of temporal scales, from years to decades to centuries to millennia, and (2) many forces working together are responsible for climate change.

Variability in available solar energy, regular changes in Earth's orbit, volcanic eruptions, changes in Earth's surface properties, and human activities are among the many factors that contribute to climate change. With the continued build-up of atmospheric carbon dioxide and

other greenhouse gases, global warming appears likely to continue at least through the present century. Scientists rely on global climate models to predict the magnitude of potential warming arising from an enhanced greenhouse effect. The impacts of global climate change on the Earth-atmosphere-ocean system are likely to be significant.

Earth's Climate System

Climate is defined as the weather of some locality averaged over some time period plus extremes in weather. Climate must be specified for a particular place and time period because, like weather, climate varies both spatially and temporally. Thus, for example, the climate of Minneapolis is different from that of Miami, and winters in Minneapolis were somewhat milder in the

1980s and 1990s than they were in the 1880s and 1890s. Extremes in weather are important aspects of the climate record because what has happened could happen again. Hence, daily weather reports usually include the highest and lowest temperatures ever recorded for the date and climatic summaries typically identify such extremes as the coldest, warmest, driest, wettest, snowiest, or cloudiest month or year on record.

Climate is usually described quantitatively in terms of normals, means, and extremes of a variety of weather elements including temperature, precipitation, and wind. Climatic summaries are available in tabular form for climatic divisions of each state and major cities along with a narrative description of local or regional climate. The U.S. National Weather Service is responsible for gathering the basic weather data used in the nation's climatological summaries. Data are processed, archived, and made available for users at NOAA's **National Climatic Data Center (NCDC)** in Asheville, NC.

THE CLIMATIC NORM

Traditionally, the **climatic norm** or normal is equated to the average value of some climatic element such as temperature or snowfall. This tradition can sometimes foster misconceptions. For one, normal may be taken to imply that climate is static when, in fact, climate is inherently variable with time. Furthermore, normal may imply a Gaussian (bell-shaped) probability distribution, although many climatic elements are non-Gaussian. For our purposes, we can think of the climatic norm of some locality as encompassing the total variation in the climate record, that is, both averages plus extremes. This implies, for example, that an exceptionally cold winter may not be "abnormal" because its mean temperature may fall within the expected range of variability of winter temperature.

By international convention, climatic norms are computed from averages of weather elements compiled over a standardized 30-year period. In 1935, the International Meteorological Conference at Warsaw, Poland selected the 30-year period of 1901-1930 as the reference for calculating normals, with subsequent recalculation at the end of each decade. Current climatic summaries are based on weather records from 1971 to 2000. Average July rainfall, for example, is the simple average of the total rainfall during each of 30 consecutive Julys from 1971 through 2000. The 30-year period is adjusted every 10 years to add the latest decade and drop the earliest one. In the United States, 30-year averages are computed for temperature, precipitation, and air pressure only. Averages of other climatic elements such as wind

speed and cloudiness are derived from the entire period of record at a particular weather station. Extremes such as the highest temperature or driest month are also drawn from the entire period of record.

Selection of a 30-year period for averaging weather data may be inappropriate for many applications because climate varies over a wide range of time scales and can change significantly in periods much shorter than 30 years. For some purposes, a 30-year period provides a shortsighted view of the climate record. Compared with the long-term climate record, the current 1971-2000 norm, for example, was unusually mild over much of the United States. Nonetheless, people find averages and extremes of past climate to be a useful guide to future expectations.

Many people assume that the mean value of some climatic element is the same as the median (middle value); that is, 50% of all cases are above the mean and 50% of all cases are below the mean. This is a reasonable assumption for climatic elements such as temperature, which approximate a simple Gaussian-type probability distribution. Hence, for example, we might expect about half the Januarys will be warmer and half the Januarys will be colder than the 30-year mean January temperature. On the other hand, the distribution of some climatic elements, such as precipitation, is non-Gaussian, and the mean value is not the same as the median value. For example, in a dry climate subject to infrequent deluges of rain during the summer, considerably fewer than half the Julys are wetter than the mean and many more than half of Julys are drier than the mean. In fact, for many purposes, the median value of precipitation is a more useful description of climate than the mean value.

CLIMATIC ANOMALIES

Climatologists find it useful to compare the average weather of a specific week, month, or year with past climate records. Such comparisons carried out over a broad geographical region show that departures from long-term climatic averages, called **climatic anomalies**, do not occur with the same sign or magnitude everywhere. For example, as shown in Figure 15.1, the average temperature during December 2004 was above the long-term average (*positive anomalies*) through much of the coterminous western and central U.S. but below the long-term average (*negative anomalies*) over most of the eastern U.S. Furthermore, the magnitude of the anomaly, positive or negative, varied from one place to another.

Precipitation anomalies typically form more complex patterns than temperature anomalies (Figure 15.2). This is due to greater spatial differences in

FIGURE 15.1
Departure of average temperature from the long-term average (1971-2000) in Fahrenheit degrees for December 2004. [NOAA, Climate Prediction Center]

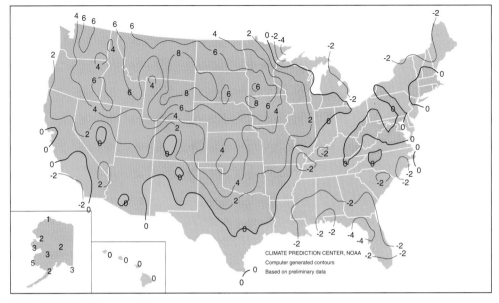

Departure of average temperature from normal (°F), December 2004

FIGURE 15.2
Percent of long-term average (1971-2000) precipitation (rain plus melted snow) for December 2004. [NOAA, Climate Prediction Center]

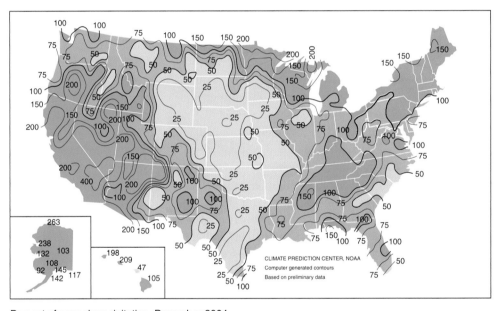

Percent of normal precipitation, December 2004

precipitation arising from the variability of storm tracks and the almost random distribution of convective showers. For these reasons, in spring and summer in middle latitudes, even adjoining counties may experience opposite rainfall anomalies (one having above-average rainfall and the other below-average rainfall). From an agricultural perspective, the geographic non-uniformity of climatic anomalies may be advantageous in that some compensation is implied. That is, poor growing weather and consequent low crop yields in one area may be compensated to some extent by better growing weather and increased crop yields elsewhere. This **agroclimatic compensation** generally applies to crops such as corn, soybeans, and other grains that are grown over broad geographical areas.

At middle and high latitudes, the geographic non-uniformity of climatic anomalies is linked to the prevailing westerly wave pattern that ultimately governs cold and warm air advection, cyclogenesis, and storm tracks (Chapter 9). Hence, the pattern of the westerlies determines the location of weather extremes such as drought or very low temperatures. In view of the number of westerly waves that typically encircle the hemisphere, a single weather extreme never occurs over an area as large as the United States; that is, severe cold or drought never grips the entire nation at the same time.

Geographic non-uniformity also applies to trends in climate. Hence, the trend in the average annual temperature of the Northern Hemisphere is not necessarily representative of all localities within the hemisphere. During the same period, some places experience cooling whereas other places experience warming regardless of the direction of the overall hemispheric (or global) temperature trend. Not only is it misleading to assume that the direction of large-scale climatic trends applies to all localities, but also it is erroneous to assume that the magnitude of climatic trends is the same everywhere. A small change in the average hemispheric temperature typically translates into a much greater change in some areas and into little or no change in other areas.

Climate Controls

The climate of a specific locale or the entire planet is constrained by physical principles associated with the conservation of energy and mass (primarily water). The globe is a mosaic of many different climate types including, for example, the hot wet tropics, warm and cold deserts, temperate regions, and polar ice caps. In this section, we describe the various controls operating in Earth's climate system.

Many factors working together shape the climate of any locality. Controls of climate consist of (1) latitude, (2) elevation, (3) topography, (4) proximity to large bodies of water, (5) Earth's surface characteristics, (6) long-term average atmospheric circulation, and (7) prevailing ocean circulation. Over a period of at least several million years, all climate controls are variable. On time scales that extend to hundreds of millions of years, continents have drifted to different latitudes, ocean basins have opened and closed, and mountain ranges have risen and eroded away—all with implications for climate. On shorter time scales (e.g., the range of human existence), for all practical purposes, the first four climate controls are essentially fixed and exert regular and predictable influences on climate.

Seasonal changes in incoming solar radiation as well as length of daylight vary with latitude and Earth's surface temperature responds to those regular variations. Air temperature drops with increasing elevation and determines whether precipitation falls in the form of rain or snow. Topography can affect the distribution of clouds and precipitation. For example, the windward slopes of high mountain barriers (facing the oncoming wind) usually are wetter than the leeward slopes (facing downwind). The relatively great thermal inertia of large bodies of water (especially the ocean) moderates the temperature of downwind localities, reducing the temperature contrast between summer and winter as well as lengthening the growing season. Earth's surface characteristics (e.g., ocean versus land, vegetative cover, semi-permanent snow and ice cover) influence the amount of incident solar radiation that is converted to heat and how that heat is used (e.g., raising air temperature, evaporating water).

Atmospheric circulation encompasses the combined influence of weather systems operating at all spatial and temporal scales ranging from sea breezes to the prevailing winds that encircle the planet. Although strongly influenced by the other climate controls, atmospheric circulation is considerably less regular and less predictable than the others. This variability is especially evident in weather systems such as thunderstorms and hurricanes that are smaller than the planetary scale. Planetary-scale circulation systems (e.g., the prevailing wind belts, subtropical anticyclones), exert a more systematic influence on climate, determining for example, where precipitation is seasonal and the location of the major biomes, such as subtropical deserts.

The ocean is a major player in Earth's climate system operating on time scales of days to millennia and spatial scales from local to global (Figure 15.3). The ocean influences radiational heating and cooling of the planet. Covering about 71% of Earth's surface, the ocean is a primary control of how much solar radiation

FIGURE 15.3
The ocean is a major player in Earth's climate system in terms of storage and exchange of heat, water, and greenhouse gases.

is absorbed (converted to heat) at the Earth's surface. Also, the ocean is the main source of the most important greenhouse gas (water vapor) and is a major regulator of the concentration of atmospheric carbon dioxide (CO_2), another greenhouse gas.

On an annual average, the ocean absorbs about 92% of the solar radiation striking its surface; the balance is reflected to space. Most of this absorption takes place within about 200 m (650 ft) of the ocean surface with the depth of penetration of sunlight limited by the amount of suspended particles and discoloration caused by dissolved substances. On the other hand, at high latitudes highly reflective multi-year pack ice greatly reduces the amount of solar radiation absorbed by the ocean. The snow-covered surface of sea ice absorbs only about 15% of incident solar radiation and reflects away the rest. At present, multi-year pack ice covers about 7% of the ocean surface with greater coverage in the Arctic Ocean than the Southern Ocean (mostly in Antarctica's Weddell Sea). The Arctic is an ocean surrounded by continents whereas the Antarctic is a continent roughly centered on the pole and surrounded by ocean. Without an Antarctic continent, much more of the Southern Ocean would be covered by sea ice.

The ocean influences the planetary energy budget not only by radiational heating and cooling, but also by contributing to the non-radiative latent and sensible heat fluxes at the air-sea interface (Chapter 4). Heat is transferred from Earth's surface to the atmosphere via latent heating (vaporization of water at the surface followed by cloud formation in the atmosphere) and sensible heating (conduction plus convection). On a global average annual basis, about ten times more heat is transferred from the ocean surface to the atmosphere via latent heating than sensible heating.

The ocean and atmosphere are closely coupled. This coupling is most apparent in the ocean's surface waters where temperatures and wind-driven currents respond to variations in atmospheric conditions within hours to days. On the other hand, the deeper basin-scale circulation responds more sluggishly to changes in atmospheric conditions, taking decades to centuries or longer to fully adjust. In turn, ocean currents strongly influence climate (Figure 9.9). Cold surface currents, such as the California Current, are heat sinks; they chill and stabilize the overlying air, thereby increasing the frequency of sea fogs and reducing the likelihood of thunderstorms. Relatively warm surface currents, such as the Gulf Stream, are heat sources; they supply heat and moisture to the overlying air, destabilizing the air, thereby

energizing storm systems. Ocean surface currents and the ocean conveyor-belt system transport heat from the tropics to higher latitudes (Chapter 4).

Recent research underscores the ocean-atmosphere climate connection with somewhat surprising findings. Winters are significantly milder in Western Europe than they are in Eastern North America at the same latitude. Since at least the mid-1800s, scientists have attributed the climate contrast primarily to the moderating influence of the warm Gulf Stream and North Atlantic Current on Western Europe. However, research results published in late 2002 call into question this assumption. Some scientists argue that the Gulf Stream is not as important as atmospheric circulation in explaining Western Europe's relatively mild winters.

Richard Seager of Columbia University's Lamont-Doherty Earth Observatory and David Battisti of the University of Washington in Seattle, WA reported that the key is the pattern exhibited by the prevailing westerlies. The westerlies blow from west to east in a wave-like pattern of ridges and troughs (Chapter 9). In winter, a cold pool of air (a *trough*) is anchored over Eastern North America resulting in a cold northwesterly flow on the western flank of the trough, but an intrusion of warm air over the North Atlantic (a *ridge*) is associated with a milder southwesterly flow over Western Europe. That is, in winter, the westerlies tend to blow from the colder northwest over Eastern North America but from the milder southwest over Western Europe. In addition, the relatively great thermal inertia of ocean water means that summer heat persists in North Atlantic surface waters long after the North American continent has cooled in fall. Hence, southwest winds blowing toward Western Europe cross relatively warm waters and are heated from below. The direction of the prevailing winds over the North Atlantic and Western Europe is primarily responsible for delivering relatively mild air masses in winter. This finding also implies that changes in the direction of the prevailing winds could alter dramatically the winter climate of Western Europe.

Global Climate Patterns

How the various controls interact to shape the climates of the continents will become clearer as we summarize the basic patterns of climate on Earth. From a global perspective, climate exhibits some regular patterns. As we examine these patterns, keep in mind that they may be significantly modified by local and regional climate controls.

TEMPERATURE

Ignoring the influence of mountainous terrain on air temperature, mean annual isotherms roughly parallel latitude circles, underscoring the influence of solar radiation and solar altitude on climate. The latitude of highest mean annual surface temperature, the **heat equator**, is located about 10 degrees north of the geographical equator. Mean annual isotherms are symmetrical with respect to the heat equator, decreasing in magnitude toward the poles.

The heat equator is in the Northern Hemisphere because overall that hemisphere is warmer than the Southern Hemisphere for several reasons. For one, the polar regions of the two hemispheres have different radiational characteristics so that the Arctic is warmer than the Antarctic. Most of the Antarctic continent is submerged under massive glacial ice sheets, so the surface has a very high albedo for solar radiation and is the site of intense radiational cooling, especially during the long polar night. By contrast, the Northern Hemisphere polar region is mostly ocean. Although the Arctic Ocean is usually ice covered, patches of open water develop in summer and lower the overall surface albedo. A second factor contributing to the relative warmth of the Northern Hemisphere is the greater fraction of land in that hemisphere's tropical latitudes. Because land surfaces warm more than water surfaces in response to the same incoming solar radiation, tropical latitudes are warmer in the Northern Hemisphere than in the Southern Hemisphere. A third contributing factor is ocean circulation which transports more warm water to the Northern Hemisphere than to the Southern Hemisphere.

Systematic patterns also appear when we consider the worldwide distribution of mean January temperature (Figure 15.4) and mean July temperature (Figure 15.5); January and July are usually the coldest/warmest months of the year in the respective hemisphere. Neglecting the influence of topography on air temperature, isotherms tend to parallel latitude circles. However, monthly isotherms exhibit some notable north-to-south bends, primarily because of land/sea contrasts and the influence of ocean currents. As the year progresses from January to July and to January again, isotherms in both hemispheres follow the sun and shift north and south in tandem. The latitudinal (north-south) shift in isotherms is greater over the continents than over the ocean; that is, the annual range in air temperature is greater over land than over the sea. Furthermore, the meridional temperature gradient is greater in the winter hemisphere than in the summer hemisphere. A steeper temperature gradient means a more vigorous circulation and stormier weather in the winter hemisphere (Chapter 9).

PRECIPITATION

The global pattern of mean annual precipitation (rain plus melted snow) exhibits considerable spatial variability (Figure 15.6). Some of this variability can be attributed to topography and the distribution of land and sea, but the planetary-scale circulation is also important. The intertropical convergence zone (ITCZ), subtropical anticyclones, and prevailing wind belts impose a roughly zonal pattern on precipitation distribution. In addition, regular shifts in these circulation features through the year are responsible for the seasonality of precipitation that characterizes the climate of many localities.

In tropical latitudes, convective activity associated with intense solar heating and the trade wind convergence triggers abundant rainfall year-round. In the adjacent belt poleward to about 20 degrees latitude, rainfall depends on seasonal shifts of the ITCZ and the subtropical anticyclones. Poleward shift of the ITCZ causes summer rains, whereas equatorward shift of the subtropical highs brings a dry winter. This climatic zone includes the belt of tropical monsoon circulation, described in Chapter 9.

Poleward of this belt, from about 20 to 35 degrees N and S, subtropical anticyclones, centered over the ocean basins, dominate the climate all year. Subsiding dry air on the anticyclones' eastern flanks is responsible for Earth's major subtropical deserts (e.g., the Sahara). On the other hand, unstable humid air on the western flanks of subtropical anticyclones causes relatively moist conditions. Between about 35 and 40 degrees latitude, the prevailing westerlies and subtropical anticyclones govern precipitation. Typically, on the western side of continents, winter cyclones migrating with the westerlies bring moist weather, but in summer, westerlies shift poleward and the area lies under the dry eastern flank of a subtropical anticyclone. Hence, summers are dry. At the same latitudes, but on the eastern side of continents, the climate is dominated by westerlies in winter and the moist airflow on the western flank of a subtropical anticyclone in summer. Thus, rainfall is triggered by cyclonic activity in winter and by convection in summer, resulting in little seasonal variability in monthly precipitation totals.

Precipitation generally declines poleward of about 40 degrees latitude as lower temperatures reduce the amount of precipitable water (Chapter 6). Although precipitation is generally not seasonal, the tendency in the continental interiors is for more precipitation in summer. The summer precipitation maximum is due to higher air temperatures, greater precipitable water, and more vigorous convection at that time of year.

FIGURE 15.4
Mean sea-level air temperature for January in degrees Celsius.

FIGURE 15.5
Mean sea-level air temperature for July in degrees Celsius.

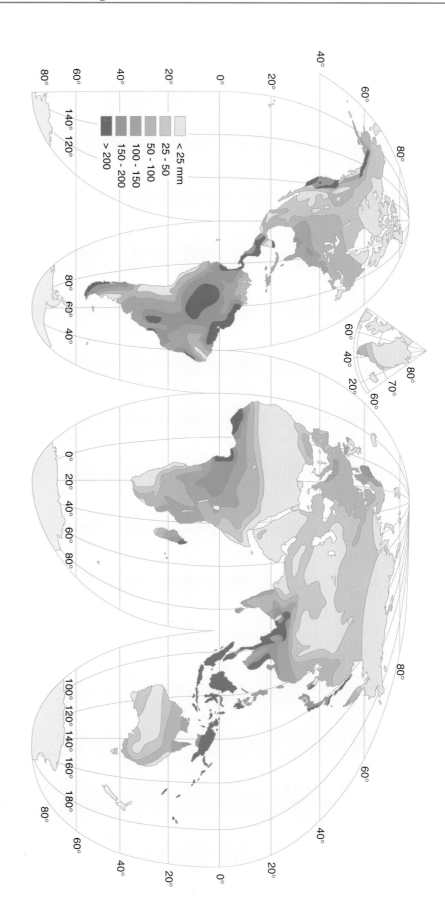

FIGURE 15.6
Mean annual precipitation (rain plus melted snow) in millimeters (mm).

Our description of the global pattern of annual precipitation is somewhat idealistic and requires some qualification. Land/sea distribution and topography complicate the generally zonal distribution of precipitation. More rain falls over the ocean than over the continents, and mountain belts induce wet windward slopes and extensive leeward rain shadows. Furthermore, annual precipitation totals fail to convey some other important aspects of precipitation, including the average daily rainfall and the season-to-season and year-to-year reliability of precipitation. As a rule, rainfall is most reliable in maritime climates, less reliable in continental localities, and least reliable in arid regions. However, drought is possible anywhere, even in maritime climates.

CLIMATE CLASSIFICATION

In response to the interaction of many controls, Earth's climates form a complex mosaic. For more than a century, climatologists have attempted to organize the myriad of climate types by devising classification schemes that group together climates having common characteristics. Classification schemes typically group climates according to (1) the meteorological basis of climate, or (2) the environmental effects of climate. The first is a genetic climate classification that asks why climate types occur where they do. The second is an empirical climate classification that infers the type of climate from such environmental indicators as the distribution of indigenous vegetation. In addition, the advent of electronic computers and databases has made possible numerical climate classification schemes that utilize sophisticated statistical techniques. Appendix III provides information on one of the more popular climate classification schemes.

The Climate Record

Climate varies not only from one place to another but also with time. Examining the record of the climate past reveals some basic understandings regarding the nature of climate behavior and provides a useful perspective on current and future climate. In most places, however, the reliable instrument-based record of past weather and climate is limited to not much more than a century or so. For information on earlier fluctuations in climate, scientists rely on reconstructions of climate based on historical documents (e.g., personal diaries, ship's logs, chronicles of weather-sensitive economic data) and longer-term geological and biological evidence such as bedrock type, fossil plants and animals, pollen profiles, tree growth rings, glacial ice

cores, and deep-sea sediment cores. Refer to this chapter's Essay for information on how past climatic data are derived from these non-instrument sources. In this section, we summarize major features of Earth's climate record from geologic time through to the present.

GEOLOGIC TIME

Throughout most of the approximately 4.5 billion years that constitute **geologic time**, information on climate is generally unreliable. Descriptions of early climates are suspect because of lengthy gaps in the record often due to more recent geological processes eradicating older records plus difficulties in determining the timing of events and correlating events that occurred in widely separated locations. Nonetheless, the available evidence supports some general conclusions regarding the climate over geologic time. For convenience of study, the geologic past and its climatic record are subdivided using the **geologic time scale**, a standard division of Earth history into eons, eras, periods, and epochs based on large-scale geological events (Figure 15.7).

Plate tectonics complicates climate reconstruction efforts that focus on periods spanning hundreds of million of years. The solid outer skin of the planet is divided into a dozen gigantic rigid plates that slowly drift over the face of the globe, moving continents and opening and closing ocean basins. Mountain building and most volcanic activity occur at plate boundaries. This model originated around 1910 when the German meteorologist Alfred Wegener (1880-1930) and the American geologist Frank B. Taylor (1860-1939) independently proposed **continental drift**, the hypothesis that the continents move over the surface of the planet. Wegener proposed that the supercontinent *Pangaea* split into *Laurasia* (encompassing present day North America and Eurasia) and *Gondwanaland* (encompassing South America, Africa, India, Australia, and Antarctica) (Figure 15.8). He based his idea on the observed close fit between continental margins, similarities in fossil plants and animals, and the continuity of rock formations and mountain ranges between continents on either side of the Atlantic. The scientific community did not widely accept the theory of plate tectonics and continental drift until the 1960s when mounting geological evidence became convincing.

Through the span of human existence, topography and the geographical distribution of the ocean and continents can be considered as essentially fixed controls of climate. This was not the case over the vast expanse of geologic time. Mountain ranges rose and eroded away; seas invaded and withdrew from the land, continents drifted over the face of the globe, and ocean basins opened

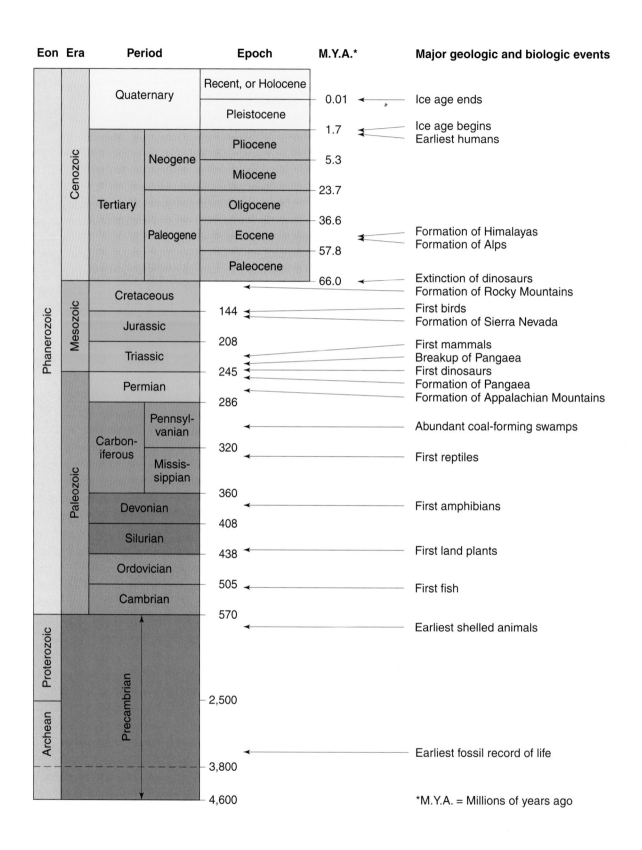

FIGURE 15.7
Geologic time scale.

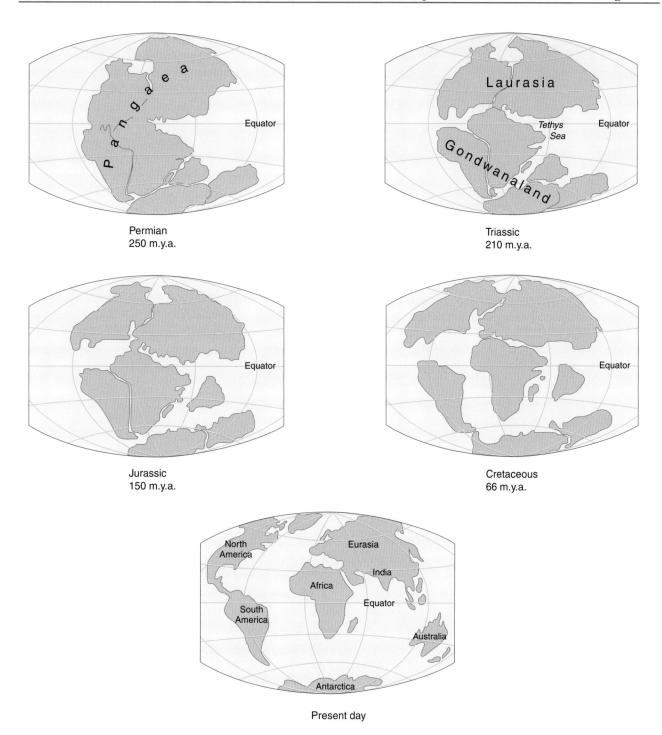

FIGURE 15.8
About 225 million years ago, the super-continent Pangaea began to split apart into separate continents that slowly drifted apart. Ocean basins opened and eventually the continents reached their present positions. Continental drift, a manifestation of plate tectonics, is responsible for climate changes operating over hundreds of millions of years. [U.S. Geological Survey]

and closed. Plate tectonics has probably operated on the planet for at least 2 billion years and explains such seemingly anomalous finds as glacial deposits in the Sahara Desert, fossil tropical plants in Greenland, and fossil coral in Wisconsin (Figure 15.9). These discoveries reflect climatic conditions millions of years ago when landmasses were situated at different latitudes than they are today. Plate tectonics also impacted global climate by altering the course of heat-transporting surface ocean currents and the ocean conveyor-belt system (Chapter 4).

FIGURE 15.9
This bedrock exposed in northeastern Wisconsin contains fossil coral that dates from nearly 400 million years ago. Based on the environmental requirements of modern coral, scientists conclude that 400 million years ago, Wisconsin's climate was tropical marine. Plate tectonics can explain such a drastic change between ancient and modern conditions.

Geologic evidence points to an interval of extreme climatic fluctuations about 570 million years ago, corresponding to the transition between Proterozoic and Phanerozoic Eons. Along Namibia's Skeleton Coast rock layers that formed in tropical seas directly overlie glacial deposits. Some scientists interpret these rock sequences as indicating abrupt climatic changes between extreme cold and tropical heat. During as many as four cold episodes, each lasting perhaps 10 million years, the continents were encased in glacial ice and the ocean froze to a depth of more than 1000 m (3300 ft). At the close of each cold episode, temperatures rose rapidly, and within only a few centuries, all the ice melted.

A relatively warm planet Earth likely persisted through much of the Mesozoic Era, from about 245 to 70 million years ago. At the boundary between the Triassic and Jurassic Periods, the global mean temperature rose perhaps 3 to 4 Celsius degrees (5.5 to 7 Fahrenheit degrees), causing substantial changes in vegetation and a major extinction of animals. At peak warming during the Cretaceous Period, the global mean temperature was perhaps 6 to 8 Celsius degrees (11 to 14 Fahrenheit degrees) higher than now. Subtropical plants and animals lived as far north as 60 degrees N and dinosaurs roamed what is now the North Slope of Alaska. Adding to the geological processes impacting climate, a great meteorite impact about 65 million years ago threw huge quantities of dust into the atmosphere, blocking sunlight, and causing global cooling that apparently was responsible for the demise of the dinosaurs. An explosion in the population of mammals followed the extinction of the dinosaurs.

The Cenozoic Era was a time of great climatic fluctuations. About 55 million years ago, methane (CH_4) released from deep-sea sediments escaped into the ocean and then into the atmosphere where it enhanced the greenhouse effect, causing an already warm planet to become even warmer. But by 40 million years ago, Earth's climate began shifting toward colder, drier, and more variable conditions setting the stage for the Pleistocene Ice Age. According to W.F. Ruddiman of Lamont-Doherty Geological Observatory of Columbia University and J.E. Kutzbach of the University of Wisconsin-Madison, mountain building may explain this change in Earth's climate, specifically the rise of the Colorado Plateau, Tibetan Plateau, and Himalayan Mountains. Prominent mountain ranges influence the geographical distribution of clouds and precipitation and can alter the planetary-scale circulation. Furthermore, mountain building may alter the global carbon cycle. Enhanced weathering of bedrock exposed in mountain ranges sequesters more atmospheric carbon dioxide in sediments thereby weakening the greenhouse effect.

In the American West, the region from the California Sierras to the Rockies, known as the Colorado Plateau, has an average elevation of 1500 to 2500 m (5000 to 8200 ft). Although mountain building began about 40 million years ago, about half of the total uplift took place between 10 and 5 million years ago. The Tibetan Plateau and Himalayan Mountains of southern Asia cover an area of more than 2 million square km (0.8 million square mi) and have an average elevation of more than 4500 m (14,700 ft). About half of total Himalayan uplift took place over the past 10 million years. These plateaus diverted the planetary-scale westerlies into a more meridional pattern, increasing the north-south exchange of air masses and altering the climate over a broad region of the globe. Also, seasonal heating and cooling of the plateaus causes low pressure to develop in summer and high pressure in winter, enhancing the monsoon circulation over southern Asia.

PAST TWO MILLION YEARS

Climate varies over a wide range of time scales so that viewing the climatic record of the past two million years in progressively narrower time frames is useful. Such an approach helps to resolve the oscillations of climate into more detailed fluctuations especially over the recent past. Over the past two million years, changes in Earth's surface associated with plate tectonics were not a major factor in climate change. For example, assuming a spreading rate of 4 cm (1.6 in.) per year, in 2 million years the Atlantic basin would spread a total distance of

80 km (50 mi), not very significant in a climatic sense. For all practical purposes, mountain ranges, continents, and ocean basins were essentially as they are today.

Compared to the climate that prevailed through most of geologic time, the climate of the past two million years was anomalous in favoring the development of huge glacial ice sheets (although evidence exists of ice ages earlier in geologic time). During much of Earth's history, the average global temperature may have been 10 Celsius degrees (18 Fahrenheit degrees) higher than it was over the past two million years. Cooling that set in about 40 million years ago culminated in the Pleistocene Ice Age that began about 1.7 million years ago and ended about 10,500 years ago.

The Swiss naturalist Louis Agassiz (1807-1873) is credited with championing the **glacial theory** during the mid-1800s. Previously, the prevailing view—as espoused by the Scottish geologist Charles Lyell (1797-1875)—attributed erratic boulders observed in Europe to rafting by icebergs during a massive flood. Erratics are large boulders that differ geologically from the local bedrock implying transport from elsewhere, in some cases over distances of hundreds of kilometers. Interestingly, Swiss peasants long thought that alpine glaciers were once more extensive and interpreted erratics, polished and striated (scratched) rock surfaces, and other landscape features as indicators of ancient glaciation. At the invitation of Jean de Charpentier, an early proponent of the glacial theory, Agassiz had an opportunity to examine such evidence near Bex, Switzerland in the summer of 1836. Agassiz quickly became convinced of the glacial origins of the landscape features and set out to develop a glacial theory.

At scientific meetings and in his writings, Agassiz argued that some time in the past (a period he called an *ice age*), large glacial ice sheets spread over Europe as far south as the Mediterranean and over much of northern Asia and North America. At first, Agassiz ideas met with considerable skepticism by the scientific establishment. However, after 1840 as more geologists examined the field evidence, an increasing number of converts to the glacial theory included prominent scientists of the day. By 1865, the theory had gained widespread acceptance on both sides of the Atlantic. A major reason for the slow pace in acceptance of the glacial theory was the fact that most geologists were unfamiliar with glaciers, not having had the opportunity to observe them or their impacts in the field. Furthermore, scientific expeditions did not discover that Greenland's glaciers formed an ice sheet until 1852 and the size of the Antarctic ice sheets was not determined until the late 19th century.

Through the 20th century much field and laboratory work was directed at working out the chronology and causes of the climate and glacial fluctuations of the Pleistocene Ice Age. During the Pleistocene Ice Age the climate shifted numerous times between glacial climates and interglacial climates. A **glacial climate** favors the thickening and expansion of glaciers whereas an **interglacial climate** favors the thinning and retreat of existing glaciers or no glaciers at all. During major glacial climatic episodes of the Pleistocene, the Laurentide ice sheet developed over central Canada and spread westward to the Rocky Mountains, eastward to the Atlantic, and southward over the northern tier states of the United States. At about the same time, mountain glaciers in the Rockies coalesced into the Cordilleran ice sheet, a relatively thin ice sheet covered the Arctic Archipelago, and an ice sheet much smaller than the Laurentide developed over northwest Europe including the British Isles and Scandinavia. The vast quantity of water locked up in these ice sheets caused sea level to drop by 113 to 135 m (370 to 443 ft), exposing portions of the continental shelf, including a land bridge linking Siberia and North America. The Laurentide and European ice sheets thinned and retreated, and may even have disappeared entirely, during relatively mild interglacial climatic episodes, which typically lasted about 10,000 years. Throughout these interglacials, however, glacial ice persisted over most of Antarctica and Greenland as it still does today.

During glacial climatic episodes, temperatures were lower than they are today but the cooling was not geographically uniform. A variety of geologic evidence indicates that during the Pleistocene, temperature fluctuations between major glacial and interglacial climatic episodes typically amounted to as much as 5 Celsius degrees (9 Fahrenheit degrees) in the tropics, 6 to 8 Celsius degrees (11 to 14 Fahrenheit degrees) at middle latitudes, and 10 Celsius degrees (18 Fahrenheit degrees) or more at high latitudes. An increase in the magnitude of a climatic change with increasing latitude is known as **polar amplification**, indicating that polar areas are subject to greater changes in climate.

Oxygen isotope analysis of the deep-sea sediment cores shows numerous fluctuations between major glacial and interglacial climatic episodes over the past 600,000 years (Figure 15.10A). Shifting focus to the past 160,000 years, resolution of the climate record improves. The temperature curve in Figure 15.10B is based on analysis of an ice core extracted from the Antarctic ice sheet at Vostok. A relatively mild interglacial episode, referred to as the *Eemian*, began about 127,000 years ago and

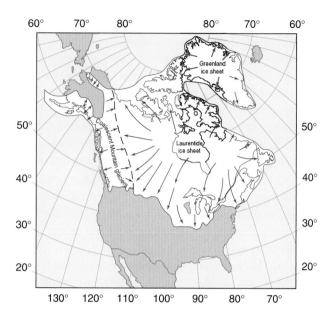

FIGURE 15.11
The extent of glacial ice cover over North America about 20,000 to 18,000 years ago, the time of the last glacial maximum.

FIGURE 15.10
(A) Variation in global glacial ice volume from the present back to about 600 million years ago based on analysis of oxygen isotope ratio in deep-sea sediment cores. (B) Temperature variation over the past 160,000 years based on oxygen isotope analysis of an ice core extracted from the Antarctic ice sheet at Vostok and expressed as a departure in Celsius degrees from the 1900 mean global temperature. [Compiled by R.S. Bradley and J.A. Eddy from J. Jousel et al., *Nature* 329(1987):403-408 and reported in *EarthQuest* 5, No. 1 (1991).]

persisted for approximately 7000 years. In some localities, temperatures may have been 1 to 2 Celsius degrees (2 to 4 Fahrenheit degrees) higher than during the warmest portion of the present interglacial. The Eemian interglacial was followed by numerous fluctuations between glacial and interglacial episodes. The last major glacial climatic episode began about 27,000 years ago and reached its peak about 18,000 to 20,000 years ago when glacial ice cover over North America was about as extensive as it had ever been (Figure 15.11).

The global mean temperature 18,000 to 20,000 years ago was about 4 to 6 Celsius degrees (7.2 to 10.8 Fahrenheit degrees) lower than at present. A general warming trend (and rise in sea level from melting ice) followed the last glacial maximum, punctuated by relatively brief returns to glacial climatic episodes (Figure 15.12). A notable example is the cold interval from about 11,000 to 10,000 years ago known as the *Younger Dryas* (named for the polar wildflower, *Dryas octopetala*, that reappeared in portions of Europe at the time). The return of glacial climatic conditions triggered short-

lived re-advances of remnant ice sheets in North America, Scotland, and Scandinavia. Glacial ice finally withdrew from the Great Lakes region about 10,500 years ago ushering in the present interglacial, the **Holocene**.

Although the Laurentide ice sheet was melting and would disappear almost entirely by about 5500 years ago, the Holocene has been an epoch of spatially and temporally variable temperature and precipitation. Cores extracted from the Greenland ice sheet and sediment cores taken from the bottom of the North Atlantic reveal that the overall post-glacial warming trend was interrupted by abrupt millennial-scale fluctuations in climate. Post-glacial warming during

FIGURE 15.12
Temperature variation over the past 18,000 years based on analysis of a variety of climatic indicators and expressed as a departure in Celsius degrees from the 1900 mean global temperature. [Compiled by R.S. Bradley and J.A. Eddy based on J.T. Houghton et al. (eds.), *Climate Change: The IPCC Assessment*, Cambridge University Press, U.K., 1990, and reported in *EarthQuest* 5, No. 1 (1991).]

the Holocene gave way to a cold episode about 8200 years ago; significant cooling also occurred between 3100 to 2400 years ago. On the other hand, at times during the mid-Holocene (classically known as the *Hypsithermal*) mean annual global temperature was perhaps 1 Celsius degree (2 Fahrenheit degrees) higher than it was in 1900, the warmest in more than 110,000 years, that is, since the Eemian interglacial. A pollen-based climate reconstruction indicates that 6000 years ago, July mean temperatures were about 2 Celsius degrees (3.6 Fahrenheit degrees) higher than now over most of Europe.

A generalized temperature curve for the past 1000 years, derived mostly from historical documents, is shown in Figure 15.13. The most notable features of this record are (1) the **Medieval Warm Period** from about 950 to 1250 CE and (2) the cooling that followed, from about 1400 to 1850 CE, a period now known as the **Little Ice Age**. The Medieval Warm Period and the Little Ice Age were not episodes of sustained warming and cooling, respectively. On the contrary, sediment and glacial ice core records plus historical documents indicate decadal fluctuations in temperature and precipitation. During much of the Medieval Warm Period, the global temperature averaged about 0.5 Celsius degree (0.9 Fahrenheit degree) higher than in 1900. The first Norse settlements were established along the southern coast of Greenland and vineyards thrived in the British Isles. Independent lines of evidence confirm that the Little Ice Age was a relatively cool period in many regions with mean annual global temperatures perhaps 0.5 Celsius degree (0.9 Fahrenheit degree) lower than it was in 1900. Sea ice cover expanded, mountain glaciers advanced, growing seasons shortened, and erratic harvests caused much hardship for many people including the end of the Norse settlements in Greenland.

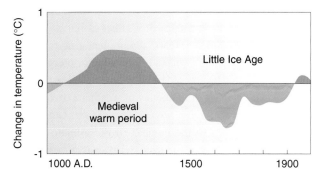

FIGURE 15.13
Temperature variation over the past 1000 years based on analysis of historical documents and expressed as a departure in Celsius degrees from the 1900 mean global temperature. [Adapted from J.T. Houghton et al. (eds.), *Climate Change: The IPCC Assessment*, Cambridge University Press, U.K., 1990, p. 202.]

INSTRUMENT-BASED TEMPERATURE TRENDS

Invention of weather instruments, establishment of weather observing networks around the world, plus standardized methods of observation and record-keeping made the climate record much more detailed and dependable. The most reliable temperature records date from the late 1800s with the birth of national weather services including those of the United States and Canada, along with the predecessor to today's World Meteorological Organization (WMO). Examination of temperature trends over the past 120 years or so is instructive as to the short-term variability of climate.

Plotted in Figure 15.14 are variations from 1880 to 2004 in (1) global (land plus sea surface) mean annual temperature, (2) global mean sea surface temperature, and (3) global mean land surface temperature. In all three cases, the temperature is expressed as a departure (in Celsius degrees and Fahrenheit degrees) from the long-term (125-year) period average. As expected, these temperature time series, assembled by the *National Climatic Data Center (NCDC)*, indicate greater year-to-year variability over land than ocean. The trend in global mean temperature was generally upward from 1880 until about 1940, downward or steady from 1940 to about 1970, and upward again through the 1990s and early 2000s. The temperature fluctuation is mostly in the range of about ±0.4 Celsius degrees (±0.7 Fahrenheit degrees) about the period average. Note that this temperature record for the globe as a whole is not representative (in direction or magnitude) of all locations worldwide; that is, the trend was amplified or reversed, or both, in specific regions.

In late 1999, the World Meteorological Organization reported that the global mean annual surface temperature was about 0.7 Celsius degrees (1.3 Fahrenheit degrees) higher at the end of the 20th century than at the close of the 19th century. In spring 2000, the NCDC reported that global warming accelerated during the final quarter of the 20th century. Since 1976, global mean annual temperature has climbed at the rate of 0.2 to 0.3 Celsius degrees (0.4 to 0.5 Fahrenheit degrees) per decade. The ten highest global mean annual surface temperatures occurred since 1990; they are 2005 and 1998 (tied for warmest), 2002 and 2003 (a tie), 2004, 2001, 1997, 1995, 1990, and 1999. During 1997 and 1998, record high global mean temperatures were set for 16 consecutive months. Furthermore, climate reconstructions (mostly in the Northern Hemisphere) indicate that the 20th century was the warmest in 1000 years. For example, analysis of ice cores extracted from a glacier at 7163 m (23,500 ft) in the Himalayan Mountains revealed that the 1990s and

Annual average temperature departures
from long term average

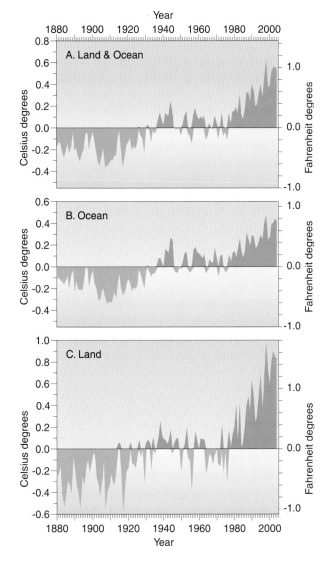

FIGURE 15.14
Anomalies in mean annual (A) global (land and ocean), (B) ocean, and (C) land temperatures. Anomalies are differences in Celsius degrees (left) and Fahrenheit degrees (right) from the long-term period average (1880-2004). [NOAA, National Climatic Data Center, Ashville, NC]

the last half of the 20th century were the warmest of any equivalent periods in a millennium.

Some critics question the integrity of hemispheric or global mean temperature records. They cite as potential sources of error: (1) improved sophistication and reliability of weather instruments through the period of record, (2) changes in location and exposure of instruments at most long-term weather stations, (3) huge gaps in monitoring networks, especially over the ocean, and (4) the warming

influence of urbanization (*urban heat islands*). By careful statistical interrogation of available data, however, global-scale temperature trends have been confirmed to a reasonable level of confidence.

Lessons of the Climate Past

What does the climate record tell us about the behavior of climate through time? The following lessons of the climate record are useful in assessing prospects for the climate future and the possible impacts of climate change.

- *Climate is inherently variable over a broad spectrum of time scales ranging from years to decades, to centuries, to millennia.* Variability is an endemic characteristic of climate. The question for the future is not whether climate will change but how climate will change and by how much.

- *Variations in climate are geographically non-uniform in both sign (direction) and magnitude.* Some areas may experience warming while other areas could undergo concurrent cooling. Large-scale trends in climate are not necessarily duplicated at a particular location although the tendency is for the magnitude of temperature change to amplify with increasing latitude (*polar amplification*). A large-scale change in climate is not likely to have the same impact everywhere.

- *Climate change may consist of a long-term trend in the various climatic elements (e.g., mean temperature or average precipitation) and/or a change in the frequency of extreme weather events (e.g., drought, excessive cold).* Recall that climate encompasses mean values plus extremes. A trend toward warmer or cooler, wetter or drier conditions may or may not be accompanied by a change in frequency of weather extremes. On the other hand, a climatic regime featuring relatively little change in mean temperature or precipitation through time could be accompanied by an increase or decrease in frequency of weather extremes.

- *Climate change tends to be abrupt rather than gradual.* In the context of the climate record, "abrupt" is a relative term. If the time of transition between climatic episodes is much shorter than the duration of individual episodes, then the transition is considered to be relatively abrupt. Analysis of cores extracted from the Greenland ice sheet indicates that cold and warm climatic episodes, each lasting about 1000 years, were punctuated by abrupt change over periods as brief as a single decade. The abrupt-change nature of climate would test the resilience of society to respond effectively to climate change.

- *Only a few cyclical variations can be discerned from the long-term climate record.* Regular cycles include diurnal and seasonal variations in incoming solar radiation (the forcing) and temperature (the response). This means simply that days are usually warmer than nights and summers are warmer than winters. Quasi-regular variations in climate include El Niño (occurring about every 3 to 7 years), Holocene millennial-scale fluctuations identified in glacial ice cores, and the major glacial-interglacial climate shifts of the Pleistocene Ice Age unlocked from analysis of deep-sea sediment cores and operating over tens of thousands to hundreds of thousands of years.

- *Climate change impacts society.* History recounts numerous instances when climate change significantly impacted society. Consider some examples. Researchers have implicated prolonged drought in the decline and fall of Middle Eastern empires around 2000 BCE, the Harappan civilization of the Indus Valley of India about 1700 BCE, the Mycenaean civilization of Greece in 1200 BCE, and the Anasazi abandonment of Mesa Verde (southwestern Colorado) around 1300 CE (Figure 15.15). The cooling trend that heralded the Little Ice Age was likely a major factor in the disappearance of Norse settlements in Greenland about 1400 CE. Although modern societies may be more capable of dealing with climate change than early peoples, a rapid and significant change in climate would seriously impact all sectors of modern society.

FIGURE 15.15
Drought apparently forced the Anasazi Indians of Mesa Verde, in southwestern Colorado, to abandon their cliff dwellings around 1300 C.E.

Possible Causes of Climate Change

No simple explanation exists for why climate changes. The complex spectrum of climate variability is a response to the interactions of many processes, both internal and external to the Earth-atmosphere-ocean system.

One way to organize our thinking on the many possible causes of climate change is to match a possible cause (or forcing) with a specific climatic oscillation (or response), based on similar periods of oscillation (Figure 15.16). For example, plate tectonics might explain long-term climate changes operating over hundreds of millions of years. Systematic changes in Earth's orbit about the sun may account for climate shifts of the order of 10,000 to 100,000 years. Variations in sunspot number and the sun's energy output may be associated with climate fluctuations of decades to centuries. Volcanic eruptions, El Niño, or La Niña may account for climate shifts lasting several months

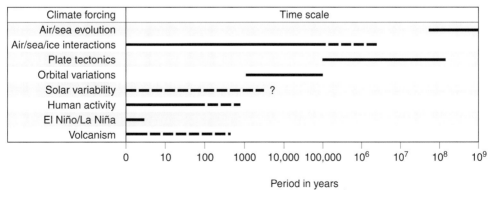

FIGURE 15.16
The various causes of climate change operate over a range of time scales.

to a few years. But matching some forcing mechanism with a climatic response based on similar periods of oscillation is no guarantee of a real physical relationship.

Another way to think about the possible causes of climate change is in terms of the global energy budget. In Chapter 4, we saw that with **global radiative equilibrium**, energy entering the Earth-atmosphere system (i.e., absorbed solar radiation) ultimately must equal energy leaving the system (i.e., infrared radiation emitted to space). Any change in either energy input or energy output will shift the Earth-atmosphere system to a new equilibrium and change the planet's climate. A number of factors can alter global radiative equilibrium, including fluctuations in solar energy output, changes in Earth's orbit about the sun, volcanic eruptions, alterations in Earth's surface properties, and certain human activities.

CLIMATE AND SOLAR VARIABILITY

Fluctuations in the sun's energy output, sunspots, or regular variations in Earth's orbital parameters are external factors that can alter Earth's climate system. Satellite measurements in the 1980s and 1990s confirmed long-held suspicions in the scientific community that the sun's total energy output at all wavelengths is not constant. Furthermore, numerical global climate models predict that only a 1% change in the sun's energy output could significantly alter the mean temperature of the Earth-atmosphere system.

Changes in solar energy output are apparently related to sunspot number. A **sunspot** is a dark blotch on the face of the sun, typically thousands of kilometers across, that develops where an intense magnetic field suppresses the flow of gases transporting heat from the sun's interior (Figure 15.17). A sunspot appears dark because its temperature is about 400 to 1800 Celsius degrees (720 to 3240 Fahrenheit degrees) lower than the surrounding surface of the sun, the **photosphere**. In 1843, the German astronomer Samuel Heinrich Schwabe

FIGURE 15.17
A sunspot is a dark blotch that appears on the sun's photosphere, typically thousands of kilometers across, that develops where an intense magnetic field suppresses the flow of gases transporting heat from the sun's interior. [Courtesy of Dr. Donat G. Wentzel, University of Maryland and the National Optical Astronomical Observatories.]

(1789-1875) reported regular variations in sunspot activity. A sunspot typically lasts only a few days, but the rate of sunspot generation is such that the number of sunspots varies systematically (Figure 15.18). The time between successive sunspot maxima or minima averages about 11

FIGURE 15.18
Variation in mean annual sunspot number since early in the 17th century. [National Geophysical Data Center]

years with a range of 10 to 12 years. Sunspot number reached a maximum in 1989, a minimum in 1996, and a maximum in 2000.

Satellite monitoring reveals that the sun's energy output varies directly with sunspot number; that is, a slightly brighter sun has more sunspots while a slightly dimmer sun has fewer sunspots. The variation in total solar energy output through one 11-year sunspot cycle amounts to less than 0.1%, with much of that change taking place in the ultraviolet (UV) portion of the solar spectrum. A brighter sun is associated with more sunspots because of a concurrent increase in bright areas, known as **faculae**, which appear near sunspots on the photosphere. Faculae dominate sunspots and the sun brightens. More sunspots may contribute to a warmer global climate and fewer sunspots may translate into a colder global climate.

How reasonable is the proposed link between global climate and sunspot number? In 1893, while studying sunspot records at the Old Royal Observatory at Greenwich, England, E. Walter Maunder found that sunspot activity greatly diminished during the 70-year period from 1645 to 1715, now referred to as the **Maunder minimum**. The scientific community for the most part ignored Maunder's finding until the 1970s when J.A. Eddy of the University Corporation for Atmospheric Research (UCAR) in Boulder, CO reinvestigated his work. Eddy pointed out that the Maunder minimum plus a prior period of reduced sunspot number, called the **Spörer minimum** (1400 to 1510 CE), occurred at about the same time as relatively cold phases of the Little Ice Age in Western Europe. Furthermore, the Medieval Warm Period coincided with an interval of heightened sunspot activity between about 1100 and 1250 CE.

Skeptics dismiss the significance of the match between the Maunder minimum and a cooler climate. They argue that relatively cold episodes occurred in Europe just prior to and after the Maunder minimum (i.e., 1605-1615, 1805-1815), and relatively cool conditions did not persist throughout the Maunder minimum and were not global in extent. Furthermore, some scientists argue that a 0.1% variation in total solar energy output during the 11-year sunspot cycle is much too weak to significantly impact Earth's climate. Other scientists counter that certain mechanisms operating within the Earth-atmosphere system could amplify the effects of changes in total solar output, making the slight brightening and dimming of the sun an important player in Earth's climate system.

In late 2001, Drew Shindell of NASA's Goddard Institute for Space Studies and his colleagues reported on their use of a global climate model to simulate what happened during the Maunder minimum. With reduced sunspot activity, less solar ultraviolet radiation reached Earth affecting the formation of ozone (O_3) in the stratosphere. Accompanying changes in the upper atmosphere circulation propagated down to the troposphere. Weakening of the mid-latitude jet stream was likely linked to changes in the Arctic Oscillation (AO) and North Atlantic Oscillation (NAO) (Chapter 9). A diminished jet stream reduced the transport of mild Pacific air into North America and mild Atlantic air into Europe. Although the change in global mean temperature during the Maunder minimum was quite small, temperatures were significantly lower regionally.

CLIMATE AND EARTH'S ORBIT

One of the earliest proposed explanations for the Ice Age was a reduction in the flux of solar radiation reaching the Earth-atmosphere system either because the sun's energy output decreased or interplanetary dust partially blocked incoming sunlight. In 1842, the French mathematician Joseph Alphonse Adhémar (1797-1862) was the first to propose that regular variations in Earth's orbit about the sun could be responsible for climatic variations that paced the glacial fluctuations of the Ice Age. Subsequently, Adhémar's ideas were expanded upon by James Croll and later by Milutin Milankovitch.

In 1864, James Croll (1821-1890), a self-educated Scottish scientist, attributed the climatic changes responsible for the Ice Age to changes in incoming solar radiation that accompanied regular changes in Earth's orbital parameters (eccentricity of the orbit, tilt of the rotational axis, and precession of the axis). On this basis, Croll worked out an Ice Age chronology, arguing that less incoming solar radiation in winter favored greater accumulations of snow. Furthermore, increases in snow cover would have a cooling effect (positive feedback) culminating in glaciation. Croll predicted multiple glaciations (rather than the single Ice Age proposed earlier by Louis Agassiz). The American geologist Thomas C. Chamberlain (1843-1928) discovered multiple layers of glacial till that confirmed Croll's view of multiple glacial advances. However, by the close of the 19th century, Croll's theory fell into disfavor when European geologists discovered a serious discrepancy between his astronomically-based Ice Age chronology and field evidence. Croll's chronology showed the Ice Age ending about 80,000 years ago whereas field evidence indicated that the date was closer to 10,000 years ago.

In the second decade of the 20th century, the Serbian astronomer Milutin Milankovitch (1879-1958) revived Croll's idea and set out to calculate the latitudinal and seasonal variations in solar radiation striking the surface of Earth (and other planets) arising from changes in Earth's three orbital parameters. For more than 25 years, Milankovitch relentlessly pursued his goal. His collaboration with the German climatologist Wladimir Köppen (1846-1940) and meteorologist Alfred Wegener convinced Milankovitch that reduced solar radiation during summer (and not winter as Croll had proposed) at high latitudes was key to initiating glaciation. In 1938, he published radiation curves for different latitudes (55 to 65 degrees N) extending back 600,000 years. In the 1930s and 1940s, support for Milankovitch's astronomical theory of the Ice Age was considerable, especially in Europe. However, in a dramatic turnaround, by the mid-1950s Milankovitch's views were rejected by most geologists.

After World War II, Willard F. Libby (1908-1980) of the University of Chicago developed the radiocarbon method of age-determination of the remains of formerly living organisms. By 1951, geologists were applying the new dating technique to deposits of the last major glacial advance. (The range of radiocarbon dating was limited to about 40,000 years.) Geologists discovered that the astronomical chronology did not match the radiocarbon chronology. However, the radiocarbon chronology was derived mostly from terrestrial sources and some scientists were convinced that a more reliable chronology could be obtained from deep-sea sediment cores extracted from the bottom of the open ocean.

Sedimentation rates in the open ocean are extremely slow, ranging from 1 to 3 mm per century. Hence, a relatively short undisturbed core could contain information on climatic fluctuations through much of the Pleistocene with a resolution of the order of 10,000 years. With the development of new age-dating techniques (based on reversals in Earth's magnetic field) and oxygen isotope analysis (described in this chapter's Essay), scientists soon had the means to reconstruct past climate oscillations from analysis of deep-sea sediment cores. An international team of scientists analyzed two cores extracted from the bottom of the Indian Ocean that spanned 450,000 years. In December 1976, scientists announced that major changes in climate occurred at essentially the same frequency as variations in the eccentricity, obliquity, and precession of Earth's orbit. Today, Milankovitch's astronomical theory is widely accepted as the explanation for the major climate fluctuations of the Pleistocene.

Milankovitch cycles are regular variations in the precession and tilt of Earth's rotational axis and the eccentricity of its orbit about the sun (Figure 15.19).

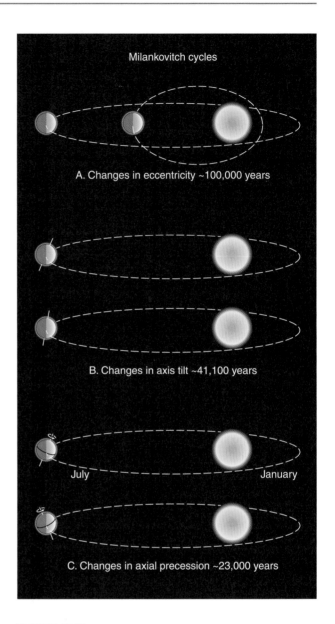

FIGURE 15.19
Milankovitch cycles likely explain the large-scale fluctuations of glacial ice cover during the Pleistocene. Note that diagrams greatly exaggerate changes in Earth-sun geometry.

These changes in Earth-sun geometry are caused by gravitational influences exerted on Earth by other large planets, the moon, and the sun. Combined, Milankovitch cycles drive climate fluctuations operating over tens of thousands to hundreds of thousands of years.

Over a period of about 23,000 years, Earth's spin axis describes a complete circle, much like the wobble of a spinning top. This precession cycle changes the dates of *perihelion*, when Earth is closest to the sun, and *aphelion*, when Earth is farthest from the sun, increasing the summer-to-winter seasonal contrast in one hemisphere while decreasing it in the other. At present, perihelion is in early January and aphelion is in early July. In about 10,000 years, those dates will be reversed (perihelion in July and aphelion in January) and the seasonal contrast will be greater than it is now in the Northern Hemisphere (i.e., colder winters and warmer summers) but less in the Southern Hemisphere (i.e., milder winters and cooler summers).

The tilt of Earth's spin axis changes from 22.1 degrees to 24.5 degrees and then back to 22.1 degrees over a period of about 41,000 years, the consequence of long-period changes in orientation of Earth's orbital plane with respect to its spin axis. (Presently, the tilt is 23.5 degrees.) As axial tilt increases, winters become colder and summers become warmer in both hemispheres. Earth's axial tilt has been slowly decreasing for about 10,000 years and will continue to do so for the next 10,000 years.

The shape of Earth's orbit about the sun changes from elliptical (high eccentricity) to nearly circular (low eccentricity) in an irregular cycle of 90,000 to 100,000 years. Variation in orbital eccentricity alters the distance between Earth and sun at aphelion and perihelion, thereby changing the amount of solar radiation received by the planet at those times of the year. When Earth's orbit is highly elliptical, the difference in the amount of radiation received at perihelion versus aphelion is greater than when the orbit is less elliptical. Also, changes in eccentricity along with the precession cycle significantly influence the lengths of the individual astronomical seasons.

Milankovitch cycles do not alter appreciably the total amount of solar energy received by the Earth-atmosphere system annually, but they do change significantly the latitudinal and seasonal distribution of incoming solar radiation. Milankovitch proposed that glacial climatic episodes began when Earth-sun geometry favored an extended period of increased solar radiation in winter and decreased solar radiation in summer at sub-polar latitudes. More intense winter radiation at these latitudes translates into somewhat higher temperatures, greater precipitable water, and more snowfall. Weaker solar radiation in summer meant that some of the winter snow cover, especially north of 60 degrees N, would survive summer and a succession of many such cool summers would favor formation of a glacier. This process, according to Milankovitch, was the origin of the Laurentide ice sheet. At other times, Earth-sun geometry favored enhanced solar radiation in summer at higher latitudes, triggering an interglacial climate and shrinkage of the Laurentide ice sheet.

Milankovitch cycles do not account for the period of climate quiescence prior to the Pleistocene. Apparently, Milankovitch cycles (which likely operated throughout Earth history) were not effective in initiating continental-scale glaciation until plate tectonics provided the appropriate boundary conditions, that is, landmasses at high latitudes and mountain ranges in place—conditions not fully achieved until onset of the Pleistocene.

Discovery of the possible relationship between systematic changes in Earth's orbital parameters and major glacial-interglacial climatic shifts prompted climatologists to search for other influences of Milankovitch cycles on climate variability. For example, J.E. Kutzbach of the University of Wisconsin-Madison has linked the Hypsithermal to Earth's precession cycle. Between 7000 and 5000 years ago, Earth was closest to the sun (perihelion) in June rather than in January as it is now. In the Northern Hemisphere, this meant about 5% more solar radiation during summer and 5% less solar radiation in winter. The consequent increase in air temperature contrast between summer and winter probably altered the planetary-scale circulation. For one, evidence suggests that the monsoon circulation of subtropical latitudes was more vigorous during the Hypsithermal than it is today.

CLIMATE AND VOLCANOES

The idea that volcanoes influence climate has been around for more than two centuries. Benjamin Franklin (1706-1790) proposed that the haze in Europe associated with the eruption of Iceland's Laki fissure zone during the summer of 1783 was responsible for the severe winter of 1783-84. The unseasonably cold summer of 1816, summarized in this chapter's Case-in-Point, followed the violent eruption of Tambora, an Indonesian volcano, in the spring of 1815. Several relatively cold years followed on the heels of the 1883 eruption of Krakatau, also an Indonesian volcano. Is the relationship between volcanic eruptions and cooling real or coincidental?

Only explosive volcanic eruptions that are rich in sulfur dioxide (SO_2) are likely to impact global or hemispheric climate and then only for a few years at most. A violent volcanic eruption can send sulfur dioxide high into the stratosphere where it combines with water vapor to form tiny droplets of sulfuric acid (H_2SO_4) and sulfate particles, collectively called **sulfurous aerosols**. The small size of sulfurous aerosols (averaging about 0.1 micrometer in diameter), coupled with the absence of precipitation in the stratosphere, allow sulfurous aerosols to remain suspended in the stratosphere for many months to perhaps a year or longer before they cycle to the Earth's surface. Successive volcanic eruptions have produced a sulfurous aerosol veil in the stratosphere at altitudes of about 15 to 25 km (9 to 16 mi). Sulfur oxide emissions from clusters of volcanic eruptions temporarily thicken the stratospheric aerosol veil.

Research conducted after the 1991 eruption of Mount Pinatubo provided new insights on the relationship between sulfurous aerosols of volcanic origin and large-scale climate fluctuations. On 15-16 June 1991, Mount Pinatubo, located on Luzon Island in the Philippines, erupted violently injecting an estimated 20 megatons of sulfur dioxide into the stratosphere (Figure 15.20). This was the most massive stratospheric volcanic aerosol cloud of the 20th century. By altering both incoming and outgoing radiation, sulfurous

FIGURE 15.20
The June 1991 explosive eruption of Mount Pinatubo (in the Philippines) was rich in sulfur dioxide. The resulting sulfurous aerosol veil in the stratosphere was responsible for cooling at Earth's surface, interrupting the post-1970s global warming trend for a few years. [U.S. Geological Survey photo]

aerosols affected temperatures in the stratosphere and troposphere, altered atmospheric circulation, and impacted surface air temperatures around the globe.

Sulfurous aerosols absorb both incoming solar radiation and outgoing infrared radiation, warming the lower stratosphere, especially in the tropics. Sulfurous aerosols also reflect solar radiation to space. NASA scientists reported that in the months following the Mount Pinatubo eruption, satellite sensors measured a 3.8% increase in solar radiation reflected to space. Also, in the presence of chlorine, sulfurous aerosols destroy ozone (O_3) especially at high latitudes, allowing more solar UV radiation to reach Earth's surface. (This is essentially the same mechanism responsible for the Antarctic ozone hole described in Chapter 3.) In the two years following the Pinatubo eruption, ozone levels at middle latitudes declined by about 5% to 8%. The combination of stratospheric warming at low latitudes and ozone depletion at high latitudes strengthens the circumpolar vortex. And associated with this large-scale circulation change is a non-uniform change in surface temperatures; that is, some places cool while other places warm.

Through its impacts on the flux of radiation and attendant changes in global circulation patterns, the Pinatubo eruption was likely responsible for the cool summer of 1992 over continental areas of the Northern Hemisphere (with surface temperatures up to 2 Celsius degrees or 3.6 Fahrenheit degrees lower than the long-term average). The Pinatubo eruption was also implicated in the temperature anomalies of the winters of 1991-92 and 1992-93, featuring higher than average temperatures over most of North America, Europe, and Siberia and lower than average temperatures over Alaska, Greenland, the Middle East, and China.

A violent sulfur-rich volcanic eruption is unlikely to lower the mean hemispheric or global surface temperature by more than about 1.0 Celsius degree (1.8 Fahrenheit degrees) although the magnitude of local and regional temperature change may be greater (Figure 15.21). The 1963 eruption of Agung on the island of Bali lowered the mean temperature of the Northern Hemisphere an estimated 0.3 Celsius degree (0.5 Fahrenheit degree) for a year or two. The violent eruption of the Mexican volcano El Chichón in March-April 1982 may have produced hemispheric cooling of about 0.2 Celsius degrees (0.4 Fahrenheit degrees). Cooling associated with the Mount Pinatubo eruption temporarily interrupted the post-1970s global warming trend; from 1991 to 1992, the global mean annual temperature dropped 0.6 Celsius degrees (1.1 Fahrenheit degrees).

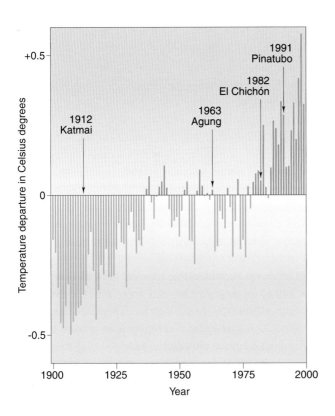

FIGURE 15.21
Large-scale cooling often followed massive volcanic eruptions that emitted sulfur dioxide into the stratosphere.

CLIMATE AND EARTH'S SURFACE PROPERTIES

Earth's surface, which is comprised of approximately 71% ocean water, is the prime absorber of solar radiation (Chapter 3). Any change in the physical properties of Earth's water or land surfaces or in the relative distribution of ocean, land or ice may affect Earth's radiation budget and climate.

Variations in mean regional snow cover may contribute to climate variability because an extensive snow cover has a refrigerating effect on the atmosphere. Fresh-fallen snow typically reflects 80% or more of incident solar radiation, thereby substantially reducing the amount of solar heating and lowering the daily maximum temperature. Snow is also an excellent emitter of infrared radiation, so heat is efficiently radiated to space, especially on nights when the sky is clear. Because of this radiational feedback, a snow cover tends to be self-sustaining. This effect may be further enhanced by the tracks of extra-tropical cyclones that tend to follow the periphery of a regional snow cover, where horizontal air temperature gradients are relatively great. This places the snow-covered region on the cold, snowy side of migrating storms, thereby adding to the snow cover and reinforcing

the chill. An unusually extensive winter snow cover favors persistence of an episode of cold weather. On the other hand, less than the usual extent of winter snow cover raises average air temperatures. Consider an example.

The average summer temperature in Arctic portions of Alaska and western Canada has increased about 1.4 Celsius degrees (2.5 Fahrenheit degrees) since 1961. According to Matthew Sturm and colleagues at the U.S. Army Cold Regions Research and Engineering Laboratory in Fort Wainwright, AK, much of this warming is due to positive feedback triggered by changes in surface albedo. In response to a warming trend in the Arctic, the end of the spring snowmelt is occurring earlier thereby lengthening the snow-free season. Hence, the surface albedo is significantly lower for a longer period of time when daylight is long, increasing the amount of sunlight absorbed by the ground by about 1.5% per decade.

Whereas changes in regional snow cover might impact climate over the short-term (seasonal), changes in Earth's sea ice or glacial ice coverage are likely to have longer-lasting effects on climate. Sea ice (formed from the freezing of seawater) covers an average area of about 25 million square km (9.6 million square mi), about the area of the North American continent. Terrestrial ice sheets, ice caps, and mountain glaciers cover a total area of about 15 million square km (5.8 million square mi), roughly 10% of the land area of the planet. Sea ice is distinct from floating ice shelves that form where glacial ice moves from land out over the ocean. Ice (especially when snow covered) is much more reflective of incident solar radiation than either ocean or snow-free land so that any change in glacial or sea-ice coverage would affect climate. As we will see later in this chapter, the Arctic climate is particularly sensitive to changes in sea ice cover.

Changes in sea-surface temperatures (SST) and ocean circulation contribute to climate change. As described in detail in Chapter 9, changes in SST patterns accompanying El Niño and La Niña contribute to interannual climate variability. Sea surface temperature patterns can exert a strong influence on the location of major features of the atmosphere's planetary scale circulation. When SST patterns change, the location of those circulation features also change. Consider an example.

Shifts in location of the highest SST in the tropical Atlantic affect the seasonal north-south shifts of the intertropical convergence zone (ITCZ), a discontinuous belt of thunderstorms paralleling the equator and marking the convergence of the trade winds of the Northern and Southern Hemispheres. The ITCZ encircles the globe and shifts north and south with the seasonal excursions of the sun—more so over land than the ocean—reaching its most northerly location in July and most southerly location in January (Figure 9.7). Displacement of the ITCZ over the tropical Atlantic Ocean affects the timing and amount of rainfall along the east coast of South American from Brazil northward into the Caribbean from March to May and in the western part of sub-Saharan Africa in August and September. With north-south shifts in the location of the highest SST, the latitude of the ITCZ changes, and regional rainfall patterns also vary. Changes in SST patterns in the eastern tropical Atlantic have been implicated in the disastrous multi-decade droughts that have afflicted sub-Saharan Africa. For more on that case, see the first Essay in Chapter 9.

Ocean circulation includes warm and cold surface currents and the ocean conveyor-belt system that transports heat throughout the world (Chapter 4). Regular changes in the strength of the conveyor belt may explain millennial-scale (1400 to 1500 year) cycles over the past 10,000 years. A strong conveyor belt brings relatively mild climate (for the latitude) to the North Atlantic and Western Europe whereas a weakening of the conveyor belt triggers cooling. Evidence shows that the actual turning of the conveyor-belt system on and off can happen in a decade or less.

CLIMATE AND HUMAN ACTIVITY

In 2001, the **Intergovernmental Panel on Climate Change (IPCC)** concluded that it is the consensus of scientific opinion that human activities are affecting Earth's climate. (The IPCC, formed in 1988 by the World Meteorological Organization and the United Nations Environmental Programme, is charged with evaluating the state of climate science as the basis for policy action.) Humans modify the landscape (e.g., urbanization, clear-cutting of forests) and thereby alter radiative properties of Earth's surface. As noted in Chapter 4, cities are slightly warmer than the surrounding countryside (urban heat island). Combustion of fossil fuels (i.e., coal, oil, and natural gas) alters concentrations of certain key gaseous and aerosol components of the atmosphere. Of these human impacts on the environment, the final one is most likely to influence climate on a global or hemispheric scale. Many scientists as well as public policy makers are concerned about the possible global climate impact of the steadily rising concentrations of atmospheric carbon dioxide (CO_2) and other infrared-absorbing gases. Higher levels of these gases appear likely to enhance the *greenhouse effect* and could be contributing to warming on a global scale (Chapter 3). In fact, the IPCC reported

that "most of the observed warming over the last 50 years is likely to have been due to the increase in greenhouse gas concentrations."

The possibility of carbon dioxide-induced global warming was first proposed in 1827 by the French mathematician Baron Joseph Fourier (1768-1830). In 1895, Svante A. Arrhenius (1859-1927), a Nobel Prize winning physical chemist, described how the radiative properties of carbon dioxide and water vapor played an important role in governing Earth's surface temperature. He argued that temperatures in the Arctic would rise some 8 to 9 Celsius degrees (14 to 16 Fahrenheit degrees) if the concentration of atmospheric CO_2 were to increase by a factor of 2.5 to 3. Arrhenius predicted that carbon dioxide and temperature would rise through the 20th century but the actual increase in CO_2 was more rapid and the rise in temperature was slower than he expected. The British engineer G.S. Callendar first reported an upward trend in atmospheric carbon dioxide in 1938.

In 1957, systematic monitoring of atmospheric carbon dioxide began at NOAA's Mauna Loa Observatory in Hawaii under the direction of Charles D. Keeling (1928-2005) of Scripps Institution of Oceanography. The observatory is situated on the slope of a volcano 3400 m (11,200 ft) above sea level in the middle of the Pacific Ocean—sufficiently distant from major sources of air pollution that carbon dioxide levels are considered representative of at least the Northern Hemisphere. Also since 1957, atmospheric CO_2 has been monitored at the South Pole station of the U.S. Antarctic Program and that record closely parallels the one at Mauna Loa. The Mauna Loa and South Pole records both show a sustained increase in average annual atmospheric carbon dioxide concentration from 316 ppmv (parts per million by volume) in 1959 to 377.6 ppmv in 2004, a long-term average increase of about 1.5 ppmv per year (Figure 3.29). Superimposed on the upward trend in the Mauna Loa record is an annual carbon dioxide cycle caused by seasonal changes in photosynthesis by vegetation in the Northern Hemisphere. Levels of carbon dioxide fall during the growing season to a minimum in October and recover over winter to a maximum in May. A weaker seasonal cycle is apparent in the South Pole record, with a maximum in October and a minimum in June.

The upward trend in atmospheric carbon dioxide was underway long before Keeling's monitoring and appears likely to continue well into the future. Humankind's contribution to the buildup of atmospheric CO_2 began roughly three centuries ago with the clearing of land for agriculture and settlement. Land clearing contributes CO_2

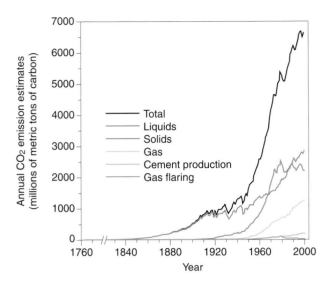

FIGURE 15.22
Estimated global annual carbon dioxide emissions by major sources. [From Marlin, Boden, and Andres, CDIAC, 2003]

to the atmosphere via burning of vegetation, decay of wood residue, and reduced photosynthetic removal of carbon dioxide from the atmosphere. By the middle of the 19th century, growing dependency on coal burning associated with the beginnings of the Industrial Revolution triggered a more rapid rise in CO_2 concentration. Carbon dioxide is a byproduct of the burning of coal and other fossil fuels (Figure 15.22). The concentration of atmospheric CO_2 is now about 31% higher than it was in the pre-industrial era. Fossil fuel combustion accounts for roughly 75% of the increase in atmospheric carbon dioxide while deforestation (and other land clearing) is likely responsible for the balance. With continued growth in fossil fuel combustion, the atmospheric carbon dioxide concentration could top 550 ppmv (double the pre-industrial level) by the end of the present century.

The ocean, a major reservoir in the global carbon cycle, is an important player in governing the amount of carbon dioxide in the atmosphere. From the beginning of the Industrial Revolution, scientists were able to estimate the amount of CO_2 released to the atmosphere by human activity. But in measuring the actual amount of carbon dioxide in the atmosphere, about 50% was missing. As it turns out, the ocean takes up about half of the carbon dioxide of anthropogenic origin (via photosynthesis and cold water absorbing CO_2 and sinking). Some anthropogenic carbon dioxide is transported with the ocean conveyor-belt system and may be sequestered for thousands of years before returning to the air/sea interface.

Besides CO_2, rising levels of other infrared-absorbing gases (e.g., methane and nitrous oxide) could also enhance the greenhouse effect. Methane's concentration in the atmosphere has increased by an estimated 1060 ppb (parts per billion) (151%) since 1750. Methane (CH_4) is the product of organic decay in the absence of oxygen and its concentration may be rising because of more rice cultivation, cattle, landfills, and/or termites, all sources of methane. The atmospheric concentration of nitrous oxide (N_2O) has increased by an estimated 46 ppb (17%) since 1750 likely because of industrial air pollution. Although occurring in extremely low concentrations, methane and nitrous oxide are very efficient absorbers of infrared radiation and are probably contributing to global warming.

Atmospheric aerosols that are byproducts of human activity apparently have the opposite effect on temperatures at Earth's surface as greenhouse gases. These aerosols vary in size, shape, and chemical composition. Larger aerosols tend to settle out of the atmosphere quickly whereas smaller ones may remain suspended for many days to weeks and can be transported thousands of kilometers by the wind, possibly impacting large-scale climate. Perhaps 90% of these aerosols are byproducts of fossil fuel burning in the Northern Hemisphere.

Sulfur oxides emitted from power plant smokestacks and boiler vent pipes combine with water vapor in the air to produce tiny droplets of sulfuric acid and sulfate particles. These *sulfurous aerosols* appear to raise the atmosphere's albedo directly by reflecting sunlight to space and indirectly by acting as condensation nuclei that spur cloud development. Greater reflectivity cools the lower atmosphere. Sulfurous aerosols in the troposphere have a shorter-term impact on climate than carbon dioxide and other greenhouse gases. Rain and snow wash sulfurous aerosols from the lower atmosphere so that the residence time of these substances is typically only a few days. On the other hand, a CO_2 molecule typically resides in the atmosphere for upwards of three-quarters of a century before being cycled out by natural processes operating as part of the global carbon cycle.

The Climate Future

What does the climate future hold? Atmospheric scientists attempt to answer this question primarily by relying on global climate models that run on supercomputers.

GLOBAL CLIMATE MODELS

A **global climate model** is a simulation of Earth's climate system. One type of global climate model consists of dozens of mathematical equations that describe the physical interactions among the various components of the climate system, that is, the atmosphere, ocean, land, ice-cover, and biosphere. A global climate model differs from numerical models used for weather forecasting in that it predicts broad regions of expected positive and negative temperature and precipitation anomalies (departures from long-term averages) and the mean location of circulation features such as jet streams and principal storm tracks over much longer time scales.

Global climate models, for example, are used to predict the potential climatic impacts of rising levels of atmospheric carbon dioxide (or other greenhouse gases). Using current boundary conditions (i.e., climate controls), a global climate model simulates the present climate. Then, holding all other variables constant, the concentration of atmospheric CO_2 (or other greenhouse gas) is elevated and the model is run to a new equilibrium state. By comparing the new climate state with the present climate, scientists deduce the impact of an enhanced greenhouse effect on patterns of temperature and precipitation.

Most modelers argue that global climate models are in need of considerable refinement. Today's models may not adequately simulate the role of small-scale weather systems (e.g., thunderstorms) or accurately portray local and regional conditions and may miss important feedback processes. A major uncertainty is the net feedback of clouds. Clouds cause both cooling (by reflecting sunlight to space) and warming (by absorbing and emitting to Earth's surface outgoing infrared radiation). The cooling effect prevails with an increase in low cloud cover whereas the warming effect prevails with an increase in high cloud cover.

Problems with global climate models stem in part from the limited spatial resolution of the models. Today's models partition the global atmosphere into a three-dimensional grid of boxes with each box typically having an area of 250 square km (155 square mi) and a thickness of 1 km (0.6 mi). Limited spatial resolution in climate models is caused by limited computational speed. Although today's supercomputers can perform trillions of operations per second, the complexity of the climate system means that simulation of climate change over a century requires months of computing time. Much greater resolution of global climate models will come with development of faster supercomputers.

An alternate approach to predicting future climate is to identify the various factors that may have contributed to past fluctuations in climate and to extrapolate their influence into the future. Atmospheric scientists have probed climate records in search of (1) regular cycles that might be extended into the future and (2) analogs that might provide clues as to how the climate in specific regions responds to global-scale climate change. Few of the quasi-regular oscillations that appear in the climate record have much practical value for climate forecasting at least over the next century.

Although the climate record yields much useful information on how climate behaves through time, the search for analogs of future global warming has been fruitless. Proposed analogs include relatively warm episodes of the mid-Holocene and the Eemian interglacial. But those analogs are inappropriate because the mid-Holocene and Eemian warming primarily affected seasonal temperatures with only a slight rise in global mean temperature. Furthermore, boundary conditions were different. During the mid-Holocene, sea level was lower, ice sheets were more extensive, and the dates of perihelion and aphelion were different from what they are now or will be over the next several centuries. Although the level of atmospheric CO_2 trended upward during the mid-Holocene, the rate of increase (about 0.5 ppmv per century) was far lower than at present (more than 60 ppmv per century). Pre-Pleistocene analogs are also inappropriate because of the absence of ice sheets and significant differences in topography and land-ocean distribution.

ENHANCED GREENHOUSE EFFECT AND GLOBAL WARMING

Over the next 10 to 20 thousand years, Milankovitch cycles favor a return to Ice Age conditions. What about the climate in the near term, over the next century or so? If all other controls of climate remain fixed, rising concentrations of atmospheric carbon dioxide and other greenhouse gases are likely to cause global warming to continue throughout this century.

How much warming might accompany a doubling of atmospheric CO_2? Based on runs of global climate models, in 2000 the Intergovernmental Panel on Climate Change (IPCC) revised upward its earlier projections of the magnitude of global warming that could accompany an enhanced greenhouse effect. Various models project that the globally averaged surface temperature will rise by 1.4 to 5.8 Celsius degrees (2.5 to 10.4 Fahrenheit degrees) over the period 1990 to 2100. Recall, however, that climate change is geographically non-uniform (in both magnitude and direction) so that this projected rise in global mean annual temperature is not necessarily representative of what might happen everywhere. For example, *polar amplification* suggests that global warming would be greater at higher latitudes. In any event, enhancement of the natural greenhouse effect could cause a climate change that would be greater in magnitude than any previous climate change in 10,000 years.

Models of global warming based on an enhanced greenhouse effect assume that all other climate controls remain constant. Whether that will actually happen is not known. Comparing the post-1957 trend in atmospheric CO_2 to the trend in mean annual global temperature strongly suggests that recent climate has been shaped by many interacting factors. The rapid rise in CO_2 concentration was not accompanied by a consistent rise in global mean temperature over the same period. Recall, for example, that sulfurous aerosols from the June 1991 eruption of Mount Pinatubo apparently were responsible for significant global-scale cooling the following year. Also as noted earlier, El Niño and La Niña influence climate in some areas of the globe over periods of 12 to 18 months. Furthermore, analysis of tiny air bubbles in cores extracted from the Greenland and Antarctic ice sheets indicate that during the Pleistocene Ice Age, atmospheric CO_2 varied between about 260 and 280 ppmv. Although CO_2 was consistently higher during milder interglacial climatic episodes than during colder glacial climatic episodes, fluctuations in carbon dioxide levels are out of phase with reconstructed variations in climate. For example, at the beginning of the last major glacial climatic episode, the decline in CO_2 concentration significantly lagged cooling in the Antarctic. Hence, fluctuations in atmospheric CO_2 may have been a response to large-scale climate oscillations rather than a cause of those oscillations.

Further complicating efforts to predict the climate future are recent indications that the global radiative budget currently is not in equilibrium. In 2005, scientists reported that the planet is now absorbing about 0.85 W/m² more energy from the sun than it is emitting as IR to space; the imbalance is approximately 0.06% of the solar constant. This conclusion is supported by measurements by satellite sensors and instrumented buoys indicating an increase in the heat content of the ocean over the past 10 years. The imbalance represents the delay in the response of Earth's climate (i.e., surface temperature) to some forcing (i.e., buildup of greenhouse gases). This delay, in turn, is the consequence of the considerable thermal inertia in Earth's climate system—due mostly to the ocean. On this basis, global climate models predict an as yet unrealized additional warming of 0.6 Celsius degree (1.1 Fahrenheit degrees) with no change in atmospheric composition as Earth shifts to a new global radiative equilibrium.

Potential Impacts of Global Climate Change

What are the potential impacts of a continued rise in global mean temperature? As noted earlier in this chapter, global-scale trends in climate do not affect all regions in the same way. But if global warming persists, societal impacts would be extensive. Rising sea level, shrinkage of the Arctic sea-ice cover, more frequent weather extremes, and disruption of agricultural systems are among the most serious potential consequences.

SEA LEVEL FLUCTUATIONS

As noted in Chapter 6, the total amount of water on the planet is essentially constant—an assumption that likely holds throughout recent geologic time. Almost all the water locked in glaciers came from the ocean via the global water cycle. Waxing and waning of glaciers plus ocean temperature fluctuations are two factors that govern the global variation in sea level. During relatively cold climatic episodes, glaciers on land thicken and expand, and the volume of water in the ocean basins decreases (i.e., sea level falls). Conversely, during relatively mild climatic episodes, glaciers on land thin and retreat, and the volume of water in the ocean basins increases (i.e., sea level rises). Furthermore, changes in ocean temperature affect water density and sea level. Seawater always contracts when its temperature drops but expands when its temperature rises. Continuation of the global warming trend appears likely to cause sea level to rise in response to melting of land-based polar ice sheets and mountain glaciers, along with thermal expansion of seawater. Expansion of warming ocean waters probably will be the greater contributor to sea level rise during the present century.

How did sea level respond to the warming trend of the 20th century? For most of the century, coastal tide gauges were the principal source of data on sea level change. Care must be taken to exclude (or adjust) those tide gauge records that might be influenced by geological forces (i.e., tectonic uplift or subsidence or post-glacial rebound). Based on adjusted tide gauge records, sea level during the 20th century rose at the rate of 1.8 ± 0.3 mm per year. Since 1993, sea level has also been measured remotely using microwave altimeters onboard the Earth-orbiting satellites TOPEX/Poseidon and its successor Jason 1 (Chapter 9). Since January 1993, satellite sensors measured a global mean sea level rise of 2.8 ± 0.4 mm per year. In total, mean sea level rose about 18 cm (7.1 in.) during the 20th century. Most mountain glaciers have been shrinking since the mid 20th century. Furthermore, portions of the Greenland ice sheet have shown recent signs of accelerated melting. How much of the recent rise in sea level was due to melting of glacial ice and how much was due to thermal expansion of the warming ocean is not known.

Amplification of the warming trend at higher latitudes would increase the threat to the Greenland and Antarctic ice sheets. About 90% of the planet's glacial ice blankets Antarctica and melting could cause a considerable rise in sea level. How likely is this to happen? Separate ice sheets cover West Antarctica and East Antarctica. The West Antarctic ice sheet sits on a former ocean bottom and is mostly below sea level whereas the East Antarctic ice sheet is situated on a continent and is well above sea level. While geological evidence suggests that the East Antarctic ice sheet has been stable for the past 15 million years, the West Antarctic sheet has undergone episodes of rapid disintegration and may have completely melted at least once in the past 600,000 years. More than 30 years ago, recognition of the relative instability of the West Antarctic ice sheet prompted some scientists to speculate that ice streams flowing from the interior of the glacier to the Ross and Ronne ice shelves might cause a total collapse of the ice sheet in a few centuries or less. Such a catastrophic event would greatly accelerate the rate of sea level rise. (Complete disintegration of the West Antarctic ice sheet would raise sea level by about 5 m or 16 ft.)

In 2001, concerns about the possible disintegration of the West Antarctic ice sheet were alleviated with the discovery that new snowfall is keeping pace with the loss of ice from bergs breaking off the Ross Ice Shelf. In early 2002, scientists at the California Institute of Technology and the University of California-Santa Cruz reported that based on satellite analysis of flow measurements of the Ross ice streams, the West Antarctic ice sheet appears to be thickening. Meanwhile, the region of the ice sheet that feeds the Thwaites and Pine Island glaciers is thinning. These glaciers transport ice directly into the ocean (rather than adding to an ice shelf) and are responsible for about 10% of the average annual rise in sea level. Nonetheless, the consensus of scientific opinion today is that the West Antarctic ice sheet is unlikely to suddenly accelerate the current rise in sea level. According to some experts, long-term gradual shrinkage of the West Antarctic ice could raise sea level at a rate of about 1 m (3.3 ft) per 500 years.

Melting (and the rate of sea level rise) could accelerate if the Antarctic ice sheets begin to feel the effects of global warming. Over most of Antarctica, the mean air temperature has fluctuated very little over the past 50 years. The Antarctic Peninsula is the only part of the continent that has shown significant warming with summer mean temperatures rising more than 2 Celsius degrees (3.6 Fahrenheit degrees) over the past half century. This warming has been accompanied by considerable ice breakup along the coast.

NASA research results released in 2000 concluded that while the central interior of the Greenland ice sheet showed no sign of thinning, about 70% of the margin was thinning substantially. Two research teams—one using a global positioning system (GPS) to monitor ice flow and the other relying on an airborne laser altimeter to measure ice thickness—reached the same conclusion based on observations made between 1993 and 1999. The maximum melting rate at the margin was about 1 m per year. An estimated 50 cubic km (12 cubic mi) of Greenland's ice melts each year, enough to raise sea level by 0.13 mm annually.

More recently, scientists at the University of Colorado reported that during the summer of 2002, surface melting on the Greenland ice sheet encompassed an area of about 695,000 square km (265,000 square mi)—about 9% greater than observed in 24 years of monitoring by satellite. In addition, melting in the northern and northeastern portion of the ice sheet occurred at elevations as high as 2000 m (6550 ft) where normally temperatures are too low for any melting. It appears that winter snowfall is insufficient to offset the summer melt so that overall the Greenland ice sheet is shrinking. Furthermore, by reducing frictional resistance within the ice mass, the greater supply of melt water accelerates the flow of Greenland ice streams into the ocean and increases the rate of rise of sea level.

According to Roger G. Barry, director of NOAA's National Snow and Ice Data Center (NSIDC) at Boulder, CO, the rate of melting of most of the world's mountain glaciers accelerated after the mid-1900s and especially since the mid-1970s (Figure 15.23). Some mountain glaciers have disappeared entirely. For example, today only 26 glaciers remain of the 150 glaciers that existed in Montana's Glacier National Park a century ago. Barry estimates that runoff from melting mountain glaciers contributes about 0.4 mm to the annual rise in sea level.

Alpine glaciers are also shrinking at an accelerating rate. According to Frank Paul of the University of Zurich-Irchel in Zurich, Switzerland, the combined area covered by almost 940 Alpine glaciers decreased by about 18% between 1973 and 1999. Paul's conclusion was based on analysis of satellite images, aerial photographs, and land surveys. Swiss glaciers are now shrinking at an annual

FIGURE 15.23
The recent global warming trend has caused mountain glaciers such as this one in Norway to retreat. Much of the melt water drains into the ocean.

rate that is more than six times the rate that prevailed from 1850 to 1973. At the present rate of shrinkage, Alpine glaciers located at elevations below 2000 m (6500 ft) will likely disappear by 2070.

In spring 2000, NOAA scientists reported that the combined Atlantic, Pacific, and Indian Ocean warmed significantly between 1955 and 1995. The greatest warming occurred in the upper 300 m (980 ft) of the ocean and amounted to 0.31 Celsius degree (0.56 Fahrenheit degree). Water in the upper 3000 m (9850 ft) warmed by an average 0.06 Celsius degree (0.11 Fahrenheit degree). In February 2002, researchers at Scripps Institution of Oceanography reported that temperatures at mid-depths (between 700 m and 1100 m) in the Southern Ocean rose 0.17 Celsius degree between the 1950s and 1980s. Although these magnitudes of temperature change may sound trivial, recall that water has an unusually high specific heat so that even a very small change in temperature of such vast volumes of water represents a tremendous heat input into the ocean. Sequestering of vast quantities of heat in the ocean may help explain why global warming during the 20th century was less than some climate models predicted based on the concurrent buildup of greenhouse gases. That is, heating of the ocean may have partially offset warming of the lower atmosphere. This finding also underscores the importance of the ocean's moderating influence on global climate change.

According to IPCC estimates, melting glaciers combined with thermal expansion of ocean water could raise mean sea level somewhere in the range of 9 to 80 cm (4 to 30 in.) over the period 1990 to 2100. Higher sea level would accelerate coastal erosion, inundate wetlands,

estuaries and some islands, and make low-lying coastal plains more vulnerable to storm surges (Chapter 12). Globally, a 50-cm (20-in.) rise in sea level would double the number of people at risk from storm surges from about 45 million at present to more than 90 million, not counting any additional population growth in the coastal zone. Rising sea level could threaten historical, cultural, and recreational resources. According to a 1997 report by the U.S. Office of Science and Technology Policy, a 50-cm (20-in.) rise in sea level would result in a substantial loss of coastal land, especially along the Gulf and southern Atlantic coasts. Particularly vulnerable is South Florida where one-third of the Everglades is less than 30 cm (12 in.) above sea level.

While higher temperatures would mean higher sea level, the level of the Great Lakes is likely to fall. Higher summer temperatures coupled with less winter ice cover on the Great Lakes are likely to translate into greater evaporation. And less winter snowfall would reduce spring runoff. Depending on the model used, forecasts call for a drop in mean water level on Lake Michigan of up to 2 m (6.5 ft) by the year 2070. Residents of the western Great Lakes may have previewed the impact of global warming during the late 1990s and early 2000s when the levels of Lakes Michigan and Huron dropped to near historical record lows.

ARCTIC SEA ICE COVER

Although melting of floating sea ice does not raise sea level, it can alter climate in a significant way by greatly reducing the surface albedo. A variety of sources provide information on the extent of Arctic sea ice cover since the early part of the 20th century. Ship and aircraft observations indicate that the multi-year Arctic ice cover remained essentially constant in all seasons through the first half of the 20th century. But beginning in the 1950s, observations by ships and aircraft detected shrinkage in the summer minimum extent of ice while the winter maximum remained nearly constant. By the mid-1970s, satellite surveillance, submarines, and ice-cores were finding a decline in the winter maximum as well.

Norwegian researchers reported that the area covered by multi-year ice in the Arctic decreased by about 14% between 1978 and 1998. Their findings were based on satellite monitoring of the spectrum of microwave energy emitted by the ice. Comparing ice-thickness measurements made by U.S. Navy submarines from 1958 to 1976 with those made during the *Scientific Ice Expedition* program in 1993, 1996, and 1997, University of Washington scientists found that ice had thinned from an average thickness of 3.1 m (10 ft) to an average thickness of 1.8 m (6 ft). Thinning at the rate of 15% per decade translates into a total volumetric ice loss of about 40% in three decades. (Upward-looking acoustic sounders mounted on the submarines were used to map ice depth.)

After 2000, the rate of reduction of Arctic sea ice cover accelerated. From analysis of satellite data, scientists from the Cooperative Institute for Research in Environmental Sciences (CIRES) at the University of Colorado reported that in 2002 the extent of Arctic sea ice was the lowest in the satellite record, likely the lowest since the early 1950s, and perhaps the lowest in several centuries. In September 2002, sea ice covered about 5.3 million square km (2 million square mi) compared to the long-term average of about 6.3 million square km (2.4 million square mi). According to scientists at NOAA's National Snow and Ice Data Center the extent of end-of-summer sea ice cover in the Arctic reached a record low in 2005 (Figure 15.24). From the late 1970s to 2001, the area of Arctic sea ice cover decreased by about 6.5% per decade. Since then, the rate of shrinkage has been about 8% per decade. If current trends continue, by 2050 there may be a 20% reduction in mean annual sea ice in the Arctic and little or no ice in summer.

Shrinkage of Arctic sea ice raises concerns about a possible **ice-albedo feedback** mechanism that would accelerate melting of sea-ice and amplify warming. Sea ice insulates the overlying air from warmer seawater and reflects much more incident solar radiation than ocean water. Snow-covered sea ice has an albedo of about 85% whereas ice-free Arctic Ocean water has an average albedo of only about 7%. As sea ice cover shrinks, the greater area of ice-free ocean waters absorbs more solar radiation, sea-surface temperatures rise, and more ice will melt. Furthermore, warmer water slows the formation of ice in

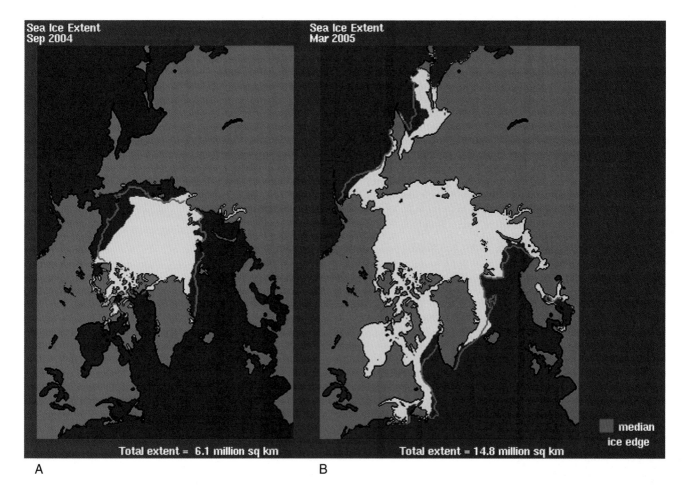

FIGURE 15.24
Total area covered by sea ice (not including the open water within the pack ice) in the Northern Hemisphere polar region in (A) September 2004 and (B) March 2005. These two months represent the times of minimum and maximum ice extent respectively over a 12-month period. Average ice conditions are estimated using passive microwave sensors on Earth-orbiting satellites. [NOAA, National Snow and Ice Data Center]

autumn. This positive feedback mechanism could rapidly reduce the sea ice cover and greatly alter the flux of heat energy and moisture between the ocean and atmosphere with possible ramifications for global climate.

Less sea ice cover on the Arctic Ocean is likely to increase the humidity of the overlying air leading to more cloudiness. As pointed out earlier in this chapter, clouds cause both cooling (by reflecting sunlight to space) and warming (by absorbing and emitting to Earth's surface outgoing infrared radiation). During the long dark polar winter, clouds would have a warming effect. In summer, the impact of a greater cloud cover depends on the height of the clouds. Cooling would prevail with an increase in low cloud cover whereas warming would likely accompany an increase in high cloud cover.

Shrinkage of the Arctic sea ice may be the direct consequence of higher air temperatures or indirectly the result of changes in ocean circulation (i.e., greater input of warmer Atlantic water under the Arctic ice). Some scientists argue that higher air and ocean temperatures in the Arctic are natural variations in climate associated with the *Arctic Oscillation (AO)* and that the ice-cover will return to normal after the AO changes phase (Chapter 9). During the present AO phase winds have been delivering warmer than usual air and seawater into the Arctic.

Mean annual air temperatures in the Arctic climbed about 0.5 Celsius degree (0.9 Fahrenheit degree) per decade over the past thirty years. Proxy climatic data indicate that present temperatures (especially in winter and spring) may be at their highest level in four centuries. In response, mountain glaciers in Alaska are shrinking at historically unprecedented rates, *permafrost* (permanently frozen ground) is beginning to thaw, and freshwater runoff into the ocean has increased. More winter precipitation combined with an increased flow of groundwater (due to melting permafrost) is likely responsible for a 7% increase in the discharge of six major Eurasian rivers into the Arctic Ocean since the 1930s.

Input of more fresh surface water (from rivers and melting glacial ice) would impact the ocean conveyor-belt system by reducing the salinity and thus the density of surface ocean waters. As part of the conveyor belt, relatively dense cold, salty water sinks at high latitudes of the Atlantic Ocean. As pointed out earlier in this chapter, changes in strength of the ocean conveyor-belt system belt affect air temperatures over the North Atlantic and Western Europe. Any alteration of the conveyor belt is likely to impact the poleward transport of heat. Paradoxically, warming at high latitudes could lead to regional cooling due to a weakening of the conveyor belt.

OTHER IMPACTS

Higher global temperatures may translate into more severe drought in some locations and floods in other places. Unfortunately, global climate models do not agree on the locations of precipitation extremes. An assessment of predictions generated by different state-of-the-art coupled atmosphere/ocean climate models underscores the rudimentary state of climate prediction at the regional scale. For example, the Canadian Climate Centre model predicts that global warming will be accompanied by drier summer soil conditions over the eastern two-thirds of the coterminous U.S. whereas Britain's Hadley Center for Climate Research and Prediction model projects wetter soils in the same area.

Whereas regional response to global climate change is uncertain, scientists and policy makers are confident that localities most vulnerable to water resource problems are places where the quality and quantity of fresh water are already a problem, that is, in semi-arid and arid regions. In the U.S., water supply problems are most likely in the drainage basins of the Missouri, Arkansas, Rio Grande, and lower Colorado Rivers. Water shortages in the Middle East and Africa may heighten political tensions especially in nations that depend on water supplies originating outside their borders.

Although global climate change is not expected to substantially impact total global food production, higher temperatures and more frequent drought may severely affect certain regions of the world. Developed nations have the capacity to adapt their agricultural systems to climate change. While overall U.S. food production is expected to climb throughout the 21st century, there will be some losers. For example, greater demand for irrigation waters may further stress important reservoirs of groundwater (e.g., the High Plains aquifer). On the other hand, the agricultural systems of developing nations are much more vulnerable to the adverse effects of warming and are most likely to experience a significant decline in food production.

Prospects of higher sea-surface temperatures prompted some scientists to predict an upturn in the number and intensity of tropical cyclones (i.e., hurricanes and tropical storms). However, as discussed in Chapter 12, relatively high sea-surface temperature is one of several factors required for tropical cyclone formation. In fact, some climate models predict stronger winds aloft accompanying a warmer climate that would inhibit tropical cyclone development. In January 2001, the IPCC concluded that in spite of the global warming trend, there is no evidence that top wind speeds or rainfall had increased in tropical cyclones during the second half of the 20th century. Resolving the likely impact of global climate change on tropical cyclones awaits the development of more realistic climate models.

Conclusions

The interaction of many factors is responsible for the inherent variability of climate. Although we can isolate specific climatic controls that are internal or external to the Earth-atmosphere system, our understanding of how these controls interact is far from complete. This state of the art limits the ability of atmospheric scientists to forecast the climatic future. Continued research on climate is needed. It is reasonable to assume that physical laws govern climatic change; that is, variations in climate are not arbitrary, random events. As scientists more fully comprehend the laws regulating climatic change, their ability to predict the climate future will improve, aided by faster supercomputers and more realistic global climate models. Meanwhile, trends in climate must be monitored closely, especially in view of the strong dependence of our food and water supplies and energy demand on climate. In spite of, or perhaps because of, the scientific uncertainty, some experts argue that we should plan now for the worst possible future climate scenario.

Basic Understandings

- Climate is defined as the weather of some locality averaged over some time period plus extremes in weather. The climatic norm (or normal) at some place encompasses the total variability of the climate record, that is, averages plus extremes.

- By international convention, climatic norms are computed from averages of weather elements compiled over a specified 30-year period. Current climate summaries are based on weather records covering the period from 1971 to 2000.

- Departures from long-term climatic averages, called anomalies, do not occur with the same sign or magnitude everywhere. At middle and high latitudes, the geographic non-uniformity of climatic anomalies is linked to the prevailing westerly wave pattern that ultimately governs cold and warm air advection, cyclogenesis, and storm tracks. Large-scale trends in climate are also geographically non-uniform.

- Many factors working together shape the climate of any locality. Controls of climate consist of latitude, elevation, topography, proximity to large bodies of water, Earth's surface characteristics, long-term average atmospheric circulation, and prevailing ocean circulation.

- The ocean is a major player in Earth's climate system. The ocean influences radiational heating and cooling, is the main source of water vapor, and a major regulator of the concentration of atmospheric carbon dioxide (CO_2). On a global average annual basis, about ten times more heat is transferred from the ocean surface to the atmosphere via latent heating than sensible heating. Coupling of the atmosphere and ocean is most apparent in the ocean's surface waters where temperatures and wind-driven currents respond to variations in atmospheric conditions within hours to days. On the other hand, the deeper basin-scale circulation responds more sluggishly to changes in atmospheric conditions, taking decades to centuries or longer to fully adjust.

- Mean annual isotherms roughly parallel latitude circles, underscoring the influence of solar radiation and solar altitude on climate. Through the course of a year, mean monthly isotherms in both hemispheres follow the sun, shifting north and south in tandem.

- The global pattern of mean annual precipitation (rain plus melted snowfall) exhibits considerable spatial variability in response to topography, distribution of land and sea, and the planetary-scale circulation.

- For information on climates prior to the era of reliable instrument-based records, scientists rely on climatic inferences drawn from historical documents, and geological/biological evidence such as bedrock, fossils, pollen, tree growth rings, glacial ice cores, and deep-sea sediment cores.

- Plate tectonics and continental drift complicate climate reconstruction of periods spanning hundreds of millions of years. In the context of geologic time, topography and the geographical distribution of continents and the ocean are variable controls of climate.

- Geologic evidence points to an interval of extreme fluctuations in climate about 570 million years ago, corresponding to the transition between

Precambrian and Phanerozoic Eons. During as many as four cold episodes, each lasting perhaps 10 million years, the planet was encased in glacial ice. At the close of each cold episode, temperatures rose rapidly, and within only a few centuries, all the ice melted. Relatively warm conditions appear to have persisted through much of the Mesozoic Era, from about 245 to 70 million years ago.

- By 40 million years ago, global climate began shifting toward cooler, drier, and more variable conditions. Scientists have implicated tectonic forces and the building of the Colorado Plateau, Tibetan Plateau, and Himalayan Mountains as the principal cause of this climate change. Cooling after 40 million years ago culminated in the Pleistocene Ice Age that began about 1.7 million years ago. During the Pleistocene, the climate shifted numerous times between glacial climatic episodes (favoring expansion of glaciers) and interglacial climatic episodes (favoring shrinkage of glaciers).

- Climate change during the Pleistocene was geographically non-uniform in magnitude; cooling was maximum at high latitudes and minimum in the tropics. This latitudinal variation in the magnitude of temperature change is known as polar amplification.

- The last major glacial climatic episode began about 27,000 years ago and reached its peak about 18,000 to 20,000 years ago when the glacial ice cover over North America was about as extensive as it had ever been.

- Notable post-glacial climatic episodes were the relatively warm mid-Holocene (the Hypsithermal), the Medieval Warm Period (from about 950 to 1250 CE), and the Little Ice Age (from about 1400 to 1850 CE). In all cases, the temperature change was geographically non-uniform in magnitude.

- The instrument-based record of global mean temperature indicates a gradual warming trend since the 1880s, interrupted by cooling at middle and high latitudes of the Northern Hemisphere from about 1940 to 1970.

- Analysis of the climate record reveals many useful observations regarding the temporal behavior of climate. Climate is inherently variable; climate change is geographically non-uniform in sign (direction) and magnitude; climate change may

involve changes in mean values of temperature or precipitation and/or changes in the frequency of weather extremes; climate change tends to be abrupt rather than gradual; only a few reliable cycles appear to operate in the climate record; and climate change can impact society.

- Matching some forcing mechanism with a climate response based on similar periods of oscillation is no guarantee of a real physical relationship. Factors that could alter the global radiative equilibrium and change Earth's climate include fluctuations in solar energy output, changes in Earth's orbital parameters, volcanic eruptions, changes in Earth's surface properties, and certain human activities.

- Changes in the sun's total energy output at all wavelengths apparently are related to sunspot activity. Solar output varies directly and minutely with sunspot number; that is, a slightly brighter sun has more sunspots (because of a concurrent increase in faculae, bright areas), and a slightly dimmer sun exhibits fewer sunspots.

- Variations in the seasonal and latitudinal receipt of solar energy available to planet Earth associated with Milankovitch cycles apparently drive climate oscillations operating over tens of thousands to hundreds of thousands of years. They were likely responsible for the major advances and recessions of the Laurentide ice sheet over North America during the Pleistocene. Cycles consist of regular variations in precession and tilt of Earth's rotational axis and the eccentricity of its orbit about the sun. These same cycles show up in deep-sea sediment cores that date from the Pleistocene Ice Age.

- Only violent volcanic eruptions rich in sulfur dioxide are likely to impact global or hemispheric-scale climate by affecting the transparency of the atmosphere to incoming solar radiation and outgoing infrared radiation from Earth's surface. Such an eruption has a non-uniform effect on surface air temperature but is unlikely to lower the mean hemispheric temperature by more than about 1.0 Celsius degree (1.8 Fahrenheit degrees).

- Earth's surface, a large fraction of which is covered by ocean water, is the prime absorber of solar radiation so that any change in the physical properties of the water or land surfaces or in the relative distribution of ocean and land may impact the global radiation balance and climate.

- Human activity may impact global-scale climate by increasing the concentration of greenhouse gases (causing warming) or sulfurous aerosols (causing cooling). The upward trend in atmospheric carbon dioxide since the beginning of the Industrial Revolution is primarily due to burning of fossil fuels and to a lesser extent the clearing of vegetation.

- A global climate model consists of mathematical equations that describe the physical laws that govern the interactions among the various components of Earth's climate system. They are used to predict broad regions of expected positive and negative temperature and precipitation anomalies.

- The climate record does not appear to contain reliable cycles that can be used to forecast the climate over a period of several centuries. Also, no satisfactory analogs exist in the climate record that would allow scientists to predict the regional response to global-scale climate change.

- Current global climate models predict that significant global warming will accompany a doubling of atmospheric CO_2 (possible by the close of this century if assumptions concerning future emission rates of this gas turn out to be correct). Warming may be greater in magnitude than during any prior climate change of the past 10,000 years.

- Projections of the magnitude of future global warming arising from carbon dioxide enhancement of the greenhouse effect assumes that all other controls of climate remain constant. To what extent this will happen is not known.

- Projected increases in global temperature would likely cause sea level to rise in response to melting of glaciers and expansion of seawater. According to IPCC estimates, melting glaciers combined with thermal expansion of ocean water could raise mean sea level somewhere in the range of 9 to 80 cm (4 to 30 in.) over the period 1990 to 2100. Higher sea level would accelerate coastal erosion, inundate wetlands, estuaries and some islands, and make low-lying coastal plains more vulnerable to storm surges. On the other hand, warming is likely to cause levels of the Great Lakes to fall in response to increased evaporation and reduced winter snow pack.

- Melting of floating sea ice can alter climate in a significant way by greatly reducing the surface albedo. Beginning in the 1950s, observations by ships and aircraft detected shrinkage in the summer minimum extent of Arctic sea ice while the winter maximum remained nearly constant. By the mid-1970s, satellite surveillance, submarines, and ice-cores were finding a decline in the winter maximum as well. Shrinkage of Arctic sea ice raises concerns about a possible ice-albedo feedback mechanism that would accelerate melting of sea ice and amplify warming.

- Higher global temperatures may translate into more severe drought in some locations and floods in other places. Unfortunately, global climate models do not agree on the locations of precipitation extremes. Arid and semi-arid localities already experiencing water supply problems are most vulnerable to the adverse effects of global climate change.

Review

1. Explain how climatic anomalies are computed.
2. List the major controls of climate.
3. Explain what is meant by the *geographical non-uniformity of climatic change*.
4. How is total solar radiational energy output related to sunspot number?
5. What are the Milankovitch cycles?
6. How does the Milankovitch theory seek to explain the major climatic shifts of the Pleistocene Ice Age?
7. How might violent volcanic eruptions influence global climate?
8. Evaluate humankind's potential contributions to climatic change.
9. What is meant by an *enhanced greenhouse effect*?
10. Describe the role of the ocean in Earth's climate system.

Critical Thinking

1. Why are climate anomalies geographically nonuniform in sign (direction) and magnitude?
2. What is the significance of the geographic nonuniformity of climatic anomalies for (a) agricultural productivity and (b) home heating and cooling demands?
3. Climatic controls are really not independent of one another. Provide some examples of linkages.
4. In general terms, describe how sensitivity to climate change varies geographically. Speculate on why polar areas appear to be more sensitive than other regions of the planet to global-scale climate change.
5. A major climate change about 18,000 years ago triggered the ultimate demise of the Laurentide ice sheet. Although the climate over most of North America was dominantly interglacial after 18,000 years ago, more than 12,000 years elapsed before all the ice melted away. Why was the Laurentide ice sheet so slow in melting?
6. Explain the notion that past climate episodes differ from present climate episodes in frequency rather than type of episode. Provide some examples.
7. A high statistical correlation between two factors does not necessarily indicate a cause-effect relationship. Give an example of how this statement applies to the search for the causes of climate change.
8. If the Milankovitch theory is correct, then the next ice age will peak about 23,000 years from now. Does this imply that each successive year from now on will get progressively colder? Explain your response.
9. In attempting to explain climate variability, we cannot focus simply on changes that occur in the atmosphere alone. We must also consider changes in the ocean and in the Earth's land-surface characteristics. Please explain why.
10. Based on conditions required for tropical cyclone development, speculate on the possible effect of CO_2-induced global warming on the intensity and frequency of hurricanes in the future.

ESSAY: Sources of Proxy Climate Data

Proxy climate data consist of information on past climates derived from analysis of climate-sensitive historical documents, geological features, and biological systems. These data serve in lieu of (as proxy for) instrument-based climate records. On land, much has been learned about past climate from study of pollen records, tree growth rings, and glacial ice cores.

Pollen is a valuable source of information on late Ice Age and Holocene vegetation and climate, especially over the past 15,000 years. *Pollen* is the tiny dust-like fertilizing component of a seed plant that is dispersed by the wind and accumulates at the bottom of lakes (and in other depositional environments) along with other organic and inorganic sediments. Scientists use a coring device to extract a sediment column (core) that chronicles past changes in pollen (and therefore, vegetation). Back at the laboratory, pollen grains are separated from the other sediment in the core, identified as to source species, and counted to determine the dominant vegetation type. Implications for past climate are drawn assuming that (1) the pollen is of local origin and (2) climate largely controls vegetation (and pollen) type. Changes in dominant pollen type with time in a core signal changes in nearby vegetation, likely in response to climate change.

Tree growth rings can yield a year-to-year record of past climate variations stretching back many thousands of years. Each spring/summer, living trees add a growth-ring whose thickness and density depend on growing season weather. A small hollow drill is used to extract a tree's growth-ring record. Although other environmental factors (e.g., soil type, drainage) can be important, tree growth rings are especially sensitive to moisture stress and have been used to reconstruct lengthy chronologies of drought prior to the era of instrument-based records. Some of the longest tree ring records have been obtained from several thousand year-old bristle cone pines found in the White Mountains of California and New Mexico (Figure 1).

Ice cores extracted from glaciers yield a record of past seasonal snowfall preserved as thin layers of ice. Cores extracted from the Greenland and Antarctic ice sheets provide detailed decadal-scale climatic information going back roughly 420,000 years (Figure 2). Using the oxygen isotope technique (described below), scientists can distinguish between cold and mild episodes in the past and through chemical analysis of tiny bubbles trapped in the ice, determine the chemical composition of ancient air. This latter information is important in tracking long-term trends in the concentration of greenhouse gases.

Figure 1
Bristlecone pines in the White Mountains of California. [Photo by Jonathan Pilcher, Palaeo-ecology Centre, Queen's University, Belfast; NOAA/NCDC/Paleoclimatology Program]

Figure 2
This 6-m (20 -ft) long ice core was extractted from the Greenland ice sheet, and is a source of information on past variations in climate and atmospheric composition. [Photo by Mark Twickler, University of New Hampshire; NOAA/NCDC/Paleoclimatology Program]

Cores taken from undisturbed layers of marine sediments that blanket the ocean floor yield a continuous record of sedimentation going back many hundreds of thousands of years. Much of what we know about the climate fluctuations of the Pleistocene Ice Age is based on analysis of the shell and skeletal remains of microscopic marine organisms that are extracted from deep-sea sediment cores. Identification of the organism plus oxygen isotope analysis of these remains enable scientists to distinguish between cold and mild climatic episodes of the past.

With *oxygen isotope analysis*, scientists use a special property of water to reconstruct large-scale climatic fluctuations of the Pleistocene Ice Age. A water molecule (H_2O) is composed of either of two stable isotopes of oxygen, O^{16} or O^{18}. (Isotopes of a single element differ in atomic mass based on the number of neutrons in the nucleus of the atom.) The lighter isotope (O^{16}) is much more abundant than the heavier isotope (O^{18}); only one O^{18} exists for every thousand or so O^{16}. Nonetheless, small but significant variations are measured in the amount of light oxygen compared to heavy oxygen circulating in the global water cycle. These variations have important implications for past fluctuations in glacial ice volume on the planet.

On average, water molecules containing the lighter O^{16} isotope move slightly faster than water molecules containing the heavier O^{18} isotope and evaporate more readily. Water molecules that evaporate from the ocean (or land) are enhanced in light oxygen compared to heavy oxygen. The amount of O^{16} compared to O^{18} is also greater in cloud particles and rain and snow versus liquid water on Earth's surface. Most precipitation either falls back into the ocean directly or drains from land back to the sea, replenishing the ocean's supply of light oxygen and maintaining a constant average ratio of O^{16} to O^{18}. However, geographical variations in the oxygen isotope ratio of seawater arise because of differences in precipitation amounts and evaporation rates. Seawater has more O^{18} at subtropical latitudes where evaporation exceeds precipitation and less in middle latitudes where rainfall is heavier.

During a glacial climatic episode, snow that accumulates on land is converted to ice. Heavy water molecules condense and precipitate slightly more readily than light water molecules so that moisture plumes moving from the tropics to high latitudes lose heavy oxygen along the way. Hence, snow falling in Canada has less O^{18} than rain falling in the tropics. The result is that growing ice sheets sequester more and more light oxygen while ocean water ends up with less and less O^{16} proportionately. With a shift to an interglacial climate, ice sheets melt and O^{16}-rich melt water drains back into the ocean increasing the amount of O^{16} compared to O^{18}. Hence, over time the proportion of light to heavy oxygen in ocean water decreases with increasing glacial ice cover.

Organic sediments on the ocean floor record fluctuations in the oxygen isotope ratio of seawater. Marine organisms such as foraminifera living in the sunlit surface waters build their shells from calcium carbonate ($CaCO_3$) that is dissolved in seawater. Shells formed during warmer interglacial climatic episodes contain more light oxygen than those formed during colder glacial climatic episodes. When these organisms die, their shells settle to the ocean bottom and mix with other marine sediments. From specially outfitted deep-sea drilling ships, scientists extract cores from an undisturbed sequence of ocean bottom sediments, with the youngest sediments at the top of the core and the oldest sediments at the bottom. In the laboratory, the core is split open, and shells are extracted and analyzed for their oxygen isotope ratio. Hence, variations in oxygen isotope ratio document changes in the planet's glacial ice volume, an indicator of large-scale climate change. Oxygen isotope analysis of deep-sea sediment cores reveals that the Pleistocene was punctuated by abrupt changes between numerous glacial and interglacial climatic episodes.

APPENDIX I

CONVERSION FACTORS

	Multiply	By	To obtain
LENGTH	inches (in.)	2.54	centimeters (cm)
	centimeters	0.3937	inches
	feet (ft)	0.3048	meters (m)
	meters	3.281	feet
	statute miles (mi)	1.6093	kilometers (km)
	statute miles (mi)	0.869	nautical miles
	kilometers	0.6214	statute miles
	kilometers	0.54	nautical miles
	nautical miles	1.852	kilometers
	kilometers	3281	feet
	feet	0.0003048	kilometers
SPEED	miles per hour (mph)	1.6093	kilometers per hour (kph)
	miles per hour	1.1516	knots (kts)
	miles per hour	0.447	meters per second (m/s)
	knots	0.869	miles per hour
	knots	0.5148	meters per second
	kilometers per hour	0.6213	miles per hour
	kilometers per hour	0.540	knots
	meters per second	1.944	knots
	meters per second	2.237	miles per hour
WEIGHTS AND MASS	ounces (oz)	28.35	grams (g)
	grams	0.0353	ounces
	pounds (lb)	0.4536	kilograms (kg)
	kilograms	2.205	pounds
	tons	0.9072	metric tons
	metric tons	1.102	tons
LIQUID	fluid ounces (fl oz)	0.0296	liters (L)

MEASURE	gallons (gal)	3.785	liters
	liters	0.2642	gallons
	liters	33.815	fluid ounces
AREA	acres (A)	0.4047	hectares (ha)
	square yards (yd^2)	0.8361	square meters (m^2)
	square miles (mi^2)	2.590	square kilometers (km^2)
	hectares	0.010	square kilometers
	hectares	2.471	acres
PRESSURE/ FORCE	pounds force (lb)	4.448	newtons (N)
	newtons	0.2248	pounds
	millimeters of mercury at 0 °C	133.32	pascals (Pa; N per m^2)
	pounds per square inch (psi)	6.895	kilopascals (kPa; 1000 pascals)
	pascals	0.0075	millimeters of mercury at 0 °C
	kilopascals	0.1450	pounds per square inch
	bars	1000	millibars (mb)
	bars	100000	pascals
	bars	0.9869	atmospheres (atm)
ENERGY	joules (J)	0.2389	calories (cal)
	kilocalories (kcal)	1000	calories
	joules	1.0	watt-seconds (W-sec)
	kilojoules (kJ)	1000	joules
	calories	0.00397	Btu (British thermal units)
	Btu	252	calories
POWER	joules per second	1.0	watts (W)
	kilowatts (kW)	1000	watts
	megawatts (MW)	1000	kilowatts
	kilocalories per minute	69.93	watts
	watts	0.00134	horsepower (hp)
	kilowatts	56.87	Btu per minute
	Btu per minute	0.235	horsepower

APPENDIX II

MILESTONES IN THE HISTORY OF ATMOSPHERIC SCIENCE

ca. 525 B.C.E.	Greek philosopher Anaximenes of Miletus proposed that winds, clouds, rain and hail are formed by thickening of air, the primary substance.
ca. 500 B.C.E.	Parmenides classified world climates by latitude as torrid, temperate, or frigid.
ca. 400 B.C.E.	Rainfall measured in India using the first known rain gauge.
350-340 B.C.E.	Aristotle produced his *Meteorologica*, the first work on the atmospheric sciences.
330 B.C.E.	Hippocrates wrote *Air, Waters, and Places,* a treatise on climate and medicine.
ca. 135 B.C.E.	The Chinese writer Han Ying first notes the hexagonal shape of snowflakes in *Moral discourses illustrating the Han text of the "Book of Songs."*
61 C.E.	Seneca complained of the air pollution of Rome.
1304	Theodoric of Friebourg (now in Germany) wrote *De iride* (On the Rainbow) describing his experiments with bulbs filled with water.
1442	Rain gauges used in Korea.
1450	Cardinal Nicholas of Cusa (1400-1464) constructed the first balance hygrometer.
1591	The English mathematician Thomas Harriot (1560-1621) notes that snowflakes have six sides.
1592	Galileo Galilei (1564-1642) invented the thermoscope, forerunner of the thermometer.
1621	Dutch physicist Willebrord Snell (1591-1626) discovered the law of refraction of light.
1637	French philosopher René Descartes (1596-1650) published *Discours de la méthode,* which includes his ideas about the rainbow and cloud formation.

1638	Galileo Galilei determined that air has weight.
1639	The first mention of a rain gauge in European literature.
1641	Ferdinand II of Tuscany (1610-1670) constructs a thermometer containing liquid.
1643	Evangelista Torricelli (1608-1647) invented the mercury barometer.
1644	Rev. John Campanius Holm recorded the first weather observations in America, near the present site of Wilmington, DE.
1648	Florin Périer ascended the Puy-de-Dôme in France, and with Blaise Pascal (1623-1662) demonstrated that air pressure decreases with increasing altitude.
1660	German scientist Otto von Guericke (1602-1686) noted that a severe storm followed a sudden drop in barometric pressure.
1666	Sir Isaac Newton (1643-1727) used a glass prism to demonstrate that sunlight is made up of a spectrum of colors.
ca. 1670	Mercury was used in thermometers for the first time.
1683	The English astronomer Edmund Halley (1656-1742) published the first comprehensive map of winds along with a partial explanation of the trade winds.
1686	Edmund Halley proposed an explanation for monsoons.
1687	Isaac Newton developed his three laws of motion.
1687	French physician Guillaume Amontons (1663-1705) invented a hygrometer.
1709	German physicist Gabriel Daniel Fahrenheit (1686-1736) constructed a thermometer with alcohol as the working fluid.
1714	Gabriel Daniel Fahrenheit introduced the Fahrenheit temperature scale.
1730	French entomologist and physicist René Réamur (1683-1757) introduced a thermometer using a water/alcohol mixture.
1735	German explorer Johann G. Gmelin (1709-1755) discovered permafrost in Siberia.
1735	George Hadley (1685-1768) proposed the Hadley cell circulation.
1742	Swedish astronomer Anders Celsius (1701-1744) introduced the Celsius temperature scale.
1743	Jean Pierre Christin inverted the fixed points on the Celsius temperature scale, producing the scale used today.
1743	Benjamin Franklin (1706-1790) deduced the progressive movement of a storm along the U.S. East Coast.

1747	Benjamin Franklin began a series of experiments on electricity that led to the use of the lightning rod.
1749	Franklin attached a lightning rod to his house in Philadelphia.
1749	In Glasgow, Scotland, Alexander Wilson used thermometers attached to a kite to obtain the first temperature profile of the lower atmosphere (up to perhaps 60 m or 200 ft).
1752	Benjamin Franklin performed his famous kite experiment demonstrating the electrical nature of lightning.
1760	Scottish chemist Joseph Black (1728-1799) formulated the concept of specific heat.
1766	English chemist Henry Cavendish (1731-1810) discovered hydrogen.
1772	Scottish medical student Daniel Rutherford was first to publish the discovery of nitrogen.
1774	Carl Scheele (1742-1786) and Joseph Priestly (1733-1804) discovered oxygen.
1778	Thomas Jefferson and James Madison took the nation's first simultaneous weather observations.
1781	Systematic weather observations began at New Haven, CT.
1783	Swiss naturalist Horace de Saussure (1740-1799) demonstrated supercooling of water.
1800	Astronomer Sir William Herschel (1738-1822) discovered energy transfer in the infrared (IR).
1802-03	British pharmacist and amateur meteorologist Luke Howard (1772-1864) developed his classification of cloud types.
1802	French physicist J. L. Gay-Lussac (1778-1850) published the *gas law*; British chemist John Dalton (1766-1844) defined *relative humidity*.
1804	J. L. Gay-Lussac and Jean Biot conducted the first manned balloon exploration of the atmosphere, reaching a maximum altitude of 7000 m (23,000 ft).
1805	British admiral Sir Francis Beaufort (1774-1857) proposed a scale of winds (now known as the *Beaufort scale*).
1811	Italian chemist Amedeo Avogadro (1776-1856) first stated Avogadro's law.
1819	Heinrich Wilhelm Brandes (1777-1834) drew the first weather map, depicting a storm over the English Channel.
1820	English chemist John Frederic Daniell (1790-1845) invented the dew-point hygrometer.
1821	Swiss geologist Ignatz Venetz (1788-1857) proposed that glaciers formerly occurred throughout Europe.
1825	E.F. August developed the psychrometer.
1827	French mathematician Baron Joseph Fourier (1768-1830) proposed the possibility of CO_2- induced global warming.

1835	Gaspard Gustav de Coriolis (1792-1843) demonstrated quantitatively how Earth's rotation affects large-scale motion in the atmosphere or ocean.
1837	Swiss naturalist Louis Agassiz (1807-1873) used the term *Eiszeit* (Ice Age) for the first time; he championed the glacial theory during the mid 1800s.
1837	James P. Espy (1785-1860) published the first U.S. weather map.
1838	British Navy adopted the Beaufort scale for estimating wind speed from the state of the sea.
1840	Agassiz publishes his *Etudes des glaciers* (*Studies on Glaciers*).
1842	Austrian physicist Johann Christian Doppler (1803-1853) first explained the Doppler Effect.
1842	French mathematician Joseph Alphonse Adhémar (1797-1862) proposed that regular variations in Earth's orbit explained climate fluctuations during the Ice Age.
1843	Samuel Heinrich Schwabe (1789-1875) discovered the sunspot cycle.
1844	Aneroid barometer invented.
1850	French chemist Jean Barrel confirmed the existence of supercooled cloud droplets in the free atmosphere.
1853	James Coffin suggested that there are three distinct wind zones in the Northern Hemisphere.
1853	First International Meteorological Conference, held in Brussels.
1856	American meteorologist William Ferrel (1817-1891) proposed a model of the general circulation of the atmosphere consisting of three cells.
1857	Lorin Blodget published *Climatology of the United States*.
1857	Dutch meteorologist Christopher Buys-Ballot (1817-1890) developed a rule that relates wind direction to the location of a low pressure center (*Buys Ballot's law*).
1862	James Glaisher and Henry Coxwell set manned balloon altitude record of 9000 m (29,500 ft) over Wolverhampton, England.
1864	Scottish scientist James Croll (1821-1890) furthered study on the astronomical theory of the Ice Age.
1869	In Cincinnati, OH Cleveland Abbe (1838-1916) prepared the first regular weather maps for part of the United States.
1870	President Ulysses S. Grant signed legislation establishing a national weather service operated by the U.S. Army Signal Corps.
1871	Cleveland Abbe appointed chief meteorologist of the new national weather service.
1874	Based on field studies, American geologist Thomas Chrowder Chamberlin (1843-1928) suggested that there were several Ice Ages separated by nonglacial epochs.

1874	Hurricane plotted for the first time on a surface weather map (offshore near Savannah, GA).
1878	The International Meteorological Organization (IMO) was founded.
1881	Lord Rayleigh (1842-1919) demonstrated that scattering of visible light by gas molecules is inversely proportional to the fourth power of the wavelength.
1884	Ludwig Boltzmann (1844-1906) derived the Stefan-Boltzmann law.
1884	International time zones were adopted at the International Meridian Conference in Washington, DC.
1884	John P. Finley of the U.S. Army Signal Corps issued the first experimental tornado forecasts.
1885	First reported sighting of a noctilucent clouds.
1886	U.S. Army Signal Corps banned the use of "tornado" in weather forecasts.
1888	Gustavus Hinrichs (1836-1923), an Iowa weather researcher, first used the word *derecho* for a straight-line windstorm.
1891	Luis Carranza, President of the Lima Geographical Society, describes a countercurrent flowing north to south from Paita to Pacasmayo and called El Niño by the local fishermen.
1891	The national weather service was transferred from military to civilian control in a new Weather Bureau within the U.S. Department of Agriculture.
1893	British astronomer E. Walter Maunder (1851-1928) identified a period of low solar activity between 1645 and 1715 (now known as the *Maunder minimum*).
1894	Wilhelm Wien (1864-1928) developed his *displacement law of radiation.*
1894	First sounding of the atmosphere using a self-recording thermometer attached to a kite at Blue Hill Observatory, Milton, MA.
1895	Swedish chemist Svante A. Arrhenius (1859-1927) pointed out that increasing carbon dioxide in the atmosphere can enhance the greenhouse effect.
1900	Russian-born German climatologist Wladimir Peter Köppen (1846-1940) first published his original climate classification scheme.
1902	French meteorologist Léon Philippe Teisserenc de Bort (1855-1913) identified and named the troposphere and stratosphere as layers of the atmosphere.
1904	Vilhelm Bjerknes (1862-1951) laid the foundations of synoptic meteorology at the Bergen School of Meteorology in Norway.
1905	Swedish physicist V. Walfrid Ekman (1874-1954) first described mathematically the coupling of surface winds and surface ocean waters (the *Ekman spiral*).
1910	German meteorologist Alfred Wegener (1880-1930) and American geologist Frank B. Taylor (1860-1939)

independently proposed the concept of continental drift.

1916	Pyranometer for measuring global radiation developed.
1917	Vilhelm Bjerknes formulated polar front theory.
1920s	Serbian astronomer Milutin Milankovitch (1879-1958) revived the theory of long-term cyclic climate change based on regular changes in Earth-sun geometry (*Milankovitch cycles*); he calculated latitudinal and seasonal changes in incoming solar radiation.
1920	Theory of atmospheric front was developed by V. Bjerknes, H. Solberg, and J. Bjerknes.
1924	Sir Gilbert Walker (1868-1958) discovered the southern oscillation.
1927	G. Stüve introduces a type of thermodynamic diagram (the *Stüve diagram*).
ca. 1928	First radiosonde developed.
1929	Robert H. Goddard (1882-1945) conducted the first rocket probe of the atmosphere.
1933	Tor Bergeron (1891-1977) published his paper on *Physics of Clouds and Precipitation*.
1935	Radar invented.
1935	Selection of the 30-year period 1901-1930 as the basis for calculating climatic normals, at the International Meteorological Conference in Warsaw, Poland.
1937	Carl-Gustav Rossby (1898-1957) introduced techniques for forecasting upper-level westerly waves.
1937	First official U.S. Weather Bureau radiosonde launch, at East Boston, MA.
1939	Work by Walter Findeisen supported Bergeron's theory of precipitation development in cold clouds (later known as the *Bergeron-Findeisen process*).
1941	Radar applied to weather systems for the first time; used to track a thunderstorm on the south coast of England.
1944	Hurd Curtis Willett produced atmospheric cross sections showing the jet stream.
1946	Vincent J. Schaefer (1906-1993) and Irving Langmuir (1881-1957) performed the first cloud-seeding experiments.
1946	John von Neumann (1903-1957) and colleagues began mathematical modeling of the atmosphere.
1946	U.S. Weather Bureau established the first River Forecast Centers at Cincinnati, OH and Kansas City, MO.
1947	American chemist Willard F. Libby (1908-1980) invented the radiocarbon dating technique, a valuable tool in reconstructing late-glacial climates.
1947	First photographs of the Earth's cloud cover obtained by a V2 rocket at altitudes of 110 to 165 km (70

to 100 mi).

1948	E.J. Fawbush and Robert C. Miller of the U.S. Air Force Air Weather Service developed and applied a method for forecasting tornadoes.
1950	A team led by the Hungarian-born American mathematician John von Neumann produced the first computer-generated weather forecasts using the ENIAC computer.
1951	The World Meteorological Organization (WMO) commenced operation.
1951	The American geographer and climatologist Arthur N. Strahler introduced a climate classification scheme based on air masses.
1952	U.S. Weather Bureau lifted the ban on the use of the word "tornado" in civilian weather forecasts.
1955	Beginning of the era when electronic computers were routinely generating weather forecasts from surface and upper-air weather observations.
1956	The British government attempted to reduce smog by limiting smoke emissions.
1957	Atmospheric CO_2 measurements began at Mauna Loa and Antarctica.
1959	A temperature-humidity index first introduced by the U.S. Weather Bureau.
1960	The United States successfully orbited the first weather satellite, TIROS-I.
1961	American meteorologist Edward N. Lorenz (1917-) observed that computer predictions of weather are highly sensitive to small differences in initial conditions, an aspect of chaos theory.
1963	Edward N. Lorenz applied chaos theory to meteorology.
1964	U.S. government introduced the first Clean Air Act to set national air pollution standards.
1966	Jacob Bjerknes (1897-1975) demonstrated a relationship between El Niño and the southern oscillation.
1967	Verner E. Suomi (1915-1995) of the University of Wisconsin-Madison processed the first geostationary satellite image.
1970s	American engineer Herbert Saffir (1917-) and meteorologist Robert Simpson (1912-) developed their hurricane intensity scale (the *Saffir-Simpson scale*).
1971	Japanese-born American meteorologist Tetsuya T. Fujita (1920-1998) with Allen Pearson introduced their tornado intensity scale (*Fujita* or *Fujita-Pearson scale*).
1972	Earth Resources Technology Satellite 1 (later called Landsat-1) was launched.
1974	The Global Atmospheric Research Program (GARP) conducted the GARP Atlantic Tropical Experiment (GATE) to improve understanding of the tropical atmosphere.
1974	M. J. Molina and F. S. Rowland warned of the CFC threat to the stratospheric ozone layer.

1975	First GOES (Geostationary Operational Environmental Satellite) was launched.
1975	The European Space Agency was formed.
1977	The first Meteosat weather satellite was launched by the European Space Agency.
1979	R.G. Steadman developed the heat index (apparent temperature index).
1979	NOAA scientists developed the SLOSH model that predicts the location and height of a storm surge.
1985	The British Antarctic Survey first reported a drastic decline in stratospheric ozone over Antarctica during the Southern Hemisphere spring.
1985	The Vienna Convention for the Protection of the Ozone Layer was convened.
1985	The Tropical Ocean-Global Atmosphere Program (TOGA) began.
1987	International adoption of the *Montreal Protocol on Substances That Deplete the Ozone Layer*.
1987	*The Joint Global Ocean Flux Study (JGOFS)* initiated to study the fluxes of carbon in the ocean.
1988	The Global Energy and Water Cycle Experiment (GEWEX) launched to examine the global hydrologic cycle.
1988	Formation of the Intergovernmental Panel on Climate Change (IPCC) by the World Meteorological Organization and the UN Environmental Programme.
1990	First Doppler radar was introduced into meteorological service.
1992	*UN Framework Convention on Climate Change* was ratified.
1992	NOAA's wind profiler network was up and running.
1994	NWS and EPA introduced the Ultraviolet (UV) Index.
1997	The Kyoto Protocol addressed reductions in greenhouse gas emissions.
1997	Launch of the TRMM satellite for remote sensing of precipitation between 40 degrees S and 40 degrees N.
1999	Landsat-7 was launched.
2001	NWS implemented a major revision of the wind-chill index.
2004	New Ultraviolet (UV) Index introduced.

APPENDIX III

CLIMATE CLASSIFICATION

Tropical Humid Climates
Dry Climates
Subtropical Climates
Snow Forest Climates
Polar Climates
Highland Climates

One of the most widely used climate classification systems was designed by German climatologist and plant geographer Wladimir Köppen (1846-1940) and subsequently modified by his students R. Geiger and W. Pohl. The Köppen system is an empirical approach to organizing Earth's myriad of climate types. Recognizing that indigenous vegetation is a natural indicator of regional climate, Köppen and his students looked for patterns in annual and monthly mean temperature and precipitation, which closely correspond to the limits of vegetative communities thereby revealing broad-scale climatic boundaries throughout the world. Records of annual and monthly mean temperature and precipitation are sufficiently long and reliable in many parts of the world that they serve as a good first approximation of climate. Since its introduction in the early 1900s, Köppen's climate classification has undergone numerous and substantial revisions by Köppen himself and by other climatologists and has had a variety of applications.

As shown in the Table, the Köppen climate classification system identifies six main climate groups; four are based on temperature, one is based on precipitation, and one applies to mountainous regions. Köppen's scheme uses letters to symbolize major climatic groups: (A) Tropical Humid, (B) Dry, (C) Subtropical (Mesothermal), (D) Snow Forest (Microthermal), (E) Polar, and (H) Highland. Additional letters further differentiate climate types.

Tropical Humid Climates

Tropical humid climates (A) constitute a discontinuous belt straddling the equator and extending poleward to near the Tropic of Cancer in the Northern Hemisphere and the Tropic of Capricorn in the Southern Hemisphere. Mean monthly temperatures are high and exhibit little variability throughout the year. The mean temperature of the coolest month is no lower than 18 °C (64 °F), and there is no frost. The temperature contrast between the warmest and coolest month is typically less than 10 Celsius degrees (18 Fahrenheit degrees). In fact, the diurnal (day-to-night) temperature range generally exceeds the annual temperature range. This monotonous air temperature regime is the consequence of consistently intense incoming solar radiation associated with a high maximum solar altitude and little variation in the period of daylight throughout the year.

Although tropical humid climate types are not readily distinguishable on the basis of temperature, important differences occur in precipitation regime. Tropical humid climates are subdivided into tropical wet (Af), tropical monsoon (Am), and tropical wet-and-dry (Aw). Although these climate types generally feature abundant annual rainfall, more than 100 cm (40 in.) on average, their rainy seasons differ in length and, in the case of Am and Aw, there is a pronounced dry season and wet season. In tropical wet climates, the yearly average rainfall of 175 to 250 cm (70 to 100 in.) supports the world's most luxurious vegetation.

TABLE
Köppen-Based Climate Classification

Tropical humid (A)
    Af tropical wet
    Am tropical monsoon
    Aw tropical wet-and-dry

Dry (B)
    BS steppe or semiarid (BSh, BSk)
    BW arid or desert (BWh, BWk)
    BWn foggy desert

Subtropical (C)
    Cs subtropical dry summer (Csa, Csb)
    Cw subtropical dry winter
    Cf subtropical humid (Cfa, Cfb, Cfc)

Snow forest (D)
    Dw dry winter (Dwa, Dwb, Dwc, Dwd)
    Df year-round precipitation (Dfa, Dfb, Dfc, Dfd)
    Ds dry summer

Polar (E)
    Et tundra
    Ef ice cap

Highland (H)

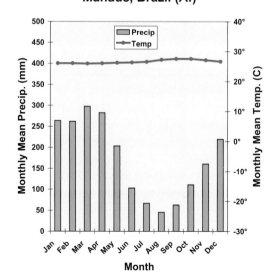

Tropical rainforests occupy the Amazon Basin of Brazil, the Congo Basin of Africa, and the islands of Micronesia. For the most part, rainfall is distributed uniformly throughout the year, although some areas experience a brief (one or two month) dry season. Rainfall occurs as heavy downpours in frequent thunderstorms triggered by local convection and the intertropical convergence zone (ITCZ). Convection is largely controlled by solar radiation and rainfall typically peaks in midafternoon, the warmest time of day. Because the water vapor concentration is very high, even the slightest cooling at night leads to saturated air and the formation of dew or radiation fog, giving these regions a sultry, steamy appearance.

Tropical monsoon (Am) climates feature a seasonal rainfall regime with extremely heavy rainfall during several months and a lengthy dry season. The principal control for these climates involves seasonal shifts in wind from land to sea, typified by the Asian monsoon. During the low-sun season, high air pressure over the Asian continent causes dry air to flow southward into parts of Southeast Asia and India. During the high-sun season, low air pressure covers the Tibetan Plateau and the winds reverse direction, advecting moisture inland from over the Indian Ocean. Local convection, orographic lifting, and shifts of the ITCZ combine to deluge the land with torrential rains. Am climates also occur in western Africa and northeastern Brazil.

For the most part, tropical wet-and-dry climates (Aw) border tropical wet climates (Af) and are transitional to subtropical dry climates in a poleward direction. Aw climates support the savanna, tropical grasslands with scattered deciduous trees. Summers are wet and winters are dry, with the dry season lengthening poleward. This marked seasonality of rainfall is linked to shifts of the intertropical convergence zone (ITCZ) and semipermanent subtropical anticyclones, which follow the seasonal excursions of the sun. In summer (*high-sun* season), surges of the ITCZ trigger convective rainfall; in winter (*low-sun* season), the dry eastern flank of the subtropical anticyclones dominates the weather.

The annual mean temperature in Aw climates is only slightly lower, and the seasonal temperature range is only slightly greater, than in the tropical wet climates (Af). The diurnal temperature range varies seasonally, however. In summer, frequent cloudy skies and high humidity suppress the diurnal temperature range by reducing both solar heating during the day and radiational cooling at night. In winter, on the other hand, persistent fair skies have the opposite effect on radiational heating and cooling and increase the diurnal temperature range.

Cloudy, rainy summers plus dry winters also mean that the year's highest temperatures typically occur toward the close of the dry season in late spring.

Dry Climates

Dry climates (B) characterize those regions where average annual potential evaporation exceeds average annual precipitation. *Potential evaporation* is the quantity of water that would vaporize into the atmosphere from a surface of fresh water during long-term average weather conditions. Air temperature largely governs the rate of evaporation so it is not possible to specify some maximum rainfall amount as the criterion for dry climates. Rainfall is not only limited in B climates but also highly variable and unreliable. As a general rule, the lower the mean annual rainfall, the greater is its variability from one year to the next.

Earth's dry climates encompass a larger land area than any other single climate grouping. Perhaps 30% of the planet's land surface, stretching from the tropics into midlatitudes, experience a moisture deficit of varying degree. These are the climates of the world's deserts and steppes, where vegetation is sparse and equipped with special adaptations that permit survival under conditions of severe moisture stress. Based on the degree of dryness, we distinguish between two dry climate types: steppe or semiarid (BS) and arid or desert (BW). Steppe or semiarid climates are transitional between more humid climates and arid or desert climates. Mean annual temperature is latitude dependent,

as is the range in variation of mean monthly temperatures through the year. Hence, a distinction is made between warm dry climates of tropical latitudes (BSh and BWh) and cold, dry climates of higher latitudes (BSk and BWk).

Dryness is the consequence of subtropical anticyclones, cold surface ocean currents, or the rain shadow effect of high mountain ranges. Subsiding stable air on the eastern flanks of subtropical anticyclones gives rise to tropical dry climates (BSh and BWh). These huge semipermanent pressure systems, centered over the ocean basins, dominate the weather year-round near the Tropics of Cancer and Capricorn. Consequently, dry climates characterize North Africa eastward to northwest India, the southwestern United States and northern Mexico, coastal Chile and Peru, southwest Africa, and much of the interior of Australia.

Although persistent and abundant sunshine is generally the rule in dry tropical climates, there are some important exceptions. Where cold ocean waters border a coastal desert, a shallow layer of stable marine air drifts inland. The desert air thus features high relative humidity, persistent low stratus clouds and fog, and considerable dew formation. Examples are the Atacama Desert of Peru and Chile, the Namib Desert of southwest Africa, and portions of the coastal Sonoran Desert of Baja California and stretches of the coastal Sahara Desert of northwest Africa. These anomalous foggy desert climates are designated BWn.

Cold, dry climates of higher latitudes (BWk and BSk) are situated in the rain shadows of great mountain ranges. They occur primarily in the Northern Hemisphere, to the lee of the Sierra Nevada and Cascade ranges in North America and the Himalayan chain in Asia. Because these dry climates are at higher latitudes than their tropical counterparts, mean annual temperatures are lower and the seasonal temperature contrast is greater. Anticyclones dominate winter, bringing cold and dry conditions, whereas summers are hot and generally dry. Scattered convective showers, mostly in summer, produce relatively meager precipitation.

Subtropical Climates

Subtropical climates are located just poleward of the Tropics of Cancer and Capricorn and are dominated by seasonal shifts of subtropical anticyclones. There are three basic climate types: subtropical dry summer (or *Mediterranean*) (Cs), subtropical dry winter (Cw), and subtropical humid (Cf), which receive precipitation throughout the year.

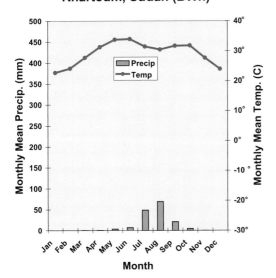

Khartoum, Sudan (BWh)

Mediterranean climates occur on the western side of continents between about 30 and 45 degrees latitude. In North America, mountain ranges confine this climate to a narrow coastal strip of California. Elsewhere, Cs climates rim the Mediterranean Sea and occur in portions of extreme southern Australia. Summers are dry because at that time of year Cs regions are under the influence of stable subsiding air on the eastern flanks of the semi-permanent subtropical highs. Equatorward shift of subtropical highs in autumn allows extra-tropical cyclones to migrate inland, bringing moderate winter rainfall. Mean annual precipitation varies greatly-ranging from 30 to 300 cm (12 to 80 in.) with the wettest winter month typically receiving at least three times the precipitation of the driest summer month.

Although Mediterranean climates exhibit a pronounced seasonality in precipitation (dry summers and wet winters), the temperature regime is quite variable. In coastal areas, cool onshore breezes prevail, lowering the mean annual temperature and reducing seasonal temperature contrasts. Well inland, however, away from the ocean's moderating influence, summers are considerably warmer; hence, inland mean annual temperatures are higher and seasonal temperature contrasts are greater than in coastal Cs localities. Climatic records of coastal San Francisco and inland Sacramento, CA illustrate the contrast in temperature regime within Cs regions. Although the two cities are separated by only about 145 km (90 mi.), the climate of Sacramento is much more continental (much warmer summers and somewhat cooler winters) than that of San Francisco. The warm climate subtype is designated Csa and the cooler subtype is Csb.

Subtropical dry winter climates (Cw) are transitional between Aw and BS climates and located in South America and Africa between 20 and 30 degrees S. Cw climates also occur between the Aw and H climates of the Himalayas and Tibetan plateau and between the BS and Cfa climates of Southeast and East Asia. Northward shift of the subtropical high pressure systems is responsible for the dry winter in South America and Africa The narrowness of the two continents between 20 and 30 degrees S means a relatively strong maritime influence and dictates against extreme dryness. In spring, subtropical highs shift southward and rains return. In Asia, winter dryness is caused by winds radiating outward from the massive cold Siberian high. As the continent warms in spring, the Siberian high weakens and eventually is replaced by low pressure. Moist winds then flow inland bringing summer rains. Mean annual precipitation in Cw climates is in the range of 75 to 150 cm (30 to 60 in.).

Subtropical humid climates (Cf) occur on the eastern side of continents between about 25 and 40 degrees latitude (and even more poleward where the maritime influence is strong). Cfa climates are the most important of the Cf climate subtypes in terms of land area and number of people impacted. Cfa climates are situated primarily in the southeastern United States, a portion of southeastern South America, eastern China, southern Japan, on the extreme southeastern coast of South Africa, and along much of the east coast of Australia. These climates feature abundant precipitation (75 to 200 cm, or 30 to 80 in., on average annually), which is distributed throughout the year. In summer, Cfa regions are dominated by a flow of sultry maritime tropical air on the western flanks of the subtropical anticyclones. Consequently, summers are hot and humid with frequent thunderstorms, which can produce brief periods of substantial rainfall. Hurricanes and tropical storms contribute significant rainfall (up to 15% to 20% of the annual total) to some North American and Asian Cfa regions, especially from summer through autumn. In winter, after the subtropical highs shift toward the equator, Cfa regions come under the influence of migrating extratropical cyclones and anticyclones.

In Cfa localities, summers are hot and winters are mild. Mean temperatures of the warmest month are typically in the range of 24 to 27 °C (75 to 81 °F). Average temperatures for the coolest months typically range from 4 to 13 °C (39 to 55 °F). Subfreezing temperatures and snowfalls are infrequent.

Melbourne, Australia (Cfb)

A strong maritime influence is responsible for the cool summers and mild winters of Cfb climates. These climates occur over much of Northwest Europe, New Zealand, and portions of southeastern South America, southern Africa, and Australia. The coldest subtype, the Cfc, is relegated to coastal areas of southern Alaska, Norway, and the southern half of Iceland. Cfb and Cfc climates are relatively humid with mean annual precipitation ranging between 100 and 200 cm (40 and 80 in.).

Snow Forest Climates

Snow forest climates (D) occur in the interior and to the leeward sides of large continents. The name emphasizes the link between biogeography and the Köppen climate classification system. These climates feature cold snowy winters (except for the Dw subtype in which the winter is dry) and occur only in the Northern Hemisphere. Snow forest climates are subdivided according to seasonal precipitation regimes with Df climates experiencing year-round precipitation whereas Dw climates have a dry winter. D climates with dry summers (Ds) are rare and small in extent. Additional distinction is made between warmer subtypes (Dwa, Dfa, Dwb, and Dfb) and colder subtypes (Dwc, Dfc, Dwd, Dfd).

The warmer subtypes, sometimes termed *temperate continental*, have warm summers (mean temperature of the warmest month greater than 22 °C or 71 °F) and cold winters. They are located in Eurasia, the

northeastern third of the United States, southern Canada, and extreme eastern Asia. Continentality increases inland with maximum temperature contrasts between the coldest and warmest months as great as 25 to 35 Celsius degrees (45 to 63 Fahrenheit degrees). The southerly Dfa climates have cool winters and warm summers and the more northerly Dfb climates have cold winters and mild summers. The freeze-free period varies in length from 7 months in the south to only 3 months in the north. The weather in these regions is very changeable and dynamic because these areas are swept by extra-tropical cyclones and anticyclones and by surges of contrasting air masses. Polar front cyclones dominate winter, bringing episodes of light to moderate frontal precipitation. These storms are followed by incursions of dry polar and arctic air masses. In summer, cyclones are weak and infrequent as the principal storm track shifts poleward. Summer rainfall is mostly convective, and locally amounts can be very heavy in severe thunderstorms and mesoscale convective complexes (MCCs). Although precipitation is distributed rather uniformly throughout the year, most places experience a summer maximum.

In northern portions, winter snowfall becomes an important factor in the climate. Mean annual snowfall and the persistence of a snow cover increase northward. Because of its high albedo for solar radiation and its efficient emission of infrared, a snow cover chills and stabilizes the overlying air. For these reasons, a snow cover tends to be self-sustaining; once established in early winter, an extensive snow cover tends to persist.

Yellowknife, Canada (Dfc)

Moving poleward, summers get colder and winters are very cold. These so-called *boreal climates* (Dfc, Dfd, Dwc, Dwd) occur only in the Northern Hemisphere as an east-west band between 50 to 55 degrees N and 65 degrees N. It is a region of extreme continentality and very low mean annual temperature. Summers are short and cool, and winters are long and bitterly cold. Because midsummer freezes are possible, the growing season is precariously short. Both continental polar (cP) and arctic (A) air masses originate here, and this area is the site of an extensive coniferous (boreal) forest. In summer, the mean position of the leading edge of arctic air (the arctic front) is located along the northern border of the boreal forest. In winter, the mean position of the arctic front is situated along the southern border of the boreal forest.

Weak cyclonic activity occurs throughout the year and yields meager annual precipitation (typically less than 50 cm, or 20 in.). Convective activity is rare. A summer precipitation maximum is due to the winter dominance of cold, dry air masses. Snow cover persists throughout the winter and the range in mean temperature between winter and summer is among the greatest in the world.

Polar Climates

Polar climates (E) occur poleward of the Arctic and Antarctic circles. These boundaries correspond roughly to localities where the mean temperature for the warmest month is 10 °C (50 °F). These limits also approximate

the tree line, the poleward limit of tree growth. Poleward are tundra and the Greenland and Antarctic ice sheets. A distinction is made between tundra (Et) and ice cap (Ef) climates, with the dividing criterion being 0 °C (32 °F) for the mean temperature of the warmest month. Vegetation is sparse in Et regions and almost nonexistent in Ef areas.

Polar climates are characterized by extreme cold and slight precipitation, which falls mostly in the form of snow (less than 25 cm, or 10 in., melted, per year). Greenland and Antarctica could be considered deserts for lack of significant precipitation, despite the presence of large ice sheets. Although summers are cold, the winters are so extremely cold that polar climates feature a marked seasonal temperature contrast. Mean annual temperatures are the lowest of any place in the world.

Highland Climates

Highland Climates (H) encompass a wide variety of climate types that characterize mountainous terrain. Altitude, latitude, and exposure are among the factors that shape a complexity of climate types. For example, temperature decreases rapidly with increasing altitude and windward slopes tend to be wetter than leeward slopes. Climate-ecological zones are telescoped in mountainous terrain. That is, in ascending several thousand meters of altitude, we encounter the same bioclimatic zones that we would experience in traveling several thousand kilometers of latitude. As a general rule, every 300 m (980 ft) of elevation corresponds roughly to a northward advance of 500 km (310 mi).

McMurdo, Antarctica (Ef)

GLOSSARY

A

Absolute humidity   The mass of water vapor per unit volume of air containing the water vapor; usually expressed as grams of water vapor per cubic meter of humid air.

Absolute instability   Property of an ambient air layer that enhances vertical motion for both saturated (cloudy) and unsaturated (clear) air parcels; the *temperature* of the ambient air is dropping more rapidly with altitude than the *dry adiabatic lapse rate*.

Absolute stability   Property of an ambient air layer that suppresses vertical motion for both saturated (cloudy) and unsaturated (clear) air parcels.   Occurs when the *temperature* in the ambient air layer drops more slowly with altitude than the *moist adiabatic lapse rate*, the temperature does not change with altitude in the ambient air layer (isothermal), or the temperature increases with altitude in the ambient air layer (temperature inversion).

Absolute zero   The theoretical *temperature* at which a body does not emit *electromagnetic radiation* and all molecular motion ceases (usually some subatomic activity takes place); 0 K (−273.15 °C or −459.57 °F).

Absorption   The energy conversion process whereby a portion of the radiation incident on an object is converted to *heat* energy.   Absorption is a function of the surface and composition of the absorbing material and the *wavelength* of the incident radiation.

Acid deposition   The combination of acid rain (or snow) plus dry deposition.

Acid rain   Rain having a pH lower than 5.6, representing the pH of natural rain water saturated with carbon dioxide.

Acoustic shadow   An area where sound is not heard due to the refraction of sound waves.

Adiabatic process   A thermodynamic process in which no *heat* is exchanged between a mass and its environment.   Within the *atmosphere*, *expansional cooling* and *compressional warming* of unsaturated air parcels are essentially adiabatic processes, that is, no heat is exchanged between the air parcels and the surrounding air.

Advanced Weather Interactive Processing System (AWIPS)   A computerized workstation that receives and organizes *Automated Surface Observing System* data and other analysis and guidance products from the *National Centers for Environmental Prediction* and enables *National Weather Service* meteorologists to display, process, and overlay images, graphics, and other data.   Inspired by *McIDAS*.

Advection fog   Ground-level *cloud* generated by the cooling of a mild, humid *air mass* (to its *dewpoint*) as it travels over a relatively cool surface.

Aeolian sound   Humming, singing, or whistling sounds produced by winds blowing over obstacles.

Aerosols   Tiny liquid or solid particles of various compositions that occur suspended in the *atmosphere*.

Aerovane A wind sensor designed to measure wind speed and direction.

Agroclimatic compensation Poor growing *weather* and decreased crop yields in one area is offset to some extent by better growing weather and increased crop yields in other areas.

Air density Mass of molecules per unit volume of air; about 1.275 kg per cubic meter at sea-level temperature of 0 °C and pressure of 1000 millibars.

Air mass A huge volume of air covering thousands of square kilometers that is horizontally relatively uniform in *temperature* and water vapor concentration (*humidity*). The specific characteristics of an air mass depend on the type of surface over which the air mass forms (its source region) and travels.

Air mass advection Movement of an *air mass* from one place to another; one air mass replaces another air mass having different *temperature* and/or *humidity* characteristics.

Air mass modification Changes in the *temperature, humidity,* and/or stability of an *air mass* as it travels away from its source region. Occurs primarily by exchange of *heat*, moisture, or both with the surface over which the air mass travels, *radiational heating* or *radiational cooling*, or adiabatic heating or cooling associated with large-scale vertical motion.

Air parcel An imaginary volume of air useful for visualizing atmospheric processes and containing a fixed number of molecules.

Air pollutant A gas or *aerosol* that occurs at a concentration that threatens the wellbeing of living organisms (especially humans) or disrupts the orderly functioning of the environment.

Air pressure The cumulative force exerted on any surface by the molecules composing air; usually expressed as the weight of a column of air per unit surface area.

Air pressure gradient Change in *air pressure* with distance.

Air pressure tendency Change in *air pressure* with time; on a surface *weather* map, the air pressure change over the prior 3 hrs.

Albedo The fraction or percent of radiation striking a surface (or interface) that is reflected by that surface (or interface); usually applied to the reflectivity of an object to visible radiation.

Altimeter Any device used to determine altitude such as an *aneroid barometer* calibrated to read in altitude or elevation.

Altocumulus clouds (Ac) Middle level *clouds* occurring as roll-like patches or puffs forming waves or parallel bands. Altocumulus are distinguished from *cirrocumulus* by the larger size of the cloud patches and by sharper edges indicating the presence of supercooled water droplets rather than ice crystals.

Altocumulus lenticularis clouds Lens-shaped *altocumulus*; *mountain-wave clouds* generated by the disturbance of horizontal airflow by a prominent mountain range.

Altostratus clouds (As) Middle level *clouds* occurring as uniformly gray or bluish white layers totally or partially covering the sky. The sun is typically only dimly visible through altostratus. These clouds are composed of supercooled water droplets and ice crystals.

Aneroid barometer A portable instrument that utilizes a flexible partially-evacuated metal chamber and spring to measure *air pressure*; may be used as an *altimeter*.

Antarctic Circle Poleward of this latitude (66 degrees 33 minutes S) there are 24 hrs of sunlight on the austral summer *solstice* and 24 hrs of darkness on the austral winter solstice.

Antarctic ozone hole A large area of significant stratospheric ozone depletion over the Antarctic continent that typically develops annually between late August and early October, and generally ends in mid-November. Ozone thinning is attributed to the action of chlorine (Cl) liberated from a group of chemicals known as chlorofluorocarbons (CFCs).

Anticyclone A dome of air that exerts relatively high surface *air pressure* compared with surrounding air; same as a *High*. Viewed from above, surface *winds* in an anticyclone blow clockwise and outward in the Northern Hemisphere but counterclockwise and outward in the Southern Hemisphere.

Aphelion The time of the year when the Earth is farthest (152 million km or 94 million mi) from the sun (currently about 4 July).

Arctic air (A) Exceptionally cold and dry *air masses* that form primarily in winter over the Arctic Basin, Greenland, and the northern interior of North America north of about 60 degrees N.

Arctic Circle Poleward of this latitude (66 degrees 33 minutes N) there are 24 hrs of sunlight at the boreal summer *solstice* and 24 hrs of darkness at the boreal winter solstice.

Arctic high A *cold-core anticyclone* originating in a source region for *arctic air*; the product of extreme *radiational cooling* over the *snow*-covered continental interior of North America well north of the *polar front*.

Atmosphere A thin envelope of gasses (also containing suspended solid and liquid particles and *clouds*) that encircles the planet.

Atmospheric boundary layer The atmospheric zone to which frictional resistance (*eddy viscosity*) is essentially confined; on average the zone extends from Earth's surface to an altitude of about 1000 m (3300 ft).

Atmospheric stability Property of ambient air that either enhances (unstable) or suppresses (stable) vertical motion of air parcels; depends on the vertical *temperature* profile or *sounding* of the ambient air and whether air parcels are saturated (cloudy), with cooling or warming at the *moist adiabatic lapse rate*, or unsaturated (clear), with cooling or warming at the *dry adiabatic lapse rate*. See *stable air layer* and *unstable air layer*.

Atmospheric windows *Wavelength* bands within which atmospheric gases absorb little or no *electromagnetic radiation*.

Aurora A luminous phenomenon in the night sky consisting of overlapping curtains of greenish-white light, sometimes fringed with pink, appearing in the *ionosphere* of high latitudes. Light is emitted by atoms and molecules that are excited by beams of electrons generated by a complex interaction between the *solar wind* and the Earth's *atmosphere*. Known as the aurora borealis (northern lights) in the Northern Hemisphere and the aurora australis (southern lights) in the Southern Hemisphere.

Automated Surface Observing System (ASOS) Meteorological sensors, computers, and fully automated communication ports that record and transmit atmospheric conditions automatically; a component of the modernization program of the *National Weather Service*. A network of ASOS units feed observational data to National Weather Service Forecast Offices and local airport control towers 24-hrs per day.

Avogadro's law The number of molecules in one mole of gas is a constant for permanent gases with a pressure of one standard atmosphere and temperature of 0° C (32 °F).

B

Back-door cold front   A *cold front* that propagates southward or southwestward along the North Atlantic coast east of the Appalachian Mountains. These fronts occur most frequently in the summer and fall and usher in Canadian *continental polar air* or Atlantic *maritime polar air*.

Barograph   A recording instrument that provides a continuous trace of *air pressure* with time; helps determine *air pressure tendency*.

Barrier island   A long, narrow strip of sand parallel to the coast and separated from the mainland by a lagoon or backwater bay. Since a barrier island faces the open ocean, it absorbs the brunt of *tropical cyclone*- and other sea storm-driven waves and *storm surge*, providing some protection for coastal beaches, wetlands, and shoreline structures.

Beaufort scale   A scale of *wind* speed based originally on visual assessment of the effects of wind on seas, and later extended to describe the effects of wind on land-based flexible objects such as trees. The scale ranges from 0 for calm conditions to 12 for *hurricane*-strength winds.

Bergeron-Findeisen process   *Precipitation* formation in *cold cloud*s whereby ice crystals grow at the expense of supercooled water droplets in response to differences in *vapor pressure* relative to water and ice surfaces; also known as the ice-crystal process.

Blackbody   A hypothetical "body" that absorbs all *electromagnetic radiation* that is incident on it at every *wavelength* and emits all radiation at every wavelength; no radiation is reflected or transmitted. The "body" must be large compared to the wavelength of incident radiation.

Blizzard   A severe storm characterized by high winds and reduced visibility due to falling or blowing snow.

Blocking system   A *cyclone* or *anticyclone* cutoff from the main westerly airflow that blocks the usual west-to-east progression of *weather* systems. A blocking system may be responsible for weather extremes, such as drought or flooding *rains* or excessive *heat* and cold.

Bowen ratio   For a moist surface, the ratio of *heat* energy used for *sensible heating* (*conduction* and *convection*) to the heat energy used for *latent heating* (*evaporation* of water or *sublimation* of *snow*). The Bowen ratio varies from one locality to another depending on the amount of surface moisture, ranging from 0.1 for the ocean surface to more than 5.0 for deserts; negative values are also possible.

Boyle's Law   When temperature is constant, the pressure and density of an ideal gas are directly proportional.

British thermal unit (Btu)   The quantity of *heat* needed to raise the *temperature* of one pound of water one Fahrenheit degree (technically, from 62 to 63 °F).

C

Calorie (cal)   The amount of *heat* needed to raise the *temperature* of one gram of water one Celsius degree (technically, from 14.5 to 15.5 °C).

Capping inversion   An elevated temperature inversion layer that caps a convective boundary layer, keeping the convective elements from rising higher into the atmosphere.

Centripetal force   An inward-directed force that acts on an object moving in a curved path, confining the object to the curved path; the result of other forces.

Charles' Law   With constant pressure, the absolute temperature (in kelvins) of an ideal gas is inversely proportional to the density of the gas.

Chinook wind   Air that is adiabatically compressed as it is drawn down the leeward slope of a mountain range. As a consequence, the air is warm and dry, causing rapid temperature rises and reduction in snow cover.

Chromosphere   Portion of the sun above the *photosphere*; consists of transparent ionized hydrogen and helium at 4000 to 40,000 °C (7200 to 72,000 °F).

Circumpolar vortex   The planetary-scale circulation regime that surrounds the cold pool of air in the polar regions.

Cirriform cloud   A thin wispy or fibrous cloud composed of ice crystals.

Cirrocumulus clouds (Cc)   High *clouds* that exhibit a wavelike pattern of small, white, rounded patches rarely covering the entire sky. Cirrocumulus are composed of ice crystals.

Cirrostratus clouds (Cs)   High, thin, layered *clouds* composed of ice crystals that form a thin white veil over the sky. Cirrostratus are nearly transparent, so the sun or moon readily shines through them.

Cirrus clouds (Ci)   High, thin, nearly transparent *clouds* composed of ice crystals and occurring as delicate silky strands, which are streaks of falling ice particles blown laterally by strong *winds*.

Climate   *Weather* of some locality averaged over some time period plus extremes in weather behavior observed during the same period or during the entire period of record.

Climatic anomalies   Departures from long-term climatic averages.

Climatic norm   The average value of some climatic element such as temperature or snowfall.

Climatology   Study of *climate*, its controls and spatial and temporal variability. In *weather* forecasting, a forecast derived from climatology is based on the type of weather that occurred on the same day in years past.

Cloud   A visible suspension of minute water droplets and/or ice crystals in the *atmosphere* above the Earth's surface. Clouds differ from *fog* only in that the latter is, by definition, in contact with Earth's surface. Clouds form in the free atmosphere primarily as a result of *condensation* or *deposition* of water vapor in ascending air that nears *saturation*.

Cloud condensation nuclei (CCN)   Tiny solid and liquid particles that promote the *condensation* of water vapor at *temperatures* both above and below the freezing point of water, may include *hygroscopic nuclei*.

Cloud forest   Tropical forests perpetually shrouded in clouds and mist.

Cloud streets   *Clouds* aligned in rows due to strong vertical shear in horizontal *wind* speed or direction; these rows often extend for hundreds of kilometers.

Cold air advection   Flow of air across regional isotherms from relatively cool localities to relatively warm localities.

Cold cloud   *Cloud* composed of ice crystals or supercooled water droplets or a mixture of both which have *temperatures* below 0 °C (32 °F).

Cold front   *Front* that moves in such a way that relatively cold (more dense) air advances and replaces relatively warm (less dense) air.

Cold-core anticyclone   Shallow high-pressure system that coincides with a dome of *continental polar air* or *arctic air*; labeled as either a *polar high* or an *arctic high*. The high's shallow anticyclonic circulation weakens rapidly with altitude and often reverses to a cyclonic circulation in the middle and upper *troposphere*.

Cold-core cyclone   An occluded low-pressure system in which the lowest *temperatures* occur throughout the column of air above the low-pressure center. Isobaric surfaces dip downward above the low center and the depth of the low increases with altitude, implying that a cyclonic circulation prevails throughout the *troposphere* and is most intense at high altitudes.

Collision-coalescence process   Growth of *cloud* droplets into raindrops within a *warm cloud*; droplets merge upon impact. This process takes place in a cloud made up of droplets of different sizes; larger droplets with higher *terminal velocity* overtake, and then collide and coalesce with smaller droplets in their paths.

Comma cloud   The pattern of cloudiness associated with a mature *extra-tropical cyclone*; the head of the comma stretches from the low center to the northwest and its tail follows along the *cold front*. This pattern reflects the strengthening of the system's circulation.

Comet   A relatively small celestial body composed of meteoric dust and ice that follows a parabolic or highly elliptical orbit around the sun.

Compressional warming   A *temperature* rise that accompanies a pressure increase on and resultant compression of a gas (or mixture of gases). The work of compressing air is converted to *heat*, raising the temperature of the gas. Air parcels that descend within the *atmosphere* undergo compressional warming in response to increasing *air pressure*.

Condensation   The process that produces a net gain of liquid water mass at the interface between liquid water and air; more water changes phase from vapor to liquid than liquid to vapor. The phase change from vapor to liquid releases the *latent heat of vaporization*.

Conditional stability   Property of an ambient air layer that suppresses vertical motion for unsaturated (clear) air parcels and enhances vertical motion for saturated (cloudy) air parcels. The *sounding* in a conditionally stable layer of air lies between the *dry adiabatic lapse rate* and the *moist adiabatic lapse rate*.

Conduction (of heat)   Transfer of kinetic energy of atoms or molecules via collisions between the neighboring atoms or molecules.

Continental drift   Slow movement of continents, which are parts of gigantic plates, across the face of the globe.

Continental polar air (cP)   Relatively dry *air masses* that develop over the northern interior of North America; these air masses are very cold in winter and relatively mild in summer.

Continental tropical air (cT)   Warm, dry *air masses* that form over the subtropical deserts of Mexico and the southwestern United States primarily in summer.

Convection   The transport of *heat* within a fluid via motions of the fluid itself; generally occurs only in liquids and gases. Convection is much more important than *conduction* in transporting heat vertically within the *troposphere*.

Convective condensation level (CCL)   The altitude at which *condensation* begins to occur through *convection*; coincides with the base of *cumuliform clouds*, typically at altitudes between 1000 and 2000 m (3600 and 6000 ft).

Converging winds   *Winds* that blow toward a central point of a column of air.

Conveyor-belt model (atmosphere)   Three-dimensional depiction of a mature *extra-tropical cyclone* and its corresponding *fronts* in terms of three interacting airstreams, often referred to as conveyor belts. This model developed out of a better understanding of upper-air circulation in the years since the *Norwegian cyclone model*.

Coordinated Universal Time (UTC)   Formerly known as Greenwich Mean Time, the time along the prime meridian, zero degree longitude.

Coral bleaching   The loss of color by coral polyps and their subsequent death caused by unusually high sea-surface temperature.

Coriolis Effect   A deflective force arising from the rotation of the Earth on its axis; affects principally synoptic-scale and planetary-scale *winds*. Winds are deflected to the right of their initial direction in the Northern Hemisphere and to the left in the Southern Hemisphere. Magnitude depends on latitude and speed of the moving object.

Corona   A series of alternating light and dark colored rings that surround the moon or sun; due to *diffraction* of light by spherical *cloud* droplets.

Crepuscular rays   Alternating light and dark bands (solar rays and shadows) that appear to diverge in a fanlike pattern from the solar disk. They can be observed at the beginning of *twilight* or during the day as the sun's rays pass through holes in *clouds* or between clouds in a hazy sky.

Cumuliform clouds   *Clouds* that exhibit significant vertical development; often produced by updrafts in *convection* currents.

Cumulonimbus clouds (Cb)   *Thunderstorm clouds* that form as a consequence of deep *convection* in the *atmosphere*; have tops that sometimes reach altitudes of 20,000 m (60,000 ft) or higher. The upper portions of these clouds are anvil-shaped and composed of mostly ice crystals, the middle portions are composed of supercooled water droplets or a mixture of supercooled water droplets and ice crystals, and the lower portions are often composed of ordinary water droplets.

Cumulus clouds (Cu)   Vertically developed *clouds* that form as a consequence of the updraft in *convection* currents; resemble balls of cotton floating in the sky. Cumulus are normally fair-*weather* clouds and consist of mostly water droplets, which may be supercooled.

Cumulus congestus cloud   Upward-building convective *clouds* with vertical development between those of *cumulus* and *cumulonimbus*; having a cauliflower appearance. Cumulus congestus can occur when the ambient air in the middle to upper *troposphere* is unstable for saturated air. These clouds consist of mostly water droplets, which are frequently supercooled.

Cup anemometer   An instrument used to monitor *wind* speed. Wind rotates the 3 or 4 open hemispheric cups, which spin horizontally on a vertical shaft, and that motion is calibrated in wind speed.

Curvature effect   The effect a curved water surface has on the ability of water molecules to vaporize from the surface. The smaller (radius) a droplet, the greater the concentration of surrounding water vapor that is necessary for the droplet to grow.

Due to differences in the bond strength of the water molecules on the droplet surface, water molecules more readily vaporize from a small droplet than a large droplet, explaining why the *saturation vapor pressure* over a small droplet is greater than over a large droplet at the same *temperature*. Tiny droplets cannot form or exist without a supersaturated environment.

Cyclogenesis   The birth and development of a *cyclone*; for an *extra-tropical cyclone*, cyclogenesis usually takes place along the *polar front* directly under an area of strong horizontal *divergence* in the upper *troposphere*.

Cyclolysis   Process whereby a *cyclone* weakens; usually takes place when the central pressure rises and winds slacken. Upper-air support for the cyclone diminishes to the point where horizontal *divergence* aloft becomes weaker than horizontal *convergence* near the surface.

Cyclone   A *weather* system characterized by relatively low surface *air pressure* compared with the surrounding air; same as a *Low*. Viewed from above, surface *winds* blow counterclockwise and inward in the Northern Hemisphere but clockwise and inward in the Southern Hemisphere.

D

Dalton's law   A scientific law that states that the total pressure exerted by a mixture of gases is equal to the sum of the partial pressures of each consftituent gas. Each gas species in the mixture acts independently of the other molecules.

Deposition   The process which produces a net gain of ice mass at the interface between ice and air; more water changes phase from vapor to ice than ice to vapor; phase change of water from vapor to ice (without first becoming liquid).

Derecho   A family of straight-line *downburst winds* in excess of 94 km per hr (58 mph) that impacts a path up to hundreds of kilometers long; may be produced by a *squall line* or a *mesoscale convective complex*.

Dew   Tiny water droplets formed by *condensation* of water vapor on a relatively cold surface. For water vapor to condense as dew on the surface of an object, the *temperature* of that surface must cool below the *dewpoint*.

Dewpoint   *Temperature* to which air must be cooled (at constant *air pressure* and constant water vapor content) to achieve *saturation* of the air relative to liquid water (if at or above 0 °C or 32 °F).

Dewpoint hygrometer   An instrument that measures the *dewpoint* of the air. In one design, air passes over the surface of a metallic mirror that is cooled electronically. An electronic sensor continually monitors the *temperature* of the mirror at the same time that a beam of *infrared radiation* is pointed at the mirror. When a thin *condensation* film forms on the mirror, the *reflectivity* of the infrared beam changes, and the mirror temperature is automatically recorded as the dewpoint.

Diffraction   The slight bending of a light wave as it moves along a boundary of an object such as a water droplet. As light waves bend, they interfere with each other, either constructively, producing a larger wave, or destructively, canceling each other out. When interference of light waves is constructive, a ring of bright light is seen, and when interference is destructive, darkness is perceived.

Dissipating stage   The final phase in the life cycle of a *thunderstorm* cell; features downdrafts throughout the system, the tapering off and ending of *precipitation*, and vaporization of *clouds*.

Distillation   The purification of water through phase changes (e.g., *evaporation* followed by *condensation*). When water vaporizes, all suspended and dissolved substances are left behind.

Diverging winds   *Winds* that blow away from a central point in a column of air.

Doldrums   An east-west equatorial belt of light and variable surface *winds* where the *trade winds* of the two hemispheres converge.

Doppler Effect   A shift in the frequency (or phase) of an electromagnetic or sound wave due to the relative movement of the source or the observer.

Doppler radar   *Weather radar* that determines the velocity of targets (*precipitation*, dust particles) moving directly toward or away from the radar unit based on the difference in frequency (or phase) between the outgoing and returning radar signal.

Downburst   A strong and potentially destructive *thunderstorm* downdraft; depending on size, classified as either a *microburst* or a *macroburst*.

Downdraft   A strong, downward-flowing air current within a thunderstorm, usually associated with precipitation.

Drizzle   A form of liquid *precipitation* consisting of water droplets having diameters between 0.2 and 0.5 mm (0.01 and 0.02 in); falls very slowly from low *stratus* clouds.

Dropwindsonde   A small instrument package equipped with a radio transmitter and parachute that is dropped from an aircraft to take altitude readings of *temperature*, *air pressure*, and *dewpoint*. This instrument package is also tracked from the air by a direction-finding antenna or global positioning system (GPS) to measure variations in horizontal *wind* direction and speed with altitude.

Dry adiabatic lapse rate   The adiabatic expansional cooling of ascending, clear (unsaturated) air parcels at the rate of about 9.8 Celsius degrees per 1000 m of uplift (or 5.5 Fahrenheit degrees per 1000 ft). If clear (unsaturated) air parcels descend in the *atmosphere*, the parcels warm adiabatically at the same rate.

Dry slot   Dry air descending behind a cold front and drawn into the center of a cyclone.

Dryline   A boundary between *continental tropical air* and *maritime tropical air* in the southeast sector of a mature *extratropical cyclone*; likely site for *squall line* and *severe thunderstorm* development.

Dust devil   A swirling mass of dust triggered by intense solar heating of dry surface areas. The most common dust devil is less than 1 m (about 3 ft) in diameter, lasts less than a minute, and is too weak to cause serious property damage.

E

Earth-atmosphere system   The Earth's surface (i.e., continents, ocean, ice sheets) plus the *atmosphere*.

Easterly wave   A ripple in the tropical easterlies (*trade winds*) featuring a weak trough of low pressure; propagates from east to west. Lower-tropospheric convergence on the east side of the wave can help organize convective activity into a *tropical disturbance*.

Eddy viscosity   Fluid *friction* (*viscosity*) arising from eddies (irregular whirls) within a fluid such as air or water.

Ekman spiral   A spiral in water motion in the top 100 m (330 ft) or so of the ocean produced by the directional change and decreasing horizontal motion of successively lower layers of water. Due to a balance between the *Coriolis Effect* and frictional drag, the surface ocean layer moves at an angle of up to 45 degrees to the right or left (depending on the hemisphere) of the surface *wind* direction. Due to the same balance of forces, the layer immediately below the surface ocean layer moves slower and at an angle to the motion of the layer above. This spiraling effect is responsible for the *Ekman transport*.

Ekman transport   The net horizontal movement of water in the top 100 m (330 ft) or so of the ocean induced by the coupling of surface *winds* with ocean surface waters. The *Ekman spiral* causes this net transport to be about 90 degrees to the right of the surface wind direction in the Northern Hemisphere and to the left of the surface wind direction in the Southern Hemisphere.

El Niño   An anomalous warming of surface ocean waters in the eastern tropical Pacific; accompanied by suppression of *upwelling* off the coasts of Peru and Ecuador.

Electromagnetic radiation   Energy in the form of waves that have both electrical and magnetic properties; these waves travel through gases, liquids, and solids, and occur even in a vacuum. All objects emit all forms of electromagnetic radiation, although each object emits its peak radiation at a certain *wavelength* within the *electromagnetic spectrum*.

Electromagnetic spectrum   Range of *electromagnetic radiation* types arranged by *wavelength* or by *wave frequency* or both. Although the electromagnetic spectrum is continuous, different names are assigned to different segments. These segments extend from the longest-wavelength (lowest frequency) *radio waves* through *microwaves*, *infrared radiation*, *visible radiation*, *ultraviolet radiation*, *X-rays*, to the shortest wavelength (highest frequency) *gamma radiation*.

Electronic hygrometer   Measures the amount of water vapor in the air based on changes in the electrical resistance of certain chemicals as they adsorb water vapor from the air. Variations in electrical resistance are calibrated in terms of *relative humidity* or *dewpoint*. An electronic hygrometer is flown aboard *radiosondes*.

Emissivity   A measure of how close a radiating object approximates a *blackbody*, a perfect radiator. The emissivity of a blackbody is 1.0 and less than 1.0 for all other objects.

Energy   The capacity for doing work.

Ensemble forecasting   A numerical model which generates several forecasts each based on slightly different sets of initial conditions.

ENSO (El Niño/Southern Oscillation)   The relationship between *El Niño* and the *southern oscillation*. An El Niño episode begins when the weakening of the surface *air pressure gradient* between the western and central tropical Pacific heralds the slackening of the *trade winds*.

Equinoxes   The first days of spring and autumn when day and night are of approximately equal length at all latitudes (except the poles) and the noon sun is directly over the equator (*solar altitude* of 90 degrees).

Evaporation   The process which produces a net loss of water vapor mass at the interface between liquid water and air; more water changes phase from liquid to vapor than vapor to liquid. The phase change from liquid to vapor requires the *latent heat of vaporization* and occurs at a *temperature* below the boiling temperature of water.

Evapotranspiration   Direct *evaporation* from Earth's surface plus the release of water vapor by vegetation (*transpiration*).

Expansional cooling   A *temperature* drop that accompanies a pressure reduction on and resultant expansion of a gas (or mixture of gases). The work of expansion requires energy, which is drawn from the internal energy of the gas, reducing its temperature. Air parcels that ascend within the *atmosphere* undergo expansional cooling in response to falling *air pressure*; expansional cooling is the principal means of *cloud* formation in the *atmosphere*.

Extra-tropical cyclone   A *synoptic-scale* low pressure system that occurs in midlatitudes, often forming along the *polar front*. This low, characterized by *fronts* and a *comma cloud* pattern, becomes a *cold-core cyclone* especially in the later stage of its life cycle.

Eye   An area of almost cloudless skies, subsiding air, and light *winds* (less than 25 km per hr or 16 mph) at the center of a *hurricane*. The eye diameter ranges from 10 to 65 km (6 to 40 mi) across and typically shrinks as the system strengthens.

Eye wall   A circle of *cumulonimbus* clouds that surrounds the *eye* of a mature *hurricane* and produces heavy *rains* and very strong *winds*. The most dangerous and potentially most destructive part of a hurricane is the portion of the eye wall where the wind blows in the same direction as the hurricane's forward motion.

F

Faculae   Relatively bright and hot areas in the solar *photosphere* that form a veined network near *sunspots*.

Fair-weather bias   The observation that fair-*weather* days outnumber stormy days almost everywhere.

Flash flood   A short-term, localized, and often unexpected rise in river or stream level causing flooding. Usually occurs in response to torrential *rain* falling over a small geographical area.

Fog   A visibility-restricting suspension of tiny water droplets or ice crystals in an air layer next to Earth's surface; *stratus* in contact with the ground.

Force   A push or pull on an object computed as mass times acceleration.

Freezing rain   Supercooled raindrops that at least partially freeze on contact with cold surfaces.

Friction   The resistance an object encounters as it comes into contact with other objects; the friction of fluid flow is known as *viscosity*.

Front   A narrow zone of transition between *air masses* of contrasting *air density*, that is, air masses of different *temperature*, *humidity*, or both. Fronts are classified as stationary, warm, cold, and occluded.

Frontal fog   *Fog* formed when *precipitation* falling from relatively warm air aloft into a wedge of relatively cool air near the Earth's surface evaporates and raises the *vapor pressure* in the cool air to saturation; occurs either just ahead of a *warm front* or just behind a *cold front*.

Frontal uplift   Ascent of air along the surface of a boundary between air masses of contrasting *air density*; often accompanied by cloud development.

Frost   Ice crystals that are formed by *deposition* of water vapor on a relatively cold surface. For water vapor to deposit as frost on the surface of an object, the *temperature* of that surface must cool below the *frost point*.

Frost point   The *temperature* to which air must be cooled at constant *air pressure* to achieve saturation at or below 0°C (32 °F).

F-scale (Fujita scale)   A six-category *tornado* intensity scale developed by T. Theodore Fujita that rates tornadoes from F0 to F5 on the basis of rotational *wind* speed estimated from property damage. Categories are weak (F0, F1), strong (F2, F3), and violent (F4, F5).

Funnel cloud   A tornadic circulation extending below *cloud* base but not reaching the ground; made visible by a cone-shaped cloud.

G

Gas law The relationship between the *variables of state* of a gas (or mixture of gases) stating that the pressure exerted by a gas is directly proportional to the product of its density and *temperature*.

Geologic time A span of millions or billions of years in the past. The geologic time scale is a standard division of time on Earth into eons, eras, periods, and epochs based on large-scale geological events.

Geologic time scale The standard division of Earth history into eons, eras, periods and epochs based on large-scale geological events.

Geostationary Operational Environmental Satellite (GOES) A *geostationary satellite*, operated by NOAA, designed to remotely monitor *weather* systems.

Geostrophic wind A hypothetical, unaccelerated horizontal *wind* that flows along a straight path parallel to *isobars* or height contours above the *atmospheric boundary layer*; results from a balance between the horizontal *pressure gradient force* and the *Coriolis Effect*.

Glacial climate Long-term average conditions favorable to the initiation and growth of glacial ice.

Glacial theory The notion that at various times in the past places that are not currently glaciated were covered by glacial ice.

Global climate model A *numerical model* that describes the physical interactions among the various components of the *climate* system: the *atmosphere*, ocean, land, ice-cover, and biosphere. Predicts broad regions of expected positive and negative *temperature* and *precipitation anomalies*, and the mean location of circulation features such as jet streams and principal storm tracks.

Global radiative equilibrium The balance between net incoming solar radiation and *infrared radiation* emitted to space by the *Earth-atmosphere system*.

Global water budget Balance sheet for the inputs and outputs of water to and from the various global water reservoirs. The global water budget indicates an annual net gain of water mass on land and an annual net loss of water mass from the ocean; the excess water mass on land flows to the sea and balances the budget.

Global water cycle The ceaseless movement of water among the atmospheric, oceanic, terrestrial, and biospheric reservoirs on a planetary scale; assumes an essentially fixed amount of water in the *Earth-atmosphere system*.

Glory Concentric rings of color about the shadow of an observer's head that appear on top of a *warm cloud* situated below the observer. A glory is caused by much the same optics as a primary *rainbow*, two important differences being the size of the reflecting and refracting particles, and the direction of reflected and refracted light. A glory is the consequence of sunlight interacting with a mass of much smaller cloud droplets that compose a *warm cloud*.

Gradient wind A hypothetical horizontal *wind* that blows parallel to curved *isobars* or height contours above the *atmospheric boundary layer*. It differs from the *geostrophic wind* in that the path of the gradient wind is curved.

Granules A network of huge, irregularly shaped convective cells in the sun's *photosphere*.

Gravity The force that accelerates air downward to the Earth's surface. It is the net result of gravitation, the force of attraction between Earth and all other objects, and the *centripetal force* arising from Earth's rotation on its axis.

Graupel   *Ice pellets*, generally 2 to 5 mm (0.1 to 0.2 in.) in diameter, formed in a *cloud* when supercooled water droplets collide and freeze on impact.

Green flash   A brilliant, thin, green rim that occasionally appears on the upper limb of the sun as it rises or sets (at *twilight*). A green flash is primarily the consequence of atmospheric *refraction* and *scattering* of light from a low sun; it is best seen on a distant horizon when the *atmosphere* is clear.

Greenhouse effect   Heating of Earth's surface and lower atmosphere as a consequence of differences in atmospheric transparency to *electromagnetic radiation*. The *atmosphere* is nearly transparent to incoming solar radiation, but much less transparent to outgoing *infrared radiation*. Terrestrial infrared radiation is absorbed and radiated primarily by water vapor and, to a lesser extent, by carbon dioxide and other trace gases, thereby slowing the loss of *heat* to space from the *Earth-atmosphere system*.

Greenhouse gases   Those gases that absorb and emit appreciable infrared radiation and contribute to the greenhouse effect in the Earth-atmosphere system. The main greenhouse gas is water vapor, others are carbon dioxide, ozone, methane and nitrous oxide.

Ground clutter   A pattern of *radar echoes* produced by *reflection* of radar signals by fixed objects such as buildings on Earth's surface.

Gust front   Leading edge of a mass of relatively cool gusty air that flows out of the base of a *thunderstorm cloud* (downdraft) and spreads along the ground well in advance of the parent thunderstorm cell; a mesoscale *cold front*. Uplift along the gust front may produce additional *cumulus* that may evolve into secondary thunderstorms cells tens of kilometers ahead of the parent cell.

H

Haboob   A dust- or sandstorm caused by the strong, gusty downdraft of a desert *thunderstorm*. The mass of dust or sand rolls along the ground as a huge ominous dark *cloud* that may be more than 100 km (60 mi) wide and may reach altitudes of several thousand meters.

Hadley cell   Thermally-driven air circulation in tropical and subtropical latitudes of both hemispheres resembling a huge convective cell with rising air near the equator in the *intertropical convergence zone* and sinking air in the *subtropical anticyclones*. Equatorward blowing surface winds and poleward directed upper-level *winds* complete the circulation.

Hail   *Precipitation* in the form of jagged to nearly spherical chunks of ice often characterized by internal concentric layering. Hail is associated with *thunderstorm* cells that have strong updrafts, an abundant supply of supercooled water droplets, and great vertical *cloud* development.

Hailstreak   Accumulation of *hail* in a long narrow path along the ground typically around 2 km (1.2 mi) wide and 10 km (6.2 mi) long.

Hair hygrometer   An instrument designed to monitor *relative humidity* by measuring the changes in the length of human hair that accompany *humidity* variations.

Halo   A whitish ring of light surrounding the sun or moon formed when the tiny ice crystals that compose high, thin *clouds* (such as *cirrus* or *cirrostratus*) refract the sun's rays.

Heat   A form of energy transferred between systems or components of a system in response to differences in *temperature*. Heat energy is always transferred from a warmer system to a colder system.

Heat conductivity   The ratio of the rate of heat transport across an area to a temperature gradient.

Heat equator   The latitude (about 10 degrees N) of highest mean annual surface air *temperature*. The mean position of the *intertropical convergence zone* approximately corresponds to the heat equator.

Heterosphere   The *atmosphere* above 80 km (50 mi) and the *homosphere* where gases are stratified, with concentrations of the heavier gases decreasing more rapidly with altitude than concentrations of the lighter gases.

Holocene   The interval since the end of the Pleistocene glaciation (approximately 10,500 years ago) that represents the present interglacial. This epoch has been characterized by spatially and temporally variable *temperature* and *precipitation*.

Homosphere   The *atmosphere* up to 80 km (50 mi) where the relative proportions of principal gases, such as nitrogen and oxygen, are constant.

Hook echo   A distinctive hook-shaped reflectivity pattern in a *radar echo* that often indicates the presence of a *severe thunderstorm* cell and perhaps tornadic circulation. This pattern is produced by rainfall being drawn around the *mesocyclone*.

Horse latitudes   Areas of persistent light *winds* or calm air between about 30 and 35 degrees N and S under *subtropical anticyclones*.

Hot-wire anemometer   An instrument that measures *wind* speed based on the rate of *heat* loss to air flowing passed a heated wire. The rate of heat loss from the wire to the air increases as wind speed increases.

Humidity   A general term referring to any one of many ways of describing the amount or concentration of water vapor in the air.

Hurricane   An intense *tropical cyclone* that originates over tropical ocean basins; called a typhoon in the western Pacific Ocean. Maximum near-surface sustained *winds* are 119 km per hr (74 mph) or higher.

Hydrostatic equilibrium   Balance between the *atmosphere's* vertical *pressure gradient force* and the equal, but oppositely directed force of *gravity*.

Hygrograph   An instrument that records a continuous trace of *relative humidity* variations with time. The most common hygrograph is a *hair hygrometer* designed to move a pen on a clock-driven drum.

Hygrometer   An instrument that measures the amount of water vapor in the air. See *dewpoint hygrometer, hair hygrometer,* and *electronic hygrometer*.

Hygroscopic nuclei   A special category of *cloud condensation nuclei* that have a special chemical affinity for water molecules, so that *condensation* may take place on these nuclei at *relative humidities* under 100%.

Hypothesis   A proposed explanation for some observation or phenomenon which is tested through the *scientific method*.

I

Ice pellets   *Precipitation* consisting of frozen raindrops 5 mm (0.2 in.) or less in diameter that bounce on impact with the ground; also called sleet.

Ice-albedo feedback Warming that causes a reduction in Arctic sea-ice cover is enhanced by the lower albedo of the open ocean waters.

Ice-forming nuclei (IN) Tiny particles that promote the formation of ice crystals at *temperatures* well below freezing; include *freezing nuclei* and *deposition nuclei*.

Ideal gas A gas which obeys Boyle's law and Charles' law precisely.

Infrared radiation (IR) *Electromagnetic radiation* at *wavelengths* ranging from 0.8 micrometer (near-infrared) to about 0.1 mm (far infrared). Infrared radiation has wavelengths shorter than *microwaves* and longer than visible red light; most objects in the *Earth-atmosphere system* have their peak emission in the infrared.

Infrared radiometer An instrument that measures the intensity of infrared radiation emitted by the surface of some object such as clouds or the ocean.

Infrared satellite image Picture or image processed from radiometers onboard a satellite that sense thermal (or infrared) radiation (typically, from *wavelengths* of approximately 8 to 12 micrometers) emitted by Earth and *cloud* surfaces of the *Earth-atmosphere system*. Infrared radiation signals are routinely calibrated to give the surface *temperature* of objects in the sensor's field of view.

Internal energy A measure of the molecular activity of a system or the summation of total energies of all molecules in a specific mass.

Interglacial climate Climate episode that favors the thinning or retreat of existing glaciers or no glaciers at all.

Intergovernmental Panel on Climate Change (IPCC) Entity established by WMO and UNEP to assess the technical, scientific, and socio-economic information relevant for the understanding of climate change and its potential impacts.

Intertropical convergence zone (ITCZ) Discontinuous low-pressure belt of *thunderstorms* paralleling the equator and marking the convergence of the Northern and Southern Hemisphere surface *trade winds*.

Inverse square law Intensity of radiation emitted by a point source (e.g., the sun) decreases as the inverse square of distance traveled.

Ion An atomic-scale particle that caries an electric charge.

Ionosphere Region of the upper *atmosphere* above 80 km (50 mi) that contains a relatively high concentration of *ions* (electrically charged particles). The ionosphere is located primarily in the *thermosphere*.

Iridescent cloud A *cloud* (usually *altocumulus*, *cirrostratus*, or *cirrocumulus*) having bright spots, bands, or borders of color, usually red or green. Iridescent clouds are produced by *diffraction* and typically appear up to about 30 degrees from the sun.

Isobar A line plotted on a map joining locations reporting the same *air pressure*. Drawing an isobar on a map of sea-level air pressures requires interpolation between reporting *weather* stations.

Isotherms Lines drawn on a map through localities having the same air temperature.

J

Jet streak   An area of accelerated air flow within a jet stream; the *wind* may strengthen by as much as an additional 100 km per hr (62 mph). Jet streaks occur where surface horizontal *temperature gradients* are particularly steep and play an important role in the generation and maintenance of synoptic-scale *cyclones*. The strongest jet streaks develop during winter in the *polar front jet stream* along the East Coasts of North America and Asia.

L

La Niña   A period of particularly strong *trade winds* and unusually low sea-surface *temperatures* (SST) in the central and eastern tropical Pacific; opposite of *El Niño*. The strong trade winds induce exceptionally vigorous *upwelling* in the eastern tropical Pacific, which causes unusually low SST.

Lake breeze   A relatively cool surface *wind* directed from a large lake toward land in response to differential heating between land and lake; develops during daylight hours.

Land breeze   A relatively cool surface *wind* directed from land to sea or land to lake in response to differential cooling between land and a body of water; develops at night.

Latent heat   The quantity of *heat* involved in the phase changes of water.

Latent heat of fusion   *Heat* released to the environment when water changes phase from liquid to solid; 80 *calories* per gm.

Latent heat of vaporization   *Heat* required to change the phase of water from liquid to vapor; 540 to 600 *calories* per gram, depending on the *temperature* of the water.

Latent heating   Transport of *heat* from one place to another within the *atmosphere* as a consequence of phase changes of water. Heat is supplied for melting, *evaporation*, and *sublimation* of water at the Earth's surface, and heat is released during freezing, *condensation*, and *deposition* within the atmosphere.

Law of energy conservation   Energy is neither created nor destroyed but can change from one form to another; same as the first law of thermodynamics.

Law of reflection   The angle of incident radiation is to equal to the angle of reflected radiation.

Lee-wave clouds   Lens-shaped (lenticular) *clouds* that form in the crests of a standing wave downwind from a prominent mountain range.

Lifting condensation level (LCL)   The altitude to which air must be lifted so that *expansional cooling* leads to *condensation* (or *deposition*) and *cloud* development; corresponds to the base of clouds.

Lightning   A brilliant flash of light produced by an electrical discharge in response to the buildup of an electrical potential between a *cloud* and Earth's surface, between different clouds, or between different portions of the same cloud.

Lightning detection network (LDN)   System that provides real-time information on the location and severity of *lightning* strokes.

Little Ice Age   The interval of the *Holocene* from about 1400 to 1850 when average global *temperatures* were lower, and alpine glaciers increased in size and advanced down mountain valleys. The Little Ice Age followed the *Medieval Warm Period.*

M

Macroburst   A *downburst* that affects a path longer than 4.0 km (2.5 mi), has maximum surface *winds* that may top 210 km per hr (130 mph), and has a life expectancy of up to 30 minutes. The leading edge of a macroburst may be marked by a *gust front.*

Magnetosphere   Region of the upper *atmosphere* above an altitude of about 150 km (95 mi) encompassed by the Earth's magnetic field; deflected by *solar wind* into a teardrop-shaped cavity.

Mammatus clouds   *Clouds* that form on the underside of a *thunderstorm* anvil and exhibit pouchlike, downward protuberances; may indicate turbulent air.

Maritime polar air (mP)   Cool, humid *air masses* that form over the cold ocean waters of the North Pacific and North Atlantic, especially north of 40 degrees N. Along the West Coast, maritime polar air contributes to heavy winter *rains* and *snows* and persistent summer coastal *fogs.*

Maritime tropical air (mT)   Warm, humid *air masses* that form over tropical and subtropical ocean waters (e.g., the Gulf of Mexico). Maritime tropical air is responsible for oppressive summer *heat* and *humidity* east of the Rocky Mountains.

Mature stage   The middle and most intense phase in the life cycle of a *thunderstorm* cell; begins when *precipitation* reaches Earth's surface and is characterized by both updrafts and downdrafts. *Rain* is heaviest, *lightning* is most frequent, and *hail,* strong surface *winds,* and *tornadoes* may develop during this stage, which typically lasts about 10 to 20 minutes.

Maunder minimum   A 70-year period from 1645 to 1715 when *sunspots* were rare.

McIDAS (Man-computer Interactive Data Access System)   A computerized data management system for *weather* information; ingests weather data and satellite images and integrates and organizes those data into guidance products for potential users. Developed by scientists at the Space Science and Engineering Center (SSEC) at the University of Wisconsin-Madison.

Medieval Warm Period   A relatively mild episode of the *Holocene* between about 950 and 1250 C.E.

Mercury barometer   A mercury-filled tube used to measure *air pressure*; the standard barometric instrument, which features great precision.

Meridional flow pattern   Flow of the *planetary-scale* westerlies in a series of deep troughs and sharp ridges; westerlies exhibit considerable amplitude. In this pattern, cold *air masses* surge southward and warm air masses stream northward, leading to strong *temperature gradients.*

Mesocyclone   A vertical column of cyclonically rotating air 3 to 10 km (2 to 6 mi) across that develops in the updraft of a *severe thunderstorm* cell; an early stage in the development of a *tornado.* A mesocyclone forms a tornado about 10% of the time.

Mesopause   Narrow zone of transition between the *mesosphere* below and the *thermosphere* above; the top of the mesosphere. Has an average altitude of 80 km (50 mi) and features the lowest average *temperature* in the *atmosphere.*

Meso-scale convective complex (MCC) A nearly circular organized cluster of many interacting *thunderstorm* cells covering an area of many thousands of square kilometers. MCCs occur mostly in the warm-season over the eastern two-thirds of the United States and develop at night during weak synoptic-scale flow. Lasting from 6 to 12 hrs, they are driven by a flow of warm, humid air at low levels and *radiational cooling* at upper levels, which work together to destabilize the *troposphere*.

Mesoscale systems *Weather* phenomena that may influence the weather in only a portion of a large city or county; includes *thunderstorms*, *sea breezes*, and *lake breezes*. These systems have dimensions of 1 to 100 km (1 to 60 mi) and last from hours to a day or so.

Mesosphere The atmospheric layer between the *stratosphere* and the *thermosphere*; *temperature* falls with increasing altitude. Located between average altitudes of 50 to 80 km (31 to 50 mi).

Meteorology The scientific study of the *atmosphere* and atmospheric processes.

Microburst A *downburst* that affects a path on the ground that is 4.0 km (2.5 mi) or shorter, has maximum surface *winds* as high as 270 km per hr (170 mph), and has a life expectancy of less than 10 minutes.

Microscale systems *Weather* phenomena that represent the smallest spatial subdivision of atmospheric circulation, such as a weak *tornado*. These systems have dimensions of 1 m to 1 km (3 ft to 1 mi) and last from seconds to an hour or so.

Midlatitude westerlies Prevailing planetary-scale *winds* in the middle and upper *troposphere* between about 30 and 60 degrees of latitude; blow on average from the southwest in the Northern Hemisphere and from the northwest in the Southern Hemisphere out of the poleward flanks of the *subtropical anticyclones*.

Mie scattering The optical effect whereby light is scattered equally at all *wavelengths*. It is produced by spherical particles having about the same diameter as the wavelength of *visible radiation;* responsible for a milky white sky when large numbers of *aerosols* are present.

Milankovitch cycles Systematic changes in three elements of Earth-sun geometry: precession of the *solstices* and *equinoxes*, tilt of Earth's rotational axis, and orbital eccentricity; affect the seasonal and latitudinal distribution of incoming solar radiation and influence climatic fluctuations over tens to hundreds of thousands of years.

Mirage An optical phenomenon that makes an object appear to be displaced from its true position. A mirage is caused by *refraction* of light rays due to the change in *air density* with altitude within the lower *atmosphere*. When an object appears higher that it actually is, it is called a superior mirage. When an object appears lower that it actually is, it is called an inferior mirage.

Mist Very thin *fog* in which visibility is greater than 1.0 km (0.62 mi). Mist is also known as light *drizzle*.

Mixing ratio Mass of water vapor per mass of the remaining dry air; usually expressed as so many grams of water vapor per kilogram of dry air.

Model comparison A comparison made among forecasts made by several different numerical models.

Moist adiabatic lapse rate A variable rate of cooling applicable to saturated (cloudy) air parcels that are ascending within the *atmosphere*. This rate is less than the *dry adiabatic lapse rate* because some of the *expansional cooling* is compensated by *latent heat* released during *condensation* or *deposition* of water vapor.

Molecular viscosity Fluid *friction* (*viscosity*) arising from the random motions and interactions of molecules composing a fluid such as air or water.

Monsoon circulation Seasonal reversals in prevailing *winds* that cause wet summers and relatively dry winters. The most vigorous monsoon circulation occurs over Africa and southern Asia.

Mountain breeze A shallow, gusty downslope flow of cool air that develops at night in some mountain valleys in response to differential heating between the air adjacent to the valley wall and air at the same altitude out over the valley floor.

Mountain-wave clouds Stationary lenticular (lens-shaped) *clouds* situated over and downwind of a prominent mountain range; formed by the disturbance of the large-scale horizontal *winds* by the mountain range.

Multi-vortex tornadoes A tornado consisting of two or more subsidiary vortices that orbit each other or about a common center within a massive tornado.

N

Nacreous clouds Rarely seen *clouds* with a soft, pearly luster that form in the upper *stratosphere*; may be composed of ice crystals or supercooled water droplets. Nacreous clouds are *cirrus* and *altocumulus lenticularis* that form on sulfuric acid nuclei. Also called mother-of-pearl clouds or polar stratospheric clouds.

National Centers for Environmental Prediction (NCEP) Centers responsible for the interpretation of weather maps and charts, and the generation of forecasts and other guidance products for the nation and for exchange with other nations.
National Climatic Data Center (NCDC) An agency of the *National Oceanographic and Atmospheric Administration* that archives climatic data of the United States; located in Asheville, NC.

National Data Buoy Center (NDBC) A network of automated weather stations attached to moored buoys in offshore locations and at lighthouses, fishing piers and offshore oil platforms.

National Hurricane Center (NHC) A branch of the Tropical Prediction Center (part of the *National Centers for Environmental Prediction*) located in south Florida that is responsible for forecasting *tropical cyclones* in the Atlantic Basin, Gulf of Mexico, and the eastern tropical Pacific Ocean.

National Oceanic and Atmospheric Administration (NOAA) The administrative unit within the U.S. Department of Commerce that oversees the *National Weather Service*.

National Weather Service (NWS) The agency of the *National Oceanic and Atmospheric Administration* responsible for *weather* data acquisition, data analysis, weather forecasting and dissemination, and storm watches and warnings.

Nebula In astronomy, an immense rotating interstellar cloud of dust, ice and gases.

Neutral air layer An ambient air layer in which an ascending or descending air parcel always has the same *temperature* (and *air density*) as its surroundings.

Newton's first law of motion An object at rest or in straight-line, unaccelerated motion remains that way unless acted upon by a net external force.

Newton's second law of motion A net force is required to cause a unit mass of a substance to accelerate; force = (mass) × (acceleration).

Nimbostratus clouds (Ns)   Low, gray, layered *clouds* that resemble *stratus* but are thicker, appear darker gray, have a less uniform base, and yield more substantial *precipitation*. Nimbostratus are composed of mostly water droplets.

NOAA Weather Radio   Low power, VHF-high-band FM radio transmitters operated by the *National Oceanic and Atmospheric Administration* that broadcast continuous *weather* information (e.g., regional conditions, local forecasts, marine warnings) directly from *National Weather Service* Forecast Offices 24 hrs per day.

Noctilucent clouds   Wavy, thin *clouds* resembling *cirrus*, but usually bluish-white or silvery; best seen at high latitudes just before sunrise or just after sunset. These rare clouds occur in the upper *mesosphere* at altitudes above about 80 km (50 mi) and may be composed of ice deposited on meteoric dust.

Norwegian cyclone model   An approximation of the structure and life cycle of an extra-tropical low-pressure system based mostly on surface observations, first proposed during World War I by researchers at the Norwegian School of Meteorology at Bergen.

Nuclei   Tiny solid or liquid particles suspended in the *atmosphere* that provide surfaces on which water vapor condenses into droplets or deposits into ice crystals; essential for *cloud* formation.

Number density   Number of molecules of a gas (or mixture of gases) per unit volume.

NWS Cooperative Observer Network   Consists of more than 8000 *weather* stations across the United States that record daily *precipitation* and maximum/minimum *temperatures* for hydrologic, agricultural, and climatic purposes. These manned stations complement observations from the *Automated Surface Observing System*.

O

Ocean conveyor-belt system   Planetary-scale ocean transport of heat energy and salt by ocean currents; plays an important role in Earth's climate system.

Occluded front   A *front* formed late in the life cycle of an extra-tropical *cyclone*; its behavior depends upon the characteristics of air behind the *cold front* and ahead of the *warm front*. Also known as an occlusion.

Orographic lifting   The forced rising of air up the slopes of a hill or mountain. Air that is forced to ascend the slopes facing the oncoming *wind* (windward slopes) expands and cools, which increases its *relative humidity*. With sufficient cooling, *clouds* and *precipitation* develop.

Outgassing   Release of gasses to the *atmosphere* from hot, molten rock during volcanic activity and from impact of meteorites on the rocky surface of the planet; the origins of most atmospheric gases.

Overrunning   The process whereby less dense air flows up and over denser air; occurs along a *warm front* and may occur along a *stationary front*. Ascending air cools by expansion, leading to the formation of *clouds* and perhaps *precipitation* over a widespread area.

P

Pacific air   Term used to describe cool, humid *maritime polar air* air swept inland from the Pacific Ocean that experiences *air mass modification* over the Rocky Mountains, emerging milder and drier to the east of the mountains. During a *zonal flow pattern*, Pacific air floods the eastern two-thirds of the United States and southern Canada, causing mild and generally dry *weather*.

Perihelion   The time of the year when the Earth's orbital path brings it closest (147 million km or 91 million mi) to the sun (at present, about 3 January).

Persistence   Tendency for *weather* episodes to continue for some period of time.

pH scale   A measure of the range of acidity and alkalinity of different substances, extending from 0 to 14. A pH of 7 is neutral. Acids have values less than 7 and alkaline substances greater than 7.

Photosphere   The intensely bright portion of the sun visible to the unaided eye; this several-hundred-kilometer-thick layer is what we perceive as the surface of the sun. Features such as *sunspots* and *faculae* are observed on the photosphere.

Photosynthesis   The process whereby plants use sunlight, water, and carbon dioxide to manufacture their food and generate oxygen as a byproduct.

Planetary albedo   The fraction (or percent) of incident solar radiation that is scattered and reflected back into space by the *Earth-atmosphere system*; measurements by satellite sensors indicate a planetary albedo of about 31%.

Planetary-scale systems   *Weather* phenomena operating at the largest spatial scale of atmospheric circulation; includes the global *wind* belts and *semipermanent pressure systems*. These systems have dimensions of 10,000 to 40,000 km (6000 to 24,000 mi) and exhibit patterns that persist from weeks to months.

Planetesimals   Large meteorites a few kilometers across.

Plate tectonics   Concept that the outer 100 km (60 mi) of solid Earth is divided into a dozen or more gigantic rigid plates that move relative to one another slowly across the surface of the planet. The drift of these plates move continents and open and close ocean basins over the vast expanse of *geologic time*; mountain building and most volcanic activity occur at plate boundaries.

Polar amplification   The tendency for a major *temperature* change to increase in magnitude with latitude.

Polar front   Narrow transition zone where the relatively mild *midlatitude westerlies* meet and override the relatively cold polar easterlies. When the *temperature gradient* across the *front* is steep, the front is well defined and is a potential site for development of *extra-tropical cyclones*.

Polar front jet stream   A corridor of strong westerlies in the upper *troposphere* between the midlatitude *tropopause* and the polar tropopause and directly over the *polar front*.

Polar high   A *cold-core anticyclone* that originates in a source region for *continental polar air*; this shallow system is the product of intense *radiational cooling* over the *snow*-covered continental interior of North America well north of the *polar front*.

Polar-orbiting Operation Environmental Satellite (POES)   A satellite whose orbital plane passes near the North and South poles. Earth rotates under the plane of the satellite.

Polar stratospheric clouds (PSCs)   Clouds composed of water ice, nitric acid and sulfuric acid which form during the Antarctic winter when extreme radiational cooling causes stratospheric temperatures to drop below $-88°$ C (-126 °F).

Poleward heat transport   Flow of *heat* from tropical to middle and high latitudes in response to latitudinal imbalances in net *radiational heating* and *radiational cooling*. Poleward heat transport is accomplished primarily by *air mass* exchange, but also by storms, and ocean circulation.

Precipitable water   The depth of water that would be produced if all the water vapor in a vertical column of air were condensed; usually the column of air extends from Earth's surface to the top of the *troposphere*.

Precipitation   Water in solid, liquid, or freezing form that falls to Earth's surface from *clouds*; can be in the form of *rain, drizzle, snow, ice pellets, hail* or *freezing rain.*

Pressure gradient force   A force operating in the *atmosphere* that accelerates air parcels away from regions of high *air pressure* directly across *isobars* toward regions of low air pressure in response to an *air pressure gradient.*

Pressure systems   Individual synoptic-scale features of atmospheric circulation; commonly denoted as highs (or *anticyclones*) or lows (or *cyclones*), less frequently ridges or troughs.

Psychrometer   An instrument used to measure the amount of water vapor in the air. It consists of two identical liquid-in-glass *thermometers* mounted side by side with the bulb of one thermometer wrapped in a muslin wick. To take a reading, the wick-covered bulb is first soaked in distilled water and then the instrument is ventilated, either by being whirled about (*sling psychrometer*) or with a small fan (*aspirated psychrometer*). The dry bulb thermometer measures the actual air *temperature.* Water vaporizes from the muslin wick into the air streaming past the wet-bulb thermometer and evaporative cooling lowers the *wet-bulb temperature* to a steady value. By referring to special psychrometric tables, the *relative humidity* or the *dewpoint* can be determined from the difference between the dry-bulb temperature and wet-bulb temperature (*wet-bulb depression*).

Pyranometer   The standard instrument for measuring solar radiation incident on a horizontal surface; calibrates the *temperature* response of a special sensor in units of radiation flux, such as watts per square meter.

R

Radar   An acronym for radio detection and ranging. In meteorology, a remote sensing tool which broadcasts and receives microwave signals back from targets for the purpose of determining the location, height, movement and intensity of precipitation areas.

Radar echo   *Microwave* signals emitted by *weather radar* that are scattered or reflected by *rain* or *snow* back to a receiver where they are electronically processed and displayed on a cathode ray tube.

Radiation fog   Ground-level *cloud* formed by nocturnal *radiational cooling* of a humid air layer near the ground so that its *relative humidity* approaches 100%; sometimes called *ground fog,*

Radiational cooling   The drop in *temperature* of an object or a surface accomplished whenever the object or surface undergoes a net loss of *heat* due to a greater rate of emission of *electromagnetic radiation* than *absorption.*

Radiational heating   The rise in *temperature* of an object or a surface accomplished whenever the object or surface undergoes a net gain of *heat* due to a greater rate of *absorption* of *electromagnetic radiation* than emission.

Radiosonde   A small balloon-borne instrument package equipped with a radio transmitter that takes altitude readings (*soundings*) of *temperature*, *air pressure*, and *humidity* in the *atmosphere.*

Rain   Form of *precipitation* consisting of liquid water drops having diameters generally between 0.5 and 6.0 mm (0.02 and 0.2 in); falls mostly from *nimbostratus* and *cumulonimbus* clouds.

Rain gauge A device for collecting and measuring rainfall (or melted snowfall); a standard rain gauge consists of a cylindrical container equipped with a cone-shaped funnel at the top.

Rain shadow A region situated downwind (often hundreds of kilometers) of a prominent mountain range and characterized by descending air and, as a consequence, a relatively dry *climate*.

Rainbow An arc of concentric colored bands formed by *refraction* and internal *reflection* of sunlight by raindrops. To see a rainbow, an observer must be looking at a distant *rain* shower with the sun at his/her back.

Rawinsonde A *radiosonde* tracked from the ground by a direction-finding antenna or global positioning system (GPS) to measure variations in horizontal *wind* direction and wind speed with altitude.

Rayleigh scattering The optical effect where light at the short-*wavelength* end of the visible *electromagnetic spectrum* is scattered much more efficiently than light at the long-wavelength end of the visible spectrum. This wavelength-dependent *scattering* is caused by spherical scattering particles having diameters much smaller than the wavelength of scattered radiation. Rayleigh scattering is responsible for the blue of the daytime sky.

Reflection The process whereby a portion of the radiation that strikes the interface between two different media is redirected such that the angle of reflection equals the angle of incidence. Reflection is a special case of *scattering*.

Refraction The bending of a light ray as it passes from one transparent medium into another (from air to water, for example). Bending is due to the differing speeds of light in the two media.

Relative humidity Compares the amount of water vapor in the air with the amount of water vapor in the same air at *saturation*. Relative humidity is a measure of how close air is to *saturation* at a specific *temperature*, always expressed as a percentage. It can be computed from either the ratio of the *vapor pressure* to the *saturation vapor pressure* or the ratio of the *mixing ratio* to the *saturation mixing ratio*.

Remote sensing The technology of measuring or acquiring data and information about an object or phenomenon with a device that is not in physical contact with it.

Ring A large turbulent eddy that forms when a meander in an ocean current forms a loop which pinches off, separating from the main current.

Roll cloud A low, cylindrically-shaped and elongated *cloud* occurring behind a *gust front*; associated with but detached from a *cumulonimbus* cloud. The cloud appears to rotate slowly about its horizontal axis.

Rossby waves Series of long-*wavelength* troughs and ridges that characterize the planetary-scale westerlies (above the 500-mb level) as they encircle the globe; also called *long waves*. Typically, between 2 and 5 waves encircle the hemisphere at one time.

S

Saffir-Simpson Hurricane Intensity Scale A five-category *hurricane* intensity scale developed by H. S. Saffir and R. H. Simpson that rates hurricanes from 1 to 5 on the basis of maximum sustained *wind* speed. Categories are 1 (weak), 2 (moderate), 3 (strong), 4 (very strong), and 5 (devastating).

Sahara air layer (SAL) An elevated mass of dry stable air originating over the Sahara Desert.

Santa Ana wind A hot, dry *chinook wind* that blows from the desert plateaus of Utah and Nevada across the Sierra Nevada and downslope toward coastal southern California. This *wind* desiccates vegetation and contributes to outbreaks of forest and brush fires.

Saturation absolute humidity The value of *absolute humidity* when air is saturated with respect to water vapor.

Saturation mixing ratio The value of the *mixing ratio* when air is saturated with respect to water vapor; varies directly with *temperature*, and to a lesser extent upon *air pressure*.

Saturation specific humidity The value of the *specific humidity* when air is saturated with respect to water vapor; varies directly with *temperature*.

Saturation vapor pressure The value of the *vapor pressure* when air is saturated with respect to water vapor; varies directly with *temperature*.

Scattering The process by which *aerosols* and molecules disperse radiation in all directions. Scattering is a function of the *wavelength* of the incident radiation and the size, surface, and composition of the scattering aerosol or molecule, where size is defined relative to the wavelength. No energy transformation results from scattering.

Scientific method A systematic form of inquiry that involves observation, speculation, and the formulation and testing of hypotheses.

Scientific model An approximate representation or simulation of a real system that omits all but the most essential variables of the system.

Scientific theory A *hypothesis* that has stood the test of time and is generally accepted by the scientific community.

Scintillation Generic term for rapid variations in apparent position, brightness, or color of a distant luminous object viewed through the atmosphere, caused by changing refraction of light passing along an atmospheric path with rapidly changing density.

Sea breeze A relatively cool mesoscale surface *wind* directed from the ocean toward land in response to differential heating of land and sea; develops during daylight hours.

Second law of thermodynamics All systems tend toward a state of disorder. A gradient in a system, such as a *temperature gradient*, signals order in the system. As a system tends towards disorder, gradients are eliminated.

Semi-permanent pressure systems Persistent areas of high and low *air pressure* that are *planetary-scale systems*. They undergo some important seasonal changes in location and surface air pressures and include *subtropical anticyclones*, the *intertropical convergence zone*, *subpolar lows*, and *polar highs*.

Sensible heating Transport of *heat* from one location or object to another via *conduction*, *convection* or both.

Severe thunderstorm *Thunderstorms* accompanied by locally damaging surface *winds*, frequent *lightning*, or large *hail*. The official *National Weather Service* criterion for the severe thunderstorm designation includes any one or a combination of the following: hailstones with diameters 0.75 in. (1.9 cm) or larger; *tornadoes* or *funnel clouds*; surface winds stronger than 58 mph (93 km per hr).

Shelf cloud A low, wedge-shaped, and elongated *cloud* that occurs along a *gust front*; associated with and attached to a *cumulonimbus* cloud. Damaging surface *winds* may occur under a shelf cloud, and this cloud may be associated with a *severe* *thunderstorm*. Also known as an arcus cloud.

Short waves Relatively small short-*wavelength* ripples (troughs and ridges) superimposed on *Rossby waves* in the planetary-scale westerlies; they propagate with the airflow in the middle and upper *troposphere*. Typically, a dozen or more short waves encircle the hemisphere at one time.

Single-station forecasts *Weather* forecasts based on observations at one location.

Sleet See *ice pellets*.

SLOSH (Sea, Lake, & Overland Surges from Hurricanes) A numerical model developed in 1979 by NOAA to predict the location and height of a storm surge.

Snow A frozen form of *precipitation* consisting of an assemblage of ice crystals in the form of flakes. Although snowflakes vary in shape and size, the constituent ice crystals are hexagonal (six-sided) and may consist of needles, dendrites, plates, or columns.

Snow grains Frozen form of *precipitation* consisting of flat particles of opaque, white ice having diameters less than 1 mm (0.04 in.); originates in the same way as *drizzle* except that particles freeze prior to reaching the ground. Also known as granular *snow*.

Snow pellets Frozen form of *precipitation* consisting of soft spherical (or sometimes conical) particles of opaque, white ice having diameters of 2 to 5 mm (0.08 to 0.2 in.). They often break up when striking a hard surface and differ from *snow grains* in being softer and larger. Formally called soft *hail* or *graupel*.

Solar altitude The angle of the sun 90 degrees or less above the horizon; influences the intensity of solar radiation that strikes Earth's surface. At a maximum possible solar altitude of 90 degrees, the solar rays are most intense; the intensity declines with decreasing solar altitude (towards 0 degrees).

Solar constant The flux of solar radiational energy falling on a surface that is positioned at the outer edge of the *atmosphere* and oriented perpendicular to the solar beam when Earth is at its average distance from the sun.

Solar corona Outermost portion of the solar atmosphere (above the *chromosphere*) that is a region of extremely hot (1 to 4 million °C or 1.8 to 7.2 million °F), highly rarefied gases extending millions of kilometers in space, to the outer limits of the solar system. The *solar wind* originates in the solar corona.

Solar wind A stream of super-hot electrically charged subatomic particles (mainly protons and electrons) flowing into space from the sun. The solar wind originates in the *solar corona*.

Solstice A time during the year when the sun is at its maximum poleward location relative to the Earth (23 degrees, 30 minutes, North or South); the first days of astronomical summer and winter.

Sonic anemometer An instrument sensor that emits sound waves to determine wind speed.

Sonic boom A shock wave caused by an aircraft flying at supersonic speeds, heard as a loud boom.

Sound wave A compressional wave consisting of alternate compressions and rarefactions of air.

Sounding Continuous altitude measurements that provide vertical profiles of such variables as *temperature*, *humidity*, and *wind* speed.

Southern oscillation   Opposing swings of surface *air pressure* between the western and central tropical Pacific Ocean. When air pressure is low at Darwin (Australia) it is high at Tahiti (a south Pacific island) and when air pressure is high at Darwin it is low at Tahiti.

Southern oscillation index   An index calculated from the monthly or seasonal fluctuations in the air pressure between Darwin, Australia and Tahiti. Positive values indicate La Niña conditions and negative values El Niño conditions.

Southwest monsoon   Also called the North American Monsoon System (NAMS); circulation brings summer rainfall to the American Southwest from moisture sources in the Gulf of California and the Gulf of Mexico.

Specific heat   The amount of *heat* required to raise the *temperature* of 1 gram of a substance by 1 Celsius degree.

Specific humidity   The ratio of the mass of water vapor (in grams) to the mass (in kilograms) of air containing the water vapor, that is, the combined mass of dry air plus water vapor.

Split flow pattern   Wave pattern in the *planetary-scale circulation* regime where westerlies to the north have a wave configuration that differs from that of westerlies to the south.

Spörer minimum   A period of reduced *sunspot* activity between about 1450 and 1550 C.E.

Squall line   An elongated cluster of intense *thunderstorm* cells that is accompanied by a continuous *gust front* at the cluster's leading edge. A squall line is located parallel to and up to 300 km (180 mi) ahead of a fast-moving well-defined *cold front*.

Stable air layer   An ambient air layer characterized by a vertical *temperature* profile such that air parcels return to their original altitudes following any upward or downward displacement. An ascending air parcel becomes cooler (denser) than the ambient air and a descending air parcel becomes warmer (less dense) than the ambient air, returning in both cases to the original altitude.

Standard atmosphere   A model that represents the state of the *atmosphere* averaged for all latitudes and seasons. It features a fixed sea-level air *temperature*, *air pressure*, and *air density* plus fixed vertical profiles of temperature and air pressure.

Station model   A conventional representation of *weather* station observations on a weather map using standard symbols for weather conditions.

Stationary front   A *front* that exhibits essentially no lateral movement; *winds* blow parallel but in opposite directions on either side of the *front*.

Steam fog   The general name for *fog* produced when extremely cold, dry air comes in contact with a relatively warm (unfrozen) water surface; has the appearance of rising streamers. Also known as Arctic sea smoke.

Stefan-Boltzmann law   A radiation law that states that the total energy radiated by a *blackbody* at all *wavelengths* is directly proportional to the fourth power of the absolute *temperature* (in kelvins) of the body. For example, the sun's energy output per square meter is about 190,000 times that of the *Earth-atmosphere system*.

Storm surge   A dome of water perhaps 80 to 160 km (50 to 100 mi) wide that sweeps over the coastline near the landfall of a tropical or extra-tropical *cyclone*, often causing considerable coastal erosion and flooding. The dome of water is caused primarily by strong onshore *winds* and, to a lesser extent, low *air pressure* associated with the storm system.

Stratiform clouds   Layered *clouds*, such as *altostratus*, often produced by *overrunning*.

Stratocumulus clouds (Sc) Low *clouds* occurring as large, irregular puffs or rolls arranged in a layer. Stratocumulus are composed of mostly water droplets.

Stratopause Transition zone between the *stratosphere* below and the *mesosphere* above; the top of the stratosphere at an average altitude of 50 km (31 mi).

Stratosphere The *atmosphere's* thermal subdivision situated between the *troposphere* and *mesosphere* and the primary site of ozone formation. Air *temperature* in the lower portion of the stratosphere is constant with altitude, and then the temperature increases with altitude to the *stratopause*; located between the *tropopause* and an average altitude of 50 km (31 mi).

Stratospheric ozone shield Ozone in the *stratosphere* that shields organisms at the Earth's surface from exposure to potentially lethal intensities of solar *ultraviolet radiation*.

Stratus clouds (St) Low *clouds* that occur as a uniform gray layer stretching from horizon to horizon. They may produce *drizzle*, and where they intersect the ground, they are classified as *fog*. Stratus are composed of water droplets.

Streamline A line that graphically portrays the flow of *wind* and can be used to identify regions of *divergence* and convergence.

Stüve thermodynamic diagram A graphical representation of *soundings* and *adiabatic processes* in the *atmosphere*.

Sublimation The process which produces a net loss of water mass at the interface between ice and air; more water changes phase from ice to vapor than vapor to ice. The phase change of water from ice to vapor (without first becoming liquid) requires the addition of the *latent heat of melting* plus the *latent heat of vaporization*.

Subpolar lows High-latitude, semipermanent *cyclones* marking the convergence of planetary-scale surface southwesterlies of midlatitudes with surface northeasterlies of polar latitudes in the Northern Hemisphere or midlatitude northwesterlies and polar southeasterlies in the Southern Hemisphere. The Icelandic low and Aleutian low are Northern Hemisphere examples.

Subtropical anticyclones Semipermanent high-pressure systems centered over subtropical latitudes (on average, near 30 degrees N and S) of the Atlantic, Pacific, and Indian Oceans. These warm-core systems extend from the ocean surface up to the *tropopause*.

Subtropical jet stream A zone of relatively strong *winds* aloft situated between the tropical *tropopause* and the midlatitude tropopause, on the poleward side of the *Hadley cell*.

Sulfurous aerosols Tiny droplets of sulfuric acid (H_2SO_4) and sulfate particles formed when volcanic eruptions send sulfur dioxide into the stratosphere to combine with water vapor.

Sundog A colored luminous spot at the same altitude as the sun produced by *refraction* of light by ice crystals. In some cases, sundogs are part of a *halo* surrounding the sun. Also called *parhelia*.

Sunspot Relatively dark, cool area that develops on the surface of the sun's *photosphere* where an intense magnetic field suppresses the flow of gases transporting *heat* from the sun's interior.

Supercell thunderstorm A relatively long-lived, large and intense *thunderstorm* cell characterized by an exceptionally strong updraft sometimes in excess of 240 km per hr (150 mph); may produce a *tornado*.

Supercooling The reduction of temperature of any liquid below the melting point of the substance's solid phase; that is, cooling beyond its normal freezing point while remaining a liquid.

Synoptic-scale systems   *Weather* phenomena operating at the continental or oceanic spatial scale; includes migrating *cyclones* and *anticyclones, hurricanes, air masses* and *fronts*. These systems have dimensions of 100 to 10,000 km (60 to 6000 mi) and last from days to a week or so.

System   An entity having components that function and interact with one another in an orderly and predictable manner that can be described by fundamental physical principles or natural laws.

T

Teleconnection   A linkage between changes in atmospheric circulation occurring in widely separated regions of the globe, often many thousands of kilometers apart.

Temperature   A measure of the average *kinetic energy* of the individual atoms or molecules composing a substance.

Temperature gradient   *Temperature* change with distance.

Terminal velocity   Constant downward-directed speed of a particle within a fluid due to a balance between *gravity* (acting downward) and fluid resistance (directed upward).

Thermal inertia   Resistance to a change in *temperature*.

Thermograph   A recording instrument that provides a continuous trace of *temperature* variations with time.

Thermometer   An instrument used for measuring *temperature* by incorporating a thermal sensor that utilizes the variation of the physical properties of substances according to their thermal states. Thermal sensors include liquid-in-glass, deformation, and electronic thermometers, along with radiometers that sense *electromagnetic radiation*.

Thermosphere   The outermost thermal subdivision of the *atmosphere* above the *mesopause* in which the air *temperature* is isothermal in the lower reaches and then increases with altitude. The thermosphere starts at an average altitude of 80 km (50 mi) and includes most or all of the *ionosphere*.

Thunder   Sound accompanying *lightning*; intense heating of air by a lightning discharge is accompanied by a tremendous local increase in air pressure that generates a shock wave. The shock wave propagates outward producing sound waves heard as thunder.

Thunderstorm   A mesoscale *weather* system produced by strong *convection* current that surges to great altitudes within the *troposphere*, sometimes reaching the *tropopause* or higher. Consists of *cumulonimbus* accompanied by *lightning* and *thunder* and often, locally heavy rainfall (or snowfall) and gusty surface *winds*. A thunderstorm consists of one or more convective cells, each of which progresses through the life cycle of *towering cumulus stage, mature stage*, and *dissipating stage*.

Tipping-bucket rain gauge   A recording *rain gauge* that collects rainfall in increments of 0.01 in. by containers that alternately fill, tip and empty.

Tornado   A small mass of air in contact with the ground that whirls rapidly about an almost vertical axis; made visible by water droplets formed by *condensation* and by dust and debris sucked into the system.

Tornado alley   Region of maximum *tornado* frequency in North America; a corridor stretching from eastern Texas and the Texas panhandle northward into Oklahoma, Kansas and Nebraska, and into southeastern South Dakota.

Towering cumulus stage   Initial stage in the life cycle of a *thunderstorm* cell when *cumulus* clouds build both vertical and laterally over a period of about 10 to 15 minutes. The updraft throughout the cell is sufficiently strong to keep water droplets and ice crystals suspended in the *cloud*; therefore *precipitation* does not occur during this stage.

Trade wind inversion   An elevated *stable air layer* that occurs on the eastern flank of *subtropical anticyclones* in the vicinity of the *trade winds*; a persistent and climatically significant feature. Formed when the subsiding, compressionally warmed air in a subtropical anticyclone encounters the marine air layer, a layer of cool, humid, and stable air formed where sea-surface *temperatures* are relatively low. A temperature inversion develops at the altitude where air subsiding from above meets the top of the marine air layer.

Trade winds   Prevailing planetary-scale surface *winds* in tropical latitudes; blow from the northeast in the Northern Hemisphere and from the southeast in the Southern Hemisphere out of the equatorward flanks of the *subtropical anticyclones*.

Transpiration   Process by which water that is taken up by plant roots escapes as vapor through tiny leaf pores. Measurements of direct *evaporation* from Earth's surface plus transpiration are usually combined as *evapotranspiration*.

Triple point   The point of occlusion in an *extra-tropical cyclone* where *cold front*, *warm front*, and *occluded front* all come together. Conditions at this location are favorable for the formation of a new extra-tropical *cyclone*.

Tropic of Cancer   A *solstice* position of the sun with a latitude of 23 degrees 27 minutes N. On 21 June, the sun's noon rays are vertical (*solar altitude* of 90 degrees) at this latitude.

Tropic of Capricorn   A *solstice* position of the sun with a latitude of 23 degrees, 27 minutes S. On 21 December, the sun's noon rays are vertical (*solar altitude* of 90 degrees) at this latitude.

Tropical cyclone   A *synoptic-scale system* of low pressure that originates over the tropical ocean; includes *tropical depression*, *tropical storm*, *hurricane*, and *typhoon*. Example of a *warm-core cyclone*.

Tropical depression   A *tropical cyclone* with sustained *wind* speeds of at least 37 km per hr (23 mph) but less than 63 km per hr (39 mph); an early stage in the development of a *hurricane*.

Tropical disturbance   A region of convective activity over tropical seas with a detectable center of low *air pressure* at the surface; the initial stage in the development of a *hurricane*. A tropical disturbance is typically triggered by the *intertropical convergence zone*, by a trough in the westerlies intruding into the tropics, or by a wave in the easterly *trade winds* (an *easterly wave*).

Tropical storm   A *tropical cyclone* having sustained *wind* speeds of 63 to 118 km per hr (39 to 73 mmph); a storm at pre-*hurricane* stage. When a tropical cyclone reaches tropical storm strength, it is assigned a name.

Tropopause   Zone of transition between the *troposphere* below and the *stratosphere* above; the top of the troposphere. Has an average altitude ranging from 6 km (3.7 mi) at the poles to about 20 km (12 mi) at the equator.

Troposphere   Lowest thermal subdivision of the *atmosphere* in which air *temperature* normally drops with altitude; the site of most *weather*. Located between Earth's surface and the *tropopause* at an average altitude ranging from 6 km (3.7 mi) at the poles to about 20 km (12 mi) at the equator.

Turbulence   A state of fluid flow characterized by irregular (eddy) motion.

Twilight   A period after sunset or before sunrise when the sky is illuminated by sunlight scattered by constituents of the upper *atmosphere*. Twilight is divided into the stages of civil twilight, nautical twilight, and astronomical twilight.

U

Unstable air layer   An ambient air layer characterized by a vertical *temperature* profile such that air parcels accelerate upward or downward and away from their original altitudes. An ascending air parcel remains warmer (less dense) than the ambient air and continues to ascend and a descending air parcel remains cooler (denser) than the ambient air and continues to descend.

Updraft   Upward-moving current of air.

Upslope fog   *Fog* formed as a consequence of the *expansional cooling* of humid air that is forced to ascend a mountain slope.

Upwelling   The upward movement of cold, nutrient-rich water from depths of 200 to 1000 m (about 650 to 3300 ft) toward the ocean surface associated with the offshore flow of near-surface waters.

Urban heat island   An area of higher air *temperatures* in a city setting compared to the air temperatures of the suburban and rural surroundings; shows up as an island in the pattern of isotherms on a surface map.

V

Valley breeze   Shallow, upslope flow of relatively warm air that develops during daylight hours within *snow*-free mountain valleys in response to differential heating between the air adjacent to the valley wall and air at the same altitude out over the valley floor.

Vapor pressure   The portion of the total *air pressure* exerted by the water vapor component of air; increases as the content of water vapor in air increases.

Variables of state   Descriptors of the physical state of a thermodynamic system; for a gas (and mixtures of gas) these include *temperature*, pressure and density. The variables of state are interrelated through the *gas law*.

Virga   Streaks of water and ice particles falling from a *cloud* that mostly vaporize before reaching Earth's surface.

Viscosity   *Friction* within fluids such as air and water.

Visible radiation (light)   *Electromagnetic radiation* that is perceptible to the human eye; *wavelengths* of visible light range from about 0.40 (violet) to 0.70 (red) micrometers. Visible radiation has wavelengths longer than *infrared radiation* but shorter than *ultraviolet radiation*.

Visible satellite image   Image processed from radiometers onboard a satellite that sense visible solar radiation reflected or back-scattered from surfaces in the *Earth-atmosphere system*.

W

Walker circulation   Direct zonal tropical circulation, thermally driven, in which air rises over the warm western Pacific Ocean and sinks over the cold eastern Pacific.

Wall cloud   A roughly circular lowered portion of the *rain*-free base of a *cumulonimbus cloud* about 3 km (2 mi) in diameter associated with a humid updraft; may develop into a *mesocyclone* and *tornado*. A wall cloud forms in the region of strongest *thunderstorm* updraft and often accompanies a mesocyclone.

Warm air advection   The flow of air across regional isotherms from a relatively warm locality to a relatively cool locality.

Warm cloud   *Cloud* composed of liquid water droplets having a *temperatures* above 0°C (32°F).

Warm front   A *front* that moves in such a way that the cold (more dense) air retreats, allowing relatively warm (less dense) air to advance. May be associated with a broad band of cloudiness and light to moderate *precipitation*.

Warm-core anticyclone   High-pressure system occupying a thick column of subsiding warm, dry air. Isobaric surfaces bulge upward above the high center and the anticyclonic circulation is most intense at high altitudes. *Subtropical anticyclones* are examples.

Warm-core cyclone   A surface, synoptic-scale stationary low-pressure system that develops as a consequence of intense solar heating of a large, relatively dry geographical area; same as a thermal low. The thermal low's shallow cyclonic circulation weakens rapidly with altitude and often reverses to an anticyclonic circulation in the middle and upper *troposphere*.

Water vapor imagery   Processed from a satellite sensor which monitors infrared radiation emitted by clouds and water vapor in the Earth's atmosphere.

Water vapor plume   Extensive stream of water vapor that often originates over tropical seas and is transported horizontally; easily identified on *water vapor satellite imagery*. A typical water vapor plume can be several hundred kilometers wide and thousands of kilometers long. Plumes supply moisture to *hurricanes*, *thunderstorm* clusters, and winter storms.

Water vapor satellite imagery   Picture or image processed from a satellite radiometer that senses *infrared radiation* at those *wavelengths* (typically near 6.7 micrometers) emitted by *clouds* and water vapor in the *atmosphere*; this imagery displays flow patterns in the middle *troposphere* near the top of the bulk of atmospheric water.

Wave frequency   Number of crests or troughs of a wave that pass a given point in a specified period of time, usually 1 second.

Wavelength   The distance between successive wave crests (or equivalently, wave troughs).

Weather   The state of the *atmosphere* at some place and time described in terms of such variables as *temperature*, *humidity*, cloudiness, *precipitation*, and *wind* speed and direction.

Weather radar   An adaptation of radar for meteorological purposes. The *scattering* of *microwave* radiation (*wavelengths* of a few millimeters to several centimeters) by raindrops, snowflakes, or hailstones is used for locating and tracking the movement of areas of *precipitation* and monitoring the circulation within small-scale *weather* systems such as *thunderstorms*.

Weather warning   Issued by the *National Weather Service* when hazardous *weather* is observed or imminent.

Weather watch   Issued by the *National Weather Service* when hazardous *weather* is considered possible based on current or anticipated atmospheric conditions.

Weighing-bucket rain gauge   A recording *rain gauge* that is calibrated so that the weight of cumulative rainfall is recorded directly in terms of water depth (in millimeters or inches).

Wet-bulb depression   On a *psychrometer*, the difference between the dry-bulb *temperature* and the *wet-bulb temperature*;

used to determine *relative humidity* or *dewpoint*.

Wet-bulb temperature   The *temperature* an air parcel would have if cooled adiabatically to saturation at constant *air pressure* by *evaporation* of water into it; measured using a *psychrometer* in which the wick-covered bulb is first soaked in distilled water and the instrument is ventilated to promote evaporation.

Wien's displacement law   A radiation law whereby the *wavelength* of maximum emission by a *blackbody* is inversely to its absolute *temperature* (in kelvins). For example, hot objects (such as the sun) emit peak radiation at relatively short wavelengths, whereas cold objects (such as the *Earth-atmosphere system*) emit peak radiation at longer wavelengths.

Wind   Air in motion measured relative to the Earth's rotating surface.

Wind shear   Change in *wind* speed or direction with distance.

Wind vane   An instrument used to monitor *wind* direction; consists of a free-swinging shaft with a vertical plate at one end and a counterweight (arrowhead) at the other end; the counterweight always points into the wind.

Windsock   An instrument used to monitor *wind* direction; consists of a cone-shaped cloth bag that is open at both ends. The larger end is held open by a metal ring attached to a pole; air enters the larger opening, rotating the sock and stretching it downwind.

Winter storm   An extra-tropical cyclone that produces any combination of frozen or freezing precipitation, including snow, ice pellets or freezing rain.

World Meteorological Organization (WMO)   The agency of the United Nations that coordinates *weather* data collection and analysis by 185 member nations and territories; based in Geneva, Switzerland.

Z

Zonal flow pattern   Flow of the *planetary-scale* westerlies almost directly from west to east; westerlies exhibit little amplitude. In this pattern, the north-south exchange of *air masses* is minimal.

INDEX

Q

R